SENIOR SECONDARY PHYSICS

P.N. OKEKE, F.N. OKEKE, S.F. AKANDE

First published , 1987
Revised, 2000, 2008, 2011

Published by

MACMILLAN NIGERIA PUBLISHERS LIMITED
Ilupeju Industrial Estate
P. O. Box 264, Yaba, Lagos
New Oluyole Industrial Estate
P. O. Box 1463, Ibadan

Companies and representatives throughout the world.

ISBN -0-333-37571-8

Printed by Repro India Ltd.

CONTENTS

PREFACE

Macmillan Senior Secondary Physics is a product of the reaction to correct the needs of students taking the West African Examination Council-conducted Senior Secondary Certificate Examination (SSCE) and the NECO fashion of the same examination. It also has an in-depth coverage of all topics required for entrance into universities, polytechnics and colleges of education through examinations conducted by the Joint Admissions and Matriculation Board (JAMB).

This book, with its easy to read approach, gives students the opportunity to go through important concepts and topics necessary for students' brilliant performance in examinations. Care is taken to sufficiently explain salient points to create a near classroom and laboratory feeling for students with the lavish use of colourful illustrations and experiments for easy assimilation.

Every effort has been made to achieve the correct language level and to present the essential material in a straightforward, uncomplicated manner. Essential mathematics is kept at a level that can easily be understood.

Many worked examples are included to illustrate the application of theory. Numerous exercises at the end of each chapter are intended to test the students' understanding of the subject. Students are thus presented with an effective means of self-diagnosis and assessment whereby they can determine their individual strengths and revision needs.

This revised edition has been painstakingly prepared to cover additional topics included in the new WASSCE syllabus.

P.N. Okeke

BOOK
1

UNITS AND MEASUREMENTS

1.1 Fundamental quantities and units

No physical quantity is meaningful unless it can be exactly measured, quantified and given a unit. In other words, we need two things to specify a physical quantity: the number or quantity and its unit of measurement.

There are three important fundamental quantities in physics. These are: **length, mass** and **time**. The units of these quantities form the base units upon which the units of other quantities depend. Other fundamental quantities are **electric current, temperature, amount of substance and luminous intensity**. Scientists all over the world try to use the same units to measure the same quantity. For example, the British and others prefer to use inches to measure length and pounds to measure weight. In most scientific measurements, the system of units now accepted internationally is called **International System of Units**, often called *SI* unit. The fundamental units are shown in the Table (1.1) below. If you consider only the first three fundamental quantities and units, i.e. length (metres), mass (kilograms), time (second), the SI unit can be referred to as **MKS (metre-kilogram-seconds) system**. Another sub system of MKS is the **cgs system** in which the standard units of length, mass and time are centimetre, gram and second respectively. The *SI* units are the principal system of units used in scientific work today.

Table 1.1 SI fundamental quantities and units

Quantity	Unit	Unit abbreviation
Length	metre	m
Mass	kilogram	kg
Time	second	s
Temperature	kelvin	K
Electric current	ampere	A
Amount of substance	mole	mol
Luminous intensity	candela	cd

1.2 Submultiples and multiples of units

Each unit can exist in multiples and submultiples form using the following prefixes.

Table 1.2 Submultiples and multiples of units

Submultiples	Prefix
10^{-1}	deci (d)
10^{-2}	centi (c)
10^{-3}	milli (m)
10^{-6}	micro (μ)
10^{-9}	nano (n)
10^{-12}	pico (p)
Multiples	
10	deca (da)
10^{2}	hecto (h)
10^{3}	kilo (k)
10^{6}	mega (M)
10^{9}	giga (G)
10^{12}	tera (T)

Some examples of units formed in this way are given below.

For length:
1000 metres (m) = 1 kilometre (km)
10^{-1} m = 1 decimetre (dm)
10^{-2} m = 1 centimetre (cm)
10^{-3} m = 1 millimetre (mm)

For mass:
10^{-3} kilogram (kg) = 1 gram (g)
10^{-6} kg = 1 milligram (mg)

For time:
24 hours (h) = 86400s = (24 x 60 x 60)s = 1 day
60 minutes (min) = 3600s = 1h
60 seconds (s) = 1 min
$\frac{1}{1000}$ second = 1 millisecond (ms)

1.3 Derived quantities and units

By simple combination of *SI* basic units we can obtain other useful units. These are called derived units. The unit of volume is obtained by multiplying the unit for length three times $m \times m \times m = m^3$ pronounced 'cubic metre' or 'metre cubed'. Density is the ratio of mass and volume. Therefore the unit of density is kgm^{-3}, pronounced kilogram per metre cubed. Speed is defined as distance divided by time; therefore the unit is ms^{-1}, pronounced metres per second. Other important derived units are listed on next page. The quantities measured in these units will be explained later in the book as they arise.

Table 1.3 Derived quantities and units

Table 1.4 physical quantities and their dimensions

Quantity	Derivation	Unit
Area	Length x breadth	m^2
Volume	Length x breadth x height	m^3
Density	$\dfrac{mass}{volume}$	kgm^{-3}
Speed	$\dfrac{distance}{time}$	ms^{-1}
Velocity	$\dfrac{displacement}{time}$	ms^{-1}
Acceleration	$\dfrac{change\ in\ velocity}{time}$	ms^{-2}
Force	Mass x acceleration	newton (N)
Weight	Mass x acceleration due to gravity	N
Momentum	Mass x velocity = Force x time	newton second (Ns)
Pressure	$\dfrac{force}{area}$	pascal (Pa)or Nm^{-2}
Energy or Work	force x distance	joules(J) or Nm
Power	$\dfrac{work}{time}$	watts (W) or Nms^{-1} or Js^{-1}

Physical quantities	Units	Dimension
Velocity	ms^{-1}	LT^{-1}
Acceleration	ms^{-2}	LT^{-2}
Force	N (ma)	MLT^{-2}
Momentum	$kgms^{-1}$	MLT^{-1}
Density	kgm^{-3}	ML^{-3}
Pressure	Nm^{-2}	$ML^{-1}T^{-2}$
Youngs modulus	Nm^{-2}	$ML^{-1}T^{-2}$
Surface tension	Nm^{-1}	MT^{-2}

Derived quantities and units are those obtained by simple combination of fundamental quantities and units.

Fundamental quantities are the basic quantities that are independent of other quantities.
Fundamental units are basic units upon which other units depend.

1.4 Dimensions of physical quantities

The dimensions of a physical quantity indicate how it is made up in terms of the *SI* base quantities. In other words the physical quantity is said to have been expressed in terms of dimensions of the three fundamental units length (L), mass (M) and time (T).

For example, the dimension of density (Unit kgm^{-3}) is mass x length^{-3}
i.e. density = $m/v = M/L^3 = ML^{-3}$

The dimension of acceleration, $a = v/t = s/t^2 = LT^{-2}$
The dimension of force, $F = ma = MLT^{-2}$
Below is a table of a few important physical quantities and their dimensions:

We can use method of dimension to verify whether a physical equation is correct or not. Consider for example, the formula given by:

$$s = ut + \tfrac{1}{2}at^2$$

where s = distance, u = initial velocity
v = final velocity, a = acceleration

The dimension of each term must be the same:
Dimension of $s = L$
Dimension of $ut = \dfrac{s}{t} \times t = \dfrac{L}{T} \times T = L$
Dimension of $\tfrac{1}{2}at^2 = \dfrac{s}{t^2} \times t^2 = \dfrac{L}{T^2} \quad T^2 = L$

Therefore the equation is correct dimensionally.
We can also use dimensions to derive the exact form of a physical equation. This will be shown in the following problem.

Example 1.1
The period T of oscillation of a simple pendulum depends on the length l, and acceleration g. Determine the exact form of the dependence.

Solution: We can assume that $T = l^x g^y$ where x and y are constant. We then determine the values of x and y as follows:

Express all the terms in dimensional form.
The dimensions of T is T, (the second T because period is measured in seconds).
The dimension of g i.e. acceleration $= LT^{-2}$ as shown earlier.
$\therefore\ T = L^x(LT^{-2})^y = L^x L^y T^{-2y}$
i.e. $T = L^{x+y} T^{-2y}$

Equating the indices of each term on both sides we get:
for $T: 1 = -2y$
for $L: 0 = x + y$

Solving the two equations $y = -\tfrac{1}{2}$, $x = \tfrac{1}{2}$
The formula $T = l^x g^y$ now reads $T = L^{\frac{1}{2}} g^{-\frac{1}{2}}$
or $T = (l/g)$

1.5.1 Measurements of length: metre rule, calipers, micrometer screw guage

In this section, we shall discuss the instruments for measuring in particular, the three basic quantities: length, time and mass.

Large distances, such as the length of your playground, are measured by means of tapes, graduated in metres (see Fig. 1.1).

Shorter distances, such as the length of your reading table can be measured with a metre rule (Fig. 1.2). Cylindrical objects can be measured with the aid of calipers and a metre rule (Fig. 1.2 and 1.3). In general, a metre rule can only read to the nearest 1mm or 0.1 cm, i.e. to the nearest millimeter. It is also possible to approximate with a meter rule to the nearest half a millimeter i.e. 0.05cm.

Fig 1.1 Graduated tapes.

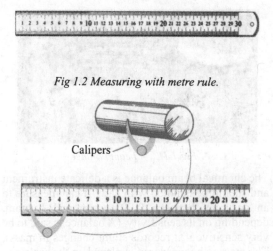

Fig 1.2 Measuring with metre rule.

Fig 1.3 Measuring with calipers.

Vernier calipers

Smaller lengths, such as the diameter of a rod (Fig. 1.4), the internal diameter of a tube, the depth of a cavity or the thickness of a plate, which cannot be measured with a metre rule, can be obtained using vernier calipers. Vernier calipers can usually measure to an accuracy of 0.01 cm or 0.1mm.

Vernier calipers have two scales, the main scale M and the vernier scale V. The vernier is a small scale which is added to the main scale to give the fraction of the smallest division on the main scale.

The main scale is calibrated in millimetres like a metre rule. The vernier is constructed by dividing nine of the 0.1cm divisions into ten equal intervals so that each vernier division has a length of 0.09cm.

When the zero of M coincides with the zero of V then the length measured is zero (Fig. 1.5), but as V slides on M, the readings on M and V together give the total reading of the distance measured.

In Fig. 1.6, the main scale reading is 4.3 and the vernier reading (i.e. where the vernier coincides with the main scale) is on the vernier mark 7. Then, the total reading will be $4.3 + 0.07 = 4.37$cm.

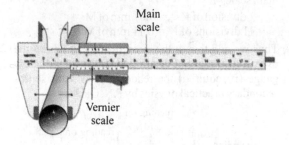

Fig 1.4 Vernier calipers

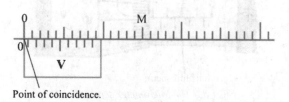

Fig 1.5 Reading 0.0

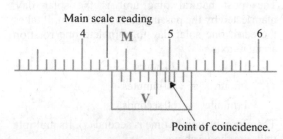

Fig 1.6 Reading 4.37

Micrometer screw guage

For certain measurements, such as the diameter of a wire, the diameter of a small ball or the thickness of paper, greater accuracy is required, so an instrument more accurate than the vernier is required. In this case a micrometer screw gauge is used. This instrument measures to an accuracy of 0.01mm. Like the vernier calipers it has a main scale, M

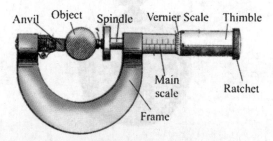

Fig 1.7 The Micrometer screw guage

graduated in millimetres with a circular vernier scale V which contains 50 divisions (Fig. 1.7). It is read by noting the main scale reading (4mm in Fig. 1.8), and then adding the vernier division, which is 11 in Fig. 1.8. The required reading is therefore 4.00 + 0.11 which is 4.11 mm or 0.411cm. The result follows from the fact that:

50 divisions of vernier (V) correspond to 0.5mm of main scale M.

$\therefore$ 1 division of V = 0.01 mm of M
11 divisions of V = 0.11 mm of M

Thus we add this to the main reading to obtain the overall reading. For detailed treatment of the screw gauge (if required) the reader may consult senior secondary practical physics by P.N. Okeke.

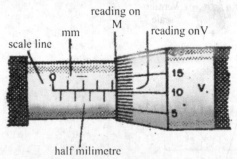

Fig 1.8   The Micrometer screw guage

1.5.2   Measurement of time

The most natural time unit is the solar day, manifested by the passing of day and night. It takes the earth one solar day to complete one rotation about its axis.

1 day	=	24 hours
1 hour	=	60 minutes
1 minute	=	60 seconds

Therefore the unit of time is second (s). Its multiple units are shown above.

All events which happen in nature involved the idea of time. In the laboratory, time is usually measured by a stop watch or a stop clock. Some stop watches can measure time to 0.1 second, while stop clocks are not as accurate, having an accuracy between 0.2 seconds and 0.5 seconds, (see Fig. 1.9). Nowadays quartz clocks and atomic clocks give a high degree of accuracy.

Fig 1.9   Stop Watch

1.5.3   Measurement of mass and weight

The mass of a body is a measure of the quantity of matter it contains.

This mass is usually measured by comparing it with standard masses, using a balance. There are various types, and one type found in some of our schools is the beam or chemical balance. A simplified diagram of a chemical beam balance is shown in Fig. 1.10 and a photograph of a beam balance is shown in Fig. 1.11 respectively.

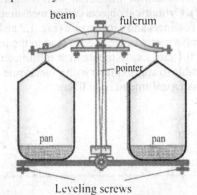

Fig 1.10   A chemical beam balance

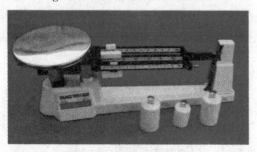

Fig 1.11   A beam balance

The chemical beam balance is a delicate instrument and should be handled with care. It can measure to an accuracy between 0.001 gram and 1 gram, depending on its sensitivity. (A balance is said to be very sensitive if it records slight changes in mass). The mass to be measured is placed on the scale pan X, and known masses are added into the other pan Y until the pointer is at the centre. The total mass in Y, is then equal to the value of the unknown mass. The physical principles involved in the working of the balance are to be discussed later. Further details of weighing techniques can be found in Senior Secondary Practical Physics by P.N. Okeke.

Note: If mass measured is obtained in grams, it can be converted to SI units (kg) using the fact that 1g = 0.001kg, i.e. by dividing by 1000.

Apart from the beam balance, we also have other types of balances. These are shown in Figs. 1.12, 1.13, 1.14 and 1.15. The first of these works like the beam balance, but the other three are graduated in grams or kilograms and the pointer gives the direct reading of the mass placed on them.

Fig 1.12 Another type of balance

Fig 1.13 A lever balance

Fig 1.14 A direct reading balance

Fig 1.15 A dial balance

In the absence of such balances for measuring mass one can obtain a rough value of the mass of an object using a uniform metre rule balanced at its centre, fig. 1.16. A known mass m_o (which is comparable to the mass m) is suspended at a convenient distance, 10cm say from the central balanced point, O. The unknown mass then suspended from the other side and its position is varied until the rule is once again balanced. Let x be its distance from O. From the principle of moments (to be discussed later), m can be calculated from the equation:

$$m \times x = m_o \times 10$$
$$\therefore \; m = \frac{M_o \times 10}{x}$$

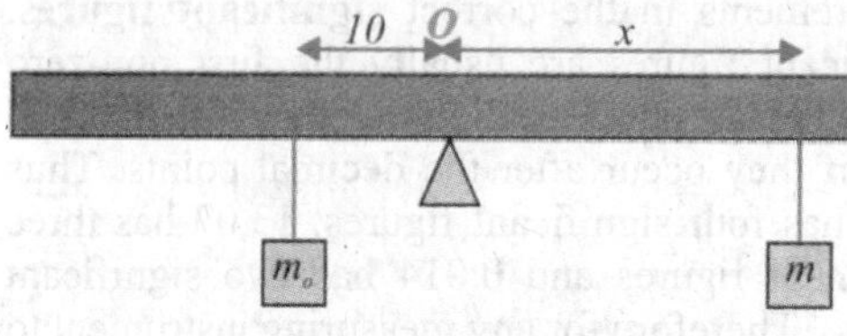

Fig 1.16 Simple measurement of mass.

Mass and weight
Sometimes we talk of measuring weight instead of mass. These two are not the same.

Mass is the quantity of matter in a body, while weight is the earth's pull on a body.

A force can either be a push or a pull, and weight is a force, (forces will be studied in detail later). It has both magnitude and direction and is therefore a vector quantity. Mass has only magnitude and is therefore a scalar quantity. Weight is measured in newtons (N), the unit of force.

Fig 1.17 A spring balance

One instrument used for measuring weight is the spring balance, (see Fig. 1.17). If the balance is calibrated in grams or kilograms, as is often the case, the reading should be converted to newtons, as follows:

A weight of one Newton corresponds to a mass of approximately 100 grams or 0.1 kilograms. Conversely, a mass of 1 kilogram corresponds to a weight of approximately 10 or more exactly 9.8 newtons.

We see later that if mass M is in kg, the weight of a body W is given by $W = mg\,(N)$
Where $g = 9.8\,ms^{-2}$.

1.5.4 Measurement of volume

(Cylinder, flask, pipettes, burette)

The volume of a liquid in cubic centimetres (cm^3) or millilitres can be measured using any of the following: measuring cylinder, measuring flask, pipette or burette, (see Fig. 1.18). The measuring cyclinder is for measuring or pouring out various volumes of liquid. The measuring flask and pipette are used for fixed pre-determined volumes. They are usually calibrated in cubic centimetres, written as cm^3, or millilitres (ml), which are equivalent units.

The volume of an irregular solid can be obtained by completely immersing the solid in a cylinder containing a liquid which does not dissolve the solid and measuring the volume of the liquid displaced. This is equal to the volume of the solid.

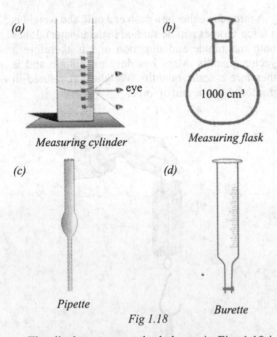

(a)

eye

Measuring cylinder

(b)

1000 cm³

Measuring flask

(c)

Pipette

(d)

Burette

Fig 1.18

The displacement method shown in Fig. 1.19 is used to measure the volume of an irregular solid. **Note**: In order to read correctly the volume of a liquid in a measuring cylinder or beaker, the eye should be along the same horizontal line as the meniscus of the liquid as in Fig. 1.18(a). This is because it is possible to make what is called a

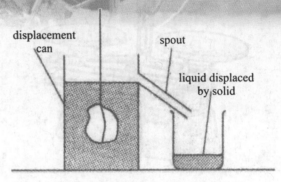

Fig 1.19 Volume of an irregular solid

parallax error; that is, to read a mark which is parallel to the surface but is not the correct one, due to the eye not being at the correct height.

The volume of a regular solid can be obtained using one of the following formulae.

Volume of a sphere $= \dfrac{4\pi r^3}{3}$ where r is radius.

Volume of a box $= l \times b \times t$
  (i.e. length $\times$ breadth $\times$ thickness).

Volume of a cylinder $= \pi r^2 l$
  (where r is radius and l is height of cylinder).

Volume of a cone $= \frac{1}{3}$ (base area $\times$ height).

1.5.5 Degree of accuracy

No measurement in physics is meaningful unless we can state the degree of uncertainty in the measurement. This uncertainty is stated as follows: for example, $31.40 \pm 0.05cm$ where 0.05cm is the *uncertainty* or *reading accuracy*. This means that the measured quantity lies between 31.35 and 31.45cm. It also gives one an idea of the instrument used in carrying out the measurement. As we can see later we can use a metre rule to read up to the nearest half a millimetre, i.e. 0.05cm. Therefore the above measurement was done with a metre rule. The number of decimal point, significant figure in a reading depends on the graduations or precision of the instrument. Sometimes, as stated above specify measurements in the correct **significant figures**. Significant figures are usually the first non-zero digit to the last non-zero digit together with the final zeros if they occur after the decimal points. Thus 27.12 has four significant figures, 13.07 has three significant figures and 0.014 has two significant figures. Therefore for any measuring instrument to be used we should first find out from the graduations to what decimal points can we obtain the reading. These are known as reading accuracies of the instrument. For example, as we shall see later, a mercury in glass thermometer has the smallest graduation as one degree. The best we estimate is half degree 0.5° which is the reading accuracy. Some stop watches for measuring time read up to one second which should be the reading accuracy.

Summary

1. *SI* fundamental quantities with units are length (m), time (s), mass (kg), temperature (K) electric current (A), amount of substance (mol) and luminous intensity (cd).

2. Fundamental quantities are basic quantities that are independent of other physical quantities.

3. Fundamental units are basic units upon which other units depend.

4. Derived quantities and units are those obtained by simple combination of fundamental quantities and units.

5. The dimensions of a physical quantity indicates how it is made up in terms of MKS units.

6. Dimensions are used in determining the units of a quantity, it can be used to verify the correctness of a physical equation and can also be used to derive the exact form of a physical equation.

7. A metre rule has a reading accuracy of 0.05cm. A venier calipers has a reading accuracy of 0.01cm and micrometer screwguage has a reading accuracy of 0.005cm.

8. Mass is the quantity of matter in a body and can be measured with beam balance and others which compare the mass with a standard mass.

9. Weight is the force of gravity on a body. It is given by $W = mg$ (N) where g is acceleration of gravity. It is measured with a spring balance.

10. We can measure volume of a liquid with a graduated cylinder, pipette or burette depending on the volume of liquid.

11. The reading accuracy of an instrument is the uncertainty in a measured quantity. It is the nearest decimal place we can measure with an instrument.

Exercise 1

1. Which of the units of the following physical quantities is not a derived unit?
   A. Area   B. Thrust   C. Pressure   D. Mass

2. Which of the following is a fundamental unit?
   A. Kgm^{-3} B. m^3 C. Nm^{-2} D. kg

3. The weight of a body is measured with
   A. spring balance.   B. beam balance.
   C. chemical balance.   D. lever balance.

4. Which of the following is not correct?
   The *SI* unit of:
   A. acceleration is ms^{-2}.
   B. momentum is Ns.
   C. work is joule.
   D. energy is watt.

5. Which instrument is best for measuring small quantity of liquid?
   A. Burette   B. Pipette
   C. Cylinder   D. Beaker

6. (a) What do you understand by the reading accuracy of a measuring instrument?

   (b) Write down the reading accuracies of the following; your watch, your ruler, a thermometer in your laboratory, vernier calipers and protractor.

7. The smallest unit on the sleeve of a micrometer screw guage is 0.5mm. There are 50 divisions on the thimble of this screw guage. What is the smallest length that can be measured with this instrument?

8. If $F = G \dfrac{Mm}{R^2}$

   Find the dimension of G, if R is a distance, F is force and Mm are masses.

9. The Young modulus of elasticity is defined as $E = \dfrac{F/A}{e/l}$.
   Obtain the dimension of E where f = force A = area, e and l are lengths.

10. For what values of x, y and z will the equation $P^x V^y T^z$ = constant, become Boyle's law?
    ($P \propto 1/V$ at constant T). P, V, T are pressure, volume and temperature respectively.

11. (i) What is the dimension of stress?

    (ii) What is the unit of frequency?

12. Find the *SI* unit of R so that the equation, velocity = $R \times$ density is dimensionally correct. R is a constant.

FUNDAMENTALS OF MOTION

Motion involves a change of position of a body with time. The study of motion of a body without involving the forces which cause motion is called **Kinematics.** The study of forces and how they affect motion of a body is called **dynamics**

2.1 Types of motion

We distinguish between four types of motion:

(a) Random motion

Objects move irregularly or at random or haphazardly or disorderly with no preferred direction or orientation. As a result of such random movement, the particles collide with one another. An example of such motion is the Brownian motion: an irregular motion of particles of various kinds suspended in water, or of smoke particles suspended in air, or the motion of gas particles.

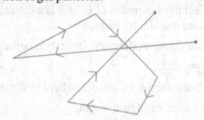

Fig. 2.1(a) Random motion.

(b) Translational linear motion

When rigid objects move from one point in space to another without rotating, the motion is said to be translational.

Examples

(i) A book sliding from one end of an inclined table to another.
(ii) A body running in a straight line from one goal post to another.
(iii) A small ball thrown vertically upwards.

Fig. 2.1(b) a ball thrown vertically upwards.

(c) Rotational motion

It involves motion of a body in a circle about a centre or axis. Examples of such motion are:
(i) rotation of the earth about its axis;
(ii) rotation of an electric fan blades;
(iii) the wheel of a moving car.

Fig. 2.2(a) Rotation of an electric fan blades.

Fig. 2.2(b)Rotation of the earth.

(d) Periodic, oscillatory or vibratory motion

Periodic motion is a type of motion that occurs very frequently in the motion of a body in a circular path with uniform speed such as the oscillation of a clock pendulum. The vibratory motion plays very important roles in many physical phenomena, especially in light, mechanics, sound and electricity. In such a motion, the path of a moving body is repeated at successive equal intervals of time. Any such motion that repeats itself at regular interval of time is known as periodic motion. Examples of such motions are: the balance wheel of watch, the vibration of a violin string and the rotation of the Earth about its axes.

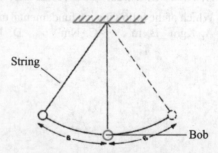

String

Bob

Fig. 2.3(a) Simple pendulum.

Fig. 2.3(b) Vibrating mass on a spring.

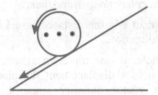

Fig. 2.3(c) Translational/rotational motion.

The motion of a body may consist of a combination of two of the above, e.g.

(i) A cylinder rolling down an inclined plane is performing both translational and rotational motion.

(ii) The earth rotating about its axis in one day and at the same time revolving about the sun in one year.

(iii) A cyclist is performing translational motion while its wheels are performing rotational motion.

2.2 Concepts associated with motion in a straight line

A straight line is the shortest distance between two points. Therefore, certain concepts need to be understood before discussing motion in a straight line. These concepts are: position, distance, bearing, scalars, vectors and displacements.

(a) Concept of position and distance

The position of a point in space is described with reference to another point whose position is known. The statement of position is determined or described by means of a frame of reference or a point of reference, which we shall call the origin. To describe the position of a point in space, we draw two lines perpendicular to each other at O as shown in Fig. 2.4, The point O is the origin.

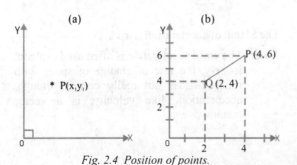

Fig. 2.4 Position of points.

The two lines known as axes of reference are OX and OY. The horizontal line OX is known as the X-axis and the vertical line OY is known as the Y-axis by convention. Points to the right of 'O' are positive, points to the left of 'O' are negative. Points above "OX" are positive in the y-direction, while points below "OX" are negative.

The position of any point such as P is determined and specified by two quantities known as the coordinates. We have the x-coordinate and y-coordinate. If we say that the coordinates of the point P are (x_1, y_1), we mean that the distance P from 'O' in the X-direction is x_1 and y_1 in the Y-direction. Suppose the point is 4 units in the X-direction and 6 units in the Y-direction, then the coordinate of P is (4,6) as shown in Fig. 2.4. Similarly the position of Q is (2,4). Sometimes the x- coordinate is called abscissa and y-coordinate is called the ordinate, the straight line joining P and Q is the distance PQ. It is

equal to $\sqrt{(4-2)^2 + (6-4)^2}$

$= \sqrt{8}$ unit

(b) Bearings and direction

The four cardinal directions are North, South, East and West. The usual way of stating the direction of a point is to state its angle in relation to the cardinal directions. We say that the direction of P is N30°E as shown in Fig. 2.5(a) and that of R is S20°W. To locate P, we face the North and move 30° to the East. Similarly to locate R we face S and move 20° to the West.

The bearing of P from O may be defined as the angle which the line OP makes with the northern direction ON in the clockwise sense. Thus if angle NOP is 30° the bearing of P from O is stated as N30°E or 030°. The figures are usually stated, North being 000°, East is 090°. South is 180° and West is 270°. Some typical bearings are shown below.

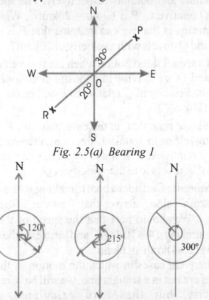

Fig. 2.5(a) Bearing 1

Fig. 2.5(b) Bearing 2

(c) Scalars and vectors

A scalar quantity is one which has magnitude but no direction.

Examples are: distance, energy, temperature, mass, and speed. All these quantities require only a number and unit to specify them. We do not have to ask, for example, the direction of mass or energy.

A vector quantity is one which has direction as well as magnitude.

For example the displacement of PQ, i.e. if we also consider the direction of PQ with respect to O apart from magnitude $PQ = \sqrt{8}$.

Other examples are: velocity, force and acceleration which are vector quantities. To specify a force, for instance, we need to define the direction in which it is acting as well as its magnitude, by stating the angle which the force makes with a fixed line, such as a horizontal.

2.3   Relative motion

Motion is change in position. Relative motion is therefore change in position of a body with respect to another. Since the Earth is always in motion, we can conclude that all motions are relative with respect to the Earth. But most of the time we assume that the Earth is at rest with respect to the motion of the body.

When two bodies move, the best way to handle the problem is to consider motion of one relative to the other assuming that the Earth is at rest. For example:

(a)   Let us consider two vehicles P and Q travelling side by side at the same speed. To the passengers in vehicle P, the vehicle Q will appear stationary. This means that the motion of each vehicle relative to the other is zero.

(b)   Let us consider the case where vehicles P and Q travel in the same direction with velocities 40 kmh^{-1} and 60kmh^{-1} respectively. The speed of Q relative to P is 60-40 = 20kmh^{-1}. What this means is that we can imagine that P is at rest and Q travels with a velocity of 20kmh^{-1}.

(c)   Consider the situation when the two vehicles P and Q are moving in opposite directions, then the velocity of Q relative to P will be 60 + 40 = 100kmh^{-1}.

(d)   Please note that, in the case two cars P and Q travelling in opposite directions, the velocity of Q relative to P is found by adding the velocity of P reversed to the velocity of Q.

Example: Consider a boat travelling with a speed of 10kmh^{-1} along a river that flows at a speed of 4kmh^{-1}. We should note that the speed of the boat down stream = $(4 + 10)kmh^{-1}$ and upstream the speed will be $(10-4)kmh^{-1} = 6kmh^{-1}$.

There are cases in which the motion of the two bodies are not in a straight line, we still have relative velocity, but these are calculated using parallelogram law of forces.

There are many other consequences of relative motion in physics. One typical example is **Doppler Effect** in sound and even in light in which there is an apparent frequency of sound or light source due to relative motion between the observer and source or light. This will be discussed in subsequent chapter.

2.4   Parameters of motion

The following parameters are required to describe motion in a straight line: *displacement*, *speed* or *velocity*, *v*, *acceleration*, *a*, and *time*, *t*.

Displacement s is the distance travelled in a specified direction.

For example, if one travels a distance of 10m eastwards, it is a displacement. Displacement is therefore a vector quantity since it has both magnitude and direction.

Speed v, is the rate of change of distance with time.

$$v = \frac{s}{t} \qquad\qquad 2.1$$

Where s and t refer to change in distance and change in time respectively. The SI unit of speed is ms^{-1}.

Uniform speed

If the ratio $\frac{s}{t}$ is constant throughout the journey, the speed v is said to be uniform. Thus, we say that speed is uniform if:

$$v = \frac{s}{t} = \text{a constant.}$$

$$\text{Average speed} = \frac{total\ distance\ travelled}{total\ time\ taken}$$

(The speed need not be constant in this case).

Velocity is speed measured in a given direction. Or velocity is the rate of change of displacement with time. It is therefore a vector quantity.

Note: In ordinary conversation, the word velocity is often used in place of speed. In science, it is important to distinguish between these two terms as we have seen above. Speed is a scalar but velocity is a vector.

Acceleration, a, is the rate of change of velocity increase with time.

$$a = \frac{v}{t} \qquad\qquad 2.2$$

The SI unit of acceleration is ms^{-2}.

Note: The word acceleration is often used to mean, loosely, the rate of change of speed with time. This is not really correct, though, acceleration, like velocity, is a vector quantity.

Uniform acceleration

If the rate of change of velocity with time is constant, the acceleration is said to be uniform. This implies that

$$a = \frac{v}{t} = \text{constant.}$$

If the velocity of a body is increasing with time, it is said to be accelerating, but if the velocity of a body is decreasing with time, the body is said to be experiencing *retardation* or *deceleration*. In this case, the acceleration is negative.

Let us apply some of these definitions.

Example 2.1

If a man walks 10m east and $10\sqrt{3}$ m northward, what is his displacement?

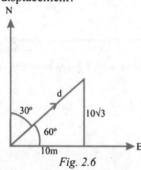

Fig. 2.6

From the figure, the man's displacement is 20m.

i.e. $\sqrt{10^2 + (10\sqrt{3})^2} = \sqrt{10^2(1 + \sqrt{3})^2} = 20\text{m}.$

The direction θ is given by:

$$\theta = \tan^{-1}\left(\frac{10\sqrt{3}}{10}\right) = \tan^{-1}(\sqrt{3}) = 60°$$

∴ his displacement is 20m, N30°E.

2.5 The equations of motion

If a body starts with initial velocity u, accelerates uniformly along a straight line with acceleration a and covers a distance s in a time t when its velocity reaches a final value v, then the distance s covered is given by s = average velocity x time:

$$s = \frac{v + u}{2} \times t \qquad \text{2.3}$$

Also, by definition, acceleration a = rate of change of velocity and since a is constant we have:

$$a = \frac{v + u}{t}$$

or $\quad v = u + at \qquad \text{2.4}$

Eliminating t from (2.3) and (2.4), we find:

$$v^2 = u^2 + 2as \qquad \text{2.5}$$

Eliminating v from (2.3) and (2.4), we find:

$$s = ut + \tfrac{1}{2}at^2 \qquad \text{2.6}$$

These four equations of motion are used in solving problems associated with uniformly accelerated motion. When using them, the following points should be noted.

(i) Ensure that all the units match. i.e., v in ms^{-1}, s in m, a in ms^{-2}, t in s; or v in kmh^{-1}, s in km, a in km/h ^{2}, t in hours.

(ii) Each of the equations contains four of the five variables u, v, s, a and t. You are normally given the value of three of them, and you are required to find one or both of the unknowns.

(iii) The best way to select which equation to use is to look at the problem and to find out which of the five variables is not given, in addition to the one which is required. Then find the equation which does not contain the variable that is not given. This gives you the required equation.

Equation (2.3) does not contain a.

Equation (2.4) does not contain s.

Equation (2.5) does not contain t.

Equation (2.6) does not contain v.

(iv) Note the conversion formulae:

$$1\,\text{kmh}^{-1} = \frac{1000}{60 \times 60}\ \text{ms}^{-1}$$

or $\quad 36\,\text{kmh}^{-1} = 10\,\text{ms}^{-1},$

or $\quad 1\,\text{ms}^{-1} = 3.6\,\text{kmh}^{-1}.$

(v) Do not confuse s for distance with the unit s for seconds.

Example 2.2

A car moves from rest with an acceleration of $0.2\,\text{ms}^{-2}$. Find its velocity when it has moved a distance of 50m.

From the problem we notice that the question does not involve t. Therefore, the required equation is (iii).

$$v^2 = u^2 + 2as$$
$$v = \sqrt{u^2 + 2as}$$

Putting $u = 0$, $a = 0.2$ and $s = 50$, we have:

$$v = \sqrt{0^2 + 2 \times 0.2 \times 50}$$
$$= \sqrt{20}$$
$$= 2\sqrt{5}\ \text{ms}^{-1} = 4.47\,\text{ms}^{-1}.$$

Example 2.3

A car has a uniform velocity of 108km/h. How far does it travel in ½ minute?

$$108\,\text{kmh}^{-1} = \frac{108 \times 1000}{60 \times 60} = 30\,ms^{-1}$$

Since the velocity is uniform $(v = u)$ we use equation (2.3).

$$s = \left(\frac{v + u}{2}\right)t = \left(\frac{v + v}{2}\right)t$$
$$s = vt$$
$$v = 30\,\text{ms}^{-1}$$
$$t = \tfrac{1}{2}\,\text{minute} = 30\text{s}$$
$$\therefore s = 30 \times 30$$
$$= 900\text{m}$$
$$= 0.9\text{km}$$

Example

A lorry travels at an average speed of 90 kmh⁻¹, what distance does it cover in 4 seconds?

Solution

First convert kmh⁻¹ to ms⁻¹:

$$90\,kmh^{-1} = \frac{90 \times 1000}{60 \times 60}\,ms^{-1} = \frac{100}{4}\,ms^{-1}$$

$$Average\ speed = \frac{distance}{time}$$

$\therefore$ distance = average speed x time

$$= \frac{100}{4} \times 4 = 100m$$

Example 2.5

A car accelerates uniformly at 2ms⁻² for 3 minutes, what is the velocity of the car in ms⁻¹?

Solution

First convert minutes to seconds:

3 minutes = 3 × 60 seconds

Acceleration $a = v/t$

$\therefore v = at = 2 \times (3 \times 60) = 360\,ms^{-1}$

Example 2.6

A train slows from 108kmh⁻¹ with a uniform retardation of 5ms⁻². How long will it take to reach 18kmh⁻¹, and what is the distance covered?

The initial velocity $u = 108kmh^{-1} = \dfrac{108 \times 1000}{60 \times 60} = 30\,ms^{-1}$

Final velocity $v = 18kmh^{-1} = \dfrac{18 \times 1000}{60 \times 60} = 5\,ms^{-1}$

Acceleration $a = -5ms^{-2}$

We are given u, v and a, we require t, we should therefore use only the equation which does not contain s, (2.4).

$$v = u + at,$$
$$5 = 30 - 5t$$
$$\therefore t = 5s$$

The distance s covered can be obtained from any of the equations involving s, since all the other parameters are now known.

Using $v^2 = u^2 + 2as$.

$$25 = 900 - 2 \times 5s$$
$$\therefore s = 87.5m$$

or, using $s = ut + \frac{1}{2}at^2$

$$s = 30 \times 5 - \frac{1}{2} \times 5 \times 5^2 = 87.5m$$

2.6 Graphical interpretation of uniform and non-uniform motion

Uniform and non-uniform velocity

We saw earlier that if a body travels with uniform velocity then velocity $v = \dfrac{s}{t} =$ constant.

This means that a graph of displacement against time will be a straight line through the origin with slope, $v = ds/dt$, as illustrated in Fig. 2.7.

Sometimes the velocity is not constant, it increases or decreases with time. In this case, the distance - time graph will not be a straight line, see Fig. 2.8. We can only define the velocity v_p at any point say P on the distance-time curve. The velocity v_p is called instantaneous velocity of the body, at point P, $v_p = ds/dt =$ slope of tangent at p.

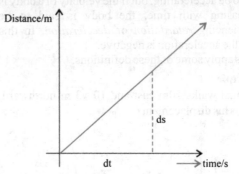

Fig. 2.7 Distance-time graph (uniform velocity)

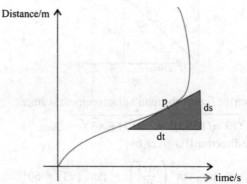

Fig. 2.8 Distance-time graph (non-uniform velocity)

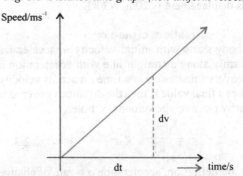

Fig. 2.9 Speed-time graph (uniform acceleration)

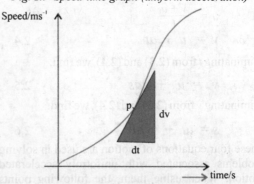

Fig. 2.10 Speed-time graph (non-uniform acceleration)

Uniform and non-uniform acceleration

For uniform motion velocity $v/t = a$ = constant, therefore if we plot a graph of velocity against time we obtain a straight-line through the origin (Fig. 2.9)

The slope of this graph at any point is constant $= \frac{dv}{dt} = $ a, the acceleration.

For non-uniform acceleration the velocity time graph (fig. 2.10) is not a straight line. The acceleration at any point P is known as instantaneous acceleration.

$$a_p = \frac{dv}{dt}.$$

2.7 Area under the velocity-time graph

Let us consider the case of a body which started moving with initial velocity u and accelerated to velocity v with uniform acceleration a. The v-t graph is shown in fig. 2.11.

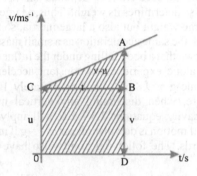

Fig. 2.11 Area under v - t graph 1

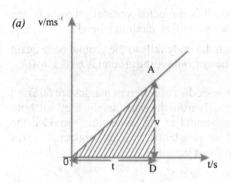

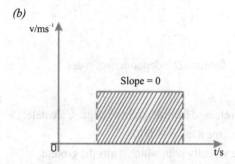

Fig. 2.12(a, b) Area under v - t graph 2

In fig. 2.11, CA represents the graph for a body accelerating uniformly, obtained by plotting v against t. $DA = v$, is the final velocity after a time t, represented on the graph by OD.

The slope of the graph $= \frac{AB}{CB} = \frac{v - u}{t} = a$

The area under the line = area of trapezium $CODA$

$$= \frac{u + v}{2} \ t = s \text{ (by definition)}.$$

Thus area under the line = distance travelled

Suppose the body starts from rest as in Fig. 2.12 (a). The total distance travelled, s = area of triangle ODA.

$$s = \tfrac{1}{2} vt.$$

Suppose the body is travelling with uniform velocity throughout, then the v-t curve takes the form of Fig. 2.12 (b). The slope of the curve = 0. Area of the rectangle represents the total distance covered.

Example 2.6

A car starts from rest and accelerates uniformly until it reaches a velocity of 30ms⁻¹ after 5s. It travels with uniform velocity for 15s and is then brought to rest in 10s with a uniform retardation.

Determine: (a) the acceleration of the car,
(b) the retardation,
(c) the distance covered after 5s,
(d) the total distance covered.

(Use both methods).

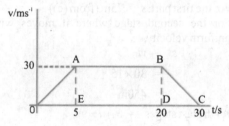

Fig. 2.13 Graphical method

The velocity-time diagram for the journey is shown in Fig. 2.13. From this diagram:

(a) the acceleration = slope of OA

$$= \frac{AE}{EO} = \frac{30}{5} = 6\text{ms}^{-2}$$

(b) the retardation = slope of BC

$$= \frac{BD}{DC} = \frac{30}{10} = 3\text{ms}^{-2}$$

Note (b) is the retardation because the speed was decreasing in the interval DC.

(c) distance travelled during accelerating
$= $ area of AEO
$= \tfrac{1}{2}(5 \times 30)$
$= 75\text{m}$

(d) Total distance covered = area of the trapezium
   OABC

$$= \tfrac{1}{2}(OC+AB)AE$$
$$= \tfrac{1}{2}(30+15)30$$
$$= 675\text{m}.$$

The method above is very simple, brief and elegant. One can also use the equations of motion, (see below) but the graphical method is recommended for such problems.

Calculation method, using equations of motion

(a) We are given that $u = 0$, $v = 30$, $t = 5$ with a as the required variable. Our problem does not involve s so we choose equation (2.4).

$$v = u + at$$

so $a = \dfrac{v-u}{t} = \dfrac{30-0}{5} = \dfrac{30}{5} = 6\text{ms}^{-2}$

(b) as in (a)

$$a = \dfrac{v-u}{t} = \dfrac{30-0}{30-20} = \dfrac{30}{10} = 3\text{ms}^{-2}$$

(c) Here we are given v, u and t and we want s. We do not want equations involving a. The only equation satisfying this requirement is equation 2.3.

$$s = \left(\dfrac{u+v}{2}\right)t = \left(\dfrac{0+30}{2}\right)5 = 75\text{m}.$$

(d) The same argument used above applies except that we need to find the various distances for the three stages of the journey and then add them.

For the first part, $s = 75$m (from (c))
For the second stage where it moves with uniform velocity,

$$s = vt$$
$$= 30 \times 15$$
$$= 450\text{m}$$

for the last stages $= \tfrac{1}{2}(u+v)t$
$$= \tfrac{1}{2}(30+0)10$$
$$= 150\text{m}$$

alternatively, we can find s in this last stage using,

$$v^2 = u^2 - 2as$$
$$0 = 30^2 - 2 \times 3 \times s$$
$$s = 150\text{m as before}$$

total distance travelled :
$$= 75+450+150$$
$$= 675\text{m}.$$

2.8   Motion under gravity

A typical example of uniformly accelerated motion is the motion of a body under the influence of gravity. It might be thought that bodies falling under the action of gravity alone fall at different rates. A heavy object has a larger force acting on it than a light object, so we would expect it to accelerate more and reach the ground sooner. This is what was thought until about 400 years ago when an Italian scientist called Galileo actually dropped two bodies of different masses to see what happened.

Galileo is supposed to have performed this historic experiment by dropping a heavy object and a light object from the top of a tower called the *Leaning Tower of Pisa*. Both objects landed at the same time. This experiment was important because it told us something about gravity. Not only this, but it also showed scientists that they should not make assumptions but should try out their ideas to see what happens. In other words, they should perform experiments.

Why do the two objects land at the same time? The reason is that the inertia of an object, or its resistance to acceleration, depends on its mass, which also determines its weight. Thus, a large mass has a large weight but also a large inertia, so that it falls with the same acceleration as a small mass. It is now known that a body falling under the influence of gravity alone experiences a constant acceleration with value g = 9.8ms^{-2}, or approximately 10ms^{-2}. Therefore, when discussing any vertical motion under gravity, equations 2.3 – 2.6, will apply, with $a = +g$ if motion is downwards, or $a = -g$ if motion is upwards. The following points also have to be noted:

(i)   If a body is simply dropped from a height, we put $u = 0$.

(ii)   When it is projected vertically upwards, the velocity $v = 0$ at maximum height.

(iii) When the body falls to the ground once again the height s above the ground is zero, $s = 0$.

Suppose two bodies of different masses are released simultaneously from the same height, they will both fall to the ground at the same time provided the effects of air resistance, etc, are neglected.   This follows from the equation:

$$s = ut + \tfrac{1}{2}gt^2$$
$$s = \tfrac{1}{2}gt^2 \;(\text{as } u = 0),$$
$$\therefore \quad t^2 = 2s/g,$$
$$t = \sqrt{(2s/g)}$$

i.e.   the time is independent of mass.

Example 2.7

A ball is released from a height of 20m. Calculate:

(a)   the time it takes to fall,

(b)   the velocity with which it hits the ground.

We are given $u = 0$, $s = 20m$, $a = g = 10ms^{-2}$.

(a) We are looking for time t. We do not know v therefore the equation we use is (2.6).

$$s = ut + \tfrac{1}{2}gt^2$$
$$or\ 20 = 0 + \tfrac{1}{2} \times 10t^2$$
$$t = 2s.$$

(b) To find v we can use $2.3 - 2.5$, since we now know everything except v.

Using (2.3): $20 = \left(\dfrac{v+0}{2}\right) \times 2$: $v = 20ms^{-1}$

Using (2.4): $v = 0 + 10 \times 2 = 20ms^{-1}$

Using (2.5): $v_2 = 0 + 2 \times 10 \times 20$
$$v^2 = 400$$
$$v = \sqrt{400}$$
$$\therefore v = 20ms^{-1}.$$

Hence any of the three formulae leads to the same result.

Example 2.8

A ball is thrown up vertically with a velocity of 40ms. Calculate:
(a) the maximum height reached;
(b) the time to reach the maximum height;
(c) the time to reach the ground again.

(a) Given $u = 40ms^{-1}$, $a = g = 10ms^{-2}$, $v = 0$ (at maximum height), we require s. The only equation not involving the unknown t is $v^2 = u^2 - 2gs$.
i.e $0 = 40 - 2 \times 10 \times s$
$$s = 80m.$$

(b) We can use $v = u + at$ to find t
i.e. $0 = u - gt$
$$t = \dfrac{u}{g} = \dfrac{40}{10} = 4s.$$

(c) The time to reach the ground again is expected to be twice the time taken to reach maximum height, i.e. $8s$. To find this we use $s = ut + \tfrac{1}{2}at_2$.
i.e. $s = ut - \tfrac{1}{2}gt^2$
$$= 0 = 40t - \tfrac{1}{2}10t$$
$$80t - 10t = 0$$
$$t(80 - 10t) = 0$$
$$t = 0\ or\ t = 8s$$

$t = 0$ corresponds to when the body started initially

$t = 8$ corresponds to when the body falls to the ground.

A body is projected horizontally from the top of a vertical cliff 40m high, with a velocity of 20ms^{-1}.

Calculate:
(a) the time taken for the body to fall to the ground;
(b) the vertical component of the velocity when the body hits the ground;
(c) the distance from the cliff when it strikes the ground.

(a) the time taken to reach the ground is independent of the horizontal motion. It is just as if the ball had been released from rest. It is therefore given by equation 2.6.
$$s = ut + \tfrac{1}{2}at^2$$
$$40 = 0 + \tfrac{1}{2} \times 10t^2$$
$$t = 2\sqrt{2}\ s = 2.83s.$$

(b) We use equation 2.5
$$v_2 = u_2 + 2as$$
$$v_2 = 0 + 2 \times 10 \times 40$$
$$v = 20\sqrt{2}\ ms^{-1} = 28.28s.$$

(c) The horizontal distance d from the cliff is just the distance travelled with the velocity of projection, 20ms^{-1} and time $t = 2\sqrt{2}$. The journey is independent of gravity.
$$\therefore\ d = ut = 20 \times 2\sqrt{2} = 56.57$$

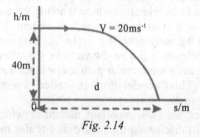

Fig. 2.14

Determination of the acceleration due to gravity
One way to find g is by timing the fall of a body from a height s. Using the equations of motion, the distance of fall is related to the time of fall t by:

$$s = \frac{1}{2}gt^2$$

Here, since the velocity is not constant, the displacement time graph will not be a straight line as we saw above, but will in fact be a parabola,

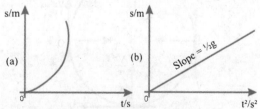

Fig. 2.15 (a) & (b) Distance-time graph for motion under gravity.

Fig. 2.15 (a). Now, if we plot a graph of s against t^2, we shall obtain a straight line through the origin with slope ½g, from which g can be calculated (see fig. 2.15(b)).

Experimental difficulties

In this experiment it is difficult to measure t accurately with an ordinary stopwatch since the time interval of fall is generally too small to be measured. Also there will be an effect on the time of fall due to air resistance which depends on the nature of the falling body. Only in a vacuum are all bodies expected to fall from the same height in the same time irrespective of their mass and shape. For this experiment to be accurate it should be performed in a vacuum and the time of fall measured with an electronic clock which can measure time to an accuracy of 0.001s.

2.9   Uniform circular motion

When an object moves with a constant speed in a circular path, we call the object's motion uniform circular motion. In this type of motion the speed of the object remains constant, but its direction is continuously changing, so that its velocity is changing.

The direction of motion at any instant is the direction of the tangent at that point. For example, the direction of motion at P is almost at right-angles with the directions at Q and is directly opposite the direction at the point R (see Fig, 2.16).

It can be shown that a body following a circular path has an acceleration which is acting towards the centre of the circle and which is responsible for making the body move in a circle. The magnitude of this acceleration can be shown to be v^2/r where r is the radius of the circular path and v is the uniform speed. This acceleration is called *centripetal acceleration*.

There are two important quantities which are useful in discussing the nature of circular motion. The first is the time **period** of the body performing circular motion. It is defined as the time taken to go round one complete circle and is measured in seconds. The second quantity is the **frequency** of the motion which is defined as the number of complete cycles described in one second. Frequency is measured in revolutions per second, or hertz (Hz).

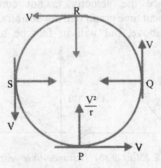

Fig. 2.16 Circular motion

The Centrifuge

This is a device used to produce large forces on objects by whirling them in a circle. In the laboratory, a centrifuge is used to whirl a test tube containing a solid in suspension, and the force produced on the particles of the solid makes them settle to the bottom of the test tube. Large centrifuges are also used to whirl test pilots and astronauts, and give them experience of large forces such as they might experience when an aeroplane turns suddenly, or a rocket takes off.

To see how a centrifuge works, consider a test tube being swung round in a circle (Fig. 2.17). As the test tube turns, the contents tend to carry on in a straight line. The test tube exerts a centripetal force on the contents to make them also turn in a circle. Thus the contents, continually tending to move forwards instead of centripetally, move outwards in relation to the test tube, and finally reach the closed end.

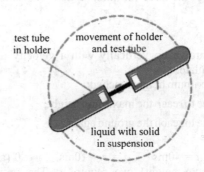

Fig. 2.17 Action of a centrifuge.

2.10   Cause of motion: Force

We have considered motion of a body without considering what makes it to move from its rest position or makes it change its state and direction of uniform motion. Such an agent that changes or tends to change the state of rest or of uniform motion of a body is called force.

Types of forces

There are two types of forces:

(a)   Contact forces   (b)   Field forces

(a)   *Contact forces* are forces which are in contact or in touch with the body to which they are applied. Examples are forces of push or pull, tension, reaction and frictional forces.

Friction is defined as a force which acts at the surface of separation between two objects in contact and tends to oppose the motion of one over the other. Detailed discussion on friction will be handled later.

(b)   *Field forces*: These are forces whose sources do not require contact with the body to which they are applied. Examples are gravitational force electrical (electrostatic) force, and magnetic force. Gravitational force is the force with which the earth attracts objects to its centre. Electrostatic force is the force between charged bodies. Magnetic forces exist around a bar magnet and a current carrying conductor. Effects of such forces are felt by bodies which are not in contact. Their actions are felt at a distance.

Summary

1. There are four major types of motion: random motion (disorderly motion as in case of gaseous particles), translational motion (motion without rotation; all points remains fixed) rotational motion(motion in a circle about a centre or axis), oscillatory motion to and fro type of motion, like a swinging pendulum).

2. The bearing of P from O is the angle which the line OP make with the northern direction ON in the clockwise sense from ON to OP. If $NOP = 30°$, we say that the bearing is N30°E.

3. A scalar quantity is one which has magnitude but no direction, e.g. distance.

4. A vector quantity is one which has magnitude as well as direction e.g. displacement.

5. Displacement is distance travelled in specified direction.

6. Speed v is the rate of change of distance or change of distance with time.

7. Average speed is (total distance travelled)/time taken.

8. Velocity is speed measured in a given direction, it is a vector quantity.

9. Acceleration is the rate of change of velocity.

10. Acceleration is uniform if the rate of change of velocity is constant.

11. For non-uniform motion, the slope of tangent at any point P in the v-t graph is the instantaneous acceleration at that point.

12. The four equations of uniformly accelerated motion are:
$$s = \left(\frac{v+u}{2}\right)t$$
$$v = u + at$$
$$s = ut + \frac{1}{2}at^2$$
$$v^2 = u^2 + 2as.$$

13. Area under the velocity time graph = total distance covered.

14. The acceleration of a body performing uniform circular motion is directed towards the centre of the circle and has magnitude v^2/r where v is the uniform tangential velocity and r is the radius of the circle.

15. There are two major types of force, contact forces and field forces. Contact force requires contact with the body to which they are applied, field forces acts at a distance.

Exercise 2

1. Which of these motions could be uniform?
   A. Molecular motion   B. Circular motion
   C. Vibrating pendulum D. Vibrational motion

2. Which of the following is incorrect?
   A. Distance is a scalar.
   B. Displacement is a vector.
   C. Speed is a vector.
   D. Velocity is a vector.

3. Which of the following equations is correct?
   A. $v = u + at$ B. $v = \frac{a}{t}$
   C. $v = u - at$ D. $v = at - u$

4. The slope of a displacement-time graph is equal to
   A. acceleration.   B. uniform velocity.
   C. uniform speed.   C. Instantaneous speed.

5. Draw a distance-time graph for uniform motion and interpret the graph.

6. Define instantaneous velocity and acceleration.

7. Use a sketch to explain the meaning of the following bearings N60°E, S40°W, 260°.

8. Distinguish between contact force and field force and give an example of each.

9. Explain clearly what is meant by average speed.

10. A body moving with a constant velocity along a straight line PQR takes 30s to go from P to Q and 10s to go from Q to R. If $PR = 4$m, find PQ.

11. An object moves in a straight line, starting from rest. There are two stages in the journey:
    (a) it gains speed uniformly for 2.0s and attains a speed of 8.0ms^{-1};
    (b) it continues at this speed for a further 1.5s.

    Draw a sketch-graph of speed against time.

    Find (i) the acceleration in stage (a);
    (ii) the acceleration in stage (b);
    (iii) the total distance moved during stages (a) and (b).

12. A train starts from rest from a station and travels with uniform acceleration $0.5ms^{-2}$ for 20s. It travels with uniform velocity for another 30s, the brakes are then applied so that a uniform retardation is obtained and the train comes to rest in a further 10s. Sketch the velocity-time graph of this motion. Using your graph, calculate the total distance travelled by the train.

13. A ball thrown vertically upwards from ground level hits the ground after 4s. Calculate the maximum height it reached during its journey ($g = 10ms^{-2}$).

14. A body is dropped from rest at a height of 80m. How long does it take to reach the ground? ($g = 10ms^{-2}$, ignore air resistance).

15. A motor car is uniformly retarded and brought to rest from a velocity $36kmh^{-1}$ in 5s. Find its retardation and the distance covered during this period.

16. A body travels from rest with acceleration $8ms^{-2}$. Find its velocity when it has covered a distance of 100m.

17. An object falls from a height of 20m. What is its velocity just before hitting the ground? (Take $g = 10ms^{-2}$).

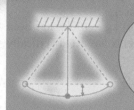

WORK, ENERGY AND POWER

Chapter 3

3.1 Forms of energy

The principles of work and energy are important in physics and engineering, especially since they are utilized in a great variety of machines upon which today's industrial technology is based. Also, the word energy appears in all branches of physics since, as we will see later, energy is shown in various forms. This is why it is one of the five themes that constitute physics.

The terms work and energy have several interpretations in ordinary conversation which include mental activity, farm work, playing, creating, destroying, etc. Therefore, a great deal of energy is required for most human activities. For man in his environment, the primary source of energy has been the muscles, combustible organic matter mainly in form of wood, coal and petroleum, rays of the sun, wind, water in motion, e.t.c.

The world energy resources are of two types: **renewable** and **non-renewable**.

Examples of the renewable resources are:

(a) *Solar energy:* When it falls on solar cells, electricity is produced. Light also is important in the production of carbohydrates in green plants.

(b) *Wind:* This turns the windmill, which produces electricity for work in the farm.

(c) *Hydroelectricity:* In dams, water turns generators and produces electricity e.g. Kainji Dam. Other examples are tides and oceans.

Examples of non-renewable resources are:

(a) *Petroleum:* The gas is used in power stations to produce electricity, e.g. a farm power station. The gas and kerosene are used as fuel for cooking. Petrol and diesel are used to drive vehicles. Thus, chemical energy is transformed to mechanical energy.

(b) *Coal:* Burning of coal produces much heat to boil water in turbines for production of electricity, and also for driving of trains and ships. Coal is used as fuel for cooking.

(c) *Nuclear energy:* This produces enormous heat to operate turbines and drive ships and aircrafts. With time, it will be put into more uses.

(d) Food eaten by man is broken down and energy released for human activities.

The world energy resources come from different sources. Solar energy comes from the sun. Wind comes from air and it is in rapid natural motion. Water comes from the rivers and oceans. Petroleum and coal are fossil fuels which were locked up in the soil millions of years ago. Radioactive materials, e.g. uranium are the sources of nuclear energy. Thus, there are many forms of energy: mechanical heat, light, electrical, atomic, solar energy, etc.

3.2 Concept of work

The term work can have several interpretations in ordinary conversation, including mental activity, such as working in the office or reading in school. In physics, however, work has only one meaning.

> Work is said to be done whenever a force moves a body through a certain distance in the direction of force, and is equal to the product of the force and the distance moved.

For example, work is done when you drag a lump of stone a certain distance, or when a body is raised through a certain distance, or when a car moves a certain distance. In each of these examples, the amount of work done is measured by the product of the force used and the distance moved in the direction of force.

Thus,

work = force x distance in the direction of force.

$$W = F \times s$$

or $W = F \times s \cos \theta$ 3.1

The SI unit of work is the joule (J).

> One joule is the work done when a force of 1 newton moves a distance of 1 metre.

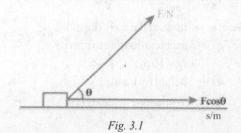

Fig. 3.1

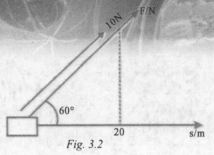

Fig. 3.2

Larger units are the kilojoule (kJ) and the megajoule (MJ).

$$1kJ = 10^3 J, \quad 1MJ = 10^6 J.$$

Example 3.1

A body is pulled along a horizontal plane by a constant force of 10N applied parallel to the plane.

(a) Calculate the work done in moving the body a distance of 20m.

(b) What work has been done if the same force is used on the body for the same distance but applied in a direction making an angle 60° to the horizontal as in Fig. 3.2?

Solution

(a) Work done is given by:

$W = F \times s$

$= 10 \times 20$

$= 200J.$

(b) The effective force moving the body is the component of the force parallel to the horizontal plane, F cos 60° (see Fig. 3.2). The movement in the direction of this force is 20m.

$W = F\cos 60° \times 20$

$= 10 \cos 60° \times 20$

$= 100J.$

Work done in a force field

The earth's gravitational field is an example of a force field. In gravitational field, there is always a force pulling a body towards the earth's centre. We defined the weight of a body as the force of attraction on the body due to the earth's gravity. This weight acts downwards. To lift a load through a height h, a pulling force must be applied to overcome the weight of the body. Therefore, when an object is lifted vertically upwards, work is done against the force of gravity. The magnitude of the work done is given by:

Work = force x distance

$= mg \times h$

$W = mgh$ 3.2

Where m = mass of the body (kg),

g = acceleration due to gravity

     (g = 10 ms⁻²),

h = height (m), and

W = Work done in joules (J).

A man of mass 80kg carries a load of bricks of mass 20kg up a vertical ladder of length 6m. What work has he done? (Take g as 10ms⁻²).

A total mass of (80 + 20) kg = 100kg has been lifted so a force of $(100 \times g)$ N has acted vertically through 6m.

Work done = $100 \times 10 \times 6$

$= 6000J$

$= 6kJ.$

Fall under gravity

If on the other hand a body of mass m falls from a vertical height h the total work done will also be equal to mgh.

Example 3.3

A stone of mass 10kg falls from a height of 2m. Calculate the work done.

Solution

Work done = mgh

$= 10 \times 10 \times 2$

$= 200 J.$

Example 3.4

A load of mass m slides down a smooth plane, with inclination, θ from point A to B. The same mass is then dropped from A to the ground C a vertical distance h. In which of the two situations is more work done?

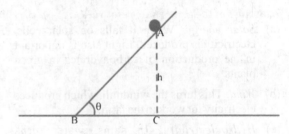

Fig. 3.3 Work depends on position, not path

In each case the force used is mg. Consider the work done along AC and AB.

Work done from A to C = mgh

Work done from A to B = $mg \times AB \sin θ$

$= mgh$

The same work is done in each case. Hence work done by gravitational force depends only on vertical distance moved and not on the path taken.

Energy can be defined as the capacity to perform work. Thus the unit of energy is the same as that of work, i.e., the *SI* unit of energy is the joule, J.

In the world we live in, energy appears in various forms as mentioned earlier.

(a) Kinetic energy, such as the energy of a moving car or a falling stone.

(b) Chemical energy, such as the energy in our food which makes us grow.

(c) Heat energy, such as the energy developed in a steam engine, or car.

(d) Electrical energy, such as the energy travelling through wires and used in driving our fans, running refrigerators and lighting houses.

(e) Light energy which enables us to see.

(f) Sound energy such as that from loudspeakers.

(g) Nuclear energy: energy from the nucleus of the atom.

(h) Elastic energy: energy stored in a spring.

Energy transformation and the conservation law

All the forms of energy listed above can be changed from one form to another by means of suitable machines or apparatus . For example, the energy in the nuclei of atoms produces heat energy, which in turn can be used to generate electrical energy. Solar energy (energy from the Sun) can be collected, stored and transformed into various forms of useful energy. The mechanical energy that moves a car comes from heat energy derived from the burning of fuel, which is stored as chemical energy. The telephone works on the principle of energy conversion from sound to electrical and back to sound. When brakes are applied to a moving car, the mechanical energy originally possessed by the car is not lost when the car stops, but is changed to heat in the brakes and tyres and some sound energy.

The principle of conservation of energy states that although energy can be changed from one form to another, the total energy of a given system remains unchanged, i.e, energy can neither be created nor destroyed during a transformation.

Or briefly, in an isolated or closed system the total amount of energy is always constant.

Mechanical energy

A body can posses mechanical energy or have the ability to work for two reasons, either by virtue of its position or because of its motion. For example, a car possesses energy due to its motion while a stone held at a height above the ground possesses energy because of its position. These two kinds of energy are called kinetic energy and potential energy respectively.

Kinetic energy is the energy a body possesses because it is in motion. The symbol is E_k.

Potential energy is the energy a body possesses because of its position. The symbol is E_p.

Potential energy

A body of mass m raised to a height h above the ground is said to possess potential energy. The quantity of energy is given by $E_p = mgh$.

Potential energy = work done
E_p = force × distance
E_p = $mg \times h$

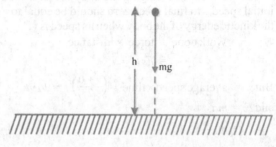

Fig. 3.4 Gravitational potential energy

This is equal to the work done when the mass m falls a distance h under gravity. The potential energy in this case is called **gravitational potential energy** because it arises from the force of gravity.

If a spiral spring is stretched a distance e, it is made to acquire an energy referred to as elastic potential energy. The magnitude of this energy can be shown to be $\frac{1}{2}ke^2$ where k is the elastic constant of the spring. A stretched catapult gives the stone potential energy, so that when released, the stone flies through the air with considerable speed.

Example 3.5

A body of mass 100kg is released from a height of 200m. With what energy does the body strike the ground? (Take $g = 10ms^{-2}$).

Gravitational potential energy is:

$E_p = mgh = 100 \times 10 \times 200$

$\qquad\qquad = 200\,000J$

$\qquad\qquad = 200kJ.$

This is all converted to kinetic energy by the time the body strikes the ground.

Kinetic energy

Kinetic energy is the energy due to motion.

Examples of kinetic energy

(i)   A rolling ball
(ii)   An object falling under gravity
(iii) Wind or air in motion
(iv)   An athlete running a race
(v)   A bullet movement
(vi)   A plane flying, e.t.c.

We should expect that the greater the speed of a body, the greater will be its kinetic energy and also the greater its mass, the greater will be the energy. For example, the kinetic energy of a lorry moving with a certain speed will be more than that of a small car moving with the same speed. A cannon ball moving with a speed of 100kmh will knock down a mud wall more easily than it would if it were moving at 2kmh^{-1}.

To obtain an expression for the kinetic energy of a body of mass m and speed v, let us assume that the body is acted upon by a constant retarding force F until it comes to rest in a distance s.

The work done in bringing the body to rest from initial speed v to final speed zero should be equal to the kinetic energy of the body when its speed is v.

$$\text{Work done} = \text{force} \times \text{distance}$$
$$= Fs$$

But $s = \text{average speed} \times \text{time} = \left(\dfrac{v+0}{2}\right) t = \frac{1}{2} vt$

and $F = ma$
$$= m\,\frac{v}{t}$$

$\therefore$ work done $= \dfrac{1}{2} vt \times \dfrac{mv}{t}$
$$= \frac{1}{2} mv^2$$
$$E_k = \frac{1}{2} mv^2$$

where m is the mass in kg, v is the speed in ms^{-1}.
i.e. work done = change in kinetic energy of the body.

Example 3.6
A boy of mass 30kg is running with a speed of 4ms^{-1}. What is his kinetic energy?

$E_K = \dfrac{1}{2} mv^2 = \dfrac{1}{2} \times 30 \times 4^2$
$$= 240J.$$

Example 3.7
A bullet of mass 40g is moving with a speed of 216kmh^{-1}. Calculate its kinetic energy.

We must convert all units to SI units before using the formula.

$40g = 0.04$kg

216kmh$^{-1} = \dfrac{216 \times 1000}{60 \times 60}$
$$= 60\text{ms}^{-1}$$

$E_K = \dfrac{1}{2} mv^2$
$$= \dfrac{1}{2} \times 0.04 \times 60^2$$
$$= 72J.$$

3.4 Conservation law of mechanical energy

As mentioned above, although energy can be transformed from one form to another, the total energy of the system remains the same.

This applies to mechanical systems. Potential energy can be transformed to kinetic energy and vice versa but in all cases the sum remains constant.
Let $K.E. = E_k$ and $P.E. = E_p$

$$E_k + E_p = \text{constant}$$
$$or \quad E_k + E_p \ \text{at any point} \qquad 3.3$$
$$= \ E_k + E_p \ \text{at another point}$$

A typical example of alternating potential and kinetic energy is that of simple pendulum.

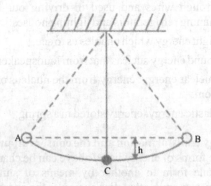

Fig. 3.5 Energy in simple pendulum.

When the pendulum swings from end to end, the energy of the system changes from potential to kinetic and vice-versa, but at each stage of the swing, the total energy remains constant.

At the furthest points from its rest position, the bob is momentarily still, and has no kinetic energy, but it is at its highest point and has maximum potential energy. As it passes through its rest position, it is at its lowest point and has no potential energy but it is moving fastest and has maximum kinetic energy. At all other positions:

$E_p + E_k = $ Constant.

E_p at furthest point, E_k at rest position.

Let the velocity at C the rest position be v_{max}
Loss in $P.E.$ at C must be equal to gain in $K.E.$
$mgh = \frac{1}{2}mv_{max}^2$

$$v = \sqrt{(2gh)} \qquad 3.4$$

Example 3.8
A stone of mass 0.5kg is thrown vertically upwards with a velocity of 10ms^{-2}. Find
(a) the potential energy at the greatest height h and the value of h,
(b) the kinetic energy on reaching the ground again (Assume $g = 10$ms and neglect air resistance).

On the ground the body has kinetic energy of $\frac{1}{2}mv^2$. The potential energy is zero since the height is zero. When it reaches the maximum height h, its velocity is zero so it has only potential energy.

Thus, applying the conservation law of energy at the ground and at the maximum height, we have,

$E_p + E_k$ on the ground $= E_p + E_k$ at maximum height

$$0 + \tfrac{1}{2}mv^2 = mgh + 0$$

(a) ∴ potential energy at maximum height

$$= mgh$$
$$= \tfrac{1}{2}mv^2$$
$$= \tfrac{1}{2} \times 0.5 \times 10^2$$
$$= 25J$$

The greatest height h is given by

$$mgh = \tfrac{1}{2}mv^2$$

$$h = \frac{v^2}{2g} = \frac{10^2}{20} = 5m.$$

The kinetic energy on reaching the ground again will have the same value, 25J, since mechanical energy is the same provided no energy has been lost due to air resistance and friction.

Example 3.9
A body of mass 2kg falls from rest through a height of 20m and comes to rest having penetrated a distance of 0.5m into sandy ground. Calculate the average force exerted by the sand in bringing the body to rest. (Take $g = 10ms^{-2}$).

If u is the velocity on reaching the ground, the conservation of energy gives.

$$\tfrac{1}{2}mu^2 = mgh \, (h = 20m)$$
$$= 2 \times 10 \times 20 = 400J.$$

This kinetic energy is converted into work which is done in penetrating a distance $s = 0.5m$ with an average force, F

$$0.5 \times F = 400$$
$$F = 800N.$$

Example 3.10
A ball of mass 2kg falls from rest from a height of 200m. Calculate its kinetic energy after falling a distance of 50m. (Neglect air resistance and take $g = 10ms^{-2}$).

Total energy at 200m $= E_p = mgh$
$$= 2 \times 10 \times 200$$
$$= 4000J$$

E_p at 150m $= 2 \times 10 \times 150$
$$= 3000J$$

Total energy at 150m $= E_p + E_k$
but $E_p + E_k = 4000J$,
where E_p (at 150m) $= 3000J$
hence, $3000 + E_k = 4000$
∴ $E_k = 4000 - 3000 = 1000J$
$$= 1kJ.$$

Power is defined as the time rate of doing work or the time rate of transfer of energy.

Average power $(P) = \dfrac{\text{work done or energy expended}}{\text{time taken}}$

$$= \text{energy or work per second}$$
$$= \frac{W}{t}$$
$$= \frac{F \times s}{t}$$
$$= F \times v \qquad\qquad 3.5$$

Where v is velocity.
The SI unit of power is called the watt (W) which is the rate of transfer of energy of one joule per second.

$$1W = 1Js^{-1}$$

Large units are the kilowatt (kW) and megawatt (MW)

$$1kW = 10^3W$$
$$1MW = 10^6W.$$

Sometimes the horse power (h.p) unit is used.

$$1 \text{ h.p} = 746 \text{ watts}$$
$$= 0.75kW.$$

A unit of energy that is sometimes used for electrical energy is the kilowatt-hour, kWh. This is the energy used by an appliance with a power of one kilowatt in one hour.

$$1kWh = 1000W \times 3600s$$
$$= 3.6 \times 10^6J$$
$$= 3.6MJ.$$

Example 3.11
Calculate the power of a pump which lifts 500kg of water through a vertical height of 4 metres in 5 seconds (assuming $g = 10ms^{-2}$).

Work is done against gravity in lifting the water

Power $= \dfrac{\text{work done}}{\text{time}} = \dfrac{\text{force used} \times \text{distance}}{\text{time}}$

$$= \frac{500 \times g \times 4}{5}$$
$$= \frac{500 \times 10 \times 4}{5} = 4000W = 4kW.$$

Example 3.12
A car travelling at a constant speed of $20ms^{-1}$ overcomes a constant frictional resistance of 300N. What is the horse power of the engine?
(Take $1 \text{h.p} = \frac{3}{4}kW$)

Engine power $= \dfrac{\text{work done}}{\text{time}} = F \times V$

$$= 300 \times 20$$
$$= 6000 \text{ watts}$$
$$= 6kW$$

$1 \text{ h.p} = \frac{3}{4}$ kW
or $1kW = \frac{4}{3}$ h.p.

∴ engine power $= 8$h.p.

If a force acts on a body and moves it in the direction of the force, we can plot a graph of force against distance. On this graph, the area under the curve represents force x distance, i.e., the work done or energy used.

Fig. 3.6 shows a force which is constant at F over a distance d.
Work done $= Fd$.

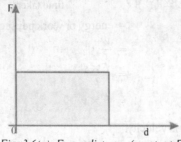

Fig. 3.6(a) Force-distance (constant F)

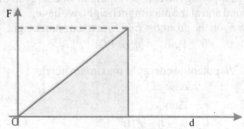

Fig. 3.6(b) Force-distance (variable F)

Fig. 3.6b shows a force which increases in proportion with distance, such as we get when stretching a spring. If the force reaches a maximum of F at extension d.

work done $=$ energy stored in spring
$=$ area of triangle
$= \frac{1}{2}Fd$.

Summary

1. Work is said to be done when a force moves a body through a distance in the direction of force. It is equal to the product of the force F and the distance s moved.

2. The unit of work is in joule, if F is in N and s is in metres. If a body of mass m moves up a distance h or falls through a distance h, the work done $= mgh$.

3. Energy is the capacity to do work. It is also measured in joules.

4. Principle of energy states that in an isolated system the total energy is always constant.

5. Kinetic energy is the energy due to motion $= \frac{1}{2}mv^2$.

6. Potential energy is energy stored in gravitational field. It is equal to mgh. In a spiral spring it is $\frac{1}{2}ke^2$.

7. Power is defined as the time rate of doing work.
Power $= W/t = Fs/t = F \times v$.
The unit is watt (W) i.e. joules per second.

Exercise 3

1. A boy of mass 60kg runs up a set of steps of total height 3m, work done in joules is.(Take $g = 10ms^{-2}$).

   A. 1800   B. 180   C. 20   D. 18

2. The speed of a bullet of mass 20g is 216 kmh⁻¹. What is its $K.E.$ in joules?

   A. 36000   B. 720   C. 36   D. 5.4

3. Which of the following statements is not correct?

   A. Elastic $P.E. = \frac{1}{2}kx^2$.   B. Power $= Fv$.
   C. Gravitational $P.E. = \frac{1}{2}gh$.   D. Unit of power is watt.

4. What is the engine power of a car with retarding force 500N moving at constant speed 20ms⁻¹?
   A. 10kW   B. 20kW   C. 30kW   D. 5kW

5. State the energy transformations which occur when a car is brought to rest by its brakes.

6. Describe the energy exchange that occurs: (i) as a clock spring unwinds (ii) as a catapult projects a stone.

7. A 2kg body is allowed to roll down an inclined plane 4m long with angle of inclination 30°. Calculate the work done. (Take g as $10ms^{-2}$).

8. A bullet of mass 0.05kg has a speed of 400ms⁻¹. What is its kinetic energy? If it hits a wall of which the average resistive force is 10000N, calculate the distance penetrated by the bullet.

9. A ball of mass 8kg falls from rest from a height of 100m. Neglecting air resistance, calculate its kinetic energy after falling a distance of 30m. (Take g as $10ms^{-2}$).

10. A boy whose mass is 40kg runs up a flight of 30 steps, each 150mm high, in 6 seconds. Find the average power developed. (Take g as $10ms^{-2}$).

11. A man strikes a nail into a wooden block, with an average force of 200N. If he continues to strike the nail with that force, estimate how much heat energy will be generated by the time the nail penetrates a depth of 0.05m.

12. An engine raises 100kg of water through a height of 60m in 20s. What is the power of the engine? (Take $g = 10ms^{-2}$).

13. A body of mass 10kg and initially at rest is subjected to a force of 20N through a distance of 10m. Calculate the change in kinetic energy of the body.

14. A certain coil spring with an unstretched length of 1m requires a force of 5N to stretch it 0.1cm. What work is done in stretching it by 1cm if the elastic limit is still not exceeded.

15. An engine pumps water from a river 10m below its own level and discharges it through a nozzle of diameter 10cm with a speed of 50ms⁻¹. Find the power required assuming: (a) no losses. (b) 70% efficiency. Water weighs $10^3 kgm^{-3}$. ($g = 10ms^{-2}$).

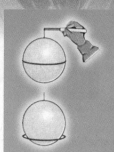

HEAT ENERGY

Chapter 4

4.1 Concept of heat and temperature

Heat makes us feel a sensation of hotness. It is a form of energy produced from different sources.

Production of heat

Heat is being produced by the sun, called *solar heat*. Heat is equally produced by friction; e.g. heat produced when we rub our palms together, vigorously for few minutes. The heat produced between the tyres of vehicles and the ground when brake is applied is due to friction. Heat could also be produced during chemical reactions, as one observes when tetraoxosulphate (VI) acid is introduced into a test tube of water.

Uses of heat

Heat serves man in various ways; like cooking our food, drying our cloths and warming our homes. In industries, heat is used for separating metals from their ores. The heat from the burning fuels in engines, provide vehicles and plane with the ability to move. Again, heat from the burning coal provides train with the ability to move.

Since heat can do all of the above work, we then define heat as a form of energy called *thermal* energy.

Heat is a form of energy which flows due to temperature difference

Concept of temperature

When a beaker of water is placed over a bunsen burner for a while, the water gets hotter. The heat from the burner has increased the temperature of the water. On the other hand, when we keep a cup of water inside a refrigerator, the temperature decreases, because heat is being drawn from the water to the refrigerator, hence the water becomes cooler.

Temperature is the degree of hotness or coldness of a body.

4.2 Effects of heat on matter

It has been observed and recorded that whenever heat is applied to a body, various changes take place. These changes include the following:

(i)   chemical changes,
(ii) change in physical property,
(iii) change in temperature of the body,
(iv) change of state of the body,
(v)   expansion of the body,
(vi) change in pressure of the body,
(vii) thermionic emission occurs (means emission of electron from metallic surface).

If one or more than one of the above changes take place after heat is applied to a body, the body may change in size or assume a different form (e.g, one can change from solid to liquid, and liquid to vapour).

4.3 Measurement of temperature

Temperature of a body is measured with an instrument called **thermometer**. There are various kinds of thermometer, each makes use of different substances, called **thermometric substances**, which change with change in temperature. (details to be discussed in future chapter).

4.4 Kinetic molecular theory

This states that:

1. all matters are made up of atoms and molecules;
2. these particles (molecules) are in a constant state of motion;
3. because they are in motion, they possess kinetic energy ($K.E.$);
4. the particles exert attractive force on one another;
5. the nearer the particles are to each other, the greater the attractive force.

Using kinetic theory to explain temperature of a body

From the statements of kinetic theory of molecules, it is obvious they possess kinetic energy of motion ($K.E.$). If heat is then applied to these moving molecules, their velocities increase and this of course, results to increase in the average kinetic energy ($\frac{1}{2}mv^2$). This no doubt leads to increase in temperature.

On the other hand, if the heat is reduced or completely withdrawn from the body, the velocities of the molecules decrease and the average kinetic energy reduces, hence the temperature decreases. These facts reveal that as the temperature of molecule increases, then the kinetic energy increases and vice versa.

4.5.1 Thermal expansion of solids

Solids expand when heated and contract when cooled. The rate of expansion and contraction differs for different types of solids. It depends on the material that the solid is made of. For example, the rate of expansion of brass is much more than that of iron and brass equally expands more than invar.

Experimental proof of solid expansion

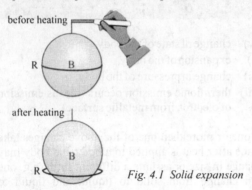

Fig. 4.1 Solid expansion

Ball and ring experiment

When the metal ball is heated for some minutes and made to pass through the ring, it is found that, it would no longer pass through the same ring it passed before heating. This is due to the expansion of the ball. If it is left to cool, and it is once more passed through the ring, it passes easily, showing that it has contracted back to its original size.

Effects of expansion in everyday life

Some of effects of expansion are observed in:
(i)   Railway lines and bridges
(ii)   Buildings
(iii) Wires (telephone, PHCN, TV, etc).

(i)   *Railway lines and bridges:* Gaps are left in between sections of rail on a railway line; this is to allow for expansion and contraction when the temperature increases or decreases respectively. In bridges (metal), one end of the bridge is allowed to rest on rollers, while one is fixed, this is to allow for expansion. During a very hot weather, as expansion occurs, the end on roller continues to roll. If the two ends are fixed, then no allowance is made for expansion, hence the bridge could bend or crack.

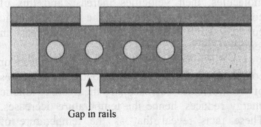

Gap in rails

Fig. 4.2(a) Expansion in a rail lines.

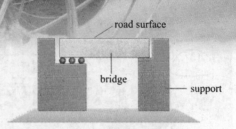

Fig. 4.2(b) Expansion of a bridge.

(ii)   *Buildings:* Expansion or contraction of galvanized iron sheets used in roofing of some buildings, generates creaking noise, which is heard when one is under the roof of such building.

(iii) *In telegraph wires:* During hot weather the metals used in constructing these wires, expand and sag, while during cold weather, they contract. To give room for these effects, the wires are originally given some allowance to allow for the expansion as well as contraction.

Applications of expansion

Expansion is applied in removing a tight stopper of a glass bottle without cracking either the bottle or the stopper. This is done by standing the bottle in boiling water, making sure the stopper is not in the water. As the bottle in boiling water expands, the stopper whose size does not alter, comes out loose.

One of the most important applications of expansion is seen in a bimetallic strip, which is used in the construction of a thermostat, a device for maintaining a steady temperature. The thermostat is used in electric laundry irons, in refrigerators and hot water storage.

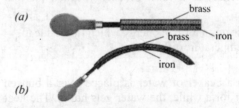

Fig. 4.3 The bimetallic strip

The bimetallic strip: This consists of two different metals rivetted together (fig. 4.3(a) and (b)). These different metals, brass and iron, when heated uniformly, it is found that the bimetallic strip bends (curves) with brass on the outside and iron in the inside (fig. 4.3 (b)). This is because, brass expands more than iron for the same temperature change. When the heat is removed, the strip cools, it straightens and gets back to its original shape.

Applications of bimetallic strip

These applications could be attributed to result of expansion. These include; the bimetallic strip thermometer, thermostat-applied in laundry iron and refrigerators, the balance wheel of clocks and watches, etc.

Bimetallic strip thermometer: This is made up of a coiled bimetallic spiral strip. The inside metal is usually made of invar or steel that hardly expands, while the outside is made up of brass. One end of the spiral strip is fixed and the other end is attached to the spindle of a pointer.

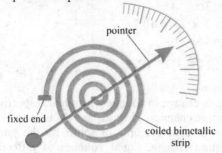

Fig. 4.4   The bimetallic strip thermometer

As the temperature is increased, the brass expands faster and more than the invar, the difference in expansion allows for the strip to curve inwards, making the pointer to move over a calibrated scale.

Working of a thermostat in electric laundry iron:
A bimetallic strip can be used to control the temperature of an electric laundry iron. When the switch is set to any desired temperature mark, then

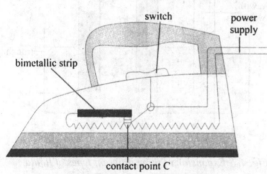

Fig. 4.5   The electric iron

the current is on, and the temperature of the iron increases. When a desired temperature is attained by the iron, the bimetallic strip (thermostat) is now curved, separates from the contact point C, thereby switching off the current, as the iron cools, the strip straightens up again and remakes contact, thus switching on the electric current once more. This make and break device regulates (controls) the temperature of the electric iron.

Linear expansivity of a solid (α)

> The linear expansivity of a solid (metal) is defined as increase in length per unit length for one degree rise in temperature.

Mathematically, it is defined as :

$$\alpha = \frac{l_2 - l_1}{l_1(\theta_2 - \theta_1)} K^{-1}$$

Where l_2, l_1 are the final and initial lengths of the solid at final and initial temperatures θ_2 and θ_1 respectively. Given that the linear expansivity or coefficient of linear expansion of iron is $12 \times 10^{-6} K^{-1}$, means that; the increase in length of a piece of iron per unit length multiplied by the change in temperature is $12 \times 10^{-6} K^{-1}$.

Example 4.1
A brass of length 100m increases to 100.5m, when heated from 50°C to 100°C. Calculate its linear expansivity (α).

Solution

$$\theta_2 = 100°C$$
$$\theta_1 = 50°C$$
$$l_2 = 100.5m$$
$$l_1 = 100.0m$$

Using;

$$\alpha = \frac{l_2 - l_1}{l_1(\theta_2 - \theta_1)} \text{ and substituting yields,}$$

$$\alpha = \frac{100.5 - 100}{100(100 - 50)}$$

$$= \frac{0.5}{100 \times 50}$$

$$= 10^{-4} K^{-1}.$$

Example 4.2
An iron rod of $\alpha = 12 \times 10^{-6} K^{-1}$ and $l_1 = 60m$, expands when heated through 100°C, Calculate (a) increase in length, (b) final length.

Solutions
(a) $l_2 - l_1 = \alpha l_1 \theta,$
$$= 12 \times 10^{-6} \times 60 \times 100$$
$$= 0.072m.$$

(b) $l_2 = l_1(1 + \alpha\theta)$
$$= 60(1 + 12 \times 10^{-6} \times 10^2)$$
$$= 60.072m.$$

Experimental determination of linear expansivity

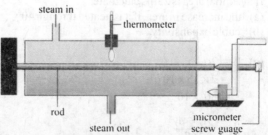

Fig. 4.6 Measurement of linear expansivity

The apparatus is as set up in figure 4.6. The length of the metallic rod is first measured and recorded, say; l_1. The initial temperature is also measured and recorded as θ_1. Then, steam is passed to the rod for some time, to allow for expansion. The final temperature of the rod is recorded as θ_2 and the micrometer screw guage is used in determining the increase in length of the rod say; (l_2-l_1). From definition of α, one can quickly determine the value of α, that is;

$$\alpha = \frac{l_2 - l_1}{l_1(\theta_2 - \theta_1)}$$

Area and volume (cubic) expansivity of solid

Here, the area and volume of a solid material are being considered. Let the initial and final areas of the solid material be A_1 and A_2 respectively. Then the initial and final temperatures be θ_1 and θ_2 respectively.

The area (superficial) expansivity (β) is given by

$$\beta = \frac{A_2 - A_1}{A_1(\theta_2 - \theta_1)}$$

Let $\quad \theta = \theta_2 - \theta_1$
$\therefore \qquad A_2 - A_1 = A_1 \beta\ \theta$

and $\quad A_2 = A_1(1 + \beta\ \theta)$

Similarly, the volume or cubic expansivity (γ) be given by;

$$\gamma = \frac{V_2 - V_1}{V_1(\theta_2 - \theta_1)}$$

$\therefore \quad V_2 - V_1 = V_1\gamma\theta$
$\qquad V_2 = V_1(1 + \gamma\theta)$

It is good to note that $\beta = 2\alpha$ and $\gamma = 3\alpha$

$\therefore \quad$ We can write $A_2 - A_1 = 2\ \alpha A_1\ \theta$
$\qquad\qquad$ and $A_2 = A_1(1 + 2\alpha\theta)$
Similarly $\quad V_2 - V_1 = 3\alpha\ V_1\theta$
And $V_2 = V_1(1 + 3\ \alpha\theta)$ (The proof is not required).

Example 4.3

The linear expansivity of a material is $15 \times 10^{-5}\text{K}^{-1}$. If the initial area is 25m^2, calculate:
(a) the increase in area, if it is heated through 40°C,
(b) cubic expansivity.

(a) $\beta = 2\alpha$
$\quad = 2 \times 15 \times 10^{-5}$
$\quad = 30 \times 10^{-5}$

$$\beta = \frac{A_2 - A_1}{A_1\theta},$$

$A_2 - A_1 \quad =$ increase in area
$\therefore \quad A_2 - A_1 \quad = A_1\beta\ \theta$
$\qquad\qquad\qquad = 30 \times 10^{-5} \times 25 \times 40$
$\qquad\qquad\qquad = 0.30\text{m}^2$.

(b) $\gamma = 3\alpha$
$\quad = 3 \times 15 \times 10^{-5}$
$\quad = 45 \times 10^{-5}$
$\quad = 0.45 \times 10^{-3}\text{K}^{-1}$.

Expansion of liquids

All liquids change in volume when their respective temperature changes. They expand about ten times as much as equal volume of solids for the same temperature change. Equal volumes of different liquids expand by different amounts when heated through the same temperature. We can demonstrate this by filling three similar glass bulbs with glass stems at the same level with water, benzene and alcohol.

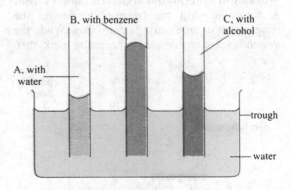

Fig. 4.7 Expansion of three different types of liquid.

The three bulbs are left in a trough of water for some time, to allow them attain the same temperature. The trough is then heated and the water in the trough is continuously stirred to ensure uniform temperature. It is observed that the levels of the three liquids rise by different amounts with water (in glass bulb A) rising least and benzene, the highest.

Volume or cubic expansivity of a liquid

Since liquids have no lengths or surface areas of their own, we only consider their volume, as they only take up the volume of containers that contain them. As such, we only discuss the volume or cubic expansivity of liquids.

In considering the above, we have to define the real (absolute) and apparent expansivity of liquids.

Real (absolute) cubic or volume expansivity (γ_r) of a liquid is defined as the increase in volume per unit volume per unit rise in temperature.

Apparent cubic or volume expansivity (γ_a) of a liquid is defined as the increase in volume per unit volume for a unit rise in temperature when the liquid is heated in an expansible vessel.

The real expansivity is normally greater than the apparent because, in apparent expansivity, the expansion of the container has to be taken into account, hence we can write:

real expansivity

= apparent expansivity + cubic expansivity

i.e. $\gamma_r = \gamma_a + \gamma$

Where γ_r = real expansivity

γ_a = apparent expansivity

γ = cubic expansivity of the material containing the liquid.

(a) Experimental determination of apparent cubic expansivity (γ_a), using pipette method

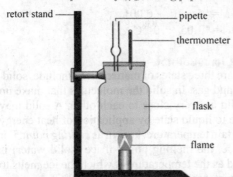

Fig. 4.8 Apparent cubic expansivity of liquid using pipette method.

This could be determined by using a pipette of a known volume, say, 20.0cm³. A flask of known volume is filled with the liquid whose cubic expansivity is to be determined. Then the pipette is placed such that the zero mark coincides with the level of water in the flask. The initial temperature of water θ_1 and the volume V_1 are recorded. Then heat is applied, and the liquid expands and fills up the pipette, the final temperature θ_2 is recorded. Then the apparent cubic expansivity γ_a is given by;

$$\gamma_a = \frac{V_2 - V_1}{V_1 (\theta_2 - \theta_1)}$$

(where $\theta = \theta_2 - \theta_1$).

Precautions

(i) The pipette must be placed in such a way that the zero mark is exactly coinciding with the level of water in the flask.

(ii) The thermometer must be placed vertically upwards.

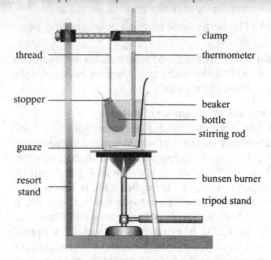

Fig. 4.9 Apparent cubic expansion of a liquid.

The coefficient of apparent expansion of a liquid such as paraffin can be determined with the apparatus as seen in the fig. 4.9.

The specific gravity bottle that has been cleaned and dried is weighed empty, and its mass recorded, say, m_1.

The bottle is then filled with paraffin and wiped dry after the stopper has been replaced. It is then re-weighed and the mass, say, m_2 is recorded.

The bottle is then suspended with its entire body immersed in the water to the depth of its tip. The initial temperature of the water is recorded say, θ_1. The whole content is heated and stirred continuously to ensure uniform temperature. It is observed that some liquid is expelled through the opening of the bottle. The water is allowed to continue boiling until no more liquid is expelled. Then the final temperature of the content is recorded. The specific gravity bottle is removed from the water and allowed to cool, after which it is again wiped dry and re-weighed, say, m_3.

Calculations

Mass of empty bottle = m_1

Mass of bottle + liquid = m_2

Mass of bottle + liquid left = m_3

Initial temperature = θ_1

Final temperature = θ_2

Mass of liquid expelled from the bottle = $(m_2 - m_3)$

Mass of liquid left in the bottle = $(m_3 - m_1)$

Temperature change = $(\theta_2 - \theta_1)$

Coefficient of apparent expansivity (γ_a)

$$= \frac{\text{mass expelled}}{\text{mass left} \times \text{temperature change}}$$

i.e. $\gamma_a = \dfrac{m_2 - m_3}{(m_3 - m_1)(\theta_2 - \theta_1)}$

Precautions

(i) The water in the beaker must be stirred constantly to ensure uniform temperature.

(ii) The bottle must be dried before adding liquid into it.

(iii) The bottle must be suspended with much care so that the water in the beaker does not enter through the mouth.

Anomalous expansion of water

It has been observed that water and few other substances do not continue to expand continuously with increase in temperature. For example; when ice at say -10°C is heated, it expands slightly until the temperature of 0°C, thereafter it melts into water at the same 0°C, and begins to contract between 0°C to 4°C, which is exceptional and abnormal. Then from 4°C to 100°C it expands, behaving as a normal liquid, and most liquids. As the mass remains constant while the volume decreases and gets to its minimum value at 4°C, the density (mass/volume) increases and reaches its maximum value at 4°C. This behaviour of water is said to be anomalous.

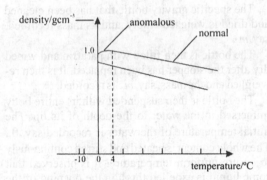

Fig. 4.10 Anomalous behaviour of water.

It is important to note that, if water is cooled below 4°C, it becomes lighter and rises. Ice at 0°C can therefore be formed at the surface of a pond, while at the bottom of the pond, water of about 4°C will still be available. This is why animals and plants can survive at the bottom of a frozen lake.

Example 4.4

A mercury in-glass thermometer has a bulb of volume $0.4cm^3$ and a tube of area $20 \times 10^{-5}cm^2$. Calculate:

(i) the apparent increase in the volume of the mercury when the temperature rises from 0°C to 100°C;

(ii) the distance between the fixed points $(\gamma_a = 12 \times 10^{-6} \, {}^\circ C^{-1})$.

Solution

(i) $\gamma_a = \dfrac{V_2 - V_1}{V_1(\theta_2 - \theta_1)}$

$V_2 - V_1 = \gamma_a v_1 (\theta_2 - \theta_1)$

$\therefore \ V_2 - V_1 = 12 \times 10^{-6} \times 0.4 \times 100$

$= 48 \times 10^{-5} cm^3$.

(ii) Volume of the tube

$20 \times 10^{-5} \times h = 0.00048$

$\therefore \ 0.0002h = 0.00048$

$h = \dfrac{0.00048}{0.0002}$

$= 2.4cm$

hence, $h = 2.4cm$.

Example 4.5

(i) Calculate the apparent expansivity of a liquid whose increase in volume is $0.05m^3$ and original volume is $10m^3$, if it is raised through a temperature of 100°C.

(ii) Assuming the expansivity of the container is $0.001°C^{-1}$, calculate the real expansivity of the liquid.

Solution

$\gamma_a = \dfrac{V_2 - V_1}{V_1(\theta_2 - \theta_1)}$ and substituting we get;

$= \dfrac{0.05}{10 \times 100}$

$= 5 \times 10^{-5} \, {}^\circ C^{-1}$.

(ii) $\gamma_r = \gamma_a + \gamma$

$= 5 \times 10^{-5} + 0.001$

$= 1.05 \times 10^{-3} \, {}^\circ C^{-1}$.

4.6 Change of state

There are three states of matter, these include, solid, liquid and gas. In solid the molecules that make up the solid are very close to each other. A solid may change to liquid state by application of heat energy at a certain temperature, known as *melting point*. For example, the melting point of ice (solid water) is defined as the temperature at which the ice melts to liquid water at the same temperature (0°C).

> This process is referred to as fusion of ice, which means the ice changes from solid state to liquid state without change in temperature when heat is supplied to ice.

On the other hand, when heat is removed from liquid it changes to solid, example is a cup of water placed in a refrigerator, gives out heat to the surrounding and hence forms block of ice. A substance changing from solid to liquid absorbs heat, while a substance changing from liquid to solid gives out heat to the surroundings. The heat absorbed by a solid substance in changing from solid to liquid is called the **latent heat of fusion**.

In liquid state, it is observed that for liquid to change to gaseous state, it will absorb some quantity of heat. At a certain temperature, vaporization starts to take place. This temperature continues to remain steady until all the liquid is vaporized. This temperature is referred to as *boiling point* of the liquid in question.

We can then define vaporization as a process by which a liquid substance changes from liquid state to gaseous state at a steady temperature when heat is supplied to it.

It is striking to note that some liquids change to vapour before their boiling point; this is known as **evaporation**. This can take place at all temperatures. In gaseous state, gases can change to liquid as they cool, that is when heat is withdrawn from them. This happens when they lose heat and condense.

4.7 Heat transfer

Heat energy may be transferred from one point to another, by any of these three modes: **conduction**, **convection** and **radiation**.

Conduction of heat: This is a process by which heat is passed along a metal object from one particle at higher temperature to another of lower temperature without the heated particle appearing to move.

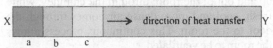

Fig. 4.11

Consider a metal rod $X Y$ (fig 4.11), with the end X placed in a flame, the other end Y, soon gets heated up. This is due to heat transfer by conduction. During this energy (heat) transfer, the particles maintain their own mean (average) position, but transfer heat by their vibrational motion.

Conductors: All metals are good conductors of heat, but the rate at which they conduct heat (thermal conductivity) differ from metal to metal. Example: copper and silver are very good conductors of heat.

Experiment to show that metals are good conductors of heat.

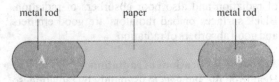

Fig. 4.12 Metal as a good conductor of heat.

A paper is wrapped round a metallic rod as shown above, and one end (A) placed in a bunsen flame for a short time. It is soon observed that the other end (B), becomes hot, while the paper is unaffected. This is because the metal AB being a good conductor, conducts heat quickly away from the paper.

When the experiment is repeated wrapping the paper round a wood and repeating the same procedure, the paper burns away because wood is a poor conductor. On the other hand, if the paper is

replaced by a metal, it is observed that the metal heats up easily.

Poor conductors are paper, cloth, glass, air, cork and asbestos.

Experiment to show that water is a poor conductor of heat.

A piece of ice is wrapped with a wire gauze and put in a test tube of water when the water is heated from above, it soon starts boiling at the top without heating the water below and the ice remains unaffected.

The test tube is held at an inclined position.

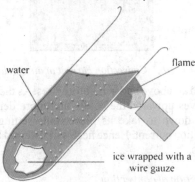

Fig. 4.13 Water as a poor conductor.

Applications of good conductors
(i)   Cooking utensils are made of metals so that heat is conducted easily and quickly through them.
(ii) In the past, Humphry Davy's lamp made use of high conductivity power of metals.

Applications of poor conductors
(i)   Roof of air conditioned rooms or heated rooms should be properly insulated, so that heat from the surroundings will not get into the house.
(ii) In cold countries, loose clothings keep the wearer warmer than tight clothings because air trapped between the clothing layers does not conduct heat away from the body easily.
(iii) Cement floors of a room is always colder on our feet than a carpet or rug lying on the same floor. This is because, the cement floor is a better conductor than the carpet or rug, and conducts heat away from our bare feet, faster than the rug or carpet.

Convection: This is the process by which heat energy is transferred in a fluid (liquid or gas) by the actual movement of the heated particles.

When fluid is heated from below or cooled from above as shown in fig. 4.14, convection current is set up. This convection current is due to expansion of air when heat is applied below. Since the mass of air remains the same, the air becomes less dense than

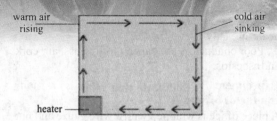

Fig. 4.14 (a) Convection current in heater.

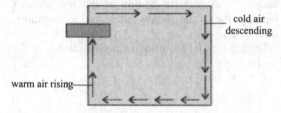

Fig. 4.14 (b) Convection current in air condition.

the cold air above and it therefore rises. As the warm air moves upwards the colder and more dense air moves down to take its place, thus setting up a convection current. Hence heat is transferred by this process.

Application of convection

The above explanation is responsible for the:
(i)   origin of land and sea breeze;
(ii)   the rise of smoke in a chimney;
(iii)   house ventilation, motor car cooling system and domestic hot water system.

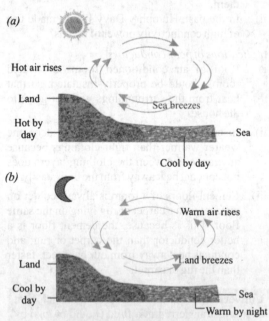

Fig. 4.15 Land and sea breezes.

During the day in summer, the land is heated up by the sun to a temperature higher than the sea temperature. The air above the land is heated and rises, and cooler air from sea takes its place. Air higher in the atmosphere completes the circulation and sea-breeze is obtained. The reverse is the case at night.

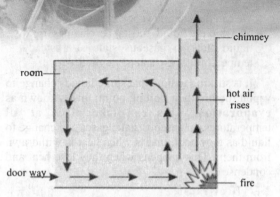

Fig. 4.16 Circulation of air in a room.

Ventilation of a room

Convection current is responsible for circulation of fresh air in a room. The air around the burning fire at one end of the room opposite the door, gets heated up, and as such, rises and finds its way through the chimney (fig. 4. 16). Fresh air moves in through the door to replace the hot air. A convection current is set up, and as the fire continues to burn, heated air rises up and out of the room through the chimney, while fresh, cool and more dense air comes through the door to the room. This continuous process allows the room to be ventilated.

Radiation

This is the process by which heat is transferred from its source to the body absorbing it without heating the intervening medium.

Convection and conduction need material medium for their propagation but radiation needs no medium for its propagation. Radiation passes quite easily through a vacuum. The heat reaching us on the earth from the sun travels through a vacuum. The radiant energy from the sun has electrical as well as magnetic properties, and is referred to as **electromagnetic radiation**.

Shiny surfaces or good radiators are poor emitters of radiation and also poor absorbers of radiation. Black surfaces or bad radiators are good emitters and good absorbers of radiation.

Practical applications of radiation

Heat from the sun gets to us mainly by radiation, so is heat from the fire. In hot climate we can keep the house cooler through reflecting back the suns rays, by having a shining roof and painting the walls with light colours. It is not advisable to wear a dark coloured jacket in the tropics because of the heat it causes to the wearer.

A thermos flask keeps hot substance hot or cold because it prevents heat loss or gain through conduction, convection and radiation.

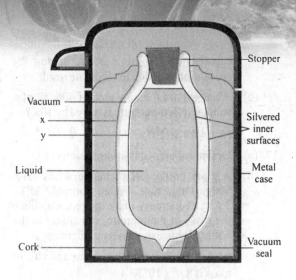

Vacuum
x
y
Liquid
Cork

Stopper
Silvered inner surfaces
Metal case
Vacuum seal

Fig. 4.17   Thermos flask

A thermos flask is used in keeping the temperature of its contents constant. This means that if a hot substance or a cold substance is placed inside the flask, they will stay hot or cold respectively.

The principal features of a thermos flask consist of a double walled glass vessel inside which has:

(i)   a vacuum between the walls,

(ii)   the two interior facing walls *x* and *y* (silvered inner surfaces) coated with silver,

(iii) insulating cork supports at the bottom,

(iv)   an insulating plastic or cork stopper.

If a hot liquid is poured into the flask, the vacuum prevents heat losses by conduction and convection. The silvered walls prevent loss of heat by radiation, this is because silver being a poor radiator, any heat radiated from one wall is reflected back by the other. The insulating stopper reduces loss of heat (from hot liquid, upwards to the outside) by convection. The insulating cork supports prevent heat loss from the glass to the surrounding flask by conduction. Thus, a hot liquid is kept hot and a cold liquid kept cold in the flask.

Summary

1. Heat is referred to as thermal energy, which can do work, unit is in Joules (J). It is a form of energy that flows due to temperature difference.

2. Temperature is a measure of degree of hotness or coldness of a body, unit is in Kelvin (K) or degree centigrade ($^{\circ}$C).

3. When heat is supplied to a body, any of the following changes can take place: temperature change, change of state, expansion, change in pressure, change in physical or chemical properties or thermionic emission can occur.

4. Kinetic theory explains that the average kinetic energy of molecules increases when the temperature increases through the addition of heat.

5. Rate of expansion and contraction differ for different types of materials. Effects of expansion are seen in railway lines, metal bridges, buildings and telegraph wires.

6. Applications of expansion are seen in thermostats, it is equally seen in bimetallic strip and thermometer.

7. Linear expansivity (α) of a solid is defined as increase in length per unit length for one degree rise in temperature.

8. Area expansivity (β) is the increase in area per unit area for one degree rise in temperature ($\beta = 2\alpha$).

9. Volume expansivity (γ) is the increase in volume per unit volume for one degree rise in temperature ($\gamma = 3\alpha$).

10. $\gamma_r = \gamma_a + \gamma$ (where γ_r is the real expansivity and γ_a is apparent expansivity and γ is the cubic expansivity of the container).

11. Water contracts between 0°C to 4°C which is exceptional and abnormal and is termed anomalous behaviour of water.

12. Three states of matter include, solid, liquid, and gaseous state. Solid state can change to liquid and to vapour and vice versa.

13. Transfer of heat is by three modes-conduction, convection and radiation.

14. Good radiators are poor emitters of radiation and also poor absorbers of radiation. (Example of this is shinny surfaces).

15. Black surfaces or bad radiators are good emitters and good absorbers of radiation.

Exercises 4

1. The heat from the sun reaches the earth mainly by the process of
    A. conduction.   B. radiation.
    C. convection.   D. reflection.

2. In which of the following is the molecules of water moving fastest?
    A. Steam   B. Ice
    C. Ice-water mixture D. Water

3. Calculate the linear expansivity (α) of brass of length 120m, that assumes a new length of 120.05m when heated through a temperature 100°C.
    A. $0.42 \times 10^{-5}K^{-1}$ B. $0.6 \times 10^{-4}K^{-1}$
    C. $0.52 \times 10^{-5}K^{-1}$ D. $0.44 \times 10^{-4}K^{-1}$

4. Using α calculated from question 3 above, determine the increase in volume of a brass container, with original volume (v_1) equals 100m³, if heated through a temperature of 50°C.

   A. 0.061m³   B. 0.042 m³

   C. 0.0044 m³   D. 0.052m³.

5. Which of the following surfaces is the best absorber of radiant energy?

   A. White   B. Black   C. Red   D. Yellow

6. All of these except one are applications of expansion in metals.

   A. Temperature control in laundry electric iron.

   B. Bimetallic strip thermometer.

   C. Compensated balance wheel of a watch.

   D. Sagging of telegraph wires.

7. 250cm³ of liquid increased by 10cm³ when heated through a temperature of 80°C. Calculate the apparent expansivity (γ_a), as well as the real expansivity (γ_r), taking cubic expansivity of the container to be $0.001 \times 10^{-3} K^{-1}$.

   A. $0.5 \times 10^{-3} K^{-1}$ and $0.500 \times 10^{-3} K^{-1}$.

   B. $0.2 \times 10^{-3} K^{-1}$ and $0.500 \times 10^{-2} K^{-1}$

   C. $0.25 \times 10^{-2} K^{-1}$ and $0.12 \times 10^{2} K^{-1}$

   D. $0.003 \times 10^{-3} K^{-1}$ and $0.001 \times 10^{-2} K^{-1}$

8. In a thermos flask, one of these prevents loss of heat by radiation:

   A. Cork stopper   B. Silvered walls

   C. Vacuum   D. Cork supports below the flask.

9. Circulation of fresh air in a room is as a result of

   A. radiation.   B. conduction.

   C. convection.   D. expansion.

10. (a) Define linear expansivity α of a solid.

    (b) The ratio of linear expansivity of copper to that of iron is approximately 1:5. A specimen of iron and specimen of copper expand by the same amount per unit rise in temperature. What is the ratio of the length of iron to that of copper?

11. (a) Describe briefly how you can experimentally determine the linear expansivity (α) of a solid, stating all precautions needed for accurate result.

    (b) What will be the new area of 400cm² of a solid, if its temperature is raised by 10K? ($\alpha = 19 \times 10^{-6} K^{-1}$).

12. (a) Define apparent cubic expansivity (γ_a).

    (b) A glass bottle full of mercury has mass 500g. On being heated through 35°C, 2.43g of mercury are expelled. Calculate the mass of the mercury remaining in the bottle. Cubic expansivity of mercury $= 1.8 \times 10^{-4} K^{-1}$) and linear expansivity of glass is $8.0 \times 10^{-6} K^{-1}$).

13. (a) Sketch a graph of density against temperature of water to show variation of water density with temperature.

    (b) Explain the term anomalous expansion of water.

    (c) Use kinetic theory to explain temperature of a substance (liquid).

14. (a) State three modes of transfer of heat.

    (b) Describe each and state any application of each in every day life.

15. (a) What materials are regarded as poor conductors? State at least five of such.

    (b) What are some of applications of poor conductors?

16. (a) Distinguish between real and apparent expansivity of a liquid.

    (b) Describe briefly experiment needed to determined the apparent expansivity of a paraffin liquid.

    (c) Given that the apparent expansivity (γ_a) of a liquid is $0.00015 \times 10^{-3} K^{-1}$, and the linear expansivity of the container is $0.00012 \times 10^{-3} K^{-1}$, calculate the real expansivity (γ_r).

ELECTRICAL CHARGES

Chapter 5

5.1 Electric charges and structure of matter

Static electricity may be defined as electric charge at rest. We can only describe the properties of such charges and their behaviour. Many effects due to static electricity can be observed.

A plastic comb rubbed with a cloth will make someone's hair stand on end if placed near it. The friction between the silk and the amber caused the amber to become charged and this helped the silk to stick to it. The word for electricity comes from the Greek word for amber elektron.

The interaction between electric charges at rest can be observed by considering a plastic rod and a piece of fur. If the rods are charged by rubbing them with fur, the rods repel each other. If glass rods are rubbed with silk, the glass rods become charged and repel each other. It is found that a charged plastic rod attracts a charged glass rod. Furthermore, the plastic rod and the fur attract each other while the glass rod and the silk attract each other. From these experiments, Benjamin Franklin (1706-1790) confirmed that there were two types of static charges; negative and positive.

Glass rubbed with silk becomes positively charged. Plastic rod rubbed with fur becomes negatively charged. Two positive charges or two negative charges repel each other. A positive charge and a negative charge attract each other. It is concluded from experiment that:

> Like (similar) charges repel; unlike (opposite) charges attract.

Cellulose acetate may be used for positive and polythene for negative charge since these are less affected by damp conditions. In addition, a clean duster may be used as a rubber instead of fur or silk.

Electric charge is one of the fundamental attributes of the particles of which matter is made. The structure of ordinary matter is made up of atoms and molecules.

The structure of atoms can be described in terms of three particles: the negatively charged **electron**, the positively charged **proton** and the uncharged **neutron**. The protons and neutrons in an atom make up a small, very dense core called **nucleus** with dimensions of the order of 10^{-15}m. Surrounding the nucleus are the electrons extending out to diameter of the order of 10^{-10} m from the nucleus. The negatively charged electrons are held within the atom by the attractive electric forces exerted on them by the positively charged nucleus. The protons and neutrons are held within the atomic nuclei by the **nuclear force**.

The masses of the individual particles are:

Mass of electron, m_e = $9.1093897 \times 10^{-31}$kg

Mass of proton, m_p = $1.6726231 \times 10^{-27}$kg

Mass of neutron, m_n = $1.6749286 \times 10^{-27}$kg.

With over 99.9% of the mass of any atom concentrated in its nucleus, m_p is about 2000 times that of m_e.

The negative charge on the electron has exactly the same magnitude as the positive charge on the proton. In a neutral atom, the number of electrons is equal to the number of protons in the nucleus. If one or more electrons are removed, the remaining positively charged structure is called a **positive ion**. A **negative ion** is an atom that has gained one or more electrons. This process of gaining or losing electrons is termed **ionization**. Fundamental principle is the "principle of conservation of charge", i.e. the algebraic sum of all electric charges in any closed system is constant.

In any charging process, charge is not created nor destroyed; it is merely transferred from one body to the other as in the glass-silk and plastic-fur cases.

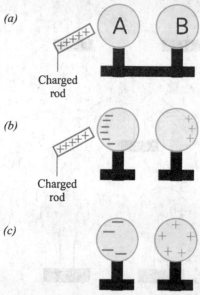

Fig. 5.1 Charging by contact.

Another important principle is that the magnitude of charge of the electron or proton is a natural unit of charge; hence charge is quantized (in discrete values). Thus the charge on any body is always either zero or an integer multiple (negative or positive) of the electron charge.

5.2   Production of charges

Charges can be produced by:
(i)   friction;
(ii)   contact; and
(iii)   electrostatic induction.

(i)   **By friction:** When an ebonite rod is rubbed with fur, the ebonite rod acquires a charge by friction; similarly, a glass rod acquires a charge by friction when rubbed with silk cloth.

Equal and opposite charges are produced by friction. Thus when an ebonite rod is rubbed with fur, negative charges are produced on the rod and an equal number of positive charges are left on the fur.

(ii)   **By contact:** Two metal spheres A and B are placed on insulating stands as in fig 5.1. The spheres are now brought together in contact, and a positively charged rod kept near A (Fig 5.1(a)). When the spheres are separated, they acquire charges as shown in fig 5.1(b), with the charged rod removed, A and B acquire opposite sets of charges as in fig. 5.1(c).

(iii)   **Electrostatic Induction:**   When a plastic rod brought near a body gives a charge of opposite sign without losing any of its own charge, this process is called **charging by induction.**

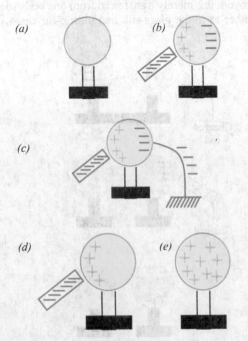

Fig. 5.2 Charging by induction.

Fig 5.2 shows an example of charging by induction. A metal sphere is supported on an insulating stand in fig 5.2(a). When a negatively charged rod is brought near it, the free electrons in the metal sphere are repelled by the excess electrons on the rod (fig 5.2(b)) and they shift toward the right, away from the rod. They cannot escape from the sphere because the stand and surrounding air are insulators. So we have negative charge at the right surface of the sphere and a net positive charge at the left surface. These excess charges are called **induced charges**.   With the plastic rod in place, a wire is used to touch the right surface of the sphere and the other end of the wire to earth (fig 5.2(c)). The earth being a conductor acts as a sink for unwanted electrons and the negative charge flows through the wire to earth.

Now if the wire is disconnected (fig5.2(d)) and the rod is removed (fig 5.2(e)), a net positive charge is left on the sphere. The charge on the negatively charged rod has not changed during this process, the earth acquires a negative charge that is equal in magnitude to the induced positive charge remaining on the sphere.

The gold leaf Electroscope - Detection of charge

An electroscope is an instrument used for the detection and testing of small electric charges, fig 5.3 illustrates a type of electroscope. It consists of a brass rod on which is placed a brass cap. At its lower end is a brass plate to which a leaf of thin gold or aluminum is attached. The leaf is protected from draughts by enclosing it in a metal case with glass windows, which is connected to earth. The brass rod is supported by passing it through a rubber bong or dry wooden cork at the top of the case. The gold leaf can be used to detect the nature of charge on a body. It is known experimentally that if the charge on the electroscope is already positive and a positively charged body is brought near the cap, the leaf is seen to diverge more; similarly if the electroscope has a negative charge and a negatively charged body is brought near, there is increase in divergence of the leaf from the brass plate.

An increase in divergence of the leaf occurs when the charge on the electroscope and the charge on the body are of the same kind, but if the charges are of different or opposite sign, there is decrease in divergence. The insulating or conducting properties of materials can be tested by the gold leaf electroscope.

The substance may be held in the hand and brought into contact with the cap of a charged electroscope if the substance is a good insulator, there will be no leakage of charge through it, and the leaf divergence will not alter. If the leaf collapses instantly, it shows that the substance is a good conductor.

Good insulators or poor conductors such as wood, wool, or cotton would produce a slow collapse of the leaf. This arises because of their moisture content, if dried thoroughly, they become good insulators.

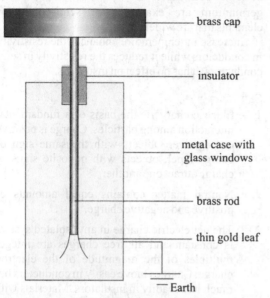

Fig. 5.3 Gold leaf electroscope

5.3. Distribution of charges on a conductor

If the distribution of charges over the surface of a conductor is examined, charges are not uniformly distributed except on spherical surfaces. In general, charges concentrate at places where the surface is sharply curved. Thus, the surface charge density or charge per unit area is very large at sharp points with very small areas. This is the case with the pear-shaped conductor in fig 5.4. It is found that the charges reside only on the outside surface of a conductor and not inside.

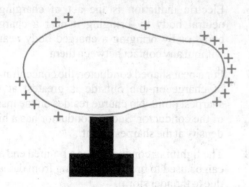

Fig. 5.4 Distribution of charges on a conductor.

Lightning and lightning conductors

The atmosphere is known to contain ions or charged particles which have been produced by ultra-violet rays, radiation from the sun, and cosmic radiation which enter the atmosphere from outer space. Lightning is a sudden discharge or neutralizing of electric charges and it occurs when charges build up in cloud.

In a thunder cloud, there is a region of positive charges and another region of negative charges. As the charges build up, the attraction increases steadily until a heavy spark or discharge is produced as the charges approach one another. This spark is observed as a very bright flash which we call lightning. During the discharge to earth, lightning strikes the tallest part of a building and the charge is conducted to the earth through the path of least resistance. The current passing may produce tremendous heat and can sometimes set the house ablaze.

In order to protect a building from damage a lightning conductor is employed. It consists of a thick strip of metal capable of carrying heavy current without melting e.g. copper. At its upper end there is a sharp point which extends above the roof. The lower end of the conductor is buried beneath the soil attached to a large sheet of copper plate to ensure good contact. When a strongly charged cloud passes over the conductor, large opposite charge is attracted to the pointed parts of the conductor. The two sets of charges exert very strong forces on the electrons and the positive charges of the air molecules between the cloud and the lightning conductor. The strong forces ionize the molecules, leaving them positively charged. Ions or charged particles are thus formed.

If the cloud were negatively charged, positive ions are attracted to the cloud. The negative charge flows to the earth as electrons. The ions neutralize the charge on the cloud, so that it loses its charge without any lightning effect taking place.

The air above the conductor now contains many positive charges. This charge makes it less likely that lightning will strike the building. If, however, lightning strikes, the charge is attracted towards the spikes and is carried safely away towards the earth through the conducting strip. The action of a lightning conductor is shown in fig 5.5.

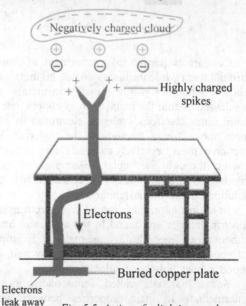

Fig. 5.5 Action of a lighting conductor.

Some materials permit electric charges to move easily from one part of the material to another while others do not. A copper wire is supported by a glass rod as in fig 5.6. If one end of the wire is touched by a charged plastic rod and the other end attached to a metal ball initially uncharged and the charged rod is then removed; when another charged body is brought close to the ball, it is attracted or repelled. Fig 5.6(b,c) indicate that the ball has been electrically charged. This shows that electric charge has been transferred through the copper wire between the ball and the surface of the plastic rod.

The wire is called a **conductor** of electricity. If the experiment is repeated using a rubber band thread in place of wire, no charge is transferred to the ball. This material is called an **insulator**.

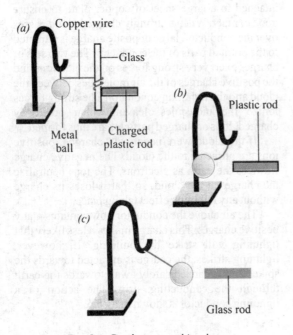

Fig. 5.6 Conductors and insulators.

Conductors permit easy movement of charge through them while insulators do not, all metals are good conductors while most non-metals are insulators. Within the metal such as copper, one or more outer electrons (valence electrons) in each atom move freely throughout the material. The motion of these negatively charged electrons carries charge through the metal. Examples of good conductors are all metals, graphite, acids, salt solutions, the earth, and human body.

In an insulator, there are no free electrons and electric charges are bound to the atom and hence cannot move freely through the material. Examples of good insulators are glass, plastic, dry hair, dry wood, rubber, polythene, sulphur, and wax.

Some materials called semi-conductors are intermediate in their properties between good conductors and good insulators. They are a class of solids with electrical resistivity between that of a conductor and an insulator. For example, the resistivity of a conductor is of the order $10^{-8}\Omega$-m and that of an insulator $10^4\Omega$-m and higher while that of a semi conductor is $10^{-1}\Omega$-m. Silicon and germanium are examples of semi-conductor elements that are widely used.

Increase in temperature enhances the resistivity in conductors while it reduces the resistivity in semi conductors. It has no effect on insulators.

Summary

1. Electric charge is the basis of a fundamental interaction among particles. Charge is positive or negative. Objects with the same sign of charge repel; objects with opposite signs of charge attract one another.

2. Neutral matter contains equal amounts of positive and negative charge.

3. The net electric charge in any isolated system is constant and all free charges are integer multiples of the magnitude of the electron charge. Charges move easily in conductors but much less readily in insulators. Materials with conductivity or resistivity between good conductors and good insulators are called semi-conductors.

4. Charges can be detected and tested using a gold leaf electroscope. Nature of charges could also be determined by the electroscope. If an unknown charge is brought near a charged electroscope and the leaf diverges more, the unknown charge is similar to the one on the electroscope.

5. Charges can be produced by friction, by contact and by electric induction.

6. Electric induction is the act of charging a neutral body by bringing it near a charged body, or by bringing a charged body near it without any contact between them.

7. For a pear shaped conductor, the concentration of charge on the outside is greatest at the sharpest point. No charge resides on the inside of the conductor. Such a conductor has a high density at the sharpest point.

8. The lightning conductor has a pointed end and can be used to protect a building from damage due to thunder storm.

Exercise 5

1. In order to charge an electroscope by induction, the following process can be followed:
    I.   Bring charge near the electroscope.
    II. Touch the cap.
    III. Remove the charge.

IV. Remove the finger.
A. I - II - III and IV   B. I - II - IV - III
C. II - I - IV - III
D. I - IV - II - III

2. Which of the following can be used to compare the magnitudes of charge on two given bodies?
A. Glass rod   B. Gold-leaf electroscope
C. Ammeter   D. Capacitor

3. Which of the following rods acquire positive charge?
I. Polythene rubbed with silk.
II. Cellulose acetate rubbed with silk.
III. Glass rod rubbed with silk.

A. II only   B. I only
C. I, II, and III   D. II and III

4. An ebonite rod rubbed with fur becomes negatively charged because
A. some negative charges are transferred from fur to the ebonite rod.
B. some positive charges are transferred from fur to ebonite.
C. the ebonite becomes deficient in positive charges.
D. some positive charges have been transferred from ebonite to fur.

5. Which of the following materials can be used to obtain positive charge?
I. Cellulose acetate
II. Polythene
III. Glass
IV. Ebonite

A. I and II only   B. I and III only
C. I, II, and III only   D. II, III and IV only

6. Explain what is meant by electrostatic induction. Given two equal metal spheres mounted on wooden supports, a glass rod and a piece of silk cloth, describe and explain how you would charge:
(a) a sphere positively by induction;
(b) one sphere positively and the other negatively to the same extent.
Illustrate your answers with diagrams.

7. With the aid of a diagram, explain the action of a lightning conductor.

8. Describe the gold leaf electroscope, and show how it can be used to determine the sign of an electric charge.
If a rod bearing a positive charge were provided, explain how the electroscope would be charged:
(a) positively   (b) negatively.

9. Write down what obtains under the following conditions:
(i) A glass rod is rubbed with silk cloth.
(ii) The rod is held near a copper ball on an ebonite stand.
(iii) The ball is touched momentarily with a finger while the rod is still held close
(iv) The rod is removed.
Show how you would use this method to charge a gold leaf negatively.

10. (a) How would you demonstrate that there are two kinds of static electricity?
(b) If a positively charged rod were brought near the cap of an electroscope of which the leaf is already charged, what will happen to the leaf?

11. Explain why in the construction of a lightning conductor, one end is made into a sharp point. Describe a laboratory experiment to support your explanation.

MAGNETS

6.1 What is a magnet and magnetic materials?

Many centuries ago, the ancient Greeks found that a certain form of iron ore, called **magnetite** or **lodestone**, had the property of always pointing the same way when freely suspended. These iron ores became known as **magnetic iron ores**. Objects showing this property and made of these iron ores are known as **magnets**.

> A substance is in general said to be magnetic if it is attracted by a magnet.

Examples of magnetic materials are iron, cobalt, nickel and certain alloys. Substances such as brass, wood, copper and glass are not attracted by magnets. These are called non-magnetic materials.

6.2 Properties of magnets and patterns

(i) Experiments show that iron filings (small pieces of iron) cling mainly to the ends of a bar magnet (see fig. 6.1(a)). This shows that the ends of a magnet are regions where the attracting power is greatest. These ends are called **poles**.

(ii) It is observed that if a bar magnet is suspended so that it swings freely in a horizontal plane, it always comes to rest with its axis pointing approximately north-south (N.S). The pole which is attracted towards the North pole of the Earth is called a **north seeking pole**, or simply a **north pole**, and the pole which is attracted towards the south pole is called a **south seeking** or just a south pole. A suspended or pivoted magnet used to find north and south is called a **compass**.

Fig. 6.1(a) A magnet with iron filings.

Fig. 6.1(b) A bar magnet showing lines of force.

(iii) Like poles of a magnet repel each other but unlike poles attract each other.

This is called the **basic law of magnetism**. Thus a north and a south pole attract each other, but two north or two south poles repel each other.

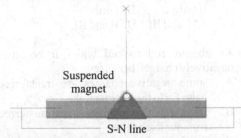

Fig. 6.2 A suspended magnet.

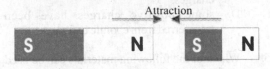

Fig. 6.3(a) Unlike poles attract.

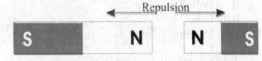

Fig. 6.3(b) Like poles repel.

Test for polarity of a magnet

The polarity of a magnet may be tested by bringing both its poles in turn near to the known poles of a suspended magnet.

Repulsion will indicate similar polarity. If attraction occurs, no firm conclusion can be drawn, since attraction would be obtained between either two unlike poles or a pole and a piece of unmagnetised magnetic material. Repulsion is therefore the only sure test for polarity.

6.3 Theory of magnetism

If we cut a magnet in two, an interesting thing happens. Instead of separating the north and south poles, we obtain two magnets. Extra north and south poles are formed and each of the two small magnets has half the strength of the original magnet.

This process can be continued, repeatedly dividing a magnet in two, and obtaining more smaller magnets. We might ask, 'How long can this go on? What is the smallest magnet we can obtain?'

Clearly, the smallest magnet is one molecule, and the original magnet must have been made up of a very large number of tiny molecular magnets. This explains the difference between iron (and the other ferromagnetic elements like nickel and cobalt) and non-magnetic materials. Their molecules are magnets, while those of non-magnetic materials are not.

When magnetic materials are unmagnetised, the molecular magnets are mixed up to point in random directions, and they cancel each other. When the material is magnetised, the molecular magnets are all turned to point the same way and reinforce each other.

Magnetising a piece of iron thus consists of turning its molecules more in line, while demagnetising it consists of mixing up the molecules again. This is, of course, a simplified view of the situation.

6.4 Magnetisation and demagnetisation of magnetic materials

A magnetic material is one which is capable of being magnetised.

These include iron, steel, cobalt and nickel. There are several methods of magnetising materials.

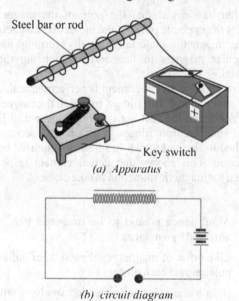

(a) Apparatus

(b) circuit diagram

Fig. 6.4 Magnetisation using electric coil.

Electrical method

The best method of magnetising is to insert it into a solenoid (a coil of wire with many turns) through which a steady direct current flows, as in Fig. 6.4. After some time, the material is removed and it is found to have become a magnet. The polarity of the magnetised specimen depends on the direction of the current. If when we look at the end of the bar the current is flowing in a clockwise direction, that end will be a south pole. If current is flowing anticlockwise, it will be a north pole.

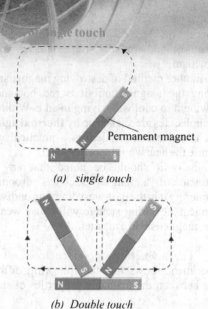

(a) single touch

(b) Double touch

Fig. 6.5 Magnetising a steel rod.

The material is stroked from one end to the other end several times in the same direction with one pole of a magnet. This pulls the opposite poles of the molecular magnets in one direction and leaves them pointing one way. A disadvantage of this is that it produces magnets in which one pole is nearer the end of the material than the other (Fig. 6.5(a)).

The method of double or divided touch

This is a better method. The material is stroked from the centre outwards with unlike poles of two magnets simultaneously, as in Fig.6.5(b)).

Demagnetisation

The process by which a magnet loses its magnetism is known as **demagnetisation**. To demagnetise a magnet, the molecules have to be shaken out of their orderly arrangement.

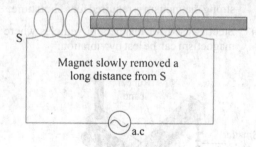

S

Magnet slowly removed a long distance from S

a.c

Fig. 6.6 Demagnetisation

The best way of demagnetising a magnet is to place it inside a solenoid through which an alternating current is flowing. The solenoid is placed with its axis pointing east to west. After a few seconds the magnet is slowly withdrawn from the solenoid and taken a long distance away. The alternating current reverses every 0.01s and hence reverses the magnetism in the material 100 times per second. This has the effect of shaking up the molecules and making the material lose its magnetism.

Another method of destroying magnetism is by heating the magnet until it is red hot and then allowing it to cool while lying in an E-W direction. The molecules are shaken up by **thermal agitation**. This is not recommended as a practical method because the heat would spoil the steel.

Finally it should be noted that any rough treatment of a magnet such as dropping it, hammering it in the east-west direction or disorderly arrangement during storage will cause weakening of the magnetism in a magnet.

6.5   The magnetic properties of iron and steel

Experiment shows that the following differences exist between the magnetic properties of steel and iron:

(I)   Iron is more easily magnetised than steel.

(II)   Iron is more easily demagnetised than steel.

(III)   In a solenoid bearing a set current, iron becomes more strongly magnetised than steel.

(IV)   Steel keeps its magnetism much longer than iron.

Because of these differences in their magnetic properties, iron and steel are used for different things.

(a)   Steel is used in making permanent magnets, such as compass needles, bar magnets, ball-ended magnets, and so on.

(b)   Iron nails are often used for experiments in magnetisation and demagnetisation because they are easier to magnetise and demagnetise.

(c)   Iron is used for making electromagnets where strong magnetism is required for a short time.

(d)   Steel is used for magnets in vehicles where magnetism can be lost by vibration.

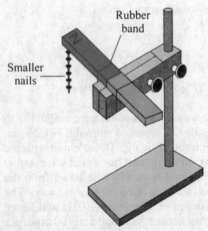

Fig. 6.7   Magnetic induction

6.6   Induced magnetism

A bar magnet is fixed in a wooden clamp as shown (do not use a metal clamp). In Fig. 6.7. Soft iron nails (unmagnetised) are placed at the north end of the magnet as shown. The nails can be placed one below the other.

The number of nails that can be hung in a single chain depends on the strength of the magnet. The stronger the magnet the larger the number of nails. Experiment shows that if the magnet is gently moved, all the nails fall off.

Explanation

It is clear that the first nail is attracted by the magnet, hence it sticks to it and becomes a magnet; it has been magnetised by induction. In the same way the second, third and fourth nails have been magnetised by the first. They will remain attached to one another as long as the magnet is there. Once the magnet which induces magnetism is removed they will fall off.

> Induced magnetism is the process of magnetising an object made of magnetic material simply by bringing a magnet near.

What happens is that the pole of the magnet attracts the opposite poles of the molecular magnets in the magnetic material, partially turning the molecular magnets in line and magnetising the material.

Now suppose an experiment is performed with a magnet, a nail and iron filings, in which the magnet does not touch the nail but is brought near it, it is found that the iron filings jump up and become attached to the nail which has been magnetised by induction. This shows that actual contact is not needed for magnetic induction to take place.

Summary

1.   A substance is said to be magnetic if it is attracted by a magnet.

2.   Like poles of magnet repel each other unlike poles attract each other.

3.   If a bar magnet is suspended freely, it will come to rest with its axis pointing north-south.

4.   A magnetic material is one which is capable of being magnetised.

5.   The best way to demagnetise a magnet is to place it in solenoid through which an alternating current is flowing.

6.   Iron is more easily magnetised or demagmatised than steel but steel keeps its magnetism much longer than iron.

7.   Induced magnetism is the process of magnetising an object made of magnetic material simply by bringing a magnet near it.

Exercise 6

1. A substance is said to be magnetic if
   A. it is attracted by a magnet.
   B. it has two north poles.
   C. it is neutral.
   D. it has no poles.

2. If a bar magnet is suspended freely
   A. it will continue to rotate.
   B. it will come to rest with its axis pointing N-S.
   C. it will point to the south.
   D. it will point to the north.

3. Which of the following statement is correct?
   A. Repulsion is not the only sure test for polarity.
   B. Like poles of magnets attract each other.
   C. Unlike poles of magnet remains at rest.
   D. Unlike poles of magnets attract each other.

4. If we cut a magnet into two
   A. we obtain two magnets.
   B. we destroy the magnet.
   C. the magnet becomes non-magnetic.
   D. like poles appear.

5. Which of the following elements are real magnetic materials?
   A. Iron, steel and nickel.
   B. Copper, steel and iron.
   C. Lead, iron and brass.
   D. Glass, lead and steel.

6. What is a magnetic material?

7. What do you understand by the term magnetic induction?

8. Describe how magnet can be magnetised and how it can be demagnetised using a coil carrying current.

9. List the magnetic properties of iron and steel.

10. Describe briefly the theory of magnetism.

11. One small magnet is sufficient to magnetise all the steel in the world without loss to itself. **True** or **false**?

CURRENT ELECTRICITY

Chapter 7

Current Electricity

In chapter 5, we studied charges at rest; now we want to consider charges in motion. An electric current consists of charges in motion from one region to another. When this motion takes place within a conducting path that forms a closed loop, this path is termed an electric circuit. These circuits are a means for conveying energy from one place to another. They constitute the heart of radio, TV transmitters and receivers, computers, household and industrial power systems.

We shall study properties of cells and how they cause current transfer in a circuit. In our analysis, we shall use the concepts of current, potential difference (or voltage), resistance and electromotive force (e.m.f.).

7.1 Definition of electric current, potential difference and resistance

A current is any motion of charge from one region to another in an electric circuit. In this section, we shall discuss current in conducting materials (wire) in an electric circuit which may consist of a cell (source of e.m.f.) connected by copper wires to one or more resistors or other components which will be described later. The cell provides an electromotive force which sets up potential differences across various circuit components and drives the current through them. The resistors offer opposition to the free flow of current.

In any electric circuit, there is a need to measure:

(i)   current, measured in amperes (A);

(ii)   electromotive force and potential difference both measured in volts (V);

(iii)   resistance, measured in ohms (Ω).

> An electric current (I) is the time rate of flow of charge (Q) round a circuit.

The quantity of electricity (Q) is measured in coulombs (C).

Hence, the electric current I

$$= \frac{\text{quantity of charge } Q \text{ in coulombs}}{\text{time in seconds}}$$

$$I = \frac{Q}{t} \qquad 7.1$$

The unit of current, one coulomb per second is called an **ampere** (A).

Currents vary in magntitudes from very large values of hundreds of amperes required to start electric motors to very small values of current in radio and television circuits expressed in milliamperes ($1mA = 10^{-3}A$), or microamperes ($1\mu A = 10^{-6}A$) and currents in computer circuits expressed in nanoamperes ($1nA = 10^{-9}A$) or pico amperes ($1pA = 10^{-12}A$).

Example 7.1

A current of 4.5A flows through a car headlight. How many coulombs of charge flow through it in 1.0hr?

Solution

$$\text{Current } I = \frac{Q}{t} \text{ (charge)}$$

$$\text{Then } Q = It$$
$$= 4.5 \times 1 \times 60 \times 60 \text{ coulombs}$$
$$= 16\,200C = 1.62 \times 10^4 \text{ C.}$$

Current measuring instruments

Electric current is measured with the ammeter. Other types of ammeter are the microammeter, the milliameter and the galvanometer. The galvanometer can measure or detect currents thousands of times smaller than a microammeter.

Fig. 7.1 The Centre-zero galvanometer

Fig. 7.2 Ammeter

For the centre-zero galvanometer, the pointer is at the central zero mark when no current flows through it. When current passes through the galvanometer, the pointer deflects to the right or to the left depending on the direction of current; such an instrument is very useful in metre bridge and potentiometer experiment to be discussed later. For measuring the exact amount of current in the circuit, ammeters are used for large currents and a milliameter or microameter for smaller currents. The circuit symbols for these instruments are shown in Fig. 7.3:

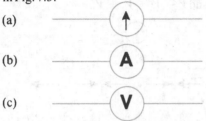

(a)

(b)

(c)

Fig. 7.3 Circuit symbols of (a) a galvanometer (b) an Ammeter (c) a voltmeter.

It should be noted that the ammeter must always be placed in a circuit so that the current to be measured flows directly through it. In fig 7.4(a) for example, the current flows through the ammeter A_1, and through the ammeter A_2 placed at P and Q; both will record the same current I. Such ammeters are said to be placed in series in the circuit. Ammeters have low resistance so that it introduces negligible resistance into the circuit.

In Fig. 7.4(b), similar ammeters A_1 and A_2 at R and S respectively are connected in parallel with each other will indicate different currents while the ammeter A_3 at T will record the main current flowing from the battery. The current $I = I_1 + I_2$.

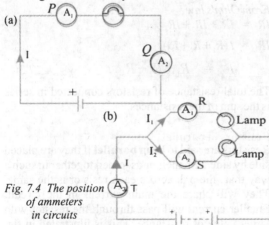

Fig. 7.4 The position of ammeters in circuits

Potential difference (p.d.)

When a current flows through a wire, a potential difference is said to exist between the ends of the wire.

> The potential difference (p.d.) between any two points in a circuit is defined as the work done, in joules, when one coulomb of electricity moves from one point to another.

The unit of potential difference is the **volt** (V) and is defined as follows: Two points are at a potential difference of 1 volt if 1 joule of work is done per coulomb of electricity passing from one point to the other.

Units of p.d. other than volts are:

$$1 \text{ microvolt} = \frac{1}{10^6} \text{ volt} \, (\mu V = 10^{-6} V)$$

$$1 \text{ millivolt} = \frac{1}{10^3} \text{ volt} \, (mV = 10^{-3} V)$$

$$1 \text{ kilovolt} = 10^3 \text{ volts} \, (1 k V = 10^3 V)$$

Instruments for measuring p.d.

The instrument for measuring p.d. is known as a **voltmeter** and is graduated in volts or millivolts. The circuit symbol is as shown in fig. 7.3 (c); since it measures the difference in potential between two points, it is therefore connected in parallel. Thus in Fig. 7.5, the voltmeter V_1 measures the p.d. across the resistor P connected between A and B. The voltmeter V_2 measures the p.d. across the resistor Q connected between C and D.

Total p.d. across the resistances = sum of individual p.ds = $V_1 + V_2$.

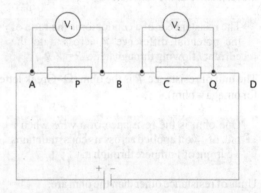

Fig. 7.5 Potential difference across series resistors.

RESISTANCE

We have seen that different materials have different conducting abilities and are accordingly known as good or poor conductors or insulators. In current electricity, we think in terms of the ability of a substance to oppose or resist the flow of electricity through it. A good conductor is therefore said to have a low resistance and a poor conductor, a high resistance. Very good insulators may be regarded as having infinite resistance. Hence no current can pass through an ideal insulator. Silver offers the least resistance to the currents; however it is too expensive for normal use and so copper is generally used as connecting wires and cables in electric circuits.

> Any component that offers opposition to the flow of current in a circuit is called a resistor.

When a high resistance is required in a circuit, constantan, manganin and nichrome wires are used.

In 1826, George Simon Ohm, a German Physicist, found by experiment, that for a good conductor, there is a relationship between the current flowing through it and the potential difference across it. This is stated as follows:

> The electric current passing through a metallic conductor (wire) at constant temperature is directly proportional to the potential difference applied between its ends.

This is known as ohm's law.
Other physical conditions such as pressure are also assumed constant.

If V represents potential difference in volts and I represents current in amperes, Ohm's law can be expressed as:

$$\frac{\text{Potential difference } (V)}{\text{Current } (I)} = \text{Constant } (R)$$

$$V = IR \qquad 7.2$$

where R is a constant of proportionality which depends on the nature of the conductor identified as the resistance of the conductor.

> The resistance R of a conductor is the ratio of the potential difference V across it to the current I flowing through it. i.e. $R = V/I$.

The unit of resistance, R is the ohm (Ω- Greek letter for omega = ohm).

> One ohm is the resistance of a wire when a p.d. of 1 volt applied across its ends maintains a current of 1 ampere through it.

Units of resistance other than the ohm are:

$$1 \text{ microohm } (\mu\Omega) = \frac{1}{1000000} \; \Omega$$
$$= 10^{-6} \text{ ohm}$$

$$1 \text{ kilo ohm } (k\Omega) = 1000\Omega$$
$$= 10^{3} \text{ ohms}$$

$$1 \text{ megaohm } (m\Omega) = 1000000\Omega$$
$$= 10^{6} \text{ ohms}$$

Formulae:
$$R = \frac{V}{I}, \quad I = \frac{V}{R}, \quad V = IR.$$

Limitations of ohm's law

Ohm's law holds for metallic conductors and certain other materials. There is the need for the temperature to be kept constant and other physical conditions to remain constant. For example, the resistance of some conductors will change if they are placed under tension or bent into a loop. Ohm's law, however, does not apply to conductors such as radio valves, transistors, semiconductors (silicon, germanium) rectifiers, neon gas and acids.

7.3   Resistance in series and parallel

Resistors in series

If three resistors R_1, R_2, and R_3 are connected end to end in such a way that the same current flows through each resistor when they are connected to a source of e.m.f., they are said to be connected in **series** as shown in Fig. 7.6(a).

The equivalent or total resistance, R of these resistors is given by $V = IR$ where V is the total p.d. across them and $V = V_1 + V_2 + V_3$.

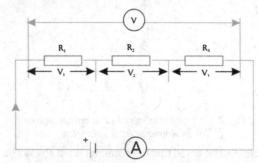

Fig. 7.6(a) Resistances in series

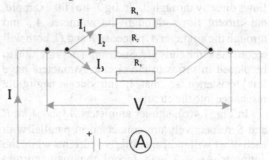

Fig. 7.6(b) Resistances in parallel

From Ohm's law
$$IR = IR_1 + IR_2 + IR_3$$
$$IR = I(R_1 + R_2 + R_3)$$
$$R = R_1 + R_2 + R_3 \qquad 7.3$$

The total resistance of resistors connected in series is the sum of the resistances.

Resistors in parallel

Resistors are said to be in **parallel** if they are placed side by side with their ends joined together in such a way that the p.d. across each resistor is the same. They will share the main current in the circuit. Smaller current will pass through the resistor with larger value of resistance. This is illustrated in fig. 7.6(b).

If R_1, R_2 and R_3 are the resistances of the resistors and I_1, I_2, and I_3 are the corresponding currents in each resistor, then the equivalent resistance R is obtained as follows:
Since $I = I_1 + I_2 + I_3$ and the p.d,. V is the same across R_1, R_2 and R_3;

Then, $\frac{V}{R} = \frac{V}{R_1} + \frac{V}{R_2} + \frac{V}{R_3}$

Dividing through by V

$$\frac{1}{R} = \frac{1}{R_1} + \frac{1}{R_2} \quad \frac{1}{R_3} \qquad\qquad 7.4$$

Special case of two resistors R_1 and R_2 in parallel

$$\frac{V}{R} = \frac{V}{R_1} + \frac{V}{R_2}$$

$$R = \frac{R_1 R_2}{R_1 + R_2}$$

For two resistors in parallel,

$$\text{Combined resistance} = \frac{\text{product of resistances}}{\text{sum of resistances}}$$

Resistance of a pure metal increases with temperature but the resistance of certain conducting materials e.g. carbon decreases with temperature. Metal alloys particularly manganin and constantan which are used for constructing standard resistors show very small changes in resistance with temperature.

Semiconductors such as silicon, germanium and selenium decrease in resistance with rising temperature.

Example 7.2

In the circuit shown below, find the reading of the ammeter, A when the key, K is (i) opened (ii) closed. Assume that the battery has negligible resistance.

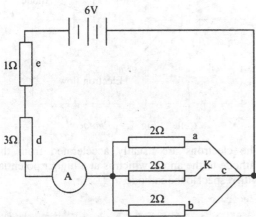

Solution

(i) When K is open, only two resistors each of 2Ω are connected in parallel. Combined resistance of a and b.

$$\frac{1}{R} = \frac{1}{2} + \frac{1}{2}$$

$$R = 1\,\Omega.$$

Total circuit resistance $= 1 + 3 + 1 = 5\Omega$

$$\text{Main current} = \frac{\text{e.m.f.}}{\text{total resistance}} = \frac{6}{5}\,\text{A}.$$

(ii) When K is closed, the three resistors a, b, c are in parallel, the combined resistance R is given by:

$$\frac{1}{R} = \frac{1}{2} + \frac{1}{2} + \frac{1}{2} = \frac{3}{2}$$

$$R = \frac{2}{3}\,\Omega$$

$$\text{Total resistance} = \frac{2}{3} + 3 + 1 = 4\frac{2}{3}\,\Omega$$

$$\text{Current} = \frac{\text{e.m.f.}}{\text{Total resistance}} = \frac{6\times3}{14} = \frac{9}{7}\,\text{A}.$$

Standard resistors and rheostats

These are components in the form of lengths of resistance wire or piece of carbon of which the resistance is accurately known. They are known as standard resistors.

To make standard resistors of various known resistances, measured lengths of resistance materials such as manganin or constantan wires are cut out, wind them on a cardboard or wood and provide terminals for connection as shown in Fig. 7.7(a).

Such resistors depend on the length, l, of the wire, the material of the wire, ρ (its resistivity) and the cross sectional area, A.

$$R = \frac{\rho l}{A}$$

Example 7.3

Determine the length and conductivity of a wire with diameter 2.0mm constructed from an alloy of resistivity $22 \times 10^{-8}\,\Omega\text{m}$, if its resistance is 0.42Ω. (Take $\pi = \frac{22}{7}$)

Solution

$$\text{resistance } R = \frac{\text{resistivity } (\rho) \text{ length } (l)}{\text{cross sectional area } (A)}$$

$$A = \pi r^2$$

$$= \frac{\pi d^2}{4}$$

$$0.42 = \frac{22\times10^{-8}\times l}{\frac{22}{7}\times(1\times10^{-3})^2}$$

$$l = \frac{0.42\times22\times10^{-6}}{7\times22\times10^{-8}}$$

$$= 0.06 \times 10^2 = 6.0\text{m}$$

$$\text{Conductivity } \sigma = \frac{1}{\text{resistivity } (\rho)}$$

$$= \frac{100}{22} \square 10^6 = 4.55\times10^6\,(\Omega\text{m})^{-1}.$$

Rheostats are variable resistors whose resistance values can be varied. The schematic is shown in Fig.

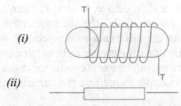

Fig. 7.7(a) Standard resistor (i) Resistor (ii) symbol

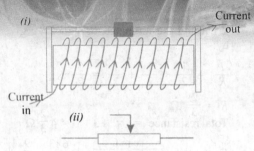

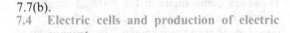

Fig. 7.7(b) (i) Rheostat (ii) Symbol

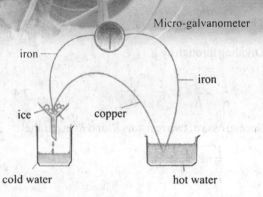

Fig. 7.8 The thermocouple

7.7(b).

7.4 Electric cells and production of electric current

A steady current is produced through continuous flow of charge. Such a continuous flow of charge can be generated from:

(a) chemical energy
(b) mechanical energy
(c) heat energy
(d) solar energy

(a) Electricity from chemical energy

Electricity is produced from chemical energy through the use of electric cells which convert chemical energy into electrical energy (see section 7.5).

(b) Electricity from mechanical energy

Most of the world's electricity is produced from the conversion of mechanical energy to electrical energy using electric generators. Such generators produce electricity by the movement of coils of insulated wire (the armature) that cut lines of force in the magnetic field between the poles of powerful magnets. The induced electric current on the wire is picked up from the copper splitting commutators by means of graphite carbon brushes (details and diagram of this mechanism are in chapter 33).

The bicycle dynamo is an example of this mechanism which generates electricity for the headlamp of the bicycle.

(c) Electricity from heat energy

An electric current can be produced when the ends of two different metal wires (e.g. copper and iron) are joined end to end. One junction is placed in hot water (hot junction) and the other in a beaker of ice chips (cold junction).

Electricity flows around the circuit formed by the two wires. Such a device, known as thermocouple produces electricity by the thermoelectric effect. The greater the difference in temperature between the two junctions, the greater is the electric current.

A micro galvanometer is connected in one arm of the thermocouple to indicate the current flow as in Fig. 7.8.

Thermocouples are used for measuring high temperatures particularly when constructed from metals or alloys with high melting point (e.g. platinum and platinum- iridium).

(d) Electricity from solar energy

When sunlight falls on a photosentive surface (e.g. surface of potassium) electrons are produced whose movement constitutes a current. A photocell or photoelectric cell consists of a photosensitive surface as a cathode and a wire ring as the anode. If visible light falls on this surface, electrons are emitted by a process called photoelectric effect and the flow of these electrons can be detected by a micro ammeter as shown in the diagram Fig. 7.9.

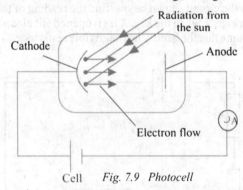

Fig. 7.9 Photocell

The electrons are usually accelerated from the cathode to the anode which is at a higher potential with respect to the cathode.

Electric cells

A cell is a device for converting chemical energy to electrical energy.

A cell consists of two **electrodes** (dissimilar metals) placed in a container in which there is a solution of acid or salt called the **electrolyte**. The positive electrode is the **anode** while the negative electrode is the **cathode**. Some examples of electrolytes are dilute tetraoxosulphate (VI) acid or a strong solution of ammonium chloride in water. Examples of electrodes are rods of aluminium, carbon (graphite), copper, iron, lead and zinc. There are two main types of cells - *primary* and *secondary* cells.

The simple primary cell (voltaic cell) (Zn-Cu cell). A simple cell consists of a copper rod and a zinc plate immersed in a container filled with dilute sulphuric acid (tetraoxosulphate (VI) acid). When the copper rod and zinc plate are connected by a wire, the zinc slowly dissolves in the acid and bubbles of hydrogen gas are formed on the copper. As a result of chemical reaction, electrons flow from zinc to copper through the wire as in Fig. 7.10. Copper is the anode (+ve electrode) and zinc is the cathode (-ve electrode). When a bulb is connected between the terminals, it lights up indicating that current is flowing in the external circuit from copper to zinc. If a voltmeter is connected across these terminals, it will register about 1.0V. The current supplied is for a short time due to some defects; and both the electrolyte and the electrodes have to be replaced.

Defects of a simple cell

There are two defects of a simple cell.
(i)   Polarization   (ii)   Local action

(i)   *Polarization:* This is due to the production of hydrogen gas bubbles around the copper plate of the cell. This is due to the reaction of zinc and dilute tetraoxosulphate (VI) acid. This reaction sets up a back e.m.f. which reduces the current in the external circuit. Polarization can be reduced by brushing the plates or by the use of a depolarizer such as manganese dioxide or potassium dichromate which oxidizes hydrogen to form water and so removes the hydrogen bubbles.

(ii)   *Local action:* This is due to impurities in the zinc plate which results in the wearing away of the electrode. These impurities (iron and carbon) set up tiny cells around the zinc surface producing bubbles of hydrogen. Zinc plate is being dissolved and washed since no current is supplied to the external circuit. Local action can be prevented by amalgamation, i.e.

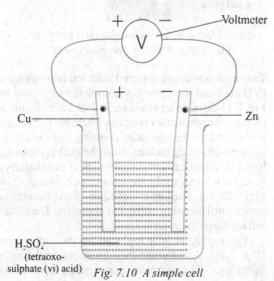

Fig. 7.10 A simple cell

cleaning the zinc with tetraoxosulphate (VI) acid and then rubbing it with some mercury which covers up the impurities and prevents their contact with the electrolyte.

The Leclanche Cell

This is a primary cell and it is of two types; the wet type (Fig. 7.11(a)), and the dry type in Fig. 7.11(b).

The wet Leclanche cell

Structure: It consists of a zinc rod, the cathode, in solution of ammonium chloride (sal ammoniac) contained in glass vessel. The anode is a carbon rod contained in a porous pot and surrounded by manganese dioxide as *depolariser*.

Action: The zinc, the carbon and the electrolyte set up an e.m.f. which drives a current from zinc to carbon through the cell. Thus the carbon is at a higher potential than the zinc. When connected with a circuit outside the cell, current flows from carbon to zinc outside, but from zinc to carbon inside.

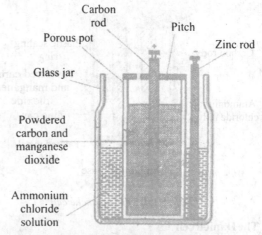

Fig. 7.11(a)   Wet Leclanché cell

The e.m.f. is set up because zinc reacts with the ammonium chloride to form zinc chloride, ammonia and hydrogen, and electrons are released. These electrons flow from the zinc plate to the carbon plate outside the cell.

Hydrogen reacts with the manganese dioxide and oxidises it to form water. The e.m.f. of a Leclanche cell is about 1.5V

Defects or Disadvantages

The wet cell has two serious defects.
(i)   Although polarisation is reduced by the presence of maganese dioxide, it cannot be completely eliminated. When the cell has worked for some time, the rate at which hydrogen is produced becomes greater than the rate at which it is oxidised by the maganese dioxide, so polarisation sets in. For this reason, the cell must be allowed to rest from time to time. Thus primary cells do not give continuous service. Their use is

restricted to a situation where intermittent current is required.

(ii) The wet Leclanche cell is cumbersome to carry about without spilling the liquid.

The dry Leclanché cell

The dry Leclanche cell was invented to overcome the second defect mentioned above.

In the dry cell, the electrolyte is a jelly-like material containing ammonium chloride; instead of the liquid solution. The positive electrode is a carbon rod surrounded by a packed mixture of manganese dioxide and powdered carbon, inside a zinc container which is the negative electrode. The working is similar to that of the wet cell.

The dry cell can be carried about easily. Ordinary torch batteries and transistor radio batteries are dry Leclanche cells. Local action cannot be completely stopped in the dry cell. So the cell deteriorates after some time.

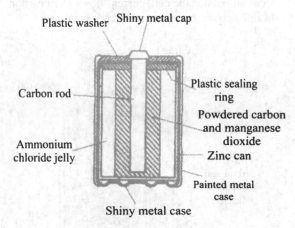

Fig. 7.11(b) Dry Leclanché cell.

The Daniell cell

The Daniell cell (Fig. 7.12) is another type of primary cell invented to counter the problem of polarization. As in the Leclanche cell, the zinc rod is the negative electrode but the positive electrode is a copper container. The electrolyte is dilute tetraoxosulphate (VI) acid contained in a porous pot around the zinc rod, and the depolarizer is copper tetraoxosulphate (VI) in the surrounding copper container. The action is similar to that of a Leclanche

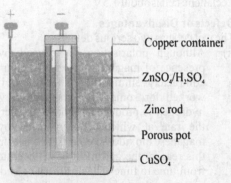

Fig. 7.12 The Daniel cell

cell but the depolarization is much more efficient. The e.m.f. of a Daniell cell does not, therefore, vary very much and has a constant value of 1.08V.

Secondary cells or accumulators

The action of a secondary cell can be shown by the following experiment:

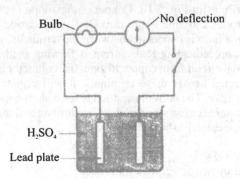

Fig. 7.13(a)

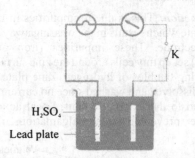

Fig. 7.13(b) Cell being charged

Fig. 7.13(c) Electric bulb lights after charging
Fig. 7.13(a, b and c) Secondary cells

Two lead plates are inserted into tetraoxosulphate (VI) acid and the circuit is completed as shown in Fig. 7.13 through an ammeter, a 2 or 3 V bulb and a plug key or some other type of switch. No deflection is obtained on the ammeter, showing that the cell is not delivering any current. Now the bulb is replaced by a 12V direct current supply (such as a car battery) in series with a variable resistor circuit, as shown in Fig. 7.13 (b). The key is closed and the resistance is varied until there is a current of about 1A. The cell is left to charge for several minutes.

The supply is now replaced by the bulb again (Fig. 7.13(c)) and when the key is closed the bulb lights up. The ammeter connections have to be reversed, showing that current is now coming out of the cell instead of being put into it. It is found that after some time, the bulb stops shining, showing that the energy in the cell has been used up. The cell is again connected to the 12V supply for some time. It is found that when this is disconnected the cell becomes energised again and lights the bulb. This time the cell will be found to be more efficient and will light the bulb for a longer time. This type of cell stores energy when current is passed through it. The electrical energy causes a chemical change, and when the change is reversed, the energy is released again. When the energy is used up, we can store more energy by passing a current through the cell again.

Daniel and Leclanche cells do not work in this way. Once their energy is used up, it cannot be restored by recharging, but only by the addition of fresh electrolyte. Such cells are known as **primary cells**. Lead-acid cells are known as **secondary cells** or **accumulators**.

When an accumulator is receiving current through a source of electricity it is being charged. When it is delivering a current it is being discharged.

Manufactured secondary cells

There are two main kinds of secondary cell: the lead-acid accumulator, and the alkaline or Nife accumulator.

The lead-acid accumulator

This is more common than the Nife accumulator. It consists of lead oxide as the positive electrode, lead as the negative electrode and tetraoxosulphate (VI) acid as the electrolyte. During discharge, when the cell is giving out current, both electrodes gradually change to lead tetraoxosulphate (VI) while the acid gradually becomes more dilute and the density decreases. When fully charged the relative density is about 1.25 and the e.m.f. of the cell is 2.2V, but when discharged relative density is about 1.15 and the e.m.f. less than 2.0V. The relative density which should not be allowed to drop below 1.15 and is measured using a special hydrometer.

A voltmeter connected across a battery will also show either the car battery is well charged or in need of charging. When newly charged, the voltage is well over 12V, but it soon falls to 12V when the battery is used. It stays constant throughout use, until the battery has run out of usage, when the voltage drops suddenly well below 12V.

The lead-acid accumulator is the same as the car battery, and needs to be carefully looked after. The liquid level must be maintained by using distilled water. The cell should be charged if the relative density of the acid falls below 1.15. The cell is fully charged when the relative density of the acid is 1.25. This can be tested with a special hydrometer. The battery should be kept clean so that current does not leak away across the casing between the terminals.

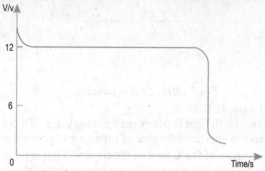
Fig. 7.14 Discharging of a car battery.

The alkaline or Nife accumulator (nickel-iron)

The name Nife comes from Ni and Fe, the chemical symbols for nickel and iron. The cell has a positive electrode made of nickel hydroxide while the negative plate is iron or cadmium. The electrolyte is potassium hydroxide dissolved in water. Alkaline cells last much longer than lead-acid cells, keep their charge longer and they require less maintenance. They are used for emergencies in factories and hospitals. They are, however, more expensive and bulky. The e.m.f. of a Nife cell is relatively small, about 1.25V.

7.5 Arrangement of cells in circuit

Cells in series

A group of cells connected together is called a battery. When cells are connected in series, the positive terminal of one being connected to the negative of the other and so on. In such an arrangement as in Fig. 7.15(a). a larger e.m.f. is obtained in the circuit and hence there is increase in current. In this case:

(i)   total e.m.f. between terminals A and B equals the sum of individual e.m.fs;

(ii)   total internal resistance equals the sum of internal resistances.

Fig. 7.15(a) Cells in series.

Cells in parallel

When identical cells are connected in parallel, all the positive terminals of the cells are connected together and the negative terminals are also connected together as in Fig. 7.15(b).

(i)   Total e.m.f. is the e.m.f. of only one cell.

(ii)   Total internal resistance is the combined resistance of the resistors (internal resistance) in parallel.

One advantage of connecting cells in parallel is that there is less current drain on the cells since they share the total current whereas with series connection, the same main current is supplied by each cell.

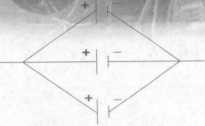

Fig. 7.15(b) Cells in parallel.

Example 7.4

Two torch light batteries each having *e.m.f.* of 1.5V and an internal resistance of 1 ohm are connected to a resistor of 5Ω. Calculate the current in this resistor if the cells are connected in (i) series (ii) parallel.

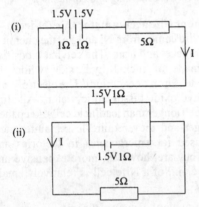

Solution

Total e.m.f. of 2 cells in series $= 1.5 + 1.5 = 3V$.
Total resistance in circuit $= 1 + 1 + 5 = 7\Omega$.

$$\text{current} = \frac{\text{e.m.f.}}{\text{total resistance}} = \frac{3}{7} = 0.43A$$

For (ii) e.m.f. of 2 cells in parallel $= 1.5V$
Resistance of 2 cells in parallel $= R$

$$\frac{1}{R} = \frac{1}{1} + \frac{1}{1}$$

$$R = 0.5\Omega.$$

Total resistance in the circuit $= 5 + 0.5 = 5.5\Omega$.

$$\text{Current} = \frac{\text{e.m.f.}}{\text{total resistance}} = \frac{1.5}{5.5} = 0.27A.$$

Electric circuit

An electric current will flow only if there is a complete circuit of conductors by which currents can leave from one terminal of the cell and flow round to the other terminal. This electric circuit is the path provided for the flow of electric current. The circuit consists of the source of e.m.f. (e.g. cell or battery) connected through a wire to a resistor or a bulb and a switch which makes (closes) or brakes (opens) the circuit. The current is the same at any point round the circuit and the flow of current stops when the switch is open.

When the circuit is closed as in Fig. 7.16(a), current flows through the inside of the cell and the external resistor (bulb) and the bulb lights up. In the open circuit, a gap exists in the path and no current flows, hence the bulb does not light as in Fig.

7.16(b). Fig. 7.16(c) is a short circuit, here the terminals of the source are joined. By convention, current flow is from positive terminal to negative terminal and the electron flow is in the opposite direction (-ve to +ve). The electric circuit with the essential components is illustrated in Fig. 7.17.

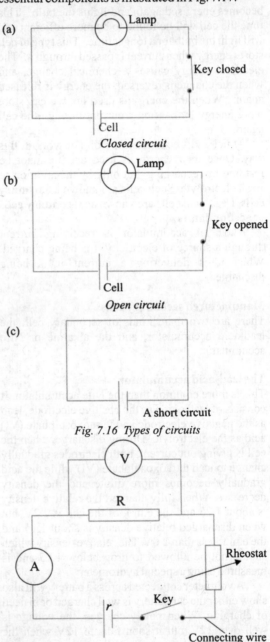

Fig. 7.16 Types of circuits

Fig. 7.17 An electric circuit

7.6 Electric conduction through materials

All materials offer a certain degree of opposition or resistance to the flow of current through them, some materials allow electric currents to flow through them more readily than others. Materials through which electricity can flow easily are known as **conductors**. Some examples are: (i) almost all metals (ii) impure water (iii) inorganic acid solutions. **Insulators** are those materials that do not allow electric currents to flow easily through them. A few of these include; ebonite, glass, drywood, and plastics.

The best metallic conductor is silver followed by copper. Most connecting wires used in circuits and electric cables are made of copper because it is less expensive than silver.

Conductors have low electrical resistance but insulators which are poor conductors have high electrical resistance to electric current flow.

7.7   Electrical energy and power

Electrical energy

Energy is used up when work is done. The units of both energy and work are joules (J). We have defined the potential difference (p.d.) between two points as the work done (in joules) when one coulomb of electricity moves from one point to another. Thus, if the p.d. applied is V (in volts) and the quantity of electricity which passes through is Q (in coulombs), the work done W is

$$W = VQ \text{ (in joules)}$$

But since $Q = It$

then, $W = VIt$ 7.5

Where t is the time in seconds (s) during which the current IA flows. Using ohm's law in the form $V = IR$ or $I = V/R$, expressions for electrical energy expended may be put in any of the following forms:

$$W = IVt$$
$$W = V^2 t/R$$
$$W = I^2 R t \qquad 7.6$$

The electrical energy can be converted into:
(i)   mechanical energy if there are motors in the circuit e.g. in electric fans and electrical machines;
(ii)   sound energy e.g. in record players and telephone;
(iii)   heat energy if heating element is present, e.g. in electric irons and immersion heaters;
(iv)   light energy, e.g. in filament lamps.

Example 7.5

A heating coil marked 1000W is used to heat water for 15 minutes. Calculate the energy given out in joules.

Solution

$$\text{Power} = \frac{\text{Energy produced}}{\text{time taken in seconds}}$$

$$1000 = \frac{\text{Energy}}{15 \times 60}$$

$$\text{Energy} = 1000 \times 15 \times 60 \text{J}$$
$$= 9 \times 10^5 \text{ J}$$

Electrical power

Power P is defined as energy W used or produced per second.

$$\text{Power} = \frac{\text{Energy produced/transferred}}{\text{Time taken}}$$

$$P = \frac{W}{t}$$

$$= \frac{IVt}{t}$$

$$= IV$$

or $P = \dfrac{V^2}{R}$

or $P = I^2 R$

The unit of power Js^{-1} or volt-ampere is called watt (W).

Large amounts of electric power are required in industry e.g.

1 kilowatt (kW)	$= 1000\text{W} = 10^3\text{W}$
1 megawatt (MW)	$= 10^6\text{W}$
1 horse power (h.p.)	$= \frac{3}{4}\text{kW}.$

Example 7.6

An electric bulb is labelled 240V, 60W. How much current is taken by the bulb?

Solution

Power $P = IV$ (current x potential difference)
$$60 = I \times 240$$
$$\frac{6}{24} = I$$
Current $I = 0.25A.$

Commercial units of electric power

Commercial power is consumed in *kilowatt-hours* (kW-h). 1kWh is the energy supplied by a rate of working of 1000 watts for 1 hour.

$$1\text{kWh} = 1000\text{W} \times (60 \times 60)\text{s}$$
$$= 3.6 \times 10^6 \text{J}.$$

Most of the electrical energy used in Nigeria is produced from Kainji Dam. The Power Holding Company of Nigeria (PHCN) distributes the electrical energy and sells it in units of kWh.

Summary

1.   Current is the time rate of flow of electric charge from one region to another in a circuit through a conductor which are invariably metals in which the charge carriers are free electrons. Current is measured in amperes (A) by an ammeter joined in series. Resistance wire is made of pure copper and alloys, such as manganin or constantan. The potential difference between two points in an electrical circuit is the work done in joules when one coulomb of electricity moves from one point to another and it is measured in volts by a voltmeter connected in parallel across the points.

2. The electromotive force (e.m.f.) E of a cell is the p.d. between its terminals when it is not delivering current to an external circuit. It is also the total work done in joules when one coulomb of electricity is conveyed through the material of the source of e.m.f. and the external circuit, V; $E = V + Ir$ and measured in volts, r is the internal resistance, I is current flowing through the circuit and Ir is the lost volts.

3. Ohm's law states that, the current flowing through a metallic conductor (wire) is directly proportional to the potential difference across it provided the physical conditions of the wire such as temperature remain constant, i.e. $\frac{V}{I} = R$.

4. The ammeter used for measuring current is placed in series in a circuit and has a low resistance. The voltmeter on the other hand is placed parallel with the circuit across the component and should always have a high resistance compared to the resistance of the component whose p.d. or e.m.f. is to be measured. An electric circuit carrying a constant, steady current must include a source of e.m.f. (cell, battery or generator) that delivers energy to the circuit and in which charges move from regions of lower to higher potential energy through conductors. Resistance is the opposition to the flow of current in a circuit, unit is in ohm (Ω). In a circuit containing resistance in series:
   (i) the current is the same in each resistance;
   (ii) the total p.d. = the sum of the individual p.ds;
   (iii) combined resistance = sum of individual resistances
   $$R = R_1 + R_2 + R_3.$$
   In a circuit containing resistances in parallel:
   (i) p.d. across each resistance is the same;
   (ii) the combined resistance is given by
   $$\frac{1}{R} = \frac{1}{R_1} + \frac{1}{R_2} + \frac{1}{R_3}$$
   if there are three wires of resistances R_1, R_2 and R_3 respectively. Resistance can be measured by voltmeter and ammeter method.

5. Simple cell has a positive copper and negative zinc electrode and an electrolyte of tetraoxosulphate (VI) acid.

6. Polarisation is due to hydrogen at the copper electrode which produces back e.m.f. and high internal resistance, Leclanche dry cell has a positive carbon and negative zinc electrode and electrolyte of ammonium chloride paste and a solid manganese (IV) oxide as depolariser. The hydrogen produced at the carbon pole is oxidised to water. The e.m.f. is about 1.5V but current is maintained for a short time.

7. Accumulator of lead-acid type has positive lead peroxide and negative lead electrodes and electrolyte of dilute tetraoxosulphate (VI) acid. Its e.m.f. is about 2V with very low resistance and can be recharged unlike primary cells.

8. The Daniell cell is another type of primary cell that has copper container as positive electrode and zinc rod as negative electrode. Its electrolyte is tetraoxosulphate (VI) acid and depolariser of copper tetraoxosulphate (VI) surrounding copper. The constant e.m.f. is 1.08V.

9. Other cells include Nife accumulator with nickel hydroxide as positive pole and iron as the negative pole. Its electrolyte is solution of potassium hydroxide. Though expensive and bulky they last much longer and require less maintainance with e.m.f of 1.25V. Other cells such as fuel cells used in space craft use hydrogen and oxygen. When a resistance R is connected to a cell with internal resistance r, the current
   $$I = \frac{E}{R + r} \text{ where } E \text{ is the e.m.f.}$$

10. For cells in series, total e.m.f. is the sum of the individual e.m.f. and total internal resistance is sum of individual internal resistance. Cells in parallel with similar cells :

    total e.m.f. = e.m.f. of **one** cell.

    total internal resistance = parallel combination of the internal resistances.

11. Current can be produced from:
    (a) chemical energy through electric cells;
    (b) heat energy through thermo electric effect;
    (c) mechanical energy through d.c. dynamo;
    (d) solar energy through solar cells.

Exercise 7

1. Five (5)-ohm resistors are connected in parallel, the equivalent resistance is
   A. 1ohm.   B. 2.5ohm.
   C. 6.5ohm.   D. 12.5ohm.

2. Two resistors 10 ohm each can be connected to give a combined resistance of
   I. 20Ω   II. 15Ω   III. 5Ω   IV. 2Ω
   A. I only   B. I and II only   C. III only
   D. I and III only

3. A tungsten bulb is marked 200V, 40 watts, what is its resistance when it is operated at the correct voltage?
   A. $\frac{1}{40}$ Ω   B. 5Ω   C. 50Ω   D. 1000Ω

4.

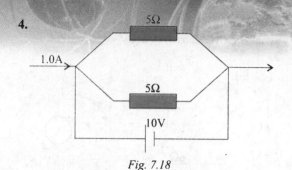

Fig. 7.18

Calculate the energy developed in 10 minutes by the system above.

A. 100J   B. 1000J   C. 1500J   D. 6000J

5. Which of the following is **not** a consequence of hydrogen bubbles covering the copper plate of a primary cell?
A. Local action.
B. Increase in resistance of the cell.
C. Polarisation.
D. Generation of less current by the cell.

6. Calculate the time in which 2.4 kJ of energy would be expended when an electric heater of resistance $3.6 \times 10_3 \ \Omega$ is used on a 240V mains supply. (Neglect heat losses to the surrounding).
A. 150.0s   B. 90.0s   C. 36.0s   D. 20.0s

7. Calculate the resistivity in ohm-m of a 5m wire whose cross-sectional area is $1.0 \times 10^{-3} m^2$ and resistance is 1ohm.
A. 1.0×10^{-2} B. 2.0×10^{-4}
C. 3.0×10^{-5} D.   2.0

8. Which statement is NOT correct about the circuit below?

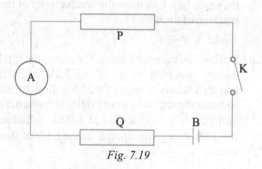

Fig. 7.19

A. B is a source of e.m.f.
B. K is the key.
C. A measures current.
D. P and Q are resistors connected in parallel.

9. Calculate the resistance of a wire of length 10cm, cross-sectional area $2.0 \times 10^{-8} m^2$ and resistivity 8.0×10^{-7} ohm m.
A. 4Ω B. 10Ω
C. 0.04Ω D. 0.004Ω

10.

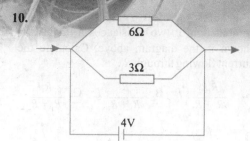

Fig. 7.20

Calculate the current I in the diagram above. (Neglect the internal resistance of the cell).
A.   2.0A   B.   4.0A
C   5.0A   D.   8.0A

11. A lamp 100W, 250V is lit for 5 hours. If it operates normally and 1kWh of electrical energy costs ₦2, what is the cost of lighting the lamp?
A. ₦1   B. ₦2   C. ₦5   D. ₦10

12. A car fuse is marked 15A and operates normally on a 12V battery, calculate the resistance of the fuse wire.
A. 0.8Ω B. 1.3Ω
C. 3.0Ω D. 27.0Ω

13.

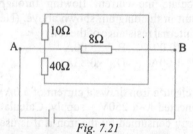

Fig. 7.21

Calculate the effective resistance between points A and B in the diagram above.
A.   27.6   B.   16.0   C.   6.0   D.   4.0

14. The electrical energy supplied by a Leclanche cell is obtained from
A. mechanical energy.
B. chemical energy.
C. solar energy.
D. magnetic energy.

15.
A battery of e.m.f. E and negligible internal

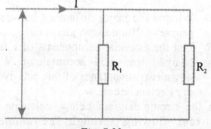

Fig. 7.22

resistance supplies a current, I to the combination of two resistances R_1 and R_2 as shown in the diagram above. Calculate the current flowing through R_1.

A. $\dfrac{R_1 R_2}{R_1 + R_2} I$ B. $\dfrac{R_2}{R_1 + R_2} I$ C. $\dfrac{R_1 I}{R_1 + R_2}$

D. $\dfrac{R_1}{R_2} I$

16. In a photocell, light energy is converted to
    A. kinetic energy.   B. heat energy.
    C. chemical energy.   D. electrical energy.

17. An electricity board transmits electrical power of 400kW through a national grid of 40kV. Calculate the current transmitted.
    A. 440.0A   B. 360.0A
    C. 100.0A   D. 10.0A

18.

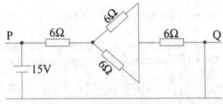

Fig. 7.23

Calculate the current flowing through the circuit in the diagram shown above. (Neglect the internal resistance of the cell)
A. 10.00A   B. 5.00A
C. 1.00A   D. 0.83A

19. An electric iron draws a current of 5.0A when connected to a $250V_{rms}$ supply. Calculate the energy consumed by the iron if it is used for 10minutes.
    A. 750.0kJ   B. 550.0kJ
    C. 41.6kJ   D. 20.0kJ

20. A wire of length 200cm and cross-sectional area 2.0×10^{-3} cm^2 has a resistance of 0.20Ω. Calculate its electrical conductivity.
    A. $2.0 \times 10^{-6}\Omega^{-1}$cm^{-1} B. $5.0 \times 10^{5}\Omega^{-1}$cm^{-1}
    C. $2.0 \times 10^{6}\Omega^{-1}$cm   D. $5.0 \times 10^{6}\Omega^{-1}$cm^{-1}

21. List two disadvantages of a simple cell. Explain briefly how these disadvantages are overcomed in the Daniell cell.

22. (a) What is the major difference between a primary cell and a secondary cell.
    (b) List the essential components of a fully charged lead acid accumulator. Write down two advantages of this cell over a dry Leclanche cell.

23. In the circuit diagram below, calculate the current flowing through the ammeter

neglecting the internal resistances of the cells if each cell has an e.m.f. of 2V.

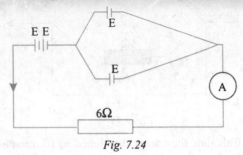

Fig. 7.24

24. Explain using diagrams what is meant by
    (i) an open circuit.
    (ii) a closed circuit.
    (iii) an electromotive force (e.m.f.) of a cell.
    (iv) potential difference.

25. State ohm's law and define resistance. Describe an experiment to demonstrate ohm's law. How can the resistance of a short piece of wire be obtained using ohm's law.

26. A battery of four cells each of e.m.f. 1.5V and internal resistance 1.0Ω is connected to a 1Ω resistor in series with a parallel combination of two 2Ω resistors. Draw the circuit diagram and calculate:
    (a) the combined external resistance.
    (b) the current in the circuit.
    (c) the lost volts in the battery.
    (d) the current in one of the two resistors.

27. Define resistivity and state its units. The resistance of a wire of length 66m and diameter 0.14m is 10⊡. Calculate the conductivity of the material of the wire.
    (Take $\pi = \dfrac{22}{7}$)

28. Define electromotice force. Calculate the total energy provided by e.m.f. of 3.0V when it causes a steady current of 0.30A to flow for 30 minutes through an electric bulb. If the battery had an internal resistance of 2.00Ω, calculate the heat energy dissipated in the bulb at that time.

29. Define the watt and the joule. An electric kettle contains a 1000W heating element, what current does it take from $240V_{rms}$ mains source?

30. An electric heater is rated 1000W, 250V.
    (a) Calculate the resistance of the heating element when in use.
    (b) If electricity is charged at ₦2 per kilowatt hour and the heater is used for 30min each day, calculate the cost per month of 30days.

31. State ohm's law and define electrical resistance. Distinguish between resistance and

resistivity. Illustrate with a circuit diagram and explain how you would connect a voltmeter and an ammeter to a given standard resistor to measure the resistance of the resistor.

32. A resistor 500Ω, an ammeter and a battery of negligible internal resistance are connected in series. A voltmeter is connected across the system. If the ammeter reading is 2.0A and voltmeter is 1.0V, what is internal resistance of voltmeter?

33. List two non-ohmic conductors and state two reasons why they are non-ohmic.

34. Fig 7.25 shows two resistors, whose resistances are 0.4Ω and 0.6Ω. and the current in the 0.4☐ resistor is 1.50A.

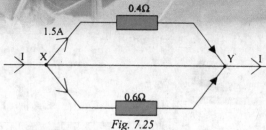

Fig. 7.25

Calculate:
(a) the potential difference between *X* and *Y* in the diagram.
(b) the current *I* in the 0.6Ω resistor.
(c) the current *I* in the circuit.

35. Calculate the resistance of the wire, 150cm long and diameter 2.0mm constructed from an alloy of resistivity $44 \times 10^{-8}\Omega m$.

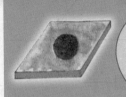

PARTICLE NATURE OF MATTER

Chapter 8

8.1 Structure of matter

Matter is what we call anything that has mass. All substances are made up of matter. All matter is acted upon by a force called gravity. On the earth, matter is attracted by gravity towards the centre of the earth. Matter exists in three different states, solid, liquid and gas. We shall now look at how matter is made up.

From very early times people wondered about the nature of matter and looked for ways of explaining the behaviour of substances. If a piece of matter, such as a piece of yam, were repeatedly cut into smaller and smaller bits, it is reasonable to think that one would eventually find the smallest particle, which could not be divided further. Such particles are called molecules.

8.2 Simple nature of molecules and atoms

A molecule is the smallest particle of a substance which can have a separate existence, whilst still keeping the properties of that substance. If the substance is an element, one of the chemically simple, basic substances, then its smallest particle is an atom.

> An atom is the smallest particle of an element which can take part in a chemical reaction.

If the substance is a chemical compound, made up of several elements, then the molecule of the substance is made up of atoms of the separate elements. Even when the substance is an element, the atoms often join together in groups to form molecules. For instance, one molecule of hydrogen, an element, is made up of two atoms of hydrogen. One molecule of water, a compound, contains two atoms of hydrogen and one atom of oxygen. We therefore talk of molecules of water, not atoms of water.

> A molecule is the smallest particle of a substance which can have a separate existence and still retain the properties of that substance.

The number of molecules contained in even a fairly small piece of a substance is quite enormous. For example, one gram of hydrogen contains about 3×10^{23} molecules.

As we are going to show later, the diameter of a molecule is of the order of 10^{-9}-10^{-10}m. It varies from substance to substance.

8.3 Determination of molecular size

An approximate length of a molecule of a substance can be found by the method first used by Lord Rayleigh. The purpose of the experiment is to measure the thickness of an oil film on the surface of water. It is argued that if an oil drop is placed on water, it spreads to form a circular film and that the thickness of this film represents the length of one molecule.

A tray is filled with clean water and when the surface is still, lycopodium powder is sprinkled lightly on it. A drop of olive oil is then formed and its diameter is estimated with the aid of a half-millimetre scale.

The drop is then gently released on the surface of the water. It immediately spreads across the water, forming a circular film. The diameter of the oil film is measured with a ruler, and hence the radius is obtained.

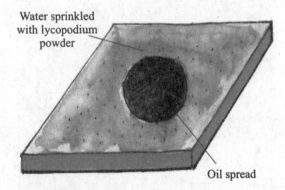

Water sprinkled with lycopodium powder

Oil spread

Fig. 8.1 Oil film experiment

Let R be the radius of the film and r the radius of the drop. Area of film = πR^2

h is the required thickness of film.

Volume of film   = $\pi R^2 h$

volume of spherical drop = $\frac{4}{3} \pi r^3$

But volume of film = volume of drop

$\therefore \quad \pi R^2 h = \frac{4}{3} \pi r^3$

Thickness of film = length of molecule

$$= \left(\frac{4}{3} \pi r^3 \right) \Big/ \pi R^2$$

$$= \frac{4}{3} \cdot \frac{r^3}{R^2}$$

Experiments of this kind have been found to give values of the order of 10^{-7} m.

Note: Instead of measuring the size of the drop to obtain its volume, we can use a pipette to measure out a known small volume, V, of the light oil which is then run from the pipette on to the surface of the water. In this case,

$$V = \pi R^2 h$$

then, $h = \dfrac{V}{\pi R^2}$

8.4 Evidences of particle nature of matter

1. Brownian motion

In 1827, Robert Brown first observed a direct effect of the movement of molecules. He was looking through the microscope at some tiny pollen particles in water. He found, to his surprise, that these particles were in a continual, haphazard motion.

Many years afterwards, it was realised that the random motion of these particles was caused by bombardment from moving water molecules. The same kind of motion is shown by smoke particles suspended in air. This random motion is called **Brownian motion**, after its discoverer.

Fig. 8.2 Brownian motion

Nowadays, Brownian motion can be observed in a school laboratory by looking at smoke form, for example, a burning straw or piece of string, trapped in a small glass cell under a microscope. When lit from the side the particles of smoke are seen in continual, random movement.

Brownian motion is important for two reasons. First, it is evidence for the existence of molecules, which are too small to be observed directly. Second, it is evidence that molecules are not still, but are in continual motion.

2. Law of definite proportion

Another evidence in favour of the particle nature of matter was obtained from analysis of chemical reactions. This crucial piece of evidence is known by chemists as the law of definite proportions which states that when two or more elements combine to form a compound, they always do so in the same proportions by weight. For example, the compound water (H_2O) is always formed by two parts of hydrogen (H) and sixteen parts of oxygen (O), and the common salt (NaCl) is always formed from 23 parts of sodium and 35 parts of chlorine by weight.

3. Diffusion

In a gas, the speed with which the molecules move about depends on their masses as well as the temperature, the lighter molecules moving faster. Two gas jars, one full of hydrogen, a light gas, and the other full of carbon dioxide, a heavy gas, are arranged as shown in Fig 8.3. The glass cover separating the two gases is carefully removed. It is found by chemical tests that after a while, both gas jars contain a mixture of both carbon dioxide and hydrogen.

The heavier carbon dioxide is able to move upwards against gravity and the lighter hydrogen moves downwards to give a uniform mixture. We would expect the heavier gas to stay at the bottom and the lighter gas at the top, but what happens is easily explained if we remember that both gases consist of molecules in continual, rapid motion.

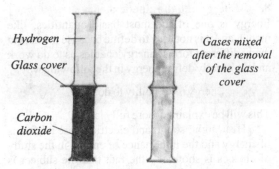

Fig. 8.3 Diffusion of gases.

The tendency of a gas to mix with another and fill an empty space as a result of the constant random motion of the molecules is called diffusion.

The rate of diffusion depends on the densities of the gases; the lighter, or less dense the gas, the more rapidly it diffuses.

If we suppose a piece of yam to represent an element (e.g. sodium), the smallest bit of the yam represents the atom of the element. The smallest particle of an element must be capable of a separate existence.

There are many theories concerning the structure of the atom. We shall discuss them later.

For now we shall consider the atom as simply consisting of two parts held together by electric forces. The two parts of the atom are (i) the *nucleus* and (ii) the *electrons*.

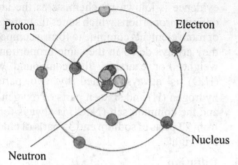

Fig. 8.4   Atomic structure

The nucleus is the heavy portion of the atom and is located at its centre. It consists of two parts the *protons* and the *neutrons*. While the protons carry a positive charge, the neutrons carry no charge.

The second part of the atom is the electron. The electrons are very light (about 1/1840 of the mass of the proton). They are negatively charged. The lightness of electrons makes it easy to transfer them when two materials are made to rub against each other. The electrons circle in orbits around the heavy nucleus and are held in place due to the electrostatic attraction between them and the protons of the nucleus.

In a neutral atom, the total charges due to the electrons must balance the total charges due to the protons.

8.5   Energy and the kinetic theory

Energy is one of the most basic quantities, like matter, and it is not easy to define because it exists in many different forms. Energy enables us to do work and we usually define energy in the following way:

> **Energy is the ability to do work.**

This will be explained more fully later.

Heat, light, sound and electricity are all forms of energy and the importance of energy in the study of physics is shown by the fact that the subject is divided into sections which deal with the different forms. A body which is moving has energy called **kinetic energy**. The faster the body moves, the greater its kinetic energy. The word kinetic means to do with movement. It is important to realise that molecules are moving all the time, and have kinetic energy, as Brownian motion shows.

The kinetic theory is the theory which takes this simple fact, that molecules are continually moving, and uses it to explain the behaviour of matter.

8.6   States of matter

(Molecules in solids, liquids and gases)

Matter exists in three states; solids, liquids and gases, which are made up of molecules in continual motion.

Solids

In solids, the molecules lie in a particular pattern. The molecules are close together and they vibrate about fixed positions. If the solid is heated, the total energy is divided among the molecules and makes them vibrate faster. Eventually they move so fast that they loose from their fixed positions. The solid melts and becomes a liquid. Some solids, such as camphor, vaporise (without melting first) by losing molecules which escape from the surface, and thereby are gradually reduced in size.

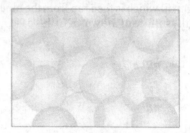

Fig. 8.5 Solid state

Liquids

The molecules of a liquid can move about within the liquid. They are in constant random motion and they also vibrate. If the liquid is heated, its molecules gain kinetic energy and move faster, until eventually molecules can escape from the surface. The liquid then vaporises and turns to a gaseous state.

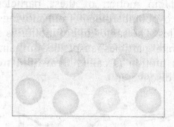

Fig. 8.6 Liquid state

Gases

The molecules of a gas are also in constant motion but the molecules are comparatively far apart. They move at high speeds, colliding with one another and with the walls of their containing vessel. They fill the vessel and exert pressure on the walls of the container. The pressure of the gas is caused by the collisions of the molecules with the walls of the container.

Fig. 8.7 Gaseous state

Summary

1. The evidence of the molecular nature of matter comes from Brownian motion, Law of definite proportion and Diffusion.

2. An atom is the smallest particle of an element which can have a separate existence. The atom consists of a central massive nucleus surrounded by light electrons moving in orbits around the nucleus. The nucleus itself consists of protons and neutrons. Protons are positively charged, electrons are negatively charged and neutrons carry no charge.

3. A molecule is the smallest particle of a substance which can have a separate existence and still retain the properties of that substance.

4. The size of a molecule is about $10^{-9} - 10^{-10}$m.

5. The three states of matter are solids, liquids and gases. In solids, the molecules are closely held together by intermolecular forces and they vibrate about a mean fixed position. In liquids, the intermolecular forces are weaker than in solids and the liquid molecules are therefore free to move. In gases, molecules are very free to move about because the intermolecular forces are very weak.

6. The kinetic energy of the molecules constituting matter increases with temperature.

Exercise 8

1. Molecule can have any of the following except:
   A. It can be made of same element.
   B. It can have different element.
   C. It is a group of atoms.
   D. They have diameters $10^{-2} - 10^{-3}$m.

2. Which of the following statements is not correct?
   A. Matter is made up of molecules.
   B. The molecules of matter are in constant motion.
   C. Brownian motion is an evidence of particle nature of matter.
   D. Molecules of a liquid are stationary.
   E. Atoms combine to form molecules

3. A drop of oil of volume 10^{-10} m³ spreads out on water to make a circular film of radius 10^{-1}m. What is the thickness of the film?
   A. 3.2×10^{-9} m   B. 3.2×10^{-8}m
   C. 1.6×10^{-9}m   D. 1.6×10^{-10}m

4. Give a brief description of the structure of the atom.

5. How would you estimate the size of a molecule of an oil?

6. Distinguish between the three states of matter.

7. What do you understand by Brownian motion? What is its significance in the theory of matter?

8. Outline the difference between solids, liquids and gases in terms of:
   (i) the separation of the molecules;
   (ii) the motion of the molecules;
   (iii) the arrangement of the molecules throughout the bulk of the material.

9. What do you understand by diffusion? Describe an experiment to demonstrate the phenomenon in the laboratory. What is the significance of diffusion in the molecular theory of matter?

10. What are the three states of matter? How do these states differ from each other? Which in general is the most compact?

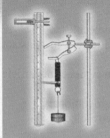

ELASTIC PROPERTIES OF SOLIDS

Chapter 9

A body is said to be elastic if it regains its original shape and size after undergoing a stretch or compression.

9.1 Hooke's law

For a wire or spring, it is found that if a gradual stretching force, F, is applied, the extension, e, produced at any time is directly proportional to the force applied. If the applied force is removed, the wire should return to its original size and shape.

This situation however does not continue indefinitely. At a certain stage the wire becomes distorted. The load becomes too much for the wire to bear, and the extension will no longer be proportional to the applied force. The wire is said to have lost its **elasticity**, or to have reached its **elastic limit**. When the stretching force is removed, it does not regain its original length. The law governing the elasticity of a wire or spring can therefore be stated as follows:

Hooke's law states that provided the elastic limit is not exceeded, the extension, e, in an elastic material (e.g. wire) is proportional to the load or applied force, F.

$$F \propto e$$
$$F = ke \qquad 9.1$$

Where k is the constant of the spring or wire, known as the **stiffness** or **elastic constant**.

If F is in newtons (N) and e is in metres (m)

$$k = \frac{F}{e} \quad \text{is in Nm}^{-1} \qquad 9.2$$

It is the force required to produce a unit extension. Hence it gives a measure of how strong a wire or spring is. Because the extension of a spring is proportional to force, the spring balance (see chapter 1) can be used to measure forces directly in newtons.

9.2 Young's modulus

Suppose a force of F (in newtons) applied to a wire of original length l_o (in metres) and cross-sectional area A (in m²) extends its length by e (m), we can also state Hooke's law as:

$$\frac{F}{A} \propto \frac{e}{l_o} \qquad 9.3$$

(provided elastic limit is not exceeded).

This equation is identical with the equation $F \propto e$, because A and l_o are all constants.

The expression F/A is known as the **tensile stress** (Nm^{-2}) and e/l is known as **tensile strain** (no units). Therefore Hooke's law may be stated as **stress** is proportional to **strain** or stress $\propto$ strain.

$\therefore$ stress $= E \times$ strain,

where E is a constant known as **Young's modulus of elasticity**, or the **Young modulus**.

The Young modulus is therefore defined as:

$$E = \frac{tensile\ stress}{tensile\ strain} \qquad 9.4$$

Example 9.1

A spring of natural length 3 m is extended by 0.01 m by a force of 4 N, what will be its length when the applied force is 12N?

From Hooke's law:

$$F = ke$$

Where $F = 4$N, $e = 0.01$m

$\therefore \quad 4 = k \times 0.01$

$\quad k = 400\,\text{Nm}^{-1}$

when $F = 12$,

$\quad F = 400 \times e$

$\quad e = \dfrac{12}{400}$

$\quad = 0.03m.$

Its length is $3.03\ m$. (i.e. 3m + 0.03m)

Example 9.2

An elastic wire extends by 1.0cm when a load of 20g hangs from it, what additional load will be required to cause a further extension of 2.0cm?

The force exerted by a mass of 20 grams

$$= (20 \times \frac{g}{1000})\,\text{N}$$

$$= 0.2\text{N}$$

By Hooke's law $F = ke$

i.e. $0.2\text{N} = k \times 0.01$

$\quad k = 20\,\text{Nm}^{-1}$

Let M (kg) be the additional load required to extend the wire by a further 2cm or 0.02m.

Total extension is now 3cm or 0.03m.
Force exerted by the new load is

$(0.02 + M) 10 = k \times 0.03$

$10M + 0.2 = 20 \times 0.03$

$10M + 0.2 = 0.6$

$\qquad M = 0.04\text{kg}$

$\qquad = 40\text{g}$

9.3 Experimental verification of Hooke's law and determination of elastic constant of a spring

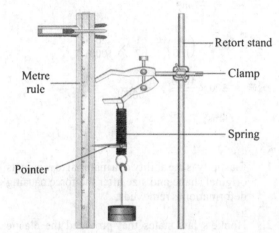

Fig. 9.1 Verification of Hooke's law.

The apparatus is set up as shown in Fig. 9.1. Without suspending any weight on the spring, the pointer reading p_o is noted. With a mass, m, of say 0.10kg suspended (depending on how stiff the spring is), the reading p is noted and hence the extension $(p - p_o) = e$ is found. The experiment is repeated for another five values of m, increasing in steps of 100 grams. The results are tabulated.

A graph of m (in kilograms) against e (in metres) is plotted. Provided that the total 0.60kg mass does not permanently deform the spring, a straight line graph through the origin should be obtained. Hence Hooke's law is verified.

If the slope of the graph is S, the force constant k is proportional to S. A mass of m (in kilograms) exerts a force of mg (in newtons).

$$k = \frac{F}{e}$$

$$= \frac{mg}{e}$$

$$= Sg \; (g = 10\text{Nkg}^{-1})$$

The graph of a strained elastic wire

The graph of load against extension for a wire which has been stretched gradually until it has exceeded its elastic limit is shown in fig. 9.2.

Up to the elastic limit, Hooke's law applies. For loads beyond this, the wire stretches permanently and if the load is removed the wire is found to have been distorted and does not return to its original length.

Still further increases in load result in a point being reached where a small increase in load produces a large extension. This is called the **yield point**.

Finally, a point is reached where the wire cannot stand any further increase in load. At this point the wire breaks. This is known as the **breaking point**.

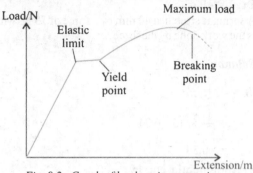

Fig. 9.2 Graph of load against extension

Up to the elastic limit, the bonds between the molecules inside the material are stretched but not broken. Beyond this, the bonds are broken, but a molecule as it moves out of position forms a bond with the next molecules along. When the force is great enough the molecules are not able to form new bonds, the molecules part permanently, and the material breaks.

9.4 Energy stored or work done on springs and elastic strings

Work is done when an elastic material is stretched or compressed. If the force stretching the material is F Newtons, then the work done is given by;

$$\text{Work} = \text{average force} \times \text{extension} \qquad 9.5$$

$$= \left(\frac{0 + F}{2}\right) \times e$$

$$= \frac{1}{2} Fe$$

But from Hooke's law, $F = ke$
where e is the extension produced by force F.

$$\therefore \; \text{work} = \frac{1}{2} ke^2 \qquad 9.6$$

Where work is in joules, e is in metres and k the elastic constant, is in Newton per metre.

Example 9.3

(i) Sketch the graph of the relation between the extension of a spiral spring and the load attached to it when it is gradually loaded up to the elastic limit.

(ii) If the spring has a stiffness of 950 Nm^{-1}, what work will be done in extending the spring by 60mm?

Solution

For the first section of the question, see fig. 9.2.

(ii)

$$W = \frac{1}{2} ke^2$$

$$= \frac{1}{2} \times 950 \times \left(\frac{60}{1000}\right)^2$$

$$= 1.71 J$$

Example 9.4

A spring is stretched 40 mm by a force of 15 N, what is the work done by the force?

Solution

$$W = \frac{1}{2} Fe$$

$$= \frac{1}{2} \times 15 \times 0.04$$

$$= 0.3 J$$

Elastic potential energy

We defined potential energy earlier as the energy possessed by a body by virtue of its state or position. Stretched or compressed spring, elastic string or rubber, possess potential energy because they are potentially able to do some works. This potential to do work arises from the fact that work is done in stretching or compressing the elastic material. This ability of the stretched or compressed elastic material to do work is called **elastic potential energy**. This is energy stored in the material as a result of its stretched or compressed state. Elastic potential energy is also given by:

$$W = \frac{1}{2} Fe$$

$$= \frac{1}{2} ke^2$$

where F is the maximum stretching or compressing force, e is the extension or compression, and k is the force constant of the material.

Elastic potential energy is stored energy which can be transformed into other forms of energy. For example when you stretch the rubber of a catapult, and project a stone from it, the elastic potential energy stored in the rubber is transformed into the kinetic energy of the flying stone according to the law of conservation of energy.

Example 9.5

A spiral spring is compressed by 0.02 m, calculate the energy stored in the spring, if the force constant is 400 Nm⁻¹.

Solution

Energy stored in the spring is given by

$$W = \frac{1}{2} Fe$$

$$= \frac{1}{2} ke^2$$

$$= \frac{1}{2} \times 400 \times 0.02^2 J$$

$$= 0.08 \text{ joules}$$

Example

A stone of mass 20 g is released from a catapult whose rubber has been stretched through 4 cm. If the force constant of the rubber is 200 Nm⁻¹, calculate the velocity with which the stone leaves the catapult.

Solution

Let the velocity of the stone be v ms⁻¹.
The elastic potential energy of the stretched rubber is transformed into the kinetic energy of the stone. Hence.

$$\frac{1}{2} ke^2 = \frac{1}{2} mv^2$$

$$\frac{1}{2} \times 200 \times \left(\frac{4}{100}\right)^2 = \frac{1}{2} \times \frac{20}{1000} \times v^2$$

$$v^2 = 200 \times \frac{1000}{20} \times \frac{16}{10000}$$

$$v = 4 \text{ms}^{-1}$$

Summary

1. Elasticity is the ability of a material to regain its original shape and size after the force causing deformation is removed.

2. Hooke's law states that provided the elastic limit of an elastic material is not exceeded, the extension of the material is directly proportional to the load or applied force causing the extension.

3. Elastic limit is the maximum stretching force beyond which the stretched material would not return to its original length when the force is removed.

4. Yield point is the point at which the elastic material loses its elasticity permanently and becomes plastic.

5. Work done in stretching or compressing a material is the same as the energy stored in the material or its elastic potential energy, and its given by:

$$W = \frac{1}{2} Fe$$

$$= \frac{1}{2} (\text{maximum force}) \times \text{extension}.$$

It is also equal to $\frac{1}{2} ke^2$.

Exercise 9

1. A spring 20 cm long is stretched to 25 cm by a load of 50 N, what will be its length when stretched by 100 N assuming that the elastic limit is not reached?
   A. 30 cm B. 10 cm C. 35 cm D. 40 cm

2. An elastic cord can be stretched to its elastic limit by a load of 2 N. If a 35 cm length of the cord is extended 0.6 cm by a force of 0.5 N, what will be the length of the cord when the stretching force is 2.5 N?
   A. 35.8cm   B. 38.0cm
   C. 35.0cm   D. 35.4 cm

3. A spring balance designed for a maximum load of 400 N was used to weigh a load of 500 N. After the 500 N load had been removed, the pointer would not return to the zero mark on the scale because the
   A. spring balance was of the cheap type.
   B. elastic limit of the spring material had been exceeded.
   C. pointer was not properly adjusted.
   D. 500 N load was removed.

4. A spring of force constant 1500 Nm^{-1} is acted upon by a constant force of 75N. Calculate the potential energy stored in the spring.
   A. 1.9 J   B. 3.2 J   C. 3.8 J   D. 5.0 J

5. A catapult is used to project a stone. Which of the following energy conversions takes place as the stone is released?
   A. The kinetic energy of the stone is converted into gravitational potential energy.
   B. The gravitational potential energy is converted into kinetic energy of the stone.
   C. The elastic potential energy of catapult is converted into the kinetic energy of the stone.
   D. The gravitational potential energy is converted to elastic energy.

6. A spring 20cm long is stretched to 25cm by a load of 50N, what will be its length when stretched by 100N, assuming that the elastic limit is not reached?

7. A spring of natural length 1.5m is extended 0.0050m by a force of 0.8N, what will its length be when the applied force is 3.2N?

8. State Hooke's law, and mention the condition under which it is obeyed.

9. A helical spring is loaded with increasing weight and the corresponding extensions of the spring are recorded until the elastic limit of proportionality is reached. Sketch a graph to show the relation between load and extension.

10. A spring of natural length 1m is stretched by an average force F (N) so that it extends to length l. Write down an expression for the work done in stretching the spring.

11. If a force of 100N stretches a spring by 0.1cm, find:
    (a) the elastic constant;
    (b) the work done in stretching the spring 0.3cm if the elastic limit is not exceeded.

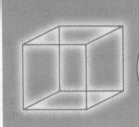

CRYSTALS

10.1 Crystal characteristics

Crystals refer to solids that have definite melting point. A crystalline compound has a definite shape, peculiar to that compound. Crystals of the same compound have the same shape. Substances of the same crystalline shape are referred to as **isomorphous**. Crystals are distinguished from each other simply by their shapes.

Crystals are made up of atoms, ions or molecules that are arranged in a regular repeating pattern.

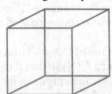

Fig. 10.1(a)   Cubic crystal

Fig. 10.1(b)   Prismatic crystal

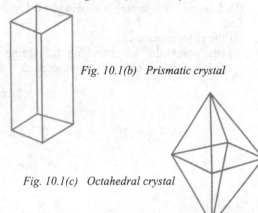

Fig. 10.1(c)   Octahedral crystal

10.2 Arrangement of atoms in crystal structure

In crystals, the atoms, molecules or ions are usually arranged in orderly regular manner, this is possible because of the force binding them. The force of cohesion holding the molecules in solid is greater than those holding them in liquid. Hence there is no free motion in crystals. The arrangement of molecules in crystals is referred to as **crystalline lattice.** Hence, different lattices produce different shapes of crystals. Crystal lattices are usually measured by X - rays.

Example

Sodium chloride is made up of sodium ions and chloride ions, then its structure is made of these ions, arranged in the form of a cube (Fig 10.2).

The ions are arranged in a way as to produce a cubic structure. Each ion of chlorine (Cl^- is surrounded by six sodium ions, just as each sodium ion is surrounded by six chlorine ions. Because the ions are of opposite charge, they are held together by **electrostatic force of attraction.** Each ion being attracted to six ions of opposite charge. Therefore, there is no free movement of ions hence the whole lattice is strong.

The melting points of crystalline substances are usually high, this is because a lot of heat energy is needed to break the strong force binding the ions together. Crystal structures of other substances are virtually being formed in the same manner as sodium chloride. Examples are zinc sulphide and potassium chloride.

Sodium chloride is an example of an ionic crystal. Sodium crystals consist of atoms held together by shared electrons like diamond, graphite

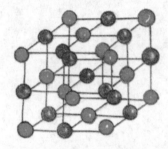

Fig. 10.2   Atomic model for sodium chloride crystal.

and quartz. Other crystals are composed of molecules arranged in an orderly manner on a crystal lattice, for example, solid carbondioxide. Crystals with atoms in their lattices are called *atomic crystals* and those with molecules in their lattices are called *molecular crystals*.

10.3 Non - crystalline or amorphous substances

Amorphous substances have no definite shapes and no definite melting points. They do not have the regular arrangement of atoms. They are more liquids than solids.

Good examples of amorphous substances are glass and plastics. Amorphous substances do not form crystals. Substances that form amorphous solids are made up of long, chain-like molecules that are interwined in the liquid state (fig. 10.3).

When amorphous substances are cooled, they behave abnormally (fig. 10.4). Crystallization of the melted material can never occur in amorphous solids because the molecules can not be untangled before they are frozen (Fig. 10.4). The cooling of the liquid continues until the substance no longer has the ability to move, at this point we say it is a solid, but it is a **super cooled liquid** not a solid. Amorphous substances soften gradually when heated, e.g. glass tubing when heated, it softens and could be bent.

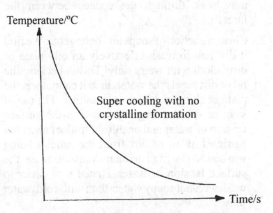

Fig. 10.4 Cooling curve for amorphous substances.

10.4 Comparison of crystalline and amorphous substances

(i) While crystalline substances have definite shape and atoms arranged in a regular pattern, amorphous substances have no definite shape.

(ii) Crystalline substances have definite melting points.

(iii) Crystalline substances are usually soluble while amorphous substances are insoluble.

(iv) For amorphous solids, crystallization of the melted material never takes place but it does in crystalline substances.

(v) Amorphous substances soften when heated, unlike the crystalline substance (e. g. ice).

(vi) Crystalline substances are either hydrated or anhydrous, all amorphous substances are anhydrous.

Summary

1. Crystalline substances (compounds) have definite melting points, and definite characteristic shape.

2. For crystals, the molecules, atoms or ions are arranged in a fairly compact and orderly manner.

3. Amorphous substances have no regular pattern or definite melting points.

4. In sodium chloride, the ions are arranged in a way as to produce a cubic structure.

5. Amorphous substances soften when heated, unlike the crystalline substances.

Exercise 10

1. Crystals have the following properties:
    I.   They have definite shape.
    II. They are insoluble.
    III. They have definite melting point.
    Which one is/are correct?
    A I only.   B I and II only.
    C I, II and III.   D I and III only.

2. Amorphous substances have the following properties: They
    I.   are all hydrated.
    II. do not have definite shape.
    III. are all soluble.
    Which of the properties is/are correct?
    A I only.   B I and II only.
    C III only.   D II only.

3. Differentiate between crystalline and amorphous substance.

4. State four characteristics of a crystal.

5. Use diagram to describe the structure of a sodium chloride crystal.

6. Explain briefly, what you understand by the word crystal lattice.

FLUID AT REST AND IN MOTION

Chapter 11

In this chapter, we shall study about forces in liquid at rest, such as surface tension, capillarity and forces in liquid in motion such as viscocity. The applications of these phenomena will also be investigated.

11.1 Surface tension

> The surface of a liquid behaves as if it were covered by an elastic skin. The surface thus appears to be under some force or tension.

> The tension or force acting parallel to the surface of the liquid is known as surface tension.

The coefficient of surface tension T is defined as the force in newton acting on a metre length drawn on the surface.

$$T = \frac{F}{L}$$

A steel needle with density greater than that of water, if placed gently on the surface of water will rest there as if it were being supported by the surface of the liquid which behaves as though covered with an elastic skin.

Some insects can walk on the surface of water, their feet make some marks in the surface but do not penetrate it. Such phenomena are examples of **surface tension**; the surface of the liquid behaves like a layer under tension.

The surface tension T, is defined as the ratio of the tangential force, F in the surface to the length, d along which the force acts.

$$T = \frac{F}{d}$$

Surface tension is a force per unit length. Its unit is newton per metre (Nm^{-1}).

Fig 11.1 shows how surface tension can support the weight of a needle resting on a water surface. Surface tension can be decreased by:
(i) increasing the temperature of the liquid;
(ii) adding detergents (soap) to the liquid.

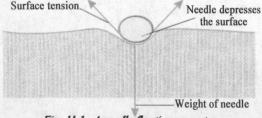

Fig. 11.1 A needle floating on water

11.2 Some applications of the effects of surface tension

1. Waterproof materials used for umbrellas, raincoats or tents, are usually treated with oil-based substances which prevent water from wetting the materials. A thin water-film is usually formed across the spaces between the threads of the fabric due to the surface tension skin on the raindrops . This skin prevents water from seeping through. If someone however touches the inside material of the umbrella, or tent, the surface film is broken and rainwater can now soak through the spaces between the threads.

2. Cleaning action of soaps and detergents: We find it difficult to wash effectively an oily plate or dirty cloth with water only. This is because the oil or dirt repels the water, thus it cannot wet the plate or cloth for effective washing .The use of soap or other detergents weakens the surface tension of water and enables it to float away the particles of oil or dirt from the articles being washed. Also high temperatures decrease the surface tension of water. Hence it is easier to wash with hot soapy water than with cold water only.

   Detergents also contain some chemicals which can combine with dirt and oil and make them soluble in water. With the dirt or oil removed, the water can then wet the material and wash it clean.

11.3 Adhesion and cohesion

Before we explain the origin of surface tension we need to distinguish between two types of forces.

> The force of attraction between molecules of the same substance is called **cohesion**.

> The force of attraction between molecules of different substances is called **adhesion**.

Adhesion of water to glass is stronger than the cohesion of water. Hence when water is spilled on a clean glass surface it wets the glass. On the other hand, the cohesion of mercury is greater than its adhesion to glass. Thus, when mercury is spilled on glass it forms small spherical droplets or large flattened drops and does not wet glass. For the same reason, when these liquids are contained in glass vessels, the water surface is concave to the air while mercury is concave to the liquid.

Fig. 11.2 Mercury drops on glass.

Molecular explanation of surface tension

The existence of surface tension can be explained by the molecular attraction between the liquid molecules.

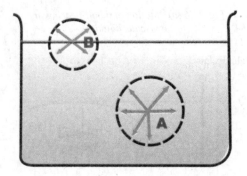

Fig. 11.3 Molecules in a liquid.

Right inside the liquid we see a molecule such as *A* is in equilibrium, since it is attracted by equal numbers of molecules all around it. There is zero net force on a molecule within the liquid. For a molecule such as *B* near the surface (Fig. 11.3), part of its sphere of molecular attraction is in air and part is in water. The liquid has far more molecules in the liquid than air. As a result of this, more molecules are attracting *B* towards the liquid than outwards.

The resultant force on *B* is hence towards the liquid. The same occurs for all molecules near the surface. Consequently the surface of the liquid is pulled inward, straining the surface molecules so that they appear to be in a state of tension.

11.4 Capillarity: definition and explanations

If a very narrow glass tube is inserted in a beaker of water we observe that water rises up the tube and its surface is concave to the air in the tube. If an identical tube is placed in a beaker of mercury , the surface is convex to the air and is depressed below the outside level.

Capillarity is defined as the tendency of liquids to rise (or fall) in narrow capillary tubes.

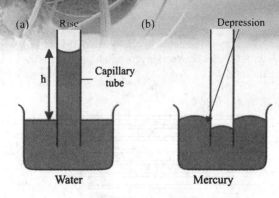

Fig. 11.4 Capillary action of water and mercury.

It is brought about by cohesive and adhesive forces. Water and some liquids which wet glass rise in a capillary tube because the force of adhesion of the liquid molecules for glass is greater than their cohesion to each other. Hence water tends to rise up the glass and the meniscus curves upwards.

In the case of mercury the cohesion of mercury molecules is greater than their adhesion to glass. The meniscus curves downwards and the mercury becomes depressed in the tube.

Similarly, blotting papers have fine pores which act like tiny capillary tubes. Ink and other liquids rise through the fine pores and enable the blotting papers to soak up the liquid.

Here are some common examples of capillary action:

(i)   water rising up the stem of a plant ,
(ii) ink held on the nib of a pen,
(iii) blood spreading through the fine capillary channels in the body,
(iv) liquid candle wax rising up the wick of a candle; there are many others.

Coefficient of surface tension and its determination

The coefficient of surface tension, *T*, is the force on a metre length of line drawn on the surface.

From Fig. 11.4, suppose water rises in the capillary tube of radius *r* to a height *h*, the weight of water in equilibrium as a result of surface tension is mg. This will balance the surface tension force $2\pi rT$.

$$\therefore \quad 2\pi rT = mg$$

$$\text{but } \rho = \frac{\text{mass}}{\text{volume}} = \text{density}$$

$$m = \rho v$$

$$v = \text{volume of cylinder}$$

$$= \pi r^2 h$$

$$mg = \rho g v$$

$$= \pi r^2 h \rho g$$

$$\therefore \quad 2\pi rT = \pi r^2 h \rho g$$

$$T = \frac{r h \rho g}{2} \qquad 11.1$$

The coefficient of surface tension can be calculated if the density ρ, height *h* and radius *r* are known.

Viscosity is the name given to internal friction which exists between layers of a liquid or gas in motion.

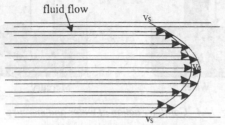

Fig. 11.5 Stream line flow of liquid.

When water or any other liquid flows through a pipe, the velocities of various layers are not the same. The velocity is greatest at the centre and least at the surface in contact with the pipe as illustrated in fig. 11.5. The resistance to flow is smaller through a large tube than a narrow one and the thicker the liquid, the more sluggish will be the flow. In general, liquids which flow and pour slowly are called **viscous** liquids, e.g. engine oil. All liquids that pour faster such as water, kerosene, turpentine are said to be less viscous than engine oil. Objects such as a ball-bearing moves faster in water than in engine oil. This is because the engine oil offers greater opposition to the movement of the ball.

Terminal velocity (speed)

A ball-bearing falling through a viscous liquid such as glycerine is acted upon by three forces, weight mg, viscous force V which opposes motion and upthrust U due to the liquid displaced as illustrated in fig 11.6(a). The equation of motion is therefore:

$$mg - V - U = ma \qquad 11.2$$

where a is the acceleration.

It is observed that at a certain stage, the ball ceases to accelerate but moves with a uniform velocity, which is called the **terminal speed**. The reason that a terminal speed is reached is that the viscous force, V, is proportional to the terminal velocity, v.

$$V = kv$$

where k is a constant.

As the ball-bearing accelerates, the speed increases and so does the viscous force V, until a point is reached where the viscous drag equals the downward force. At this stage $a = 0$ so that the above equation 11.2 becomes

$$mg - V - U = 0$$

or $\quad V = mg - U \qquad\qquad$ 11.3

Since we can calculate the value of the upthrust, the value of the viscous force, V can be estimated from the above equation. Figure 11.6(b) shows the graph of velocity versus time in a viscous liquid.

Raindrops do not accelerate for long before reaching a fairly low terminal speed due to the viscous drag of the air. If this did not happen, raindrops would hit us with a dangerously high velocity! Particles of a suspension in a liquid also fall with steady terminal speed, and this can be used to estimate the average size of the particles.

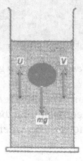

Fig. 11.6 (a) Motion of a ball-bearing in a viscous liquid.

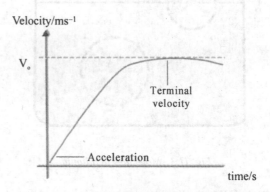

Fig. 11.6 (b) Graph of velocity versus time in a viscous liquid.

11.6   Applications of viscosity

One way of reducing friction in machine is to lubricate surfaces which are sliding over each other with a liquid, usually an oil. This places a layer of liquid between the metal surfaces and as metals slide through liquids with less friction than they slide over each other, friction is reduced.

Summary

1. The surface of a liquid behaves as if it were covered by an elastic skin. It thus appears to be under some forces or tension. This surface tension can be explained by the molecular attraction between the liquid molecules.

2. The coefficient of surface tension is the force per unit length acting on a line drawn on the surface.

3. Capillarity is the rise or fall of liquids in a capillary tube of narrow bore. It is due to the combined effects, of surface tension, adhesion and cohesion forces in liquids.

4. Cohesion is the force of attraction between molecules of same substance, while adhesion is the force of attraction between molecules of the different substances.

5. Water wets glass because the force of adhesion of the liquid molecules for glass is greater than their cohesion to each other. Hence water has a concave meniscus.

6. Mercury does not wet glass because the cohesion of mercury molecules is greater than their adhesion to glass. Hence mercury has a convex meniscus.

7. Viscosity is the internal friction which exists between layers of a liquid or gas in motion.

8. Viscous oils are used as lubricants.

Exercise 11
1. Which of the following is not a surface tension phenomenon?
   A. The floating of a needle in water.
   B. The walking of insects on water.
   C. The floating of a ship in water.
   D. A spherical drop of water forming slowly from a tap.

2. The action of water rising up the stem of a plant is due to
   A. surface tension.   B. osmosis.
   C. transpiration.   D. Capillarity.

3. Which of the following statements are correct?
   I. The meniscus of water in a capillary tube is concave.
   II. The meniscus of mercury in a capillary tube is concave.
   III. The meniscus of mercury in a capillary tube is convex.
   IV. The meniscus of water in a capillary tube is convex.

   A. I & II   B. I & IV
   C. II & III   D. I & III

4. The fall of a mercury in a narrow tube is due to
   A. the capillarity action of the liquid.
   B. the viscosity of the liquid.
   C. the osmotic pressure of the liquid.
   D. the friction between the walls of the tube and the liquid.

5. Which of the following statements is/are true?
   I. Water wets glass because adhesion of water to glass is stronger than the cohesion.
   II. Water wets glass because cohesion of water to glass is stronger than the adhesion.
   III. Cohesion is the force of attraction between molecules of same substances.

   A. I & III   B. II & III   C. I only
   D. III only

6. The following are viscous liquids except
   A. palm oil.   B. engine oil.
   C. water.   D. glycerine oil.

7. In fig 11.6, which of the equations is correct for the terminal velocity v?

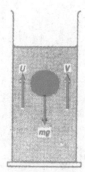

Fig. 11.6

A. $V = mg - U$ B. $mg - V - U = ma$
C. $V = kv$ D. $U = mg - V$

8. (a) Define surface tension.
   (b) Explain why mercury spilled on a horizontal sheet of clean glass runs along it.

9. How does a piece of blotting paper absorbs a drop of ink on a sheet of writing paper?

10. Explain briefly why a steel nail may float on water.

11. Two capillary tubes of the same diameter are dipped into water and mercury respectively. Describe and explain what happens in the tubes.

12. Explain why a ball bearing falls more rapidly in a column of water than in a column of engine oil.

BOOK
2

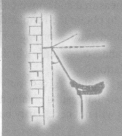

VECTOR

12.1 Vectors and scalars

In chapter 2, we mentioned that physical quantities may be divided into two types: scalars and vectors.

> A scalar quantity is one which has only magnitude, for example, distance, speed, temperature and volume.

> A vector quantity is one which has direction as well as a magnitude.

For example, displacement (which is defined as distance in a given direction), velocity (which is defined as speed in a given direction) and force (which is specified by stating its magnitude and the direction of its line of action). The weight of a body, for example, is a force which acts in a vertical direction downwards.

Scalars can be added and subtracted easily by using ordinary algebra. Vectors, however, have to be added and subtracted by other methods, using, for example, vector diagrams.

12.2 Representation of a vector

A vector can be represented by a line in a diagram, say OA in Fig. 12.1. The magnitude of the vector is represented by the length of the line. We can refer to the vector as OA, meaning that the vector has magnitude equivalent to length OA and acts from O to A.

A vector of 40 units may be represented on paper by any convenient length, e.g. 5cm, in which 1cm represents 8 units. The direction of the vector OA is represented by the angle θ of which it makes with a given line, say, OX. The sense of the vector, that is from O to A rather than from A to O, is shown on the diagram by an arrow.

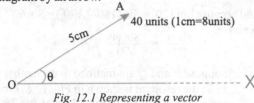

Fig. 12.1 Representing a vector

12.3 Addition of two vectors (compounding two vectors)

In general, two or more vectors acting on a body in given directions can be combined to give a single vector which produces the same effect. The single vector is called the **resultant**. Let us consider two forces of magnitude $P = 30N$ and $Q = 40N$, acting on a body O in any of the following possible directions:

(i) P and Q act in the same direction;
(ii) P and Q act in opposite directions;
(iii) P and Q act at right angles to each other;
(iv) P and Q act at an acute angle $\theta = 60°$;
(v) P and Q act at an obtuse angle $\theta = 120°$.

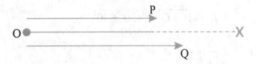

Fig. 12.2 P and Q act in the same direction.

We are required in each of the above cases to find the magnititude and direction of the resultant force.

(i)   In this case the resultant, R, is the algebraic sum of the two forces.
$$R = P + Q = 30 + 40$$
$$= 70N \text{ along } OX$$

(ii) In this case the resultant is obtained by simple subtraction.
$$R = Q - P = 40\text{-}30$$
$$= 10N \text{ along } OX$$

Note: It is obvious that if the forces P and Q are equal and opposite the resultant $R = 0$.

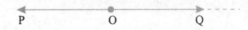

Fig.12.3 P and Q act in opposite direction.

(iii) In the case where the two forces are inclined to each other, the resultant cannot be obtained by algebraic addition, but by what is called vector **addition**. We use the **parallelogram law** of vectors, and trigonometric ratios or scale drawings to obtain the magnitude and direction of the resultant.

> The parallelogram law of vectors states that if two vectors are represented in magnitude and direction by the adjacent sides of a parallelogram, the resultant is represented in magnitude and direction by the diagonal of the parallelogram drawn from the common point.

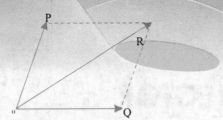

Fig. 12.4 The parallelogram law of vectors.

Both trigonometric and scale drawing methods of finding resultants will be discussed below. In vector notation, the sum of two vectors is represented by R which is written as $R = P + Q$. The diagonal of the parallelogram is represented by the resultant R.

We now consider the case when P and Q are acting at right angles (see Fig. 12.5).
The magnitude of the resultant (from Pythagoras' Theorem) is given by:

$$R = \sqrt{P^2 + Q^2} = \sqrt{30^2 + 40^2}$$
$$= 50N$$

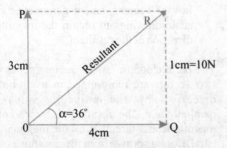

Fig. 12.5 Vectors at right angles.

The direction of the resultant with respect to a given line OX is the angle which R makes with OQ. It is given by:

$$\tan \alpha = \frac{\text{Opposite side}}{\text{adjacent side}}$$
$$= \frac{P}{Q}$$
$$= \frac{3}{4}$$

$$\therefore \alpha = 36.9°$$

Alternatively, we can find R and α by scale drawing. We represent P and Q using a suitable scale, say 1cm = 10N so that P (30N) is represented by 3cm and Q (40N) by 4cm. We then complete the rectangle, as shown in dotted lines in Fig. 12.6.

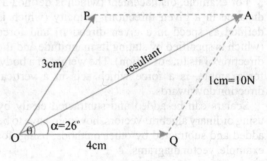

Fig. 12.6 Using scale drawings.

The length of a diagonal is measured and converted to newtons, using our scale, to obtain the resultant. The angle α is also measured with a protractor. From Fig. 12.6., $R = 50N$ and $\alpha = 36.6°$, which agrees with our earlier calculations.

Note: The scale drawing method gives only approximate values so that results obtained by different students will not necessarily be exactly equal.

(iv) Suppose P and Q are inclined at an angle $\theta = 60°$. The scale drawing method of obtaining the resultant is recommended at this level. Again we use the scale 1cm = 10N. We draw the length 4cm to represent Q (40N): using a protractor we draw the angle of 60°, then we draw the length 3cm to represent P (30N). We then complete the parallelogram. The resultant R, and its direction can now be obtained as before (see Fig. 12.7).

Fig. 12.7, $\theta = 60°$

Length of $R = 6cm$, $R = 60N$, $\alpha = 26°$
We can also obtain R by mathematical method using the cosine formula:

$$R^2 = P^2 + Q^2 - 2PQ \cos(180° - \theta)$$
and because $\cos(180 - \theta) = -\cos\theta$, we have

$$R^2 = P^2 + Q^2 + 2PQ \cos\theta$$

Where θ is the angle between P and Q
The angle α can be found using the sine rule:

$$\frac{\sin \alpha}{QA} = \frac{\sin 120}{OA}$$

and because $\sin 120° = \sin(180° - 120°) = \sin 60°$ we have:
$$\frac{\sin \alpha}{QA} = \frac{\sin 60}{OA}$$

(v) Suppose P and Q are inclined to each other at 120°, the resultant is shown in Fig. 12.8. From scale drawing, length of $R = 3.8cm$; $R = 36$ N and $\alpha = 46°$

from cosine rule
$$R^2 = P^2 + Q^2 + 2PQ \cos 120°$$
$$= P^2 + Q^2 - 2PQ \cos 60° \, [\cos 120° = -\cos 60°]$$
$$= 36N$$

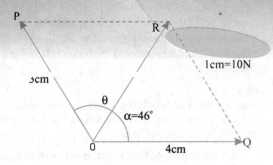

Fig. 12.8, θ = 120°

Example 12.1

(a) A man travels 7.0km due north, then 10.0km east. Find the resultant displacement.
(b) If he travels 7.0km 30° east of north, then 10.0km east, find the resultant displacement.
(c) If he travels 7.0km 40° west of north, then 10.0km east, find the resultant displacement.

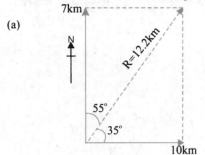

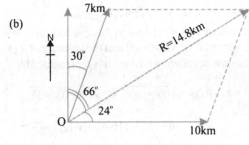

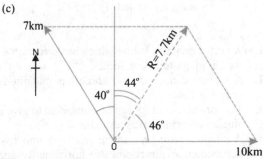

Fig 12.9 Example 12.1

The resultants for the various cases are shown in Fig 12.9(a), (b) and (c).

For (a) $R = 12.2$km, N55°E

For (b) $R = 14.8$km, N66°E

For (c) $R = 8.0$km, N44°E

12.4   Resolution of a vector

A vector, such as a force $OA = 10$N acting at an angle of 30° with the direction of OX, can be broken or resolved into two perpendicular parts. We can find these parts, or components, by drawing a rectangle for which the force will be represented by a diagonal (Fig. 12.10).

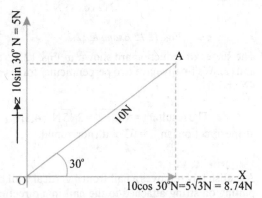

Fig. 12.10 Resolution of a Vector.

Using simple trigonometrical ratios we can then find the two components which are represented by the sides of the rectangle.

$$OX = 10\cos 30°$$
$$OY = 10\sin 30°$$

These two components, or resolved parts of the force, applied at O in Fig. 12. 10 will produce the same effects as the original force OA. The component of OA along OX can be called the horizontal component and that along OY can be called the vertical component.

12.5   The resultant of more than two vectors

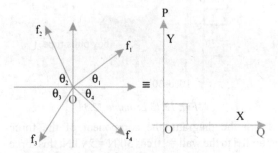

Fig. 12.11. Resultant of more than two vectors.

To find the resultant of several forces, $f_1, f_2, f_3, f_4, \ldots$ acting a point O, we first reduce the whole system to two perpendicular forces and then compound these two forces as before to obtain the resultant. To reduce the system to two perpendicular forces we simply find the components of each force $f_1, f_2, f_3, f_4, \ldots$ along two perpendicular directions OX and OY say, and then add them to obtain P and Q say. We illustrate the method with an example below.

Example 12.2

Find the resultant of the system of forces given in Fig. 12.12 (a).

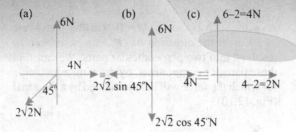

(a) 6N
4N
45°
2√2N

(b) 6N
2√2 sin 45°N
4N
2√2 cos 45°N

(c) 6–2=4N
4N
4–2=2N

Fig. 12.12 Example 12.2

The stages of reduction are shown in Fig. 12.12(b) and (c). We finally have two perpendicular forces of 4N and 2N.

$$\text{The resultant} = \sqrt{4^2 + 2^2} = 2\sqrt{5}\,N = 4.5N$$

in the direction $\tan^{-1}2 = 63°$ with horizontal.

Example 12.3

A foolish boy removes a nail from a vertical wall by pulling on string attached to the nail in a direction 30° to the wall. If the tension in the string is 10N, calculate the magnitude of the force which is not effective in removing the nail and the effective force used in pulling out the nail. Is it possible to remove the nail this way if the minimum force required is 7N? Why is the boy foolish?

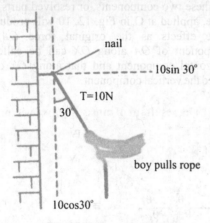

nail
10sin 30°
T=10N
30
boy pulls rope
10cos30°

Fig. 12.13 Example 12.3

From the diagram, the component of the force parallel to the wall = 10 cos 30°N = 5 √3 N; this force is not effective. The component perpendicular to the wall is the one which is effective in removing the nail. It has a value of 10 sin 30°N = 5N The minimum force required is 7N. Since this value is less that 7N he cannot remove the nail this way as long as the tension remains 10N and the angle of inclination to the wall is less than 30°. He is foolish because if he had applied the force of 10N perpendicular to the wall the nail would be removed easily.

12.6 Relative motion

If two bodies A and B are moving in a straight line, the velocity of A relative to B is found by adding the velocity of B reversed to the velocity of A.

Example 12.4

A car travelling on a straight road at 100kmh⁻¹ passes a bus going in the same direction at 60kmh⁻¹. The velocity of the car relative to the bus is (−60 + 100) = 40kmh⁻¹.

Example 12.5

Suppose the car (100kmh⁻¹) and the bus (60kmh⁻¹) are moving in opposite direction, what will be the velocity of car relative to bus?

Then the velocity of car relative to bus in this case will be (60 + 100) = 160kmh⁻¹

Example 12.6

Suppose the car A is travelling at 100 kmh⁻¹ due south of a place O and the bus B is travelling at 60 kmh⁻¹ due east of O, what is the velocity of A relative to B?

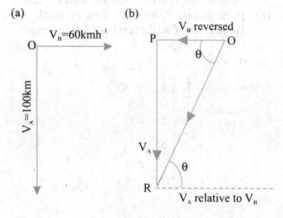

(a)
V_B=60kmh⁻¹
O
V_A=100km

(b)
V_B reversed
P
O
θ
V_A
θ
R
V_A relative to V_B

Fig. 12.14

The velocity of A relative to B is the resultant of the velocity of B (V_B) reversed and the velocity of A (V_A). Using the parallelogram law, it is represented by

$$RO = \sqrt{100^2 + 60^2} = \sqrt{100(100+36)}$$

$$RO = 10\sqrt{136} = 116.6km \text{ with angle}$$

$$\theta = \tan^{-1}\left(\frac{100}{60}\right) = \tan^{-1}\left(\frac{5}{3}\right) = 59°$$

Summary

1. A vector quantity is one which has direction as well as magnitude, e.g. force.

2. A scalar quantity is one which has magnitude only, e.g. time.

3. Two or more vectors can be combined to give a single vector known as resultant.

4. A single vector, a, can be resolved into two perpendicular directions say horizontally and vertically with components $a\cos\theta$, and $a\sin\theta$ respectively. Where θ is the angle the vector makes with the horizontal.

5. To find the resultant of several vectors, we reduce each to two perpendicular directions, sum up and then compound the two components.

Exercise 12

1. The speed of a boat in still water is 20kmh^{-1}. At what angle should it be heading in order to travel directly across a river whose current has a speed of 12 kmh^{-1}?

   The angle is θ where tan θ is:

   A. $\dfrac{5}{3}$　　B. $\dfrac{14}{5}$　　C. $\dfrac{5}{7}$　　D. O

2. Two forces of resultant 100N are perpendicular to each other. If one of them makes angle 60° with the resultant. Calculate the magnitude of the forces.
   (sin 60° = 0.87, cos 60°=0.50)
   A. 200.0N B. 173.2N C. 115.5N D. 86.6N

3. The resultant of two forces F_1 and F_2 will be greatest when the angle between F_1 and F_2 is
   A. 0°   B. 90°   C. 45°   D. 180°

4. Distinguish between a vector quantity and a scalar quantity. A boy walks 1.0km due west and the 1.0km due north. Find the resultant displacement.

5. What is the resultant of two equal forces each of magnitude F acting at right angles to each other?

6. A tug tows a small boat with a rope inclined upwards at 30° to the horizontal. The tension in the string is 2000N. What is the force tending to raise the boat out of water?

7. State the parallelogram law of forces.

8. Obtain the resultant and direction of each pair of the forces in fig. 12.15.

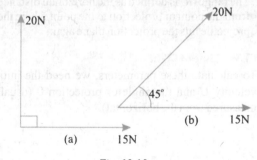

Fig. 12.15

9. An aircraft is flying northwards at 300kmh^{-1} where steady wind is blowing westwards at 80kmh^{-1}. What is the actual direction the aircraft travels over the ground?

10. What do you understand by (a) vector, (b) scalar? A swimmer wishes to swim with speed 1.0ms^{-1} across river to a point *A* directly opposite him. There is uniform current with speed 0.50ms^{-1}. Find the direction in which the swimmer must head to do this.

11. A car travels 3.0km due south and then 4.0km west. What is its displacement from the starting point?

12. Two forces 10N and 20N are inclined at an angle 60° to each other. Find the resultant force by graphic and by mathematical methods. If the two forces are now made to be inclined at 120° to each other, find the magnitude of the new resultant force.

13. Which of the following is a vector?
    A. Speed　　　B. Mass
    C. Time　　　D. Weight

14. Which of the following is a scalar?
    A. Displacement　　B. Acceleration
    C. Time　　　　　　D. Velocity

15. A vector of magnitude 3 units in the north direction is combined with another vector to give a zero resultant, the other vector is?
    A. 1 5 units in North direction.
    B. 5 units in East direction.
    C. 3 units in South direction.
    D. 10 units in the West direction.

16. Obtain the resultant of the system of forces shown in fig. 12.16.

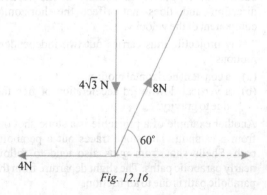

Fig. 12.16

PROJECTILES

13.1   Projectile motion

If we throw a tennis ball against a vertical wall, as the ball returns to the ground, it traces out a curved path, as shown in Fig. 13.1.

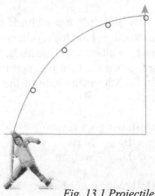

Fig. 13.1 Projectiles

If we stand on top of a building and throw a ball with an initial horizontal velocity over the building, the falling ball traces the same type of curved path. In each case the path of the motion of the falling ball will be a portion of a parabola.

If a ball falls freely from rest at the same time that another ball is projected or thrown horizontally from the same height, both will strike the ground at the same time. We conclude from this that the downward acceleration of the projectile (the body moving along the curved path) is the same as that of a freely falling body. This is true whatever the height from which the body falls. The acceleration on both bodies due to gravity is entirely in the vertical direction and does not affect the horizontal component of the velocity.

Any projectile thus carries out two independent motions:

(a)   a constant horizontal motion;

(b)   a vertical downward acceleration of free fall due to gravity.

Another example of a projectile is a stone shot out from a catapult. The stone traces out a parabolic path. Shells shot from guns also tend to follow nearly parabolic paths. The slight departure from the parabolic path is due to air friction.

> A projectile is an object thrown into the air or launched into space and moves freely by itself under the influence of gravity and air resistance.

Examples are found in sports and warfare.
For sports: Kicked football in the air, thrown javelin, thrown discuss, thrown shot put, high jumper, etc.
For warfare: thrown bomb, missiles, fired bullet, thrown stone, shot arrow etc.

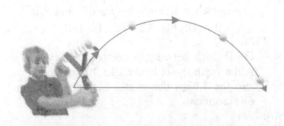

Fig. 13.2 Path of a stone shot from a catapult.

13.2.   Definition of time of flight, maximum height and range of a projectile

> We define the time of flight (T) of a projectile as the time required for it to return to the same level from which it was projected.

> The maximum height (H) is defined as the highest vertical distance reached as measured from the horizontal projection plane.

> The range (R) is defined as the horizontal distance from the point of projection to the point where the projectile hits the projection plane again.

13.3   Time of flight

To calculate these parameters, we need the initial velocity U and the angle of projection θ (usually measured from the horizontal).

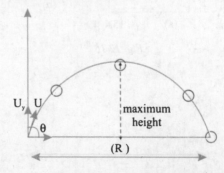

Fig. 13.3 Path of a projectile showing H and R.

We resolve the initial velocity U into horizontal (x) and vertical (y) components.

Horizontal component, $U_x = U\cos\theta$ 13.1

vertical component, $U_y = U\sin\theta$ 13.2

The horizontal component U_x is unaffected by the acceleration of free fall and remains constant.

At maximum height, the vertical component of the speed is zero, i.e. $V_y = 0$

We put this in the equation of motion

$$v = u + at \qquad 13.3$$

v = final velocity

u = initial velocity

$a = g$ = acceleration of free fall

t = time taken to reach maximum height

In this case,

$v = 0$

$u = U\sin\theta$

a is $-g$ which is negative because g is downward whereas the positive y-direction is upwards, t is time to reach maximum height.

Putting this in equation 13.3,

$$0 = U\sin\theta - gt$$

$$U\sin\theta = gt$$

$$t = \frac{U\sin\theta}{g} \qquad 13.4$$

The time taken to rise from ground level to maximum height is equal to the time to fall from maximum height to ground level. Therefore

$$\text{total time of flight} = 2t = \frac{2U\sin\theta}{g}$$

$$\therefore \text{time of flight, } T = \frac{2U\sin\theta}{g} \qquad 13.5$$

13.4 Maximum height

To find the maximum height H, we apply the equation.

$$v^2 = u^2 + 2as \qquad 13.6$$

In this case $v = 0$

$u = U\sin\theta$

$s = H$

$a = -g$

Substituting in equation (13.6)

$$0 = u^2\sin^2\theta - 2gH$$

$$H = \frac{U^2\sin^2\theta}{2g} \text{ or } \frac{U_y^2}{2g} \qquad 13.7$$

where U_y^2 is the vertical component of initial velocity.

13.5 Range

To find the range R we use the equation

$$s = ut + \frac{1}{2}at^2 \qquad 13.8$$

Here $s = R$

$u = U\cos\theta$, the horizontal component of the velocity

$$= T = \frac{2U\sin\theta}{g}$$

$a = 0$, as there is no horizontal acceleration.

$$\therefore R = (U\cos\theta) \times \frac{2U\sin\theta}{g}$$

i.e. $R = \dfrac{2U^2\sin\theta\cos\theta}{g}$ 13.9

Using trigonometry, it can be shown that

$$2\sin\theta\cos\theta = \sin 2\theta$$

Hence, from equation 13.9 we have:

$$R = \frac{U^2\sin 2\theta}{g} \qquad 13.10$$

From the above relation for R, we see that to obtain a maximum range, for a given U, sine 2θ must be maximum. The maximum value of the sin 2θ is 1, when $2\theta = 90°$, since $\sin 90° = 1$.

$$\therefore \theta = 45°$$

So to attain a maximum range, the angle of projection must be $45°$

Substituting in equation 13.10

$$R_{max} = \frac{U^2}{g} \qquad 13.11$$

Example 13.1

A cannon ball is projected so as to attain a maximum range. Find the maximum height attained if the initial velocity is U.

To attain a maximum range, we recall that the angle of projection should be $45°$.

Putting $\theta = 45°$ in equation 13.10,

$$\sin^2 45° = \frac{1}{2}$$

$$\therefore H = \frac{U^2}{4g}$$

Example 13.2

A tennis ball is hit with a velocity of $3\,ms^{-1}$ at an angle of $60°$ to the horizontal. Calculate the:

(a) time of flight;

(b) maximum height;

(c) range.

Take $g = 10\,ms^{-2}$.

(a) From equation 13.5,

$$T = \frac{2U\sin\theta}{g} = \frac{2 \times 3\sin 60}{10} = \frac{2 \times 3 \times 0.866}{10} = 0.52s$$

(b) Use equation 13.7,

$$H = \frac{U^2\sin^2\theta}{2g} = \frac{3^2\sin^2 60}{2g} = \frac{9 \times 0.866^2}{2 \times 10} = 0.3375m$$

$$= 33.75cm$$

(c) For the range, use equation 13.10,

$$R = \frac{U^2\sin 2\theta}{g} = \frac{3^2\sin 120°}{10} = \frac{9 \times 0.866}{10} = 0.779m$$

$$= 78cm$$

13.6 Alternative approach to projectile problems

Instead of the use of formulae, we are advised to work from first principle as illustrated in the following examples: The two fundamental equations are:

$$y = ut\sin\theta \pm \frac{1}{2}gt^2; x = ut\cos\theta$$

Example 13.3

A ball is thrown into the air with initial velocity of 50 ms^{-1} at 37° to the horizontal. Find the total time the ball is in the air and the total horizontal distance it travels, giving that $g = 10$ms^{-2}.

Solution

The horizontal and vertical distances covered by the ball are given by:

$$x = 50\cos 37° t$$
$$y = 50\sin 37° t - \frac{1}{2}gt^2$$

The ball gets to the ground again when $y = 0$

$$\therefore (50\sin 37° - \frac{1}{2}10t)t = 0$$

$$\therefore t = 0, t = \frac{50\sin 37°}{5} = \frac{30}{5} = 6s$$

The horizontal distance covered at this time $t = 6$s is given by

$$x = 50\cos 37° (6)m$$
$$= 40 \times 6 = 240m$$

You can see from above that it is sometimes easier and better to work from first principles, i.e. from the two equations for x and y, instead of using formula, which may be quoted wrongly. The two basic equations for projectile motion to use are:

$$y = U t\sin\theta - \frac{1}{2}gt^2, \qquad 13.12$$

$$x = U t\cos\theta \qquad\qquad 13.13$$

Let us apply this method again in the following example:

Example 13.4

A projectile is fired at an angle of 60° to the horizontal and with the initial velocity 80ms^{-1}. Calculate the:

(i) time of flight;
(ii) maximum height attained and the time taken to attain it;
(iii) range attained;
(iv) velocity of projection 2 seconds after being fired ($g = 10$ ms^{-2}).

Solution

In general, the vertical and horizontal distances covered are given by

$$y = ut\sin\theta - \frac{1}{2}gt^2, x = ut\cos\theta$$

(i) The time of flight T is obtained by equating $y = 0$

then, $t = T = 2u\dfrac{\sin\theta}{g}$

put $u = 80$ ms^{-1}, $\theta = 60°$. $T = 13.8$ seconds

Time to reach maximum height is half the time t of flight

i.e. $\dfrac{13.8}{2} = 6.9$ seconds

Maximum height given by $y = ut \sin\theta - \frac{1}{2}gt^2$

when $t = 6.9, u = 80$ms^{-1}, $\theta = 60°$

i.e. at maximum height $y_{max} = H$

$$= 80 \times 6.9\sin 60 - \frac{1}{2} \times 10 \times 6.9^2$$
$$= 240m$$

You can verify that same answer is obtained by using

$$H = \frac{U^2\sin^2\theta}{2g}$$

(iii) The Range is given by $X_{max} = R = Ut\cos\theta$ when

$$U = 80\text{ms}^{-1}, t = 13s, \theta = 60°$$

$$R = 80 \times 13.8\cos 60 = 552m$$

You can verify that the formula

$$R = \frac{U^2\sin 2\theta}{g} \text{ also give same result.}$$

(iv) At any point on the trajectory the projectile has vertical and horizontal components of velocities given by:

$u_y = u\sin\theta - gt$ which depends on t

$u_x = u\cos\theta$ which is always the same and independent of t.

Therefore 2 seconds after the projection

$$u_y = 80\sin 60° - 10 \times 2 = 49.6\text{ms}^{-1}$$
$$u_x = 80\cos 60° = 40\text{ ms}^{-1}$$

Resultant velocity $v = \sqrt{U_y^2 + U_x^2} = \sqrt{(49.6)^2 + 40^2}$

$$= 63.5 \text{ ms}^{-1}$$

The direction α is given $by \tan\alpha = \dfrac{U_y}{U_x} = \dfrac{49.6}{40}$

Summary

1. A projectile is an object thrown into the air or launched into space and moves freely by itself under the influence of gravity and air resistance.

2. The time of flight T is the time for the projectile to return to the same level from which it was projected.

3. The maximum height H is the highest vertical distance attained.

4. The range R is the maximum horizontal distance reached.

5. $T = \dfrac{2u\sin\theta}{g}$,

   $H = \dfrac{u^2\sin^2\theta}{2g}$,

   $R = \dfrac{u^2\sin 2\theta}{g}$.

6. It is advisable to work from first principles with equations:

   $y = ut\sin\theta - \frac{1}{2}gt^2$

   $x = ut\cos\theta$

Exercises 13

1. Which of the following is not correct about projectile?

   A. The motion along the horizontal is constant.

82

B. The motion along the vertical varies.
C. It has a vertical downward acceleration.
D. The motion carries out one independent motion.

2. Which of the following statements about range, time of flight and maximum height of projectile is correct?
   A. Range depends   the angle of projection only.
   B. Time of flight is shorter the higher the velocity of projection.
   C. Maximum height is the minimum vertical distance reached.
   D. Range is the maximum horizontal distance traversed by projectile.

3. A tennis ball is projected with a velocity of $3ms^{-1}$ at an angle of $30°$ to the horizontal, calculate the time of flight in seconds. (Take $g = 9.8ms^{-2}$).
   A. 5.2   B. 2.6   C.   0.3   D.   0.15

4. A stone is thrown vertically upwards with speed u, at what time will the stone return to the starting point.
   A. $\frac{u}{g}$ B. $\frac{2u}{g}$ C. $\frac{u^2}{g}$ D. $\frac{2u^2}{g}$

5. An arrow is shot into the air with an initial velocity of $100\ ms^{-1}$ at an elevation of $60°$. Find the
   (a) time of flight;
   (b) maximum heights attained;
   (c) range.

6. A ball thrown with a speed of $100ms^{-1}$ attains a height of 150m. (Take $g = 9.8ms^{-2}$)Calculate the:
   (a) time of flight;
   (b) angle of projection;
   (c) range.

7. An anti-aircraft gun fires at an elevation of $60°$ at an enemy aircraft at 10000m above the ground. At what speed must the cannon be shot to hit the plane at that height? (Take $g=9.8ms^{-2}$).

8. A ball is thrown horizontally from the top of a cliff 20m high. If the initial horizontal velocity is $8.0ms^{-1}$, find:
   (a) how long it takes to reach the horizontal plane at the foot of the cliff;
   (b) how far from the foot of the cliff it strikes the ground;
   (c) the speed with which it strikes the ground. (Take $g=9.8ms^{-2}$).

9. A rocket is fired at $60°$ to the horizontal with an initial speed of $200\ ms^{-1}$. Calculate its time of flight and its range on a horizontal plane. (Take $g=10ms^{-2}$).

EQUILIBRIUM OF FORCES

Chapter 14

14.1 Concept of equilibrium

An object acted upon by several forces is in equilibrium if it does not move or rotate. This means that the resultant force acting on the system as well as resultant moment are separately zero.

14.2 Moment of a force

Apart from the tendency of force to accelerate a body, it can also make a body rotate or turn about a point. This turning effect is called its moment.

> The moment of a force about a point is defined as the product of the force and the perpendicular distance from the point to the line of action of the force.

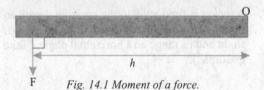

Fig. 14.1 Moment of a force.

The point at which the body turns is called the **fulcrum**. In fig. 14.1, moment = Fh, where F is the force and h is the perpendicular distance of F from O.

In Fig. 14.2, moment = $F \times PO$

Where PO is given by $\dfrac{PO}{h} = \sin \theta$

$$\therefore PO = h \sin \theta$$
$$\therefore \text{moment} = F \times h \sin \theta$$

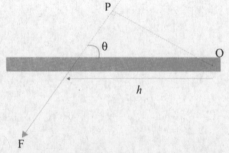

Fig. 14.2 Moment of an oblique force.

If F is in newtons and h is in metres, the SI unit of moment is the Newton metre (Nm). It follows from the definition above that two factors control the magnitude of a moment, the force F applied and the perpendicular distance from the point of rotation to the line along which the force acts (line of action of

force). A very large moment can be produced with a small force provided the distance is large. For this reason, for example, it is easier to loosen a tight nut with a long spanner than with a short one.

14.3 Couples

Sometimes a system of forces can succeed only in causing a body to undergo rotation, and will not produce any linear motion. Such a system is called a **couple**.

> A couple is a system of two parallel and equal but opposite forces not acting along the same line.

The resultant force is zero but the resultant moment is not zero. It is equal to Fh (Fig. 14.3) where h is the perpendicular distance between the lines of action of the two forces.

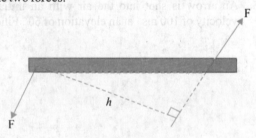

Fig. 14.3 A couple

> The turning moment of a couple is the product of one of the forces and the perpendicular distance between the lines of action of the two forces.

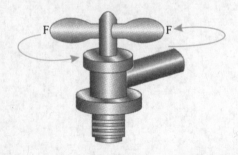

Fig. 14.4 A water tap

Examples of couples can be seen in the action of a corkscrew, or turning a water tap on or off. In Fig. 14.4, equal and opposite forces F are applied to either side of the tap by the finger and thumb.

14.4 Equilibrium under parallel forces

A body acted on by several forces is said to be in equilibrium if it does not accelerate or rotate

This means that the forces acting on the body along any direction cancel each other out, i.e. the resultant force is zero. For example, when a body is in equilibrium, the total forces acting upwards must equal the total forces acting downwards, or the body would move vertically.

Equilibrium also means that the resultant moment about any point is zero, and this can be expressed as follows:

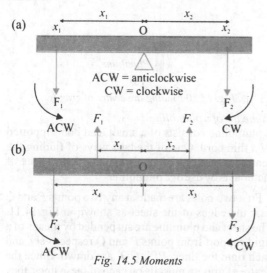

Fig. 14.5 Moments

The principle of moments states that if a body is in equilibrium then the sum of the clockwise turning moments acting upon it about any point equals the sum of the anticlockwise turning moments about the same point.

When there are several forces acting on a body the resultant moment on the body about any point O can be found by finding the algebraic sum of the various moments. If we take the clockwise turning effect (CW) as positive, and the anticlockwise effect (ACW) as negative, then the principle of moments says that the algebraic sum of the moments is zero.

For example in Fig. 14.5 (a) clockwise moment about O, CW, $F_2 x_2$. Anticlockwise moment about O, $ACW = F_1 x_1$. Sum of moments $= F_2 x_2 - F_1 x_1$. If the bar is in equilibrium, $F_2 x_2 - F_1 x_1 = 0$, or $F_1 x_1 = F_2 x_2$.

In Fig. 14.5(b), the resultant clockwise moment of the system about O for the four forces in action is:
$$F_1 x_1 - F_2 x_2 + F_3 x_3 - F_4 x_4$$
If the bar is in equilibrium,
$$F_1 x_1 - F_2 x_2 + F_3 x_3 - F_4 x_4 = 0$$
or $F_1 x_1 + F_3 x_3 = F_2 F_2 + F_4 x_4$

Please note that taking moment about any point O, A

or B will give the same result, i.e. clockwise moments are equal to anticlockwise moments. However some strategic point for taking moment is preferred in order to make calculation easier.

Example 14.1
Find the moment of the force of 20N (Fig. 14.6) about the points A and B.

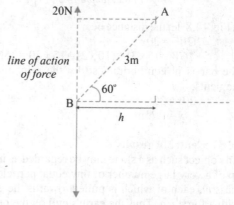

Fig. 14.6 Example 14.1

The moment of the 20N force about B is zero since the distance from B is zero. In other words, a force has no turning effect about the axis through which its line of action passes. The moment about $A = 20h$.

But $\dfrac{h}{3} = \cos 60°$

$\therefore h = 3 \cos 60°$

Moment about $A = 20 \times 3 \cos 60°$
$= 30\text{Nm}$

Example 14.2
What is the magnitude of the couple which acts on a rotating circular disc of radius 2m pivoted at its centre by a constant tangential force of 4N?

From Fig. 14.7, the tangential force is perpendicular to the radius, and there is an equal and opposite reaction as the axis. Hence the moment of the couple is simple $(4 \times 2) = 8\text{Nm}$.

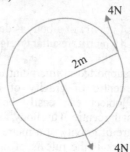

Fig. 14.7 Example 14.2

Example 14.3
A light (weightless) bar is pivoted at its centre and weights of 5N and 10N, placed 3m and 2m respectively from the pivot on one side, are balanced by a weight of 20N on the other side. How far is the 20N weight from the pivot?

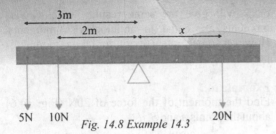

5N   10N   20N
Fig. 14.8 Example 14.3

In Fig. 14.8, let the distance be x

$CW = 20x$

$ACW = (5 \times 3) + (10 \times 2) = 15 + 20 = 35Nm$

The bar is in equilibrium, so by the principle of moments:

$20x = 35$

$x = 1.75m$

14.5 Centre of gravity

Any object such as a stone may be regarded as made up of a very large number of tiny equal particles of mass m, each of which is pulled towards the earth with a force mg. Thus the earth's pull on the object consists of a large number of equal parallel forces. These parallel forces have a resultant

$= (mg + mg + \ldots) = Mg$, say, where $M = (m + m + \ldots)$.

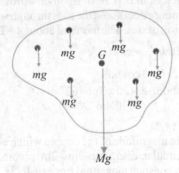

Fig. 14.9 Centre of gravity

This resultant is also a vertical force and acts through a point which is known as the centre of gravity.

> The centre of gravity of a body is defined as the point through which its resultant weight acts.

If a body is supported at this point it will remain stable. The centre of gravity of any uniform symmetrical object can easily be determined, because it is at the centre of the body, for example,

(i)   the centre of gravity of a metre rule is at the 50cm mark if the rule is of uniform cross-section;

(ii) the centre of gravity of a circular object is at the centre of the circle;

(iii) the centre of gravity of a sphere is at the centre of the sphere;

(iv) the centre of gravity of a rectangle or square or a parallelogram is at the point of intersection of the diagonals;

(v)   the centre of gravity of a cylinder is at the centre of the cylinder.

A body suspended vertically has its centre of gravity vertically below the point of suspensions (Fig. 14.10). This fact helps us to find the centre of gravity of an irregular object, as discussed below:

Fig. 14.10 Finding the centre of gravity.

By means of a plumbline

A plumbline consists of a small lead bob supported by a thin cord. One of the best ways of finding the centre of gravity of an irregular plane sheet of material is by use of a plumbline.

First two holes are made at any two points P and Q near the edges of the sheet as shown in Fig 14.11. The sheet and plumbline are suspended by means of a rigid support from points P and Q respectively, and each time the lines, PP', QQ' are drawn. Since the centre of gravity must lie on each of these lines, they may be expected to intersect at the centre of gravity as shown. As a check, the sheet can be suspended from a third point R. It should be found that, within the limits of experimental error, the plumbline passes through the intersection of the lines.

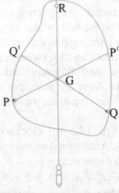

Fig. 14.11 Locating the centre of gravity using a plumbline.

By a balancing method

The centre of gravity of a long thin object such as a metre rule or a rod can be found by balancing it on a knife edge (fig. 14.12). The line of balance helps find the position of the centre of gravity. It lies vertically above the knife edge and is at the centre of the body.

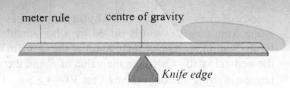

meter rule   centre of gravity

Knife edge

Fig. 14.12 Finding the centre of gravity by balancing.

14.6 The triangle of forces

If two forces act on a body to keep it in equilibrium, then they must be equal and opposite forces acting along the same line of action, e.g. if a body is supported on a spring balance, the weight downwards is balanced by the force in the spring upwards.

If three forces act on a body to keep it in equilibrium, we can use a special method of dealing with such problems.

> When a body is in equilibrium under the action of three forces all acting in the same plane, the three forces can be represented in magnitude, direction and sense by the three sides of a triangle taken in order.

This is best illustrated by an example.

Example 14.4

A bucket full of water and weighing 200N is supported by two men holding the handle at each side, each pulling sideways at an angle of 30° to the vertical. Find the force in each man's arm.

The situation is shown in Fig. 14.13.

$W = 200N$

We draw a vertical line representing the weight of the bucket $W = 200N$, using a suitable scale, Fig. 14.13(b). We then draw in X_1 and X_2, the supporting forces, each at 30° to W. Note that they follow anticlockwise round the triangle in order.

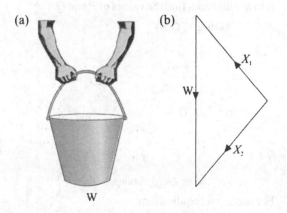

(a)   (b)

X_1

W

X_2

W

Fig. 14.13 Example 14.4

The required force $X_1 = X_2$ is found by measuring the sides of the triangle, and will be found to be 115N.

Note: (a) Problems involving equilibrium under the action of three forces can also be solved by resolving vertically and horizontally, as will be explained in later examples.
(b) A single force which will balance two others and keep them in equilibrium is called an equilibrant. In a triangle of forces, any one of the forces is an equilibrant of the other two.

Further notes on equilibrium

The word particle in mechanics refers to a small body, which can be represented by a point. For such a body, forces can only succeed in making it move or tend to move in a straight line, and cannot cause any rotation.

Equilibrium of a large or long body

In this case, forces can move or tend to move the body in a straight line, but they can also have the effect of causing rotation. We have to consider moments as well.

Normal reactions

A body pressed onto a rigid, solid surface by a force receives a reaction from the surface which acts normally, or perpendicular, to the surface. A simple example is a body resting on a table top, where the weight of the body downwards is balanced by a normal reaction upwards from the table, which is equal and opposite (Newton's third law).

Resolving vertically and horizontally

When a body is in equilibrium, we can say that the algebraic sum of the vertical components of all the forces acting must be zero, i.e. the upward components must equal the downward components.

Similarly, the algebraic sum of the horizontal components of all the forces acting must be zero, i.e. the components to the left must equal the components to the right. This applies in fact to components in any direction, not just vertical and horizontal components.

14.7 Conditions for equilibrium of non-parallel forces

A *For the action of parallel coplanar forces*

(i) The algebraic sum of the forces acting on the body in any direction must be zero. In other words, the sum of the upward forces must be equal to the sum of downward forces, and similarly for those forces along the other directions.

(ii) *Moments:* The algebraic sum of the moments of all the forces acting about any point must be zero. In other words, the sum of clockwise moments about any point must be equal to the sum of anticlockwise moments about the same points.

This is also known as the **principle of moments**.

B. For the action of non-parallel coplanar forces

(i) The vector sum of all the forces acting on the body must be zero. In other words, the algebraic sum of the forces or components of forces acting on the body in any two perpendicular directions must be zero. Put more elegantly:

(a) The algebraic sum of the horizontal components equals zero.

$$\Sigma x = 0 \qquad\qquad 14.1$$

(b) The algebraic sum of the vertical components equals zero.

$$\Sigma y = 0 \qquad\qquad 14.2$$

(ii) *Moments*: The algebraic sum of the moments of all the forces about any point in the plane must be zero. That is, the sum of the clockwise moments must be equal to the sum of anticlockwise moments about the same point.

Tension in a string or wire

If a force is exerted by a pull on a string or wire, the force in the string or wire is called a **tension**. Each point in the string or wire can be considered to be in equilibrium, so that at any point there is a force equal to the tension pulling each way, i.e. equal and opposite forces balancing each other.

These points are illustrated by the following examples.

Example 14.5

A small object of mass 20kg is placed on a horizontal table. What is the magnitude of the normal reaction of the table on the body? (Take $g = 10\text{ms}^{-2}$).

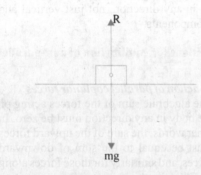

Fig. 14.14 Example 14.5

Let R be the normal reaction of the table on the body (i.e. a force which is vertically opposite the direction of the weight mg).

Since the body is in equilibrium, $R = mg$

$$\therefore \quad R = (20 \times 10) = 200\text{N}$$

Example 14.6

A body of mass 3kg is suspended by an inextensible string from a nail O and is pulled by a horizontal force F until the angle of inclination of the string to the vertical is 30°. Calculate the value of F and the tension in string. (Take $g = 10\text{ms}^{-2}$, $\tan 30° = \dfrac{\sqrt{3}}{3}$, $\cos 30° = \sqrt{\dfrac{3}{2}}$)

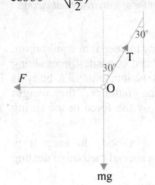

Fig. 14.15 Example 14.6

The three forces acting on the body are shown in Fig. 14.15. Let T be the tension in the string. We take vertical and horizontal components. For vertical equilibrium,

$$T\cos 30° = mg \qquad \text{.... (i)}$$

For horizontal equilibrium,

$$T\sin 30° = F \qquad \text{...... (ii)}$$

(ii) ÷ (i) gives

$$\frac{F}{mg} = \frac{T\sin 30°}{T\cos 30°} = \tan 30°$$

$$\therefore F = mg\tan 30° = 10\sqrt{3}\,\text{N}$$

Also $T = \dfrac{mg}{\cos 30°} = \dfrac{3 \times 10}{\dfrac{\sqrt{3}}{2}} = 20\sqrt{3}\ \text{N} = 34.6\text{N}$

Note: This example and the rest can also be done using the triangle of forces, and the student should try this alternative.

Example 14.7

Three forces act at point O (fig. 14.16). If the point O is in equilibrium, find the values of P and Q.

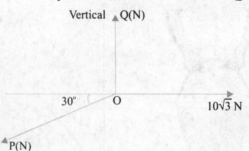

Fig. 14.16 Example 14.7

For horizontal equilibrium:

$$P\cos 30° = 10\sqrt{3}$$

$$P\,\frac{\sqrt{3}}{2} = 10\sqrt{3}$$

$$\therefore P = 20\text{N}$$

For vertical equilibrium:
$$Q = P \sin 30° = 20 \times \frac{1}{2} = 10N$$

Example 14.8

A body of mass 1kg rests on a smooth plane inclined at 30° to the horizontal. What is the magnitude of the force P which, applied along the plane, keeps it from sliding down? What is the normal reaction R between the plane and the body? (Take $g = 10 \text{ms}^{-2}$).

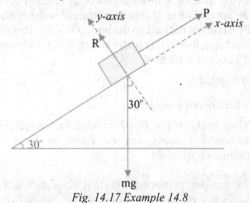

Fig. 14.17 Example 14.8

First we draw the diagram and insert the three forces acting, indicating the direction of each of them with respect to the inclined plane. In all inclined plane problems, it is best to take two perpendicular directions, along the plane and perpendicular to it. Resolving along the plane for equilibrium we have:
$$P = 10 \sin 30° = 5N$$
Resolving perpendicular to the plane we have:
$$R = 10 \cos 30° = \frac{10\sqrt{3}}{2} = 5\sqrt{3} \text{ N} = 8.7N$$

Example 14.9

A uniform bar with weight 20N rests on two supports P and Q as shown and weights are suspended as shown in Fig. 14.18. Calculate the reactions at P and Q on the supports.

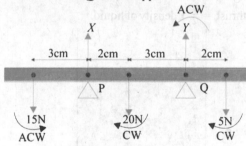

Fig. 14.18 Example 14.9

These are parallel forces.
For vertical equilibrium
$$X + Y = 15 + 20 + 5 = 40 \qquad \text{(i)}$$
Taking moments about P gives:
Anticlockwise moment = clockwise moment
$$Y \times 5 + 15 \times 3 = 2 \times 20 + 5 \times 7$$
$$\therefore Y = 6N \qquad \text{(ii)}$$
Using this value in (i) we have $6 + X = 40$
$$\therefore X = 34N$$

Note:

(a) The moment of X about P is zero.
(b) We could have worked out the problem by taking moments about Q.
(c) Any other point could have been used for taking moments but P and Q have the advantage of assisting us to eliminate one of the unknowns.

14.8   Stability of a body: Types of equilibrium

Stable equilibrium

A body is said to be in a position of stable equilibrium when, on receiving a slight displacement, it tends to return to its original position.

A body with large base and low centre of gravity is usually stable, e.g. a cone resting on its base (Fig. 14.19(a), a pendulum, the beam of an ordinary balance, a racing car.

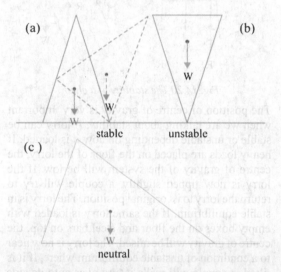

Fig. 14.19 Stability

A necessary condition for stability is that the centre of gravity is at its lowest position.

Unstable equilibrium

A body is said to be in position of unstable equilibrium when, on receiving a slight displacement, it tends to move on, farther away from its original position.

A body with a small base and high centre of gravity is usually unstable, e.g. a cone resting on its vertex or egg standing on its pointed end.

Neutral equilibrium

A body is in neutral equilibrium when on receiving a slight displacement it tends to come to rest in its new position, e.g. a cone resting on its curved surface, a ball or an orange rolling on a horizontal surface.

A low armchair is more stable than a high chair or a tall stool. A chair which is normally quite stable can be put into an unstable position by tilting it back on its legs. (Fig. 14.20).

In (a) the weight of the man W is acting downwards between two reactions R_1 and R_2 in the chair legs (as seen from the side) which clearly results in stable equilibrium. In (b), the man has tilted the chair back so that a couple is formed by his weight and the reaction R in the back legs of the chair. This clockwise couple is overturning him backwards.

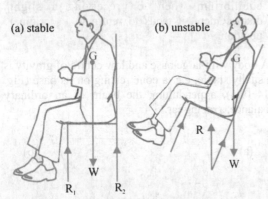

(a) stable   (b) unstable

Fig. 14.20 The stability of a chair.

The position of centre of gravity is very important when we are talking about stability. A lorry can be stable or unstable depending on how it is loaded. If heavy loads are placed on the floor of the lorry, the centre of gravity of the system will be low. If the lorry is now tipped slightly, a couple will try to return the lorry to its original position. The lorry is in stable equilibrium. If the same lorry is loaded with empty boxes on the floor and steel bars on top, the centre of gravity will be raised. The lorry is now near to a condition of unstable equilibrium where, if it is tilted, a couple will make it turn over onto its side (see fig. 14.21). Similarly, the centre of gravity and stability of a loaded boat will depend on how it is loaded or constructed.

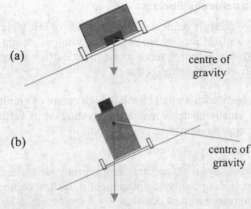

(a)

centre of gravity

(b)

centre of gravity

Fig. 14.21 How a heavy load affects the centre of gravity.

14.9 Equilibrium of bodies in liquid

When a heavy object is immersed in a liquid the object appears to become lighter. Consider the experience when a bucket of water is being drawn out of a well. While still under water the bucket appears very light and becomes very heavy as soon as it is out of water.

It was Archimedes who explained this puzzle by showing that while in water, the body is acted upon by an upward force U called upthrust of water on the body. Hence if the pull on the bucket is T, i.e. tension on the rope, then while under water, the equilibrium of the bucket is given by:

$$T = W - U \qquad\qquad 14.3$$

where W is the weight.

Thus, upthrust $U = W - T$ which is loss in weight. The equation above can be stated in form of Archimedes principle:

Archimedes' principle states that when an object is wholly or partially immersed in a fluid, it experiences a loss in weight or an upthrust which is equal to the weight of the fluid displaced by the object.

For the purpose of solving problems, I will like to deduce from the above that, an object which is completely immersed in a liquid will displace completely a volume of liquid which is equal to the volume of the object.

Thus, weight of liquid displaced = upthrust
= volume of liquid
x density of liquid
= volume of object
x density of liquid

If for example, a body is partially immersed so that the fraction of the volume, $\frac{V}{2}$ is immersed, then
upthrust = $\frac{V}{2}$ x density of liquid.

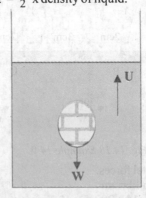

Fig. 14.22 Upthrust

Floatation

Let W be the weight of an object in water and U the upthrust. We consider three possible cases:
If $W > U$, the body will sink.
If $W < U$, the body will rise.
If $W = U$, the body will rest or float.

To summarise the above three cases, one can say that if a body is denser than the liquid, it will completely sink in it, but if the density of the body is less than that of the liquid, the body sinks until the weight of liquid displaced is just equal to the weight of the body.

The body then floats and is said to be in equilibrium. This is the condition necessary for a body to float.

$$W = U. \qquad 14.4$$

This is known as the principle of floatation which can be stated as:

> A floating body displaces its own weight of the liquid in which it floats or a body floats when the upthrust exerted upon it by the fluid is equal to the weight of the body.

The floatation principle has a lot of important practical applications. For example, ships float in water even though they are made of steel which is denser than water. This is because they are hollow objects containing large amount of air and so able to displace a large amount of water, given an upthrust large enough to support the weight of the ship. The weight of a balloon and its content is equal to the upthrust of air on the balloon.

The construction of a hydrometer is based on the displacement principle. It will be shown later that the depth h to which the floating tube sinks in a liquid is related to the density of the liquid ρ by $\rho \propto 1/h$.

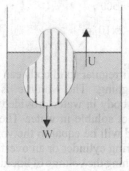

Fig. 14.23 The principle of floatation.

Example 14.10

An object weighs 0.08N in air and 0.01N in a liquid of density 700kgm³ . Calculate the:

    (i)   upthrust of the liquid on the solid;
    (ii) volume of the solid.

Solution

Upthrust = loss in weight = $(0.08 - 0.01) = 0.07$N

Mass = 0.007kg (1kg = 10N)

If we convert mass = 0.007kg = 7g

and density = $700\text{kgm}^{-3} = 0.7\text{gcm}^{-3}$

Volume of liquid displaced $V = \dfrac{m}{\rho} = \dfrac{7}{0.7} = 10\text{cm}^3$.

Example 14.11

An object of density 20gcm⁻³ weighs 200g when suspended from a spring balance. It is then inserted into a liquid of density 0.6gcm⁻³ until $\frac{1}{3}$ of its volume is immersed in the liquid. Calculate the tension in the spring in newtons.

Solution

Convert to *SI* units

$1\text{gcm}^{-3} = 1000\text{kgm}^{-3} = 10^3\text{kgm}^{-3}$

Density of the object $= 20 \times 10^3\text{kgm}^{-3}$

Density of liquid $= 0.6 \times 10^3\text{kgm}^{-3}$

Weight of 200g $= \dfrac{200 \times 10}{1000} = 2$N

Volume of object $= \dfrac{0.2}{20 \times 10^3} = 0.01 \times 10^{-3} = 1 \times 10^{-5}\text{m}^3$

Volume of object immersed $= \frac{1}{3} \times 10^{-5}\text{m}^3$

Mass of liquid displaced   = volume × density of liquid

                $= \frac{1}{3} \times 10^{-5} \times 0.6 \times 10^3$

                $= 0.2 \times 10^{-2} = 0.002$kg

Weight of liquid displaced $= 0.002 \times 10 = 0.02$N

Upthrust = weight of liquid displaced = 0.02N

Tension in spring = weight of object – upthrust
                $= (2 - 0.02)\text{N} = 1.98$N

14.10   Density and upthrust

Definition of density

It is well known that, in general, a given volume of one material has a mass different from that of the same volume of some other material. For example, we say that iron is heavier than wood. This means that any given volume of iron is heavier than the same volume of wood. To make the comparison exact, we measure 1m³ each of iron and wood respectively and find that their masses are 7900kg and 500kg respectively. These are called the densities of iron and wood. That is, the density of a substance is the mass of 1m³ of the substance.

> The density of a substance is its mass per unit volume.

$$\text{Density} = \frac{\text{mass}}{\text{volume}} \quad \text{or} \quad \rho = \frac{m}{v} \qquad 14.5$$

Where ρ (rho) is a Greek letter representing density. Although the *SI* unit of density is kgm⁻³, in laboratory work, results may be obtained in gcm⁻³. There will be no difficulty in converting to *SI* units.

Example 14.12

Convert the density of 0.2gcm³ to *SI* units.

Since $1\text{g} = \dfrac{1}{10^3}$ kg and $1\text{cm} = \dfrac{1}{10^2}$ m,

We have $0.2\text{gcm}^{-3} = 0.2 \times 10^{-3}/(10^{-2})^3 \text{kgm}^{-3}$
                    $= 0.2 \times 10^3 \text{kgm}^{-3}$

Thus, the conversion to kgm^{-3} is achieved by multiplying the density in gcm^{-3} by 10^3 or 1000.
The density of water is about 1 gcm^{-3} or 1000 kgm^{-3}. This is not an accident; the gram was originally defined as the mass of 1 cm^3 of water. Mercury is an important liquid for laboratory work. It has a very high density of 13.6gcm^{-3} or 13600kgm^{-3}.

Below is the list of densities of some important substances in descending order of magnitude.

Substance	Density $(\times 10^3)kgm^{-3}$
Gold	19.3
Mercury	13.6
Lead	11.3
Brass	8.9
Iron	7.9
Aluminium	2.7
Glass (varies)	2.6
Water	1.0
Ice	0.92
Paraffin oil	0.80
Wood (varies)	0.75
Petrol	0.70
Air	0.0013

Relative density (R.d.)

Since water is the most common substance and its density is 1000kgm^{-3} or 1gcm^{-3}, it is convenient to use it as a standard for comparing the densities of other substances.
The relative density ($R.d.$) of a substance is defined as follows:

$$R.d. = \frac{\text{density of the substance}}{\text{density of water}}$$

$$= \frac{\text{mass of substance}}{\text{mass of equal volume of water}}$$

$$= \frac{\text{weight of substance}}{\text{weight of equal volume of water}}$$

Relative density has no units. For example, the relative density of mercury is 13.6. Relative density is used to be known as specific gravity.

Determination of density of solids by direct method

Regular solid

For a regular solid, the volume can easily be found by measuring its dimensions. The mass can be obtained by direct weighing. Hence density can be calculated.

Example 14.13

Find the density of the material of a cylinder of base radius $= r = 0.1$m and height $h = 0.5$m, if the mass of the cylinder is 44kg. What kind of material is this drum likely to be made of?

Volume of cylinder $= \pi r^2 h = \frac{22}{7} \times (0.10)^2 \times 0.50 m^3$

Density $= \frac{\text{mass}}{\text{volume}}$

$$= \frac{44}{\frac{22}{7} \times (0.10)^2 \times 0.50}$$

$$= \frac{44 \times 7 \times 10^2 \times 10}{22 \times 5}$$

$$= 2800 kgm^{-3}$$

From the table, this is very close to the density of aluminum. Hence the material is probably aluminum.

Example 14.14
The relative density of an alloy is 6.5.
(a) Find the mass of a solid alloy cube of side 20cm.
(b) What volume of the alloy has a mass of 13kg?

(a) $\qquad \rho = \frac{m}{V}$
$\qquad \therefore m = \rho V$

since $R.d. = 6.5$, density $= 6500$ kgm^{-3}

volume of cube $= \frac{20 \times 20 \times 20}{100^3}$ m^3

$\therefore m = \frac{6500 \times 20 \times 20 \times 20}{100^3}$

$\qquad = \frac{5.2 \times 10^7}{10^6} = 52kg$

(b) $\qquad V = \frac{m}{\rho}$

$m = 13$kg, $\rho = 6500$

$\therefore V = \frac{13}{6500}$

$\qquad = \frac{1}{500}$

$\qquad = 2 \times 10^{-3} m^3$

Irregular solid
The mass of an irregular solid body can be obtained by direct weighing. The volume is found by immersing the body in water provided it will sink and that it is not soluble in water. The volume of water displaced will be equal to the volume of the solid. A measuring cylinder or an overflow may be used in determining the volume of liquid displaced.

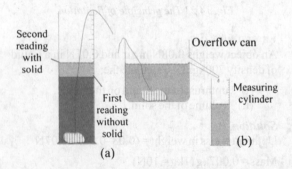

Fig. 14.24(a) (b) Finding volume by displacement.

Relative density of liquid by direct method

A relative density bottle can be used to find the density of a liquid directly.

The relative density bottle is weighed empty, and has mass m. It is then filled with liquid and weighed and has mass m_1. Finally it is emptied, dried and refilled with water and weighed again, when it has mass m_2.

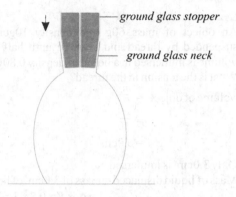

Fig. 14.25 A relative density bottle

$$R.d. = \frac{\text{density of liquid}}{\text{density of water}}$$

$$= \frac{\text{mass of liquid}}{\text{mass of equal volume of water}}$$

$$= \frac{m_1 - m}{m_2 - m}$$

Example 14.15

An empty relative density bottle weighs 25g. It weighs 65g when filled with a liquid and 75g when filled with water. Calculate the density of the liquid.

$$\begin{aligned}
\text{Relative density of liquid} &= \frac{\text{mass of liquid}}{\text{mass of equal volume of water}} \\
&= \frac{65-25}{75-25} \\
&= \frac{40}{50} \\
&= 0.8
\end{aligned}$$

Since density of water $= 1\,\text{gcm}^{-3}$

$$\begin{aligned}
\text{Density of liquid} &= 0.8\,\text{gcm}^{-3} \\
&= 800\,\text{kgm}^{-3}
\end{aligned}$$

Example 14.16

If 32g of kerosene of density 0.80 gcm^{-3} are mixed with 8g of water, what is the density of the resulting mixture?

Volume of water $= \dfrac{8}{1} = 8\,\text{cm}^3$

Volume of kerosine $= \dfrac{m}{\rho}$

$$= \frac{32}{0.8}$$

$$= 40\,\text{cm}^3$$

Total volume of mixture, $V = 48\,\text{cm}^3$ (i.e. 40+8)
Total mass of mixture, $M = 32 + 8 = 40\text{g}$

$$\begin{aligned}
\text{Density of mixture} &= \frac{M}{V} \\
&= \frac{40}{48} \\
&= \frac{10}{12} \\
&= 0.83\,\text{gcm}^{-3} \\
&= 830\,\text{kgm}^{-3}
\end{aligned}$$

Relative density of a solid in the form of a powder e.g. sand or steel ball bearing

We can use the relative density bottle to measure the relative density of sand.

The density bottle is weighed empty (m_1) and again weighed when about one-third full of sand (m_2). The bottle with sand is filled up with water and reweighed (m_3). Finally the bottle is emptied of its content, filled full with water, and weighed (m_4).

The relative density $(R.d.)$ of sand is then obtained as follows:

$$\begin{aligned}
R.d. &= \frac{\text{mass of any volume of sand}}{\text{mass of equal volume of water}} \\
&= \frac{m_2 - m_1}{(m_4 - m_1) - (m_3 - m_2)}
\end{aligned}$$

14.11 Archimedes' principle and floatation

When a heavy object is completely immersed in water, common experience shows that the object appears to become lighter. This is experienced when a bucket of water is being drawn out from a well. The bucket appears very light when it is still under water and can be drawn out very easily with one hand, but it becomes very heavy as soon as it is out of water, so that you need to use two hands to draw it out.

This puzzle was first explained by a Greek scientist called Archimedes. He showed that while it is in water, an upward force is exerted by the water on the body. This force is called the upthrust U of water on the object. Hence, the resultant pull experienced as tension in the rope when the object is under water is $T = W - U$ where W is weight of the object when it is out of water. From the above equation, the upthrust U can be written as:

$U = W - T =$ loss in weight.

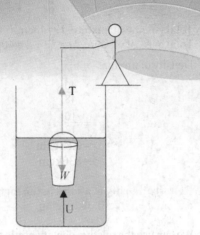

Fig. 14.26 Lifting water from a well.

14.12 Applications of Archimedes' principle

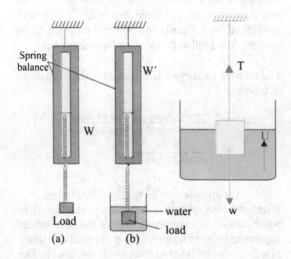

Fig. 14.27 Archimedes' principle

An object is suspended from a spring balance and its weight W(N) is noted (Fig. 14.27 (a)).
It is then completely immersed in water and the weight in water W' is noted (Fig. 14.27 (b)).
The water displaced is also collected and weighed. Let the weight be w.
Upthrust or loss in weight = $W - W'$
Weight of water displaced = w
It is found that $W - W' = w$
We therefore conclude that upthrust equals weight of water displaced, which verifies Archimedes' principle.

Example 14.17
A solid weighs 0.09N in air and 0.02N in a liquid of density $700kgm^3$ or $0.7gcm^3$. Calculate the:
(a) upthrust of liquid on the solid;
(b) volume of the solid.

(a) Upthrust = loss in weight = (0.09–0.02)N = 0.07N
(b) Mass = 0.007kg (since 1kg has a weight of 10N)
        = 7g

$\therefore$ Mass of liquid displaced = 7g
volume of liquid displaced $V = \dfrac{m}{\rho}$

$$= \dfrac{7}{0.7}$$

$$= 10cm^3$$

But volume of liquid displaced = volume of solid
Volume of solid = $10cm^3$

Example 14.18
An object of mass 60g and density $10gcm^3$ is suspended by thread and lowered until half of its volume is immersed in a liquid of density $0.80gcm^3$. What is the tension in the thread?

Volume of object $= \dfrac{m}{\rho}$

$$= \dfrac{60}{10}$$

$$= 6.0cm^3$$

Only $3.0cm^3$ is immersed.
Mass of liquid displaced = mass of $3.0cm^3$ of liquid
                          = $\rho \times V$ = 0.8 x 3 = 2.4g
                          = 0.0024kg
                  $\therefore$ upthrust = 0.024N
Mass of object = 60g = 0.06kg, weight = 0.6N
Tension = weight of object – upthrust
        = 0.60 – 0.24
        = 0.36N

Density measurements using Archimedes' principle

Density of solid
The density of a solid can be found using Archimedes' principle. A solid is weighed in air using a spring balance. It is then suspended and completely immersed in water and the spring balance reading is noted.
Let the mass in air = m (in grams)
Let the mass in water = m'
Upthrust = $(m-m')g$ = mass of water displaced g

$$\text{Density} = \dfrac{\text{mass}}{\text{volume}}$$

$$\therefore \text{volume} = \dfrac{\text{mass}}{\text{density}}$$

$\therefore$ Volume of water displaced = $(m-m')$ (in cm^3)
  (since relative density of water = 1)
Now the object displaces an amount of water equal to its own volume.
 Volume of object = $(m-m')/1$ cm^3
The relative density of the object can be found by using the formula,

$$R.d. = \dfrac{m}{m-m'}$$

$$\text{or } R.d. = \dfrac{\text{Weight in air}}{\text{apparent loss of weight under water}}$$

So Density = $R.d. \times 1000kgm^3$

To measure the relative density of a solid that floats in water (e.g. Cork), we make use of a "sinker".

The sinker is weighed when fully immersed in water (W_1). The cork is attached to the string above the water level and a new weight (W_2) is obtained with the sinker fully immersed in water but the cork in air. Finally sinker and cork are tied together and both are immersed in water. The new weight on the spring balance is read (W_3).

Weight of cork in air = $W_2 - W_1$

Upthrust of cork in water = weight of water displaced

$$= W_2 - W_3$$

$R.d.$ of cork $= \dfrac{\text{weight of cork in air}}{\text{weight of equal volume of water}}$

$$= \dfrac{W_2 - W_1}{W_2 - W_3}$$

Density of liquid

A solid is first weighed in air (let this weight be W) then in water (let this weight be W') and finally in the given liquid (let this weight be W'')

From Archimedes' principle,

weight of water displaced $= W - W'$

Weight of liquid displaced $= W - W''$

Since the same solid is used, the volume of liquid displaced is the same as the volume of water displaced.

Relative density of liquid

$$= \dfrac{\text{weight of liquid displaced}}{\text{weight of water displaced}}$$

$$= \dfrac{(W - W'')}{W - W'}$$

Example 14.19

An object weighs 10.0N in air 7.0N when immersed totally in water and 7.6N when immersed in a liquid. Calculate the relative density of the liquid.

Relative density of liquid

$$= \dfrac{\text{weight of liquid displaced (upthrust in liquid)}}{\text{weight of water displaced (upthrust in water)}}$$

$$= \dfrac{10 - 7.6}{10 - 7}$$

$$= \dfrac{2.4}{3}$$

$$= 0.80$$

Floating objects and applications

If a body is denser than a liquid it sinks in it completely, but when a body with density which is less than that of the liquid is placed it, the body sinks until the weight of liquid displaced by the submerged volume is just equal to its own weight. It then floats and the body is in equilibrium (see Fig. 14.28).

If the upthrust, which is the weight of liquid displaced, is U and W is the weight of the body in air, then the condition for the body to float is that the upthrust should equal the weight of the body.

$W = U$

The above statement is known as the principle of floatation which can be stated as follows:

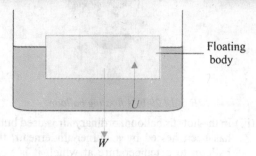

Fig. 14.28 A floating object

A floating body displaces its own weight of the fluid in which it floats.

Alternatively, it can be restated.

A body floats when the upthrust exerted upon it by the fluid in which it floats equals the weight of the body.

Some applications of floatation

(i) Although ships are made of steel, which is denser than water, they still float on water. This is because they are hollow objects, containing a great deal of air, and thus the average density is less than that of water, so they are above to displace a large amount of water; consequently the upthrust is large enough to support the weight of the ship and so keep it floating in equilibrium. The shaded portion of the boat is that which displaces a weight of water equal to the weight of the ship.

Upthrust = weight of ship

Fig. 14.29(a) A floating ship

(ii) For the same reason, a toy balloon floats in air if it displaces a volume of air which has a weight equal to that of the balloon fabric plus the gas filling it. Sometimes a light gas, such as helium which is 14 times less dense than air, is inside the balloon. Thus the total weight of the balloon is much less than the weight of air it displaces. Hence the balloon rises in the air.

Fig. 14.29(b) A floating balloon

(iii) In the hot-air balloon, ordinary air is used but it has been heated by a burner underneath the balloon to a temperature at which it is very much less dense than the air outside. The balloon as a whole is thus lighter than air, and floats upwards.

(iv) Icebergs are huge pieces of ice or frozen water which have been formed in the polar regions and are floating in the sea. Icebergs float because when water freezes it expands, and the solid is less dense than the liquid. An iceberg floats with about 0.9 of its volume under water, so it is actually much bigger than it looks. The fraction of a floating object under a liquid gives the ratio of its density relative to that of the liquid. The densities of ice and seawater are about $920 kgm^{-3}$ and $1020 kgm^{-3}$ respectively.

14.13   The hydrometer

A hydrometer is an instrument for measuring the density of liquids. Its construction and operation are based on the fact that the depth to which a tube sinks depends on the density of the liquid in which it is floating. A simple hydrometer can easily be constructed if you load a small test-tube with some lead shot or small Pebbles so that it can float vertically in water. A graduated scale can be attached inside the tube to enable you to read the depth to which it sinks in a liquid. You can calibrate your barometer using water (density $1000 kgm^{-3}$) and paraffin oil (density $800 kgm^{-3}$) and work out a scale to measure densities of other liquids.

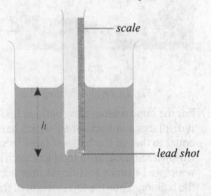

Fig. 14.30(a) A simple hydrometer

The work in principle is as follows

$$\therefore \text{Volume of liquid displaced} = \frac{mass}{density}$$
$$= \frac{W}{g\rho}$$

Where ρ = density of liquid and g is used to convert weight to mass. If the cross-sectional area of the test-tube is A and the length of tube submerged in the liquid is l then:
volume of liquid displaced = Al

$$\therefore Al = \frac{W}{g\rho}$$
$$\therefore l = \frac{W}{Ag\rho} \quad (W, A \text{ and } g \text{ are constants})$$

Then $l \propto \dfrac{1}{\rho}$

From the above, we see that the length of the test tube submerged in a liquid is inversely proportional to the density of liquid: the higher the density of the liquid the shorter the length of the tube immersed, and vice versa.

Practical hydrometers

A practical hydrometer is an instrument which gives a direct density reading of the liquid in which it floats. It consists of a narrow glass tube or stem and a bulb or float chamber which is loaded with lead shot to keep the tube upright in liquid. The practical hydrometer works from the principle that the less the density of the liquid, the further the hydrometer sinks into it:

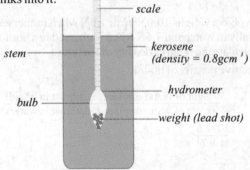

Fig. 14.30(b) A practical hydrometer

The stem is therefore directly calibrated in densities, with the lowest at the top. The instrument can be used in testing milk, when it is called a **lactometer**, and the purity of some liquid substances of which the density is known.

It is also used in testing the concentration of acid in batteries. The acid in a fully charged cell should have a relative density of 1.25, and if the cell is discharged it will be 1.15. This is a better way of testing a cell than using a voltmeter which tends to give the same reading whatever the state of charge of the battery. A battery hydrometer, inside a special pipette for taking acid from the cell, is shown in Fig. 14.30(c).

It is important to ensure that the density of acid in car batteries is not too low, or they will be permanently spoiled.

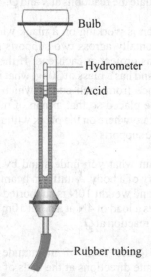

Fig 14.30(c) A battery hydrometer

Summary

1. Moment of force about a point is defined as the product of the force and the perpendicular distance from the point to the line of action of the force.

2. A couple is a system of two parallel and equal but opposite forces not acting along the same line.

3. A body acted upon by several forces is said to be in equilibrium if it does not accelerate or rotate.

4. The condition for equilibrium of a body under the action of a system of forces are summarised in the usual notation $\Sigma F_x = 0$, $\Sigma F_y = 0$, Moment= 0.

5. Centre of gravity of a body is defined as the point through which the resultant weight of the body acts.

6. A body is said to be in a position of stable equilibrium, when on receiving a slight displacement it tends to return to its original position. Stability also implies that the vertical line through the centre of gravity must lie within the base of the body.

7. The magnitude of upthrust acting on a body immersed in water is given by the Archimedes' principle. This states that when a body is totally or partially immersed in a fluid, it experiences an upthrust which is equal to the weight of fluid displaced.

8. The principle of floatation states that an object will float in a fluid when the upthrust exerted

upon it by the fluid in which it floats is equal to the weight of the object.

9. The density of an object is its mass per unit volume *S.I.* unit is kgm^3. Relative density is weight of substance/weight of equal volume of water.

10. A hydrometer is an instrument for measuring density of liquid. Its construction and operation is based on the fact that the depth l to which a tube sinks in the liquid depends on the density ρ:
$$l \propto \frac{1}{\rho}$$

Exercise 14

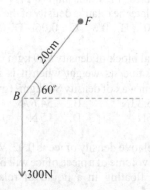

Fig. 14.31

1. Find the moment of 300N force about B.
   A.   300 Nm   B.   30 Nm
   C.   10 Nm   D.   5 Nm

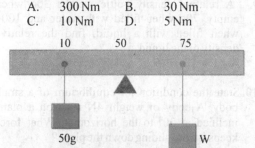

Fig. 14.32

2. With reference to the diagram (Fig. 14.32), find the value of *W.*
   A. 80g   B. 50g   C. 40g   D. 20g

3. A metre rule balances on a knife edge at the 55cm mark when a mass of 40g is hung from 95 cm mark. Find the mass of the rule.
   A. 10.3kg B. 4.3 kg C. 0.32kg D. 0.1kg

4. What is the *SI* unit of moment?
   A. kg B. Nm   C. Nm^{-1} D. Jm

5. Fig. 14.33 shows three planar forces *P, Q, R* which maintain θ in equilibrium. It follows that

   A. $\frac{P}{\sin \alpha} = \frac{R}{\sin \theta}$ B. $P + Q = R$

   C. $\sin \alpha = \sin \gamma \sin \theta$ D. $Q \sin \theta = P \sin \gamma$

97

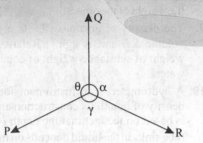

Fig. 14.33

6. A body weighs 0.30N in air, 0.25N when fully immersed in water and 0.27N in a liquid. Calculate the relative density of the liquid.
   A. 6.0   B. 0.6   C. 0.06   D. 0.006

7. A metal block of density 900 kgm^{-3} weighs 60N in air, find its weight when it is immersed in paraffin wax of density 800kgm^3 (g=10ms^2).
   A. 5.33N   B. 54.67N
   C. 6N   D. 15 N

8. The relative density of ice is 0.92. What fraction of the volume of a piece of ice will be submerged when floating in a liquid of relative density 1.11?
   A. 27%   B. 40%   C. 83%   D. 93%.

9. A relative density bottle weighs 30g when empty, 70g when filled with water and 100g when filled with a liquid, find the relative density of the liquid.
   A. 1.1   B. 1.5   C. 1.75   D. 2.0

10. State the condition for equilibrium of a small body. A body of weight 4N rests on a plane inclined at $30°$ to the horizontal. What force keeps it from sliding down the plane?

11. A uniform metre rule of mass 100g balances at the 40cm mark when a mass X is placed at the 10cm mark. What is the value of X?

12. A body of weight 150N is supported by a thin cord attached to a point in the ceiling. Another cord is attached to the weight and pulled horizontally until the supporting cord makes an angle of $30°$ with the vertical. Draw the diagram of the arrangement and calculate the tension in each string.

13. A pole AB of length 10.0m and weight 600N has its centre of gravity 4.0m from the end A, and lies on horizontal ground. Draw a diagram to show the forces acting on the pole when the end B is lifted by a vertical force. Calculate the force required to begin to lift this end. Prove that this force, applied at the end B, will not be sufficient to lift the end B.

14. A uniform beam 6.0m long and weighing 4kg rests on supports P and Q placed left and right 1.0 metre from each end of the beam. Weights of mass 10kg and 8kg are placed near P and Q respectively, one on each end of the beam. Calculate the reactions at P and Q.

15. A man is working on a plank which is placed horizontally across two supports so that equal lengths project at each end. If the plank is 5m long and has a mass of 30kg, what is the greatest distance from each end at which the supports can be placed so that a man of mass 80kg can stand anywhere on the plank without him falling off the supports?

16. Explain what you understand by the centre of gravity of a body. A uniform beam PQ of length 40m and weight 10N is supported at P and Q. It carries a load of 4N at a point 10m from P. What is the reaction at Q?

17. Two forces each of magnitude 10N act in opposite directions at the ends of a table. If the length of the table is 50cm, calculate the resultant force and moment acting on the table.

18. State the triangle rule of forces and describe an experiment to illustrate it.

19. (a) Explain with the aid of a diagram what is meant by the moment of a force about a point.
    (b) State the conditions of equilibrium for a number of coplanar parallel forces.
        A metre rule is found to balance at the 48cm mark. When a body of mass 60g is suspended at the 6cm mark, the balance point is found to be at the 30cm mark. Calculate (i) the mass of the metre rule (ii) the distance of the balance point from the zero end, if the body were moved to the 13cm mark.

20. (a) Define the centre of gravity of a body and describe how it can be determined for an irregular shaped thin lamina.
    (b) With the aid of suitable force diagrams, explain how the position of the centre of gravity of a solid cone affects its stability when it is gradually tilted.
    (c) A non-uniform rod XY of mass 40kg and length 50cm lies on the horizontal ground. Its centre of gravity is 2.0m from the end X. Calculate the vertical force P, that will just be sufficient to lift the end Y from the ground. Why would the force P, if applied at the end X not be sufficient to lift the end X from the ground? (g = 10ms^2).

21. Show that the relative density of a substance is equivalent to the ratio:

$$\frac{\textit{weight of any volume of a substance}}{\textit{weight of equal volume of water}}$$

22. Distinguish between density and relative density.

23. An object volume $4m^3$ is totally immersed in a liquid of density $1030 kgm^3$. Calculate the upthrust of liquid on the object. A body has mass 10kg in air and 4kg when immersed totally in water. Calculate the volume of the body and its density.

24. A body of mass 20g appears to have a mass of 13g in oil and 12g in water. What is the relative density of oil?

25. A solid rectangular block measures 0.100m x 0.080m x 0.060m and floats freely in a liquid of density $13546 kgm^{-3}$. If the depth of liquid is 0.045m up the block's largest side find the density of the block.

26. State Archimedes' principle. A body of density $9.0 gcm^3$ appears to have mass 27.0g in a liquid of density $1.2 gcm^3$, what is the volume of the solid?

27. A substance of density $4 gcm^3$ causes 60g of turpentine (density $0.80 gcm^3$) to overflow from a displacement vessel. What is the mass of the substance?

28. A lump of gold is suspected to contain some quantity of aluminum. If the gold sample has mass 500g and is found to have a relative density of 5.2, find what mass of gold is present if the relative densities of gold and aluminum are respectively 19.3 and 2.6.

29. A body of mass 50g is weighed in water and then in a liquid of unknown density. If the apparent masses in water and liquid are 46g and 45.5g respectively, find
    (a) the density of the body.
    (b) the density of the liquid.

30. A U-tube contains some mercury of relative density 13.6.
    (a) Kerosene of relative density 0.8 is poured into one arm of the U-tube until the height of mercury in that arm is reduced by 1.5cm. Calculate the height of kerosene.
    (b) Water is now poured into the other arm of the U-tube until the levels of mercury in both arms are again the same. Calculate the height of the water column. (The density of water = $1 gcm^3$).

31. A body of mass 2kg and volume $5 \times 10^{-4} m^3$ is hung from a balance graduated in Newtons. What would the balance read when the body is in air, fully immersed in water, fully immersed in paraffin? Density of paraffin is $800 kg \, m^{-3}$.

32. An 80kg man floats with 4% of his volume above the surface in fresh water. What is his volume? What volume would be above the surface in sea water? How great is the upthrust on him in air due to the air he displaces? Density of sea water = $1030 kgm^3$, Density of fresh water = $1000 kgm^3$.

33. A piece of metal, mass 3.6 kg is suspended from a spring balance. What is the reading of the balance (in N)
    (a) with the metal in air?
    (b) with the metal in water?
    (c) with the metal in brine? and
    (d) what is the density of a liquid in which it gives a reading of 33N ?
    (Density of brine 1200 kgm^3, density of metal = 9000 kgm^3).

PRESSURES IN FLUIDS

Chapter 15

15.1 Concept of pressure

The word pressure is frequently used by people at random to mean several things. For example, we talk of pressure of work, the pressure of the atmosphere, blood pressure, a pressure cooker, and so on. In physics however, pressure has just one meaning.

> Pressure is defined as the force acting normally (perpendicular) per unit area of surface.

The *SI* unit of pressure is the pascal (Pa) or newton per square metre (Nm^2). If *A* represents area in square metres and *F* is force in newtons, then pressure *p* is given by:

$$P = \frac{F}{A} \quad \text{(in Pa or Nm}^{-2}\text{)}$$

From the above equation, it follows that when *A* is very small, pressure is large and when *A* is large pressure is small. Thus the pressure exerted on the ground by a person wearing narrow heels is much greater than that exerted by the same person wearing flat heels. The sharp point of a needle or the sharp blade of a knife pierces very easily even when a small force is applied because the area involved in very small. An elephant with its large feet can exert less pressure on the ground than a gazelle with small hooves.

Example 15.1
If a force of 40N acts on an area of 5m^2, what is the pressure exerted on the surface?

$$\text{Pressure, } p = \frac{F}{A} = \frac{40}{5} = 8\text{Pa}$$

Example 15.2
What weight of water would exert a pressure of 2000Pa on the base of a rectangular water tank with dimensions 20cm by 30cm?

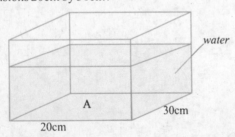

Fig. 15.1 Example 2

$$\text{Area } A = (20 \times 30)\text{cm}^2 = \left(\frac{20 \times 30}{10000}\right) m^2$$

$$P = \frac{F}{A}$$
$$F = P \times A$$
$$= \frac{2000 \times 20 \times 30}{10000}$$
$$= 120\text{N}$$

Weight of water = 120N

15.2 Pressure in a liquid

When considering pressure in liquids it is often useful to consider a property which does not vary. Density is such a property. The density of a substance is the mass of one cubic metre, measured in kilograms. The units of density are kgm^{-3} (or gcm^{-3}).

Consider a column of liquid *h* metres above the level *PQ* of liquid in a cylinder.

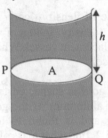

Fig. 15.2. Pressure in a liquid.

The volume of liquid resting on a horizontal area *A* at this level is *hA*.

Now mass = density x volume

The mass of the liquid is, therefore, ρhA

ρ is the density).

The weight *W* of the liquid is ρhAg, since $W = mg$

The term *g* is a conversion factor by which we convert masses to weights, and has value 9.8 (often approximated to 10) Nkg^{-1}.

The pressure or force per unit area, is $\frac{W}{A}$.

$$P = \frac{W}{A} = h\rho g \text{ (measured in pascals)}$$

We can summarise the characteristics of pressure in a liquid as follows:

(i) The pressure in a liquid increases in direct proportion to the depth of the liquid.

(ii) The pressure in different liquids at the same depth varies directly with density.

(iii) The pressure at any point in the liquid acts equally in all directions.

(iv) The pressure at all points at the same level within a liquid is the same.

We can illustrate (i) by means of a tall vessel full of water with side tubes fitted at different heights (Fig. 15.3 (a). A can with holes in it will serve the purpose.

It is found that the lower the holes, the more powerful are the jets of water produced. This shows that pressure increases with depth.

We can illustrate (iv) by pouring water or any liquid into the communicating tubes shown in Fig. 15.3 (b). The liquid stands at the same level in each tube. This shows that the pressure must be the same at the same horizontal level. If this were not so, the liquid would be forced from the areas of high pressure to areas of lower pressure and the levels in the three columns would be different.

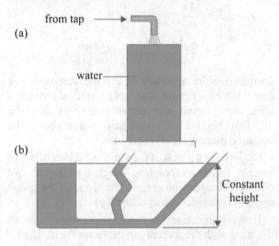

Fig. 15.3 Examining pressure in liquid.

Example 15.3

What is the pressure due to water at the bottom of a tank which is 10m deep and is half full of water? (Density of water $= 10^3$ kgm^3, $g = 10$Nkg^1).

pressure $= \rho h g$
$= 10^3 \times 10 \times 10 = 10^5$ Pa or 100kPa

Example 15.4

A jar, 0.5m deep is full of liquid of density 1800kgm^3. At what depth below the surface of the liquid is its pressure equal to 900 Nm^{-2}? (Take g = 10Nkg^1).

Let h be the height below the surface of liquid when the pressure is 900 Pa.

Pressure $= \rho h g$

$900 = h \times 1800 \times 10$
$h = 0.05$m

15.3 Applications

(a) Pascal's principle

Pascal's principle deals with the transmission of pressure in fluids.

Pascal's principle states that the pressure applied to an enclosed fluid is transmitted undiminished to every portion of the fluid and the walls of the containing vessel.

The principle holds for liquids and gases. The operation of the hydraulic press and the car brake system is based on Pascal's principle.

(b) The hydraulic press

A press is a device used to produce a very large force, to compress something, for example in a printing press where a large force presses the type with ink on it against the paper.

The general principle of a hydraulic press is that pressure is transmitted equally to all parts of a liquid at the same level. It consists of two cylinders joined by a connecting tube as shown in Fig. 15.4(a). The bore of one cylinder is much smaller than that of the other. A tight piston is fitted in each cylinder with a liquid between the pistons. A small force f(N) acting on the small piston of cross-sectional area a (m^2) transmits pressure $p = \frac{f}{a}$ (Pa), via the liquid to the piston in the wide cylinder of area A. (This is possible from the principle that pressure applied at one place in a liquid is also transmitted to other places in the liquid).

The force F on this area is therefore given by

$$\text{Pressure} = \frac{f}{a} = \frac{F}{A}$$
$$\therefore \frac{f}{a} = \frac{F}{A}$$
$$\text{i.e.} \ F = \frac{A}{a} f$$

Since A is very large compared with a, F will be very large compared with f. Hence with a small effort f we are able to achieve a great output force F as a result of transmission of liquid pressure.

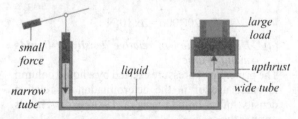

Fig. 15.4 (a) Hydraulic press or lift

The large force "F" in the hydraulic machine can be used to raise a heavy car as in the hydraulic jack or to compress bales of cotton or wool as in a hydraulic press.

Hydraulic devices

The principle of transmission of liquid pressure employed in the hydraulic press has many applications. Some car jacks work with this principle, and tractors use the hydraulic principle to lift heavy loads.

Car brakes use the principle to transmit pressure from the foot pedal to the brake. The footbrake of a car operates like a hydraulic press. The movement of the foot pedal operates a piston in a master cylinder and a hydraulic fluid transmits the pressure to slave cylinders, which operate the brakes at each wheel. By properly calculating the diameters of the master and slave cylinders, the correct force can be obtained on the brakes at the wheels. Because the fluid transmits the pressure equally to the brakes at all four wheels, the braking action is much better balanced than it would be with a system of rods, cables and levers to operate it.

However, it is important in a car braking system that no air should enter the pipe containing the hydraulic fluid. Air, unlike liquids, can be compressed, so with air present the brakes will not work properly.

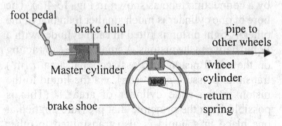

Fig. 15.4(b) Car braking system

Example 15.5

A mass of 20kg is placed on the small cylinder of a hydraulic press. Find the useful force produced at the large cylinder, the area of small and large cylinders being 10cm^2 and 10 000cm^2 respectively (g = 10ms^{-2}).
Let F be the force on large cylinder:

$$\frac{f}{a} = \frac{F}{A}$$

i.e. $\frac{20 \times 10}{10} = \frac{F}{10\,000}$

$$\therefore F = 200\,000 = 2 \times 10^5 N$$

(d) Determination of relative density of liquids using U-tube

The principle of pressure exerted by a liquid column is made use of in the determination of relative density of a liquid using a **U-tube or Hare's apparatus**.

(i) U-tube

We obtain a U-tube and pour a little mercury into it enough to cover the length of the bend. A liquid of known density, e.g. water, is poured into the right-hand limb and the liquid of whose density is required (e.g. Oil) is poured into the left-hand limb

until the mercury level is the same in both limbs as shown in Fig. 15.5.

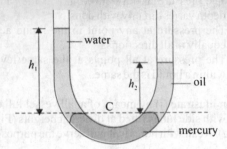

Fig. 15.5 Relative density by U-tube method

We then measure the heights (h_1) of water and (h_2) of oil above the mercury level. The relative density of the liquid is calculated as follows:
Pressure (P) exerted at the common level of mercury C, is the same in both limbs.

$$\therefore P = h_1\rho_1 g = h_2\rho_2 g$$

Where ρ_1 = density of water, ρ_2 = density of oil. Hence relative density of liquid is given by

$$\frac{\rho_2}{\rho_1} = \frac{h_2}{h_1}$$

$$= \frac{\text{height of water column}}{\text{height of liquid column}}$$

To improve the accuracy of the measurement, we repeat the experiment four more times by pouring a little more liquid and water and measuring the different heights of liquid and water above the common mercury level each time.

By plotting a graph of the various heights of water against the corresponding heights of liquid, we obtain a straight line graph. The slope of the graph gives the relative density of the liquid.

If the liquid does not mix with water, we can dispense with the mercury in the experiment. The U-tube is filled with water to about one-third of the way up each limb. The liquid is then poured through one limb until the difference in the levels of water and liquid become clearly distinct. (Fig. 15.6).

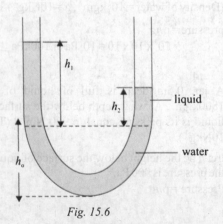

Fig. 15.6

The heights h_1 and h_2 are measured as before from above the common level, h_0.

More liquid is poured and the experiment is repeated as before. The relative density of the liquid is calculated as before.

(ii) Relative density using Hare's apparatus

Hare's apparatus consists of two vertical glass tubes with wide bores. The tubes are connected at the top by a glass T-shaped tube bearing a clip C. The lower ends of the tubes dip respectively into beakers A and B containing water and the liquid (e.g. turpentine) whose relative density is required. With the clip open, air is sucked out of the tubes at P and the clip is then closed. Removal of air brings about a reduction in the pressure inside the tubes. As a result, the liquid and water are pushed up the tubes by atmospheric pressure. The rise in the levels of liquid and water continues until the pressures exerted at the base of each column are equal to the atmospheric pressure. The heights y and x of the water and the liquid are measured. The experiment is repeated about five more times allowing the liquids to rise higher in the tubes in each occasion.

The corresponding heights above the water and liquid surfaces $y_1....y_6$ and $x_1.....x_6$ respectively are measured and recorded. A graph of y against x is plotted and the slope gives the relative density of the turpentine.

The principle of the experiment can be explained as follows:
The pressure at the base of each column is the same. Hence, we state that:

$$P + \rho_1 yg = P + \rho_2 xg$$

$$\text{Hence, } \frac{\rho_2}{\rho_1} = \frac{y}{x}$$

To obtain accurate results, the following precautions should be taken:
(a) Measure the height of the columns only when the levels are steady, i.e. when there are no more movements of liquid levels.
(b) Measure the height from the base of the meniscus. Hare's apparatus is used for comparing the densities of two miscible liquids.

Table 15.1 Densities of commonly used liquids

Substance	Density X 10^3 kgm^{-3}
Acetone	0.80
Alcohol	0.80
Castor oil	0.95
Glycerine	1.30
Olive oil	0.90
Paraffin oil	0.80
Petroleum	0.80
Sea water	1.03
Turpentine	0.85

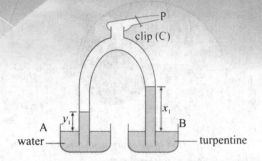

Fig. 15.7 Hare's apparatus

15.4 Atmospheric pressure

The atmosphere is the name given to the whole body of air surrounding the Earth. What we call atmospheric pressure is, in fact, the pressure of a column of air from ground or sea level to the height at which the atmosphere ceases to exist about 80km.

Air has weight; this is why it exerts pressure. Also, air is found to be more dense at sea level and the higher one goes the less dense the air becomes, the density being quite negligible by the time one gets to a height of about 80km. This is why we say that atmospheric pressure can be taken as the pressure exerted by a column of air about 80km high. This pressure acts on all objects on the surface of the Earth. At sea-level, it has a magnitude of about 10^5 Pa. We are not conscious of this enormous pressure because our blood pressure is slightly greater than the atmospheric pressure.

There are various simple experiments that can be carried out to show the enormous pressure of the atmosphere.
(i) A large tin with a screw top, such as a one gallon oil can, is heated with a small amount of water in it. The water boils and the can filled with steam, the air being driven out. The tin is removed from the heat and the top is screwed on firmly. Then the steam condenses and leaves a partial vacuum in the can, which is crushed by the air pressure.
(ii) A glass beaker inverted underwater and then raised above the surface remains full of water. The air pressure on the water surface is holding the water up inside the beaker.
(iii) In 1654, the Mayor of Magdeburg in Germany carried out an experiment to show the pressure of the atmosphere. Two large hemispheres were placed in air-tight contact and the air was pumped out of the sphere thus formed. The atmospheric pressure held the hemispheres together so tightly that sixteen horses could not pull them apart. Many schools have a smaller version of this Magdeburg hemispheres experiment.

Since the atmospheric pressure is due to the weight of air above the place on Earth at which the measurement is made, atmospheric pressure decreases with height (altitude).

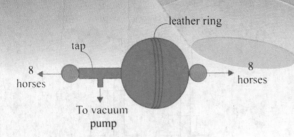

Fig. 15.8 Magdeburg hemispheres

Measurement of gas pressure

All gases exert pressure. Winds are practical evidence of the existence of air pressures: air moves from an area of high pressure to one of low pressure. Sailing boats depend upon partial vacuums which form in front of the sail. When a vehicle tyre is inflated, the high pressure of air in the tube becomes obvious; after the tyre is pumped up, this pressure can be measured using a pressure gauge.

In the laboratory, the pressure of a gas in a container is normally measured by means of an instrument known as a **manometer**. The manometer consists of a U-tube which contains water. When both arms are open to the atmosphere the same atmospheric pressure (a.*p*.) is exerted on the water surface *A* and *B* and these are at the same horizontal level Fig. 15.9 (a). To measure the gas pressure, the tube at *A* is connected to a gas tap by a length of rubber tubing, (Fig. 15.9 (b)). When the tap is turned on, the gas exerts pressure on the surface *A* causing *B* to rise until the pressure at *C* on the same horizontal level as *A* becomes equal to the gas pressure.

The pressure of gas
$$= a.p. + \text{pressure due to water column } BC$$
$$= a.p. + h\rho g$$

Hence the excess pressure of gas above a.*p*. is $h\rho g$ (in Pa) or simply *h* millimeters of water. Sometimes a higher density liquid such as mercury (chemical symbol *Hg*) is used instead of water in constructing a manometer, especially, when a very high pressure is to be measured. In this case, excess pressure is given in mmHg.

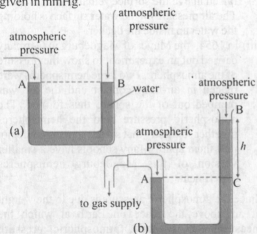

Fig. 15.9 The manometer

Another type of pressure gauge is the **Bourdon gauge**. This works on the principle that a bent tube tends to straighten out when the pressure of air inside it increases. This can be seen in Fig. 15.10. The straightening action of the tube operates a system of levers and moves the pointer on the scale.

Fig. 15.10 The Bourdon gauge

Note: The instrument used for measuring a patient's blood pressure in hospital is known as a **sphygmomanometer**. It reads in millimetres of mercury.

15.5 Simple barometer

In section 15.4 we explained what we mean by air pressure and atmospheric pressure. A very simple system for measuring atmosphere pressure (a.*p*.) was first designed as far back as 1643. The instrument is known as a **simple barometer.** It can easily be constructed in the laboratory as follows.

A clean dry glass tube of length about 1 metre, open at one end and closed at the other is nearly filled with mercury. The open end is covered with the thumb (wear plastic gloves!), and then the tube is rapidly inverted several times to remove any bubbles of air which might be trapped in the tube. The tube is then completely filled with mercury, the open end is covered with the thumb and the tube is inverted; the open end is placed below mercury in a crucible. When the thumb is removed the mercury level in the tube falls leaving a vacuum, or empty space, at the top. The height of the mercury column is found to be approximately 0.76m. This is the height of mercury which the atmosphere can support. The atmospheric pressure (a.*p*.) acts on the surface of mercury in the dish; hence the height *h* of mercury in the tube is a measure of atmospheric pressure. The normal value of atmospheric pressure at sea level is given by

$$h = 760 \text{ mmHg. or in Pa,}$$
$$\text{atmospheric pressure} = h\rho g$$
$$= (0.76 \times 13600 \times 10)\text{Pa}$$
$$(\text{for Hg, } \rho = 13600 \text{kgm}^{-3})$$
$$= 103360 \text{ Pa.}$$

Suppose another liquid such as water (density 1000 kgm^{-3}) were used in a barometer, the height to which water would rise in the tube can easily be calculated as follows:

$$hpg = 103360$$
$$h \times 1000 \times 10 = 103360$$
$$h = 10.3m$$

Imagine the large height involved. It would not be convenient to provide such a length of pipe for the experiment. Hence low density liquids such as water are not used in constructing a barometer.

It is also noted that the vertical height of mercury remains constant even when the tube is tilted. Fig. 15.11(b).

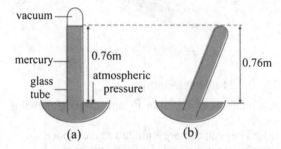

Fig. 15.11 The simple barometer

Defects of a simple barometer

The simple mercury barometer discussed above is not a very accurate instrument for the following reasons:

(i)   It is difficult to make the barometer without allowing some air or water vapour into the space above the mercury. In this respect the space does not contain a real vacuum. The air or water vapour has the effect of making the barometer read less than the true atmospheric pressure.

(ii)   There is no provision for an accurate scale for reading the height h. Only a rough estimate can be made by using a metre rule. Hence we cannot use this barometer to measure small daily variations of the atmospheric pressure.

The Fortin barometer

When an accurate measurement of atmospheric pressure is required, a Fortin barometer is used. This is a very accurate type of barometer extensively used in laboratories. It was first designed by a British naval officer called Fortin. The physical principle involved is the same as that of a simple barometer but the second defect mentioned above has been eliminated in the construction of a Fortin barometer.

The main components of the Fortin barometer are listed here.

(a)   A vertical glass tube containing mercury with a vacuum above

(b)   A reservoir of mercury at the base

(c)   A fixed millimetre scale as well as a movable vernier scale for reading the mercury level accurately

(d)   A fixed ivory index at the bottom which is the 'zero' of the millimetre scale

The levelling screw is used to ensure that the ivory index just touches the level of mercury in the reservoir, to ensure that the height reading in the scale is measured from the zero mark.

The aneroid barometer

The anaeroid barometer shown in Fig. 15.13 is a type of barometer which works without mercury or liquid. It is more compact and convenient to carry. Changes in atmospheric pressure cause the thin slides of the partially evacuated metal box to move in or out. This movement is transmitted by a spring and a system of levers (not all shown) to a pointer which moves over a graduated scale.

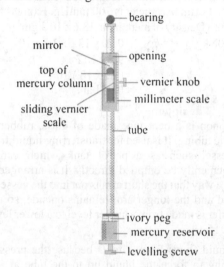

Fig. 15.12. The Fortin barometer

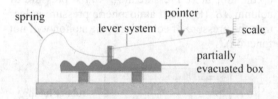

Fig. 15.13 Aneroid barometer

15.6   Practical uses of barometer

One important use of a barometer is to determine altitude. Once we know how the atmospheric pressure depends on altitude, we can use the barometer reading to find our height. The altimeter of an aeroplane is an aneroid barometer with the scale marked directly in height units.

The other main use of the barometer is in forecasting weather conditions. Contrary to general belief, moist air is less dense than dry air, water vapour itself being only about 5/8 is as dense as dry air. Since it is less dense, moist air exerts less pressure, and so in moist weather the barometer falls. This gives us a way of predicting what kind of weather we will have in the immediate future. Hence the meteorologists (those who forecast weather) are able to compile information obtained from stations all over the country, from which a forecast can be made for any locality.

15.7 Various units of atmospheric pressure

The average pressure of the atmosphere has been shown to be 760 mmHg which is approximately 10^5 Pa.

In meterology this pressure of 10^5 Pa is called one bar.

The sub-unit is 1 millibar $= \dfrac{10^5}{10^3} = 100$ Pa.

Example 15.6

On a certain hill, the atmospheric pressure as read from a Fortin barometer is 700 mmHg. Express this in bars. (Density of mercury is 13.6×10^3 kgm^{-3}, g = 10 Nkg^{-1}).

$$P = h\rho g = 0.70 \times 13.6 \times 10^3 \times 10$$
$$= 9.5 \times 10^4 \text{Pa}$$
$$= (9.5 \times 10^4)/10^5$$
$$= 0.95 \text{ bar}$$

15.8 The siphon

A siphon is a bent tube made of glass, rubber or plastic tubing. It is used for transferring liquid from a vessel such as a petrol tank which cannot conveniently be emptied directly. It is arranged in such a way that the short arm is put into the vessel of liquid and the longer arm remains outside, so that transfer is made from a higher level to a lower level, (Fig. 15.14).

Liquid flows from *A* to *D* because the pressure tending to force the liquid up to the tube at *A* is greater than the pressure tending to force the liquid up the tube at *D*. Pressure at *A* = a.p.– pressure of column *AB*. (Hence if atmospheric pressure is less than the pressure of column *AB*, the siphon will not function).

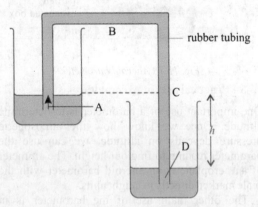

Fig. 15.14 The siphon

Also, pressure at *D* = a.p.– pressure of column *BD*
Pressure at *A* = pressure at *C*.
Pressure at *A* is greater than pressure at *D*.
The actual difference in pressure causing the liquid to flow from *A* to *D* is *h*ρg, where *h* is the difference in height of *A* and *D*.

15.9 The syringe

In a syringe (see Fig 15.15) a piston is operated in a tube to draw liquid into the cylinder. As the piston is drawn back, atmospheric pressure pushes the liquid into the tube. The liquid can then be pushed out again by the opposite action, to inject a drug into the body, for example, in the hypodermic syringe used in medicine.

Fig. 15.15 A syringe

15.10 The bicycle pump

Air pumps can function in one of the following ways:
(a) They can compress air into a given space.
(b) They can evacuate air from a given space.

A bicycle pump is a typical form of compression pump, the structure is shown in Fig. 15.16(a).
The pump has a flexible leather washer at the end of a piston. It is connected to the bicycle tyre which has a rubber valve in it, Fig. 15.16 (b).

When the piston is drawn out, air below it expands and pressure is reduced below atmospheric pressure. Air from outside the pump then flows past the leather washer into the barrel.

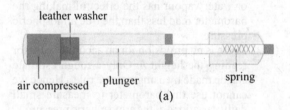

(a)

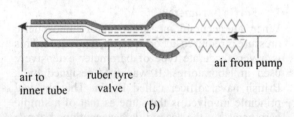

(b)

Fig. 15.16 The bicycle pump

During this time the tyre valve remains closed. When the piston is pushed down, the air compressed below it forces the leather washer against the sides of the barrel so that no air enters and this air is forced into the tyre through the valve, which is now open. In this way air from outside is forced into the tyre with each stroke of the piston.

15.11 The lift pump

The common pump or lift pump is used for raising water from wells. It consists of a piston working in a barrel or cylinder to which is attached the uptake pipe, which reaches down into the well of water. The piston head has a hole through it which can be closed by a valve A, while the second valve B closes the barrel at its base. The piston is operated by a handle lever. There are four stages involved in the working of the pump. We describe these stages briefly.

(i) As the piston moves downwards, the valve B closes and valve A opens.

(ii) As the piston moves upwards valve A closes, pressure inside the barrel decreases and the valve B opens. Atmospheric pressure causes water to flow in to occupy space above B.

(iii) On the next down stroke, pressure increases, valve B closes and A opens allowing water to flow above A.

(iv) On the next upward stroke valve A closes and water is raised to the outlet pipe where it escapes. At the same time atmospheric pressure forces water past valve B as before.

Owing to the fact that atmospheric pressure cannot support a column of water more than 10m high, it means that the maximum height to which a lift pump can raise water is theoretically about 10m.

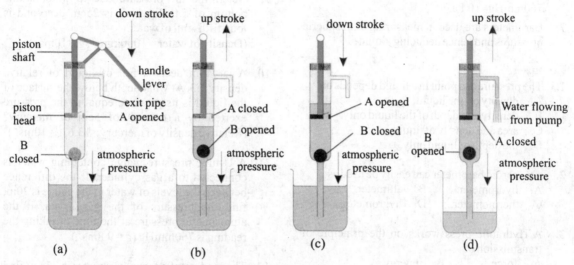

Fig. 15.17 Lift pump

15.12 The force pump

For lifting water to a height greater than 10m a force pump is used (Fig. 15.18).

(i) As the piston moves up, atmospheric pressure pushes water through valve B into the pump. Valve A is closed.

(ii) As the piston moves down, water is forced through valve A and upwards. There is theoretically no limit to how high the water can be forced, but of course in practice this will depend on the force used and the quality of the pump.

The chamber C has in it air which acts as a cushion, so that instead of coming through in bursts, the water comes through more evenly.

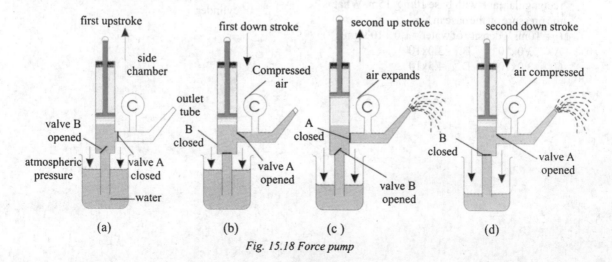

Fig. 15.18 Force pump

Summary

1. pressure is force acting normally per unit area of surface.
2. Fluid exerts pressure in all direction.
3. The pressure inside a liquid at the height of h is given by $P = \rho g h$ where h is height and ρ density.
4. Pascal's principle states that the pressure applied to an enclosed fluid is transmitted to every portion of the fluid and the walls of the containing vessel.
5. The density of liquid can be measured using Hare's apparatus or U–tube.
6. The average atmospheric pressure is $760 \text{mmHg} \approx 10^5 \text{Pa}$.
7. Barometers are used in measuring atmospheric pressures and hence deducing altitude.

Exercise 15

1. The pressure at a point in a liquid depends on
   A. density of the liquid.
   B. density and depth of the liquid only.
   C. area and density of liquid.
   D. the depth of liquid only.

2. An aneroid barometer can easily be used as
   A. hydrometer.   B. altimeter.
   C. thermometer.   D. hygrometer.

3. A Hydraulic press works on the principle of transmission of
   A. force.   B. energy.
   C. volume.   D. pressure.

4. Hydraulic press had a cylindrical piston of diameter 40cm and a cylindrical plunger of diameter 10cm. Find the distance moved by the piston when the plunger moves 8cm.
   A. 8.0cm   B. 4.0cm
   C. 2.0cm   D. 0.5cm

5. Water is poured to a depth of 3m into a rectangular tank with base 10m x 15m. What is the pressure on the base in Nm^2 ?
   ($g = 10 \text{ms}^2$, density of water $= 1.0 \times 10^3 \text{kgm}^3$)
   A. 3.0×10^2 B. 3.0×10^3
   C. 3.0×10^4 D. 4.5×10^4

6. Define pressure and give two units in which it is measured.

7. A rectangular solid block has length 10cm, breadth 5cm and height 2.0cm. If it lies on a horizontal surface, and has density 1000 kgm^3, calculate the pressure it exerts on the surface. ($g = 9.8 \text{ms}^2$)

8. A cylindrical jar of radius 7.0cm and height 25cm, is filled with a liquid 0.80gcm^3. What is the pressure exerted at the bottom of the jar by the liquid? ($g = 9.8 \text{ms}^2$)

9. Determine the pressure due to water at the bottom of a tank which is 25cm deep and is four-fifths full of water.
   (Density of water $= 1000 \text{kgm}^3$, $g = 10 \text{ms}^2$).

10. A jar 40m deep is full of liquid of relative density 1.3. At what depth below the surface of the liquid is its pressure equal to the pressure exerted by a column of 5cm of mercury? (Relative density of mercury $= 13.6$, $g = 10 \text{ms}^2$).

11. A U-tube pressure gauge containing water is connected to a gas cylinder. If the difference between the levels of water in the gauge is 20m, find the pressure of the gas in Pa, if the atmospheric pressure at the time of taking the reading is 760mmHg ($g = 9.8 \text{ms}^2$).

12. The reading of a fortin barometer is 75cm; find the atmospheric pressure in bars, $g = 10 \text{ms}^2$, density of mercury $= 13.6 \times 10^3 \text{kgm}^3$.

13. A hydraulic press consists of two cylinders of cross-sectional area 0.2m^2 and 5.0m^2. The piston in the smaller cylinder is pushed down with a force of 100N through a distance of 0.2m. calculate:
    (a) the pressure transmitted by fluid;
    (b) the force exerted by the piston in the large cylinder.

SIMPLE HARMONIC MOTION (S.H.M.)

Chapter 16

16.1 Definition of simple harmonic motion

A periodic motion (or vibration or oscillation) is a type of motion that occurs very frequently in physics. In such a motion, the path of a moving body is repeated at successive equal intervals of time. Examples of such motions are the motion of a body in a circular path with uniform speed, the oscillation of a clock pendulum, the vibrations of the balance wheel of a watch, the vibrations of a violin or guitar string and the rotation of the earth about its axis. Such vibrations play a very important role in many physical phenomena, especially in light, mechanics, sound and electricity.

A very important type of periodic motion is the Simple Harmonic Motion, which can be defined thus:

> If a small body or a particle vibrates or moves to and fro along a straight line under the influence of a force so that its acceleration towards a fixed point (or its equilibrium position) is proportional to its distance or displacement from that point, the body is said to perform simple harmonic motion.

The force influences the body's motion in such a way as to always direct the body back to its equilibrium position. Such a force is called a **restoring force** since it tends to restore the body to its equilibrium position.

16.2 Illustrations of simple harmonic motion

(a) Mass on a spring

One example of simple harmonic motion is the motion of a mass fastened to the end of a spring.

Let the mass be hung in equilibrium from the lower end of the spring, the other end of which is firmly clamped from a rigid support.

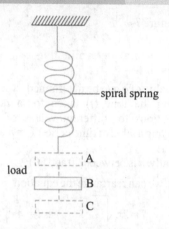

Fig. 16.1 The spring with mass executing simple harmonic motion.

When the mass, originally at the position B, is pulled down to C and then released, it is observed to move up and down in a regular fashion. The body performs simple harmonic motion provided that the spring still obeys Hooke's law; that is, that the elastic limit of the spring is not exceeded in the pull. Hence it is necessary to pull the spring only slightly.

(b) The simple pendulum

This consists of a small lead weight, or bob, suspended from a rigid support by means of a thread. If it is displaced through a small angle as shown in Fig. 16.2, it performs simple harmonic motion. The amplitude of motion is a.

It is observed that the motion of the pendulum does not continue indefinitely. This is because frictional forces and air resistance gradually reduce the motion until the amplitude a becomes zero.

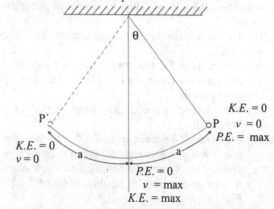

Fig. 16.2 The simple pendulum

The period of motion T of the simple pendulum of length l can be shown to be equal to

$$T = 2\pi \sqrt{\frac{l}{g}} \qquad\qquad 16.1$$

where g is the acceleration due to gravity. This expression is valid provided that the angular displacement θ or the amplitude of motion a is very small.

Therefore $T \propto \sqrt{l}$

Experimental determination of g using simple pendulum

The value of g can be determined experimentally by finding the time (t) taken for a number (n) of oscillations for different values of l, and hence obtaining a table of time period $T = \bar{n}$ and l.

(Usually, n is between 20 and 50)

Since we can rearrange the equation

$$T = 2\pi \sqrt{\frac{l}{g}}, \qquad \text{as } l = \frac{g}{4\pi^2} T^2$$

a graph of l against T^2 will be a straight line, the slope of which will be $\frac{g}{4\pi^2}$ from which g can be calculated (see fig 16.3).

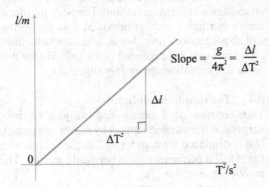

Slope $= \dfrac{g}{4\pi^2} = \dfrac{\Delta l}{\Delta T^2}$

Fig. 16.3 Determination of g

When performing the above experiment, certain precautions should be taken to obtain an accurate result.

(i) The amplitude of oscillation must be very small.

(ii) The support for the cord must be rigid. The arrangement shown in Fig. 16.4 is one way of achieving this.

(iii) The string should be very light and inextensible.

(iv) Care should be taken to count from when the bob passes the centre of the oscillation. A vertical mark arranged behind the thread when it is in its equilibrium position is helpful (see Fig. 16.4).

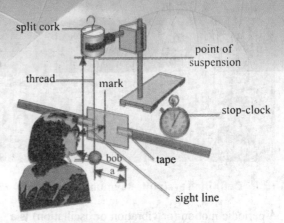

Fig. 16.4 The apparatus for finding g .

(c)   Loaded test-tube in a liquid

Another example of simple harmonic motion can be demonstrated in the laboratory using a test-tube loaded with sand. Put just enough sand into the test-tube so as to make it stand vertically erect in a liquid, e.g. water. Depress the tube into the water and release it. The tube is seen to move up and down in the water in a regular fashion. The loaded test-tube performs simple harmonic motion in the liquid.

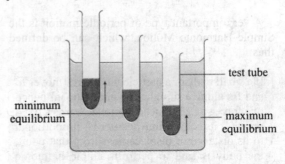

Fig. 16.5 Loaded test-tubes moving with simple harmonic motion.

16.3 Relationship between simple harmonic motion and circular motion

Let us consider a point Q (Fig. 16.6) moving round a circle of radius, r, with uniform speed, v.

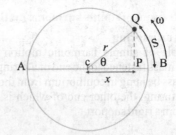

Fig. 16.6 Circular motion

Let us imagine that at every instant a perpendicular line can be drawn from Q to meet the diameter AB of the circle at P. As Q moves once round the circle, the foot of the perpendicular P moves from B through C to A and back B.

Thus the point, P, will move along AB with simple harmonic motion while the point Q moves round the circle. The velocity of P along AB changes continuously as the point moves along AB. It has its greatest velocity at C, the centre of the motion of P, but a zero velocity at A and B. This means the point P is momentarily at rest at A and B before changing its direction of motion.

As Q moves round the circle, the angle θ between QC and CP also changes. This angle changes from $0°$ to $360°$ (or 2π radians) as the point Q moves round the circle once. We define the angular velocity (ω) of the point Q as:

$$\omega = \frac{\text{Angle turned through by the body}}{\text{time taken}}$$

$$\omega = \frac{\theta}{t} \quad \text{(radians per second)} \quad 16.2$$

Thus $\theta = \omega t$, which is analogous to the formula "distance = uniform velocity x time" for motion in a straight line.

The corresponding linear velocity is given by $v = \frac{s}{t}$ where s is the length of the arc between B and Q at a time t. The angle θ (in radians) is related to the arc length s, and the radius of the circle r through the formula:

$$\theta = \frac{s}{r} \quad \text{or} \quad s = r\theta \quad 16.3$$

That is, when the arc length s equals the radius r the angle equals one radian. This is the definition of an angle in radians. Remember also that $360° = 2\pi$ radians, as the relationship between degrees and radians.

The relationship between linear and angular velocity

The angular velocity (ω) is given by

$$\omega = \frac{\theta}{t}$$
$$= \frac{s/r}{t}$$
$$= \frac{s}{t} \cdot \frac{1}{r}$$
$$= v\frac{1}{r}$$
$$= \frac{v}{r}$$
$$\text{i.e. } \omega = \frac{v}{r}$$

$$v = r\omega \quad 16.4$$

Linear velocity equals the product of the radius and the angular velocity.

Example 16.1

A stone is attached to the end of an inelastic string and whirled round in a circular path of radius 30 cm. If the stone makes 9 complete revolutions in 3 seconds, find its angular and linear velocities during this period.

Angular velocity, $\omega = \frac{\theta}{t}$

The stone moves through an angle equal to $9 \times 2\pi$ radians in 3 seconds (1 complete revolution = $360°$ or 2π radians)

$$\therefore \omega = \frac{9 \times 2\pi}{3} \quad \text{radians per second}$$
$$= 6\pi \text{ radians per second}$$

Linear velocity $v = r\omega$
$$= 30 \times 6\pi$$
$$= 180\pi \text{ cms}^{-1}.$$

16.4 Acceleration of simple harmonic motion

A body performing simple harmonic motion experiences a constant acceleration directed towards the centre of the motion C. For example, our point Q in Fig. 16.6 has a centripetal acceleration given by v^2/x or $\omega^2 x$ where x is the amplitude of the motion and is equal to r, the radius of the circle.

The acceleration of P is the component of the centripetal acceleration of the point Q along the line AB. Since the centripetal acceleration of Q is v^2/x or $\omega^2 x$ the acceleration of P may be written as:

$$a_p = -\omega^2 x \sin\theta = -\omega^2 r \text{ where } r = x\sin\theta$$

The negative sign indicates that the acceleration of P is always directed towards C, while displacement x is measured from C outwards. The above equation also shows that the acceleration of P is proportional to its displacement (x) from C, so that P executes true simple harmonic motion.

Relation between angular acceleration and linear acceleration

Angular acceleration (α) is the rate of change of angular velocity (ω) with time (t).

The unit of angular acceleration is radians per second (rads^{-2}). Suppose the angular velocity (ω) of a body changed from ω_o to ω_t in t sec., then angular acceleration (α) is given by:

$$\alpha = \frac{w_t - \omega_o}{t}$$

But $\omega = \frac{v}{r}$ or $v = r\omega$

Hence $\alpha = \frac{1}{r} \frac{(v_t - v_o)}{t}$

$$\therefore \alpha = \frac{a}{r}$$

Where a is the linear acceleration

$$a = \alpha r \quad 16.5$$

Linear acceleration equals the product of angular acceleration and the radius (or displacement) of the particle from its central position.

16.5 Period, frequency and amplitude of simple harmonic motion

For any body performing simple harmonic motion, we can define the following terms:

Period *T*: This is the time required to make one complete revolution about a point of reference.

Period is measured in seconds (s).

For example, let a body executing simple harmonic motion have an equilibrium position *C*. Let the maximum displacement from *C* be as shown in Fig. 16.7. The time taken to move from *C* to *B* to *A* and back to *C* (i.e. one complete revolution) is the period of the oscillation.

Fig. 16.7 Amplitude in simple harmonic motion

Frequency *f* is the number of complete revolutions per unit of time.

Frequency is measured in Hertz (H$_z$) or per second (s^{-1}). 1Hz = 1 cycle per second.

Frequency is the reciprocal of the period.

$$f = \frac{1}{T}$$

Amplitude, *A* is defined as the maximum displacement of the body from the equilibrium position, i.e. *CA* or *CB*.

Some important features of simple harmonic motion

(i)   The period of motion is independent of the amplitude. For example, in a simple pendulum, the period is given by $T = 2\pi\sqrt{\frac{l}{g}}$ where *l* is the length of the string and *g* is the acceleration due to gravity. The amplitude of the simple harmonic motion does not appear in the expression.

(ii) When the displacement is maximum, in either direction, the speed is zero, since the velocity must now change its direction. This implies that the body comes momentarily to rest at *A* or *B*, before it changes its direction of motion. The acceleration at this instant of change of direction is maximum but is directed opposite to the displacement.

(iii) At the equilibrium position *C*, the displacement is zero, the speed of the body is maximum and the acceleration is zero.

(iv) As the body moves from *B* to *C*., the speed increases towards *C* and then decreases as it moves out to the maximum displacement at *A*.

16.6 Energy of simple harmonic motion

Since force and displacement are involved in simple harmonic motion, energy is also involved. At any instant of the motion, the system may contain some energy as kinetic or potential or both. For example,

consider a mass suspended from the end of a spring which is made to execute a simple harmonic motion. The force necessary to stretch the spring a distance, *x* is given by

$$F = kx$$

where *k* is the force constant or stiffness of the spring. The work done in stretching the spring is given by work = average force x displacement

$$\tfrac{1}{2}kx \text{ x } x = \tfrac{1}{2}kx^2$$

Thus the energy stored in the stretched spring is $\tfrac{1}{2}kx^2$. Maximum energy stored or maximum potential energy (P.E.) in a stretched spring is given by

$$P.E._{max} = \tfrac{1}{2}kx^2$$

Where *x* is the maximum displacement or amplitude of the motion. This maximum energy is conserved throughout the simple harmonic motion.

The kinetic energy (*K.E.*) at any instant of the motion is $\tfrac{1}{2}mv^2$, where *m* is the mass of the body and *v* is its velocity at that instant. When the oscillating spring is momentarily at rest at the position of maximum displacement, where *v* = 0 and kinetic energy equals zero, the potential energy equals $\tfrac{1}{2}kx^2$.

$$\text{Total energy} = K.E. + P.E. = \tfrac{1}{2}kx^2$$

At the equilibrium position where the speed is maximum, total energy is in the form of kinetic energy i.e. $\tfrac{1}{2}mv^2$ and P. E. equals zero since *x* is zero at this point. Since the total energy of the system is always conserved, the total energy = $\tfrac{1}{2}mv^2$.

At any position *x*, total energy = $\tfrac{1}{2}mv^2 + \tfrac{1}{2}kx^2$

As another example, we consider the simple harmonic motion of a simple pendulum.

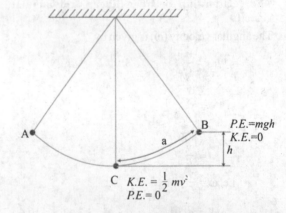

Fig. 16.8(a) Simple pendulum

At *A* or *B*, where the bob momentarily comes to rest, total energy is potential energy = *mgh* where *h* is the height of *B* above the equilibrium point *C*, *m* is mass of bob and *g* is acceleration due to gravity. At *C*, where the speed of the bob is maximum, and *h* is zero, all energy is kinetic (*K.E.* = $\tfrac{1}{2}mv^2$).

At other positions of motion, the *K.E.* and *P.E.* each contribute energy where the sum is always equal to *mgh*, the maximum potential energy.

16.7 Damped oscillation

An ideal simple harmonic motion is one which continues to vibrate with maximum amplitude forever. Unfortunately this is not true in practice. The amplitude of oscillation continues to decrease gradually until the vibrating eventually stops. A simple pendulum, for example, does not continue to vibrate for ever. Its amplitude gradually decreases until the motion stops. Such a motion in which the amplitude gradually decreases with time is said to be a damped motion. The reason for this to happen is as a result of dissipative forces such as air resistance which gradually damps the motion. The result of such damped motion is shown in fig. 16.8(b).

Fig. 16.8(b) Damped Oscillation
(Amplitudes a, gradually decreases to zero).

16.8 Forced vibration and resonance

It is observed that the amplitude of vibration in simple harmonic motion never really remains constant but becomes smaller and smaller. For example the amplitude of the bob of a simple pendulum diminishes slowly. This is as a result of energy losses arising from the viscosity or friction between the air and the bob. A vibration whose amplitude becomes progressively smaller is said to be damped.

Thus, in order to maintain an oscillating system in constant and continuous motion, some external periodic force needs to be applied to the system. For example, the simple harmonic motion of a simple pendulum oscillating at its natural frequency ($f = 1/T$) will normally be damped. However when the bob is subject to an oscillatory external force, the frequency is no longer the natural frequency, but that of the external force. Such vibrations resulting from an external periodic force acting on a system are called **forced vibrations**.

Examples of forced vibrations are seen when a bridge vibrates under the influence of marching soldiers, and when a tuning fork vibrates when exposed to the periodic force of a sound wave. You can demonstrate forced vibration in your home using a dinner fork. If we set the prongs of the fork vibrating by pinching them together, it is noticed that the sound is very faint. The sound is observed to be remarkably loud when the end of the handle of the fork is pressed firmly on a hard table.

The vibrating fork has been made to transmit its movement to another body having a larger surface. A larger amount of air is set into motion, thus a louder sound is produced. The above demonstration of forced vibration illustrates the principle of a sounding board of piano or the diaphragm of a loud-speaker.

Resonance

The response of a body to an external periodic force depends on the relation between the forced frequency and the natural frequency.

> **Resonance** is a vibration set up in a body due to a transfer of energy from another body which is vibrating with a period (or frequency) the same or nearly the same as that of the first.

A simple mechanical example of resonance is seen in a 'child' swing. A very slight force applied each time the swing reaches its maximum point will soon build up a wide movement in the swing. Thus in order to make it swing high, it should not be pushed at random but in nearly the same tempo as its natural frequency of motion.

Resonance is also seen in the rattling of windows when a low-flying aeroplane passes overhead, especially if the natural frequency of vibration of the window happens to be the same as one of the frequencies that make up the noise of the plane's engine.

> Resonance is a phenomenon which occurs whenever a particular body or system is set in oscillation at its own natural frequency as a result of impulses or signals received from some other system or body which is vibrating with the same frequency.

Example 16.2

A particle makes 240 r.p.m. on a circle of 2m radius. Find its period, angular velocity, linear velocity and its acceleration.

Period, $T = 1/\text{frequency}$

Frequency = 240 rev. per min = 4 rev. per second

$$T = \frac{1}{4} \text{ s}$$

$$= 0.25 \text{ s}$$

Angular velocity, $\omega = \frac{\theta}{t} = 2\pi \times 4 \text{ radians s}^{-1}$

($\theta = 2\pi$ radians for 1 revolution)

$\omega = 8\pi \text{ radians}^{-1}$

Linear velocity $v = \omega r$

$v = 2 \times 8\pi = 16\pi \text{ms}^{-1}$

acceleration $= \omega^2 r$

$$= 64\pi^2 \times 2$$

$$= 128\pi^2 \text{ ms}^{-1}$$

Example 16.3

A particle moves with simple harmonic motion. If its acceleration in ms^{-2} is 100 times its displacement in metres, find the period of the motion.

If $x =$ displacement,
acceleration $= \omega^2 x$
$\qquad = 100x$
$\therefore \omega = 10$ radians/second

Period $= \dfrac{2\pi}{\omega}$

$\qquad = \dfrac{2\pi}{10}$

$\qquad = \dfrac{\pi}{5}$ s

Example 16.4

A 10kg mass is suspended from the end of a spring and released. If the spring oscillates in simple harmonic motion with a period of 0.5s, find the energy given to the 10 kg mass if the amplitude of oscillation is 2cm. For the oscillating system, period

$$T = 2\pi \sqrt{\dfrac{m}{k}}$$

Where m is mass suspended and k is the spring's stiffness constant

$$0.5 = 2\pi \sqrt{\dfrac{10}{k}}$$

Squaring both sides, we have

$$0.25 = 4\pi^2 \dfrac{10}{k}$$

$$k = \dfrac{4\pi^2 \times 10}{0.25}$$

$$\qquad = 160\pi^2 \text{kgs}^{-2}$$

Energy given to the system is given by

$$E = \dfrac{1}{2}kx^2$$

Where x is the amplitude of oscillation $= 2.0$ cm $= 0.02$m

Energy $= \dfrac{1}{2}kx^2$

$$\qquad = \dfrac{1}{2} \times 160\pi^2 \times 4 \times 10^{-4} \text{ Joules,}$$

$$\qquad = 0.03\pi^2 \text{J}$$

Summary

1. A motion is said to be simple harmonic if the acceleration is always directed towards a fixed point and is proportional to the distance from the fixed point.

2. In a simple harmonic motion the following parameters are defined as follows:

    Angular velocity $\omega = \dfrac{\theta}{t}$

    Acceleration $a = \omega^2 x$, $a_{max} = -\omega^2 A$, A is amplitude

    Period, $\qquad T = \dfrac{2\pi}{\omega}$

    Frequency, $\quad f = \dfrac{1}{T} = \dfrac{\omega}{2\pi}$

    Linear velocity $v = \pm \omega \sqrt{A^2 - x^2}$

3. For a simple pendulum of length l to perform simple harmonic motion, the period of motion is given by

    $$T = \dfrac{2\pi}{\omega} = 2\pi\sqrt{\dfrac{l}{g}}$$

    For a loaded spring, $T = 2\pi\sqrt{\dfrac{m}{k}}$, k is spring constant.

4. Damped oscillation is one in which the amplitude gradually decreases with time.

5. Vibrations resulting from the action of an external periodic force on an oscillating body are called force vibrations.

6. Resonance occurs when the forcing frequency coincides with the natural frequency of the vibrating body.

Exercise 16

1. When a body is performing simple harmonic motion, its acceleration
    A. is constant.
    B. varies with displacement from equilibrium positions.
    C. is zero.
    D. moves irregularly with time.

2. The acceleration of a body undergoing a uniform circular motion is given by
    A. $\omega^2 x$.
    B. $\omega x r$.
    C. ωr^2.
    D. $\dfrac{\omega}{r}$.

3. When a body is performing simple harmonic motion,
    A. its acceleration is always directed towards a fixed point and is proportional to the distance from it.
    B. its acceleration is constant and directed towards a fixed point.
    C. its acceleration is proportional to the square of distance from the fixed point.
    D. the part of motion is straight.

4. When a simple harmonic motion is affected by severe air resistance, the motion is said to be
    A. damped.
    B. forced motion.
    C. natural motion.
    D. sinusoidal.

5. What is the angular speed (in rads^{-1}) of a body whose frequency is 50Hz?
    A. 200π
    B. 100π
    C. 50π
    D. 10π

6. Explain what you understand by simple harmonic motion, frequency, amplitude and period of the motion.

7. Describe the simple energy transformations that occur in a simple harmonic motion.

8. (a) Distinguish between 'damped oscillation' and 'forced vibration'.
   (b) What do you understand by 'forced oscillation' and 'resonance'?

9. What effect, if any, does the
   (a) amplitude of oscillation and
   (b) length of pendulum have on an oscillating bob?

10. The period of a simple pendulum X is 1.5s. What is the period of a simple pendulum Y which makes 500 vibrations in the time it takes X to make 400 vibrations?

11. When a cord is attached to the bob of an oscillating pendulum, the pendulum comes to rest much more quickly. Explain.

12. Is a body moving with constant speed in a circular path undergoing acceleration? Give reasons for your answer.

13. Define simple harmonic motion. An object moving with simple harmonic motion has an amplitude of 5cm and a frequency of 50 Hz. Calculate the:
    (a) period of oscillation;
    (b) acceleration at the middle and end of the oscillation;
    (c) velocity at the corresponding instants.

14. Explain the terms:
    (a) damped oscillation,
    (b) force oscillation, and
    (c) resonance.

15. Explain simple harmonic motion. What is meant by the period, frequency, and amplitude of such motion? What is the relationship between period and frequency?

16. Explain how you can measure the acceleration due to gravity at your laboratory by using simple pendulum. What precautions will you take to obtain accurate results? Such a simple pendulum has a period of 4.2s. When the length of the pendulum is shortened by 1m, the period is 3.7s. Calculate the:
    (a) original length of the pendulum;
    (b) value of the acceleration due to gravity.

NEWTON'S LAWS OF MOTION

Chapter **17**

17.1 Dynamics

In chapter 2, we studied the motion of bodies without any reference to the force responsible for the motion. In this chapter, we will study the effect of forces on bodies that are in motion. This branch of study is called **dynamics**.

The study of motion involves also the study of forces producing the motion. We define:

> force as any agent that changes or tends to change the state of rest or of uniform motion of a body in a straight line.

We have seen earlier that there are two types of forces in physics: (i) contact forces, and (ii) field forces.

Contact forces are such forces that are in contact with the body they affect. Examples are tension and reaction forces, frictional forces, forces of pull or push.

Field forces are forces whose sources do not require contact with the body on which they act. Examples are gravitational forces, electrical forces and magnetic forces. The effect of such forces is felt at a distance, or in a **field** of the force.

A field is an area through which the effect of the force can be felt, e.g. gravitational field, magnetic field and electrical field.

Galilei Galileo initiated the study of dynamics, and immediately after his death the work was continued by Sir Isaac Newton, (1642-1727). Among other things, Newton formulated the basic laws of motion, which are still valid today.

17.2 Newton's first law and its applications

> A body will continue in its present state of rest or, if it is in motion, will continue to move with uniform speed in a straight line unless it is acted upon by a force.

This tendency of a body to remain in its state of rest or uniform motion is called the **inertia** of the body. For this reason, Newton's first law is sometimes called 'the law of inertia'.

As an example of inertia, think of the effect on a car driver if his car is standing still and another car crashes into his car from behind. His car is suddenly knocked forward. His body is pushed forward by the seat, but his head stays still, in its state of rest, and is jerked back in relation to his body. For this reason, neck injuries are common in accidents where cars are hit from behind and many modern cars have headrests to protect drivers and passengers from injury.

It is important to realise that once a body is moving with uniform speed in a straight line, it needs no force to keep it in motion provided there are no external opposing or accelerating forces. For example, we know that once a rocket has been thrust into space it will carry on to its destination, perhaps the moon, without any further force. It will neither decrease or increase its speed nor change direction until it is acted upon by the attraction of the moon which compels it to change its path.

In general, however, from common experience it does not appear that Newton's first law is obeyed. It is known that a body moving in a straight line with uniform speed does not mean that the first law is not valid. The body comes to rest because opposing forces such as air resistance and friction gradually reduce its speed. For example, when a body is thrown up into the air, its motion is opposed by air resistance and the pull of gravity. Sooner or later it returns to the earth. If air resistance and gravitation could be eliminated the body would go on moving in a straight line for ever.

As another example, we observe the consequences of the first law when a moving vehicle is suddenly brought to rest by the application of the brakes. The passengers are suddenly jerked forward as they tend to continue in their straight line motion. Passengers in the front may hit the windscreen unless they apply enough force backwards. This is why it is advisable to use a safety belt while at high speed.

Momentum

Momentum is an important property of a moving object. It explains its tendency to continue moving in a straight line.

> The momentum of a body is defined as the product of its mass and its velocity

Momentum = mv

The unit of momentum corresponds to kg ms^{-1}, but the usual SI units of momentum will be discussed later. Thus a bullet having a small mass 0.01kg, moving with a high velocity of 10000 ms^{-1} and a heavy ball of mass 100kg moving with a small speed of 1 ms^{-1} have the same momentum. We also note that the greater the momentum of the bullet the more deadly it is, i.e. the greater the force it will exert on the body it hits.

More powerful brakes are required to stop a heavy lorry than a light car moving with the same speed.

17.3 Newton's second law and its applications

The rate of change of momentum of a body is directly proportional to the applied force and takes place in the direction in which the force acts.

$$\text{Force} \propto \frac{\text{Change in momentum}}{\text{time}}$$

Suppose a force F acts on a body of mass m for a time t and causes it to change its velocity from u to v, then Newton's second law can be stated as:

$$F \propto \frac{mv - mu}{t}$$

$$\text{So } F \propto \frac{m(v - u)}{t}$$

$$\text{but } \frac{v - u}{t} = a \text{ (acceleration)}$$

$$\therefore F \propto ma, \quad F = kma$$

If we take $m = 1$kg and $a = 1$ms^{-2}, the unit of force is chosen to make $F = 1$ when $k = 1$. The *SI* unit of force is called the Newton (N), and it is the force which produces an acceleration of 1ms^{-2} when it acts on a mass of 1kg. Thus when F is in newtons, m in kg, a in ms^{-2} we have

$$F = ma \qquad 17.1$$

This equation is recognised as a fundamental equation of dynamics and is one of the most important equations of physics. It must be noted that, when using the above equation, the force F must be the resultant force acting on the body.

Example 17.1
A body of mass 2 kg undergoes a constant horizontal acceleration of 5ms^{-2}. Calculate the resultant horizontal force acting on the body. What will be the resultant force on the body when it moves with a uniform velocity of 10ms^{-1}?
Given that $a = 5$ms^{-2}, $m = 2$kg, then Newton's fundamental equation

$F = ma$ becomes:
$F = 5 \times 2 = 10$N,

which is the resultant force on the body. If the object moves with uniform velocity, it means that it is not accelerating, i.e. $a = 0$.

$F = ma$
$\quad = m \times 0 = 0$

The resultant force on the body is zero.

Example 17.2
A car of mass 600kg, moving with a forward acceleration of 5ms^{-2} is acted upon by a constant resistive force of 1000N. Calculate the force exerted from the engine to maintain this forward acceleration.

Let F be the force of the engine. Resultant force acting on the car $= F - 1000$.
$\therefore$ Newton's equation becomes $F - 1000 = ma$
Using $a = 5ms^{-2}$ and $m = 600$kg, we have:
$F - 1000 = 600 \times 5$
$\quad F = 1000 + 3000 = 4000$N
$\quad \quad = 4$kN (4 kilonewtons)

Deductions from Newton's second law
Impulse of a force

$$\text{Now } F = \frac{m(v - u)}{t}$$

$$\text{or} \quad Ft = mv - mu \qquad 17.2$$

The quantity Ft is called the **Impulse** I of the force.

Impulse is the product of a large force and a very short time during which it acts.

The unit of impulse is the newton second (Ns). Since this quantity is equal to change in momentum it means that momentum can also be expressed in Ns.

$$\therefore \quad I = Ft = \text{change in momentum} \qquad 17.3$$

Example 17.3
A force of 10N acts for 20s. What is the change in momentum of the body?

Impulse $= Ft =$ change in momentum
$\therefore$ Change in momentum $= 10 \times 20 = 200$ Ns

Example 17.4
A body of mass 5kg moving with a speed of 30ms^{-1} is suddenly hit by another body moving in the same direction, thereby changing the speed of the former body to 60ms^{-2}. What is the impulse received by the first body?

Impulse $=$ change in momentum
$\quad = mv = mu$
$\quad = m(v - u)$
$\quad = 5(60 - 30) = 150$ Ns
Weight of a body (expressed in newtons)

We saw in chapter 2 that all bodies whatever their mass have the same acceleration ($g = 9.8$ms^{-2}) when they fall freely under gravity. Thus for a body of mass m falling under gravity alone, the force of gravity, F, acting on it is given by

$$F = ma$$

i.e. $F = mg$ (measured in newtons)
This force is called the weight W of the body.

Hence we write $\quad W = mg \qquad 17.4$

To summarise, we note that weight is a force and should be expressed in newtons (N). The weight of a mass known in kg is obtained by multiplying by g. When using Newton's equation of motion, the force F must be expressed in newtons.

Example 17.5

A body of mass 5kg is to be given an acceleration of $20ms^{-2}$. Calculate the force required when the acceleration is vertically upwards. Take $g=10ms^{-2}$.

Let F be the force required, expressed in newtons, and applied vertically upwards in the direction of acceleration. The weight of the body mg acts downwards. Therefore, the resultant force on the body upwards is: $F-mg$

$\therefore$ The equation of motion is $F-mg=ma$
Using $m=5kg$, $a=20ms^{-2}$, $g=10ms^{-2}$
We have $F-5\times10=5\times20$
$$F=50+100$$
$$F=150N$$

Difference between mass and weight

The mass m of a body is a measure of the quantity of material in a body and is constant anywhere in the universe. Weight W is the force of gravity on the body. The two quantities are related by $W=mg$. From this relation, it follows that since g varies slightly from place to place on earth, the weight W also varies from place to place although m remains constant. The value of g and W is greatest at the poles and decreases gradually towards the equator and so it is least at the equator.

The reason for this is that the Earth is spinning, and the weight of a body at the equator is partly used up in providing centripetal force to keep the body moving in a large circle. In fact it is a very small effect, but it reduces g slightly. Also, because the earth was spinning as it cooled from its liquid state in pre-historical times, it is slightly flattened, and its radius at the equator is greater than at the poles. Thus objects on the equator are farther from the earth's centre than objects at the poles, and g is less.

If we took an object to the Moon or some other planet where g had a different value, the weight would be quite different. It would be less on the surface of the Moon, since g is less, but the mass would still be the same.

Weight of a body in a lift (weightlessness)

A lift is a device operated electrically and used for moving people and load up or down a tall building.

For a man standing on the lift, there are two forces acting on him, (a) his weight (W) acting downwards and (b) the reaction R of the floor of the lift on the man acting upwards.

(i)   When the lift is stationary or moving with a constant velocity we have that

$$W=mg=R \qquad 17.5$$

where m is the mass of the man.

(ii) When the lift accelerates upwards with an acceleration a, the man is pulled upwards with an acceleration a. The unbalanced force (F) on him is given by:
$$F=R-mg=ma$$
$$\text{Hence } R=m(a+g)$$

Apparent weight of the man when the lift accelerates upwards is given by

$$W=R=m(a+g) \qquad 17.6$$

The man thus appears to weigh more under this condition.

(iii) When the lift moves downwards with an acceleration, a, the unbalanced force (F) on the man is given by $F=mg-R=ma$

His apparent weight is now
$$W=R=mg-ma$$

or $$W=m(g-a) \qquad 17.7$$

Thus the man appears to weigh less under this condition

(iv) When the lift descends with an acceleration $a=g$, (free fall) then we can see from (iii) above that $W=0$. Thus the man's apparent weight is zero, i.e. he appears to have no weight. Such a situation is referred to as "*weightlessness*".

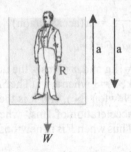

Fig. 17.1 A man in a lift accelerating or decelerating

17.4 Newton's third law and its applications

To every action there is an equal and opposite reaction

When we place an object on a table the reaction of the table on the object (the vertical force exerted on the object by the table) is equal and opposite to the action of the object on the table (the weight of the object bearing down on the table).

Again, if a moving car A hits a stationery car B, the force exerted on B by A (the reaction) will be the same as the action of B on A. This is why both cars are damaged.

When a bullet is shot out of a gun the person firing it experiences the backwards recoil force of the gun (a reaction) and this is equal to the propulsive force (action) acting on the bullet.

Note: Since force is proportional to change in momentum, it follows that the momentum of the bullet is equal and opposite to the momentum of the gun. Thus for a bullet of mass, m, and velocity, v, the velocity V of recoil of the gun is given as $MV = -mv$

$$V = \frac{-mv}{M} \qquad\qquad 17.8$$

where M is the mass of the gun.

Newton's third law has a very useful application in the operation of jet aeroplanes and rockets. The application is based on the fact that a large mass of very hot gases issues from the nozzle behind the jet or rocket. The velocity and mass per second of the gases are so high that considerable momentum is imparted to the stream of gas. An equal and opposite momentum is imparted to the rocket or aeroplane which undergoes a forward thrust (see Fig. 17.2).

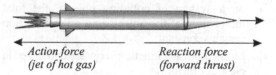

Action force
(jet of hot gas)

Reaction force
(forward thrust)

Fig. 17.2 The Rocket

Law of conservation of momentum

Newton's second and third laws enable us to formulate an important conservation law known as the law of conservation of momentum.

> In a system of colliding objects the total momentum is conserved, provided there is no net external force acting on the system.

It can also be stated as follows:

> The total momentum of an isolated or closed system of colliding bodies remains constant.
> Thus if two or more bodies collide in a closed system, the total momentum before collision is equal to the total momentum after collision.

By a **closed** or **isolated** system we mean that system on which no external forces act.

Let u_1, u_2 and v_1, v_2 be the initial and final velocities of two colliding bodies of masses m_1 and m_2. The conservation law can be stated as:

$$m_1 u_1 + m_2 u_2 = m_1 v_1 + m_2 v_2 \qquad 17.9$$

Note: All the velocities must be measured in the same direction along the same line, with correct positive or negative signs.

The above law follows from the fact that the action of body 1 on body 2 is equal to the reaction of body 2 on body 1, and that both forces act for an exactly equal time.

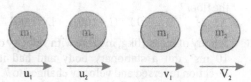

Fig. 17.3 Conservation of momentum.

This argument applies to bodies which are elastic and rebound from each other after collision with different velocities. It also applies to bodies which are inelastic and join together after the collision and move away with the same velocity. In this case.

$$v_1 = v_2 = v$$

$$\therefore m_1 u_1 + m_2 u_2 = (m_1 + m_2)v \qquad 17.10$$

Example 17.6

A body of mass 4kg moving with a velocity of $10 ms^{-1}$ collides with a stationary body of mass 6kg. If the two bodies move together after the collision, calculate their common velocity.

In this case, $m_1 = 4$kg, $u_1 = 10 ms^{-1}$, $m_2 = 6$kg but $u_2 = 0$. Since they move together after collision, let their common velocity be v.
Then using $m_1 u_1 + m_2 u_2 = v(m_1 + m_2)$
We have $4 \times 10 + 0 = v(4 + 6)$, $v = 4 ms^{-1}$

Example 17.7

Object A of mass 20kg moving with a velocity of $3 ms^{-1}$ makes a head-on collision with object B, mass 10kg moving with a velocity of $2 ms^{-1}$ in the opposite direction. If A and B stick together after collision, calculate their common velocity v in the direction of A.

Let u_A, u_B be the initial velocities and v the final common velocity

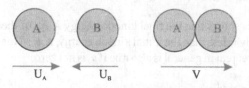

Fig. 17.4

$u_A = 3 ms^{-1}$, $u_B = 2 ms^{-1}$, $m_A = 10$kg, $m_B = 15 kg$
Using $m_A u_A + m_B u_B = v(m_A + m_B)$
We have
$20 \times 3 + 10 \times (-2) = v(20 + 10)$
$60 - 20 = 30v$
$v = \frac{4}{3}$ ms^{-1}

Elastic and inelastic collisions

There are two major types of collisions, elastic and inelastic collisions.

Elastic collision

In an elastic collision both momentum and kinetic energy are conserved. This means that for two colliding bodies with masses m_1 and m_2 and initial velocities of u_1 and u_2 and final velocities after collision of v_1 and v_2.
Then $m_1 u_1 + m_2 u_2 = m_1 v_1 + m_2 v_2$

$$\frac{1}{2} m_1 u_1^2 + \frac{1}{2} m_2 u_2^2 = \frac{1}{2} m_1 v_1^2 + \frac{1}{2} m_2 v_2^2$$

An example of perfectly elastic collision is a ball which bounces off the ground back to its original height.

Inelastic collision

In this case momentum is conserved but not the kinetic energy. The kinetic energy usually decreases as it is converted into heat, sound, or elastic potential energy and in this way causes deformation.

In a complete inelastic collision, the two objects join together after an impact and move with the same velocity v, so that conservation of momentum equation becomes

$$m_1 u_1 + m_2 u_2 = (m_1 + m_2) v$$

The $K.E.$ of the system before impact is

$$K.E._1 = \frac{1}{2} m_1 u_1^2 + \frac{1}{2} m_2 u_2^2$$

The final $K.E.$, $K.E._2 = \frac{1}{2}(m_1 + m_2)v^2$

Consider a special case when the body m_2 is at rest, then

$$K.E._1 = \frac{1}{2} m_1 u_1^2$$

$$K.E._2 = \frac{1}{2}(m_1 + m_2)v^2$$

but $v = \frac{m_1 u_1}{m_1 + m_2}$

$$\therefore K.E._2 = \frac{1}{2} \frac{m_1^2 u_1^2}{m_1 + m_2}$$

then $\frac{K.E._1}{K.E._2} = \frac{m_1}{m_1 + m_2}$

This shows that the final kinetic energy $K.E._2$ of the body is less than the initial kinetic energy, $K.E._1$ This statement in general is also true if u_2 is not zero.

Summary

1. The momentum of a body in motion is defined as the product of the mass and velocity of the body. It acts in the same direction as the velocity.

2. A body at rest has no momentum.

3. The impulse of the force acting on a body is the product of the force and the time for which it acts on the body. Impulse $I = F \times t$ (F = force, t = time).

4. The impulse of the force, F, acting on a body of mass (m) and changing the velocity of the body from v_0 to v in time interval $t - t_0$ is given as:

$F(t - t_0) = m(v - v_0)$, that is, impulse of the force on the body = change in momentum of the body.

5. Unit of momentum = Unit of impulse
   = Newton second (Ns)
   = $kg\,ms^{-1}$.

6. Newton's first law of motion states that a body will continue in its state of rest or uniform velocity unless acted upon by an external force to act otherwise.

7. Newton's second law of motion states that the change of momentum of a body per unit time is directly proportional to the force causing the change and takes place in the same direction of the straight line along which the force acts.

8. Newton's third law of motion states that action and reaction are equal and opposite. Thus, if a body A exerts a force F on a body B, then B exerts a force of F on A.

9. The principle of conservation of linear momentum states that, if no external forces act on a system of colliding objects, the total momentum of the objects in a given direction remains constant.

10. Momentum and kinetic energy are conserved in elastic collision.

11. Momentum is conserved and kinetic energy usually decreases in inelastic collision.

12. Momentum is conserved but kinetic energy increases during an explosion.

13. The inertia of a body is its reluctance to start motion and its reluctance to stop once it has begun to move. Inertial is a measure of the mass of a body and is known as the inertia mass.

Exercise 17

1. The unit of impulse of a force is
   A. N B. Ns C. Ns^{-1} D. Nm

2. For elastic collision,
   A. energy is doubled and momentum is halved.
   B. energy is conserved.
   C. momentum is conserved.
   D. kinetic energy and momentum are conserved.

3. The property of a body to remain at rest or to continue to move in a straight line, is known as
   A. force.   B. impulse.
   C. momentum.   D. inertia.

4. A resultant force of 15.00 N acts on a body for 4s mass 4 kg. Calculate the change in momentum of the body within this period.
   A. 60Ns   B. 11Ns
   C. 3.5Ns   D. 0.3 Ns

5. A ball of mass 100g falls from a height of 5m onto a floor and rebounds to a height of 3m. What energy is lost as a result of the impact on the floor?
   A. 2J   B. 20 J C. 100J   D. 1,00J

6. A body of mass 10kg, moving with velocity of 10 ms^{-1}, hit a stationary body and had its direction reversed and velocity changed to 7.5 ms^{-1} in 5 seconds. Calculate the force of impact.

A. 3.5N B. 35.0N
C. 175.0N D. 875.0N

7. In an elastic collision, (i) energy is conserved (ii) energy is decreased (iii) energy is increased (iv) linear momentum is conserved.
A. (i) only
B. (ii) only
C. (iii) only
D. (i) and (iv) only

8. A motor car of mass 800kg travelling at 20ms^{-1} is brought to rest by brakes in 100m. Calculate the average braking force required.

9. A body moving with constant force has a constant acceleration. Is this statement true? Give reasons.

10. Define momentum and derive its units.

11. Define the impulse of a force. If a force of 6.0N acts on a body for five seconds, what is the change in momentum?

12. Explain why the velocity of a recoiling gun is lower than that of the ejected bullet.

13. A bullet of mass 0.045kg is fired from a gun of mass 9kg, the bullet moving with an initial velocity of 200ms^{-1}. Find the initial backward velocity of the gun.

14. A body of mass 2kg moving with velocity of 6ms^{-1} collides with a stationary object of mass 0.5kg. If the two bodies move together after the impact, calculate their common velocity.

15. Calculate the force required to impart an acceleration of 5ms^{-2} to a mass of 10kg.

16. What force would be required to accelerate an electron (mass of electron = 9 x 10^{-31} kg) from rest to a velocity of 10^{4}ms^{-1} in 10 seconds?

17. State Newton's first law of motion. What do you understand by inertia? Describe an experience you have had in which inertia was involved.

18. A block of weight 7.0N rests on a level floor. The frictional force between the block and the floor is 1.0N. A horizontal force of 1.4N is used to pull the block for 4 seconds. What is the velocity of the block after this time?

19. A player hits a ball of mass 0.3kg which was moving eastwards with a velocity of 10ms^{-1}, causing it now to move with velocity 15ms^{-1} westwards. The force of the blow acts on the

ball for 0.01s. Calculate the average force exerted on the ball by the player.

20. A body of mass 10 kg is pulled along a horizontal floor by a horizontal force of 48 N with an acceleration of 3.0 ms^{-2}. Calculate the frictional force between the body and the floor.

21. A ball of mass 200g, travelling with velocity of 100 ms^{-1}, collides with another ball of mass 800 g, moving at 50 ms^{-1} in the same direction. If they stick together, what will be their common velocity?

22. A steel block, S, is placed on a concrete platform, B. The weight of the block is 5 N. A steadily increasing force is applied horizontally to the block so that it just begins to move. If the coefficient of friction is 0.2, calculate the minimum force required to move the block.

23. A rocket expels gas at the rate of 0.4 kgs^{-1}. If the average force of the gas is 120N, calculate the velocity of the gas. State the law used in your calculation.

24. A player hits a ball of mass 0.24 kg moving northwards with a velocity of 15 ms^{-1} thereby causing it to move with a velocity of 20 ms^{-1} southwards. The force of the blow acts on the ball for 0.025s. Calculate the average force exerted on the ball by the player.

25. A jet engine takes in 20 kg of air per second at 150 m. The air is compressed, heated and discharged at 500 ms^{-1}. What force is developed in the engine?

26. Explain the terms velocity and momentum. What is the relation between force and momentum? State the law of conservation of momentum. Explain why the recoil velocity of a gun is much less than the velocity of the bullet.

27. State Newton's third law of motion. Use it to explain how and why care should be taken in shooting a gun. In such a case, what is the sum total of the momenta of the bullet and the gun?

28. State the principle of the conservation of linear momentum. A ball of mass 50 g travelling with a velocity of 10 ms^{-1} collides with another ball of mass 60 g moving with 5 ms^{-1} in opposite direction. If they stick together, what will be their common velocity and in what direction?

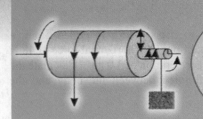

MACHINES

18

18.1 Definition and types of machines

In physics, a machine is not necessarily a complicated piece of mechanism. It is simply a device used to do work.

> A machine is a device by means of which work can be done more conveniently.

Essentially, it is a contrivance by means of which a force called an effort *(E)* applied at one point can be used to overcome a force known as a load *(L)* at some other point. In most cases, but not all, the machine enables a large load or resistance to be overcome by a small effort.

Examples of machines include pulley systems, car lifting jacks and crowbars. In the discussion of the general principles and mode of operation of machines, certain terms are generally employed. These are mechanical advantage *(M.A.)*, velocity ratio *(V.R.)* and efficiency *(ε)*. We will now discuss the general meanings of these.

18.2 Mechanical advantage *(M.A.)* and velocity ratio *(V.R.)*

Note: Mechanical advantage is now often referred to as Force Ratio *(F.R.)*.

In Fig. 18.1, we show the general form of any machine. The symbols *L, E, x and y* represent the **load,** the **effort,** the **distance moved by the effort** and the **distance moved by the load** respectively.

> The *M. A.* of a machine is defined as the ratio of the load to the effort.

i.e. $M.A. = L/E$

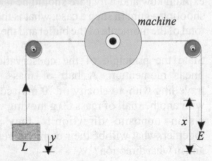

Fig 18.1 General principles of a machine.

> The *V. R.* of a machine is defined as the ratio of the distance moved by the effort to the distance moved by the load.

$$V.R. = \frac{x}{y}$$

Comments

(a) If the load *(L)* is bigger than the effort *(E)*, the *M.A.* is greater than one.

(b) In this case the small applied effort moves through a large distance *x*, while the large load overcome moves through a small distance *y*, so that the *V. R.* is greater than one.

(c) In practice, part of the effort in a machine has to overcome frictional forces present, and also often has to lift part of the machine. Hence mechanical advantage depends in part on friction and the quality of construction of the machine. From the relation *M.A. = L/E*, it is clear that the smaller the friction, the smaller will be the effort *E* and hence the larger the *M.A.*

(d) Since *V.R.* depends only on the geometry of the moving parts, it is independent of friction.

Efficiency (ε) and its relation to *V.R.* and *M.A.*

The ratio of useful work done by the machine to the total work put into the machine is called the **efficiency (ε)** of the machine. It is usually expressed as a percentage, and is defined as follows:

$$\varepsilon = \frac{\text{work output}}{\text{work input}} \times 100\%$$

Since work = force x distance

$$\frac{\text{work output}}{\text{work input}} = \frac{\text{load x distance moved by load}}{\text{effort x distance moved by effort}}$$

$$= \frac{Ly}{Ex}$$

$$= \frac{L}{E} \Big/ \frac{x}{y}$$

$$= \frac{M.A.}{V.R.}$$

$$\varepsilon = \frac{M.A.}{V.R.} \times 100\%$$

Comments

(a) Since *M.A.* decreases with an increase in friction but *V.R.* is independent of friction, it follows that efficiency (ε) decreases with increase in friction.

(b) The above equation is found to be very useful in solving problems but is not the basic definition of efficiency. It is only a relationship between efficiency, *M.A.* and *V.R.*

Example 18.1

What does it mean that the *M.A.* of a machine is 4?

It means that the ratio of load to effort is 4:1

Example 18.2

What does it mean that the *V.R.* of a machine is 5?

It means that the distance moved by the effort is five times the distance moved by the load.

Example 18.3

A machine with *V. R.* 5 requires 1000J of work to raise a load of 500N through a vertical distance of 1.5m. Find the efficiency and *M.A.* of the machine.

The efficiency $\varepsilon = \dfrac{\text{work ouptput}}{\text{work input}} \times 100\%$

So $\varepsilon = \dfrac{\text{load x distance moved by load}}{\text{work input}} \times 100\%$

$ = \dfrac{500 \times 1.5}{1000} \times 100\%$

$ = 75\%$

Also $\varepsilon = \dfrac{M.A.}{V.R.} \times 100\%$

$75 = \dfrac{M.A.}{5} \times 100\%$

$\therefore M.A. = 3.75$

Example 18.4

A machine has a velocity ratio 5 and is 80% efficient. What effort would be needed to lift a load of 2000N with the aid of this machine?

Efficiency ε is given by

$$\varepsilon = \frac{M.A.}{V.R.}$$

$$= \frac{L/E}{V.R.}$$

but $\varepsilon = 80\%$

$\therefore \quad \dfrac{80}{100} = \dfrac{2000/E}{5}$

or $\quad E = \dfrac{2000}{4} = 500N$

Effort required = 500N

18.3 Classification, uses and applications of machines

The following are different classes of machines which we need to consider: the lever, pulleys, the inclined plane and wedge, the screw, the hydraulic press and the wheel and axle.

The lever

The lever is a simple form of machine. The term *lever* is applied to a rigid body pivoted about a point called a **fulcrum (*F*)**. An **effort (*E*)** is applied at one point on the lever and this overcomes a **load (*L*)** at some other point.

First order levers

In a lever the relative positions which *F*, *E* and *L* can occupy may vary, and hence we have three different types of levers for the three possible arrangements. The first order lever type is one in which *F* is between *L* and *E*.

Simple examples of first order levers are the crowbar, the claw hammer and pliers (see Fig.18.3). Pliers are an example of a double first order lever. The lever is based upon the principle of moments and we can show that the *V.R.* is the ratio of the two arms of the lever. The *M.A.* increases when this ratio increases.

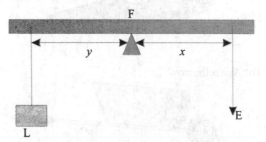

Fig 18.2 *First order levers.*

(a) Claw hammer

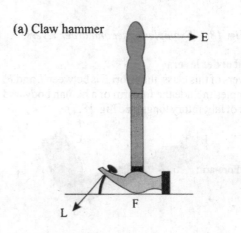

(b) Crowbar

(c) Pliers

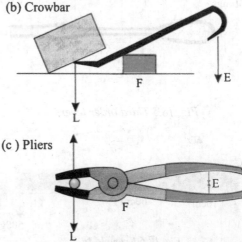

Fig. 18.3 Examples of first order levers.

If y and x represent the distances of load L and effort E from the fulcrum F in each of the above levers, then taking moments about F gives

$$y \times L = x \times E$$

$$\frac{L}{E} = \frac{x}{y} \Rightarrow M.A. = V.R.$$

Second order levers

This is the class of levers in which the load L is between the fulcrum F and effort E. Examples include nut crackers and wheel barrows (see Fig. 18.4).

(a) Nutcracker

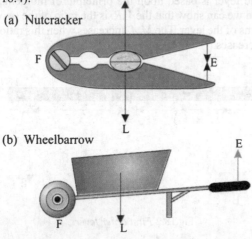

(b) Wheelbarrow

Fig. 18.4 Examples of second order levers.

Third order levers

In levers of this class, the effort E is between L and F. Examples include the forearm of a human body and a pair of laboratory tongs (see Fig. 18.5).

(a) Fore-arm

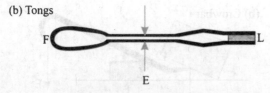

(b) Tongs

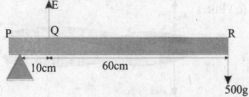

Fig. 18.5 Third order levers

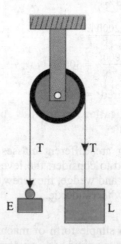

Fig. 18.6 Example 18.5

Example 18.5

In Fig. 18.6, $PQ = 10$cm and $QR = 60$cm; calculate the effort E.

Taking moments about P.

$$L \times 70 = E \times 10$$
$$L = 500g = 5N$$
$$so, 5 \times 70 = E \times 10$$
$$\therefore E = 35N$$

Example 18.6

What type or order of lever is shown in Fig. 18.5 opposite?

Since the effort is between load and the fulcrum, it is a third order lever.

Example 18.7

Which one of the following levers is not in the same order as the others in respect to the location of load, effort and fulcrum: a crowbar, a wheelbarrow, a common balance, a pair of scissors, a seesaw?

Only the wheelbarrow is a second order lever in which the load is between the fulcrum and effort, but all the others are first order levers where the fulcrum is between the effort and load.

Pulleys

A simple pulley is a fixed wheel with a rope passing round a groove in its rim. A load, L, is attached at one end of the rope while the effort, E, is applied at the other end. If we neglect friction at the wheels and the weight of the rope, then tension, T, in the rope will be the same throughout.

Therefore, when there is no friction, $L = T = E$.
The mechanical advantage $(M.A.) = 1 = V.R.$ if there is no friction present.

Next, consider a simple movable pulley as shown in Fig. 18.8. The velocity ratio is 2 because for every distance d the load rises, the effort has to be pulled far enough to take up a length $2d$ of rope (remember there are two vertical parts of the rope).

Fig 18.7 A fixed pulley

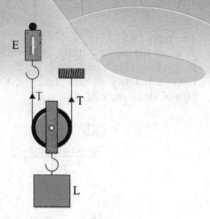

Fig. 18.8 A movable pulley

Systems of pulleys

Pulleys can be combined to form machines used for lifting loads. They are used by builders for hauling heavy loads to high floors or in loading and unloading ships. The aim of combining pulleys is to achieve a larger velocity ratio and thus also a higher mechanical advantage.

Figure 18.9 illustrates a number of practical pulley systems, with various velocity ratios.

In the system shown in Fig. 18.9(a) with two movable and two fixed pulleys, when E moves through a distance, d, L moves d/4, since there are four ropes supporting the load.

$$\therefore V.R. = \frac{d}{\frac{d}{4}}$$
$$= 4$$

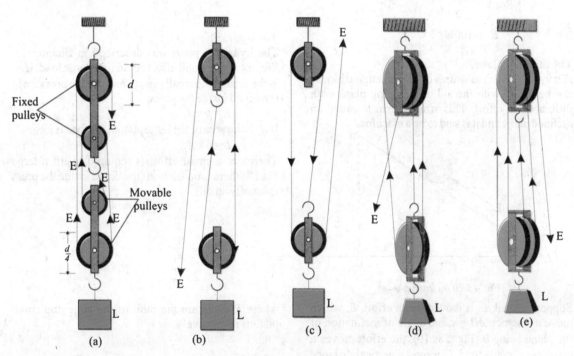

Fig. 18.9 Systems of pulleys

In general, it is shown that for a block and tackle with n strings supporting the load, the M.A. also increases as n increases.

     V.R. = n

If a greater load needs to be lifted, we can use more pulleys, thus increasing the M.A. However, this increased load increases friction at the axles, and also more pulleys have to be lifted, so that the efficiency is reduced.

With a particular pulley system, larger loads give greater efficiency because the weight of the pulley attached to the load is less, in proportion to the load.

Example 18.8

A block and tackle consisting of 5 pulleys is used to raise a load of 400N through a height of 10m. If the work done against friction is 1000J, calculate:
(a) the work done by the effort,
(b) the efficiency of the system,
(c) the effort applied.

(a) Work done by effort = work done in raising the load + work done against friction
$$= (400 \times 10) + 1000$$
$$= 5000J.$$

(b) Efficiency $= \dfrac{\text{work output}}{\text{work input}} \times 100\%$

$$= \frac{400 \times 10}{5000} \times 100\%$$

125

$$= \frac{4000}{5000} \times 100\%$$

$$= 80\%$$

(c) Since $\frac{M.A.}{V.R.} \times 100\% = \varepsilon$

$$M.A. = \frac{V.R. \times \varepsilon.}{100}$$

For a block and tackle with 5 pulleys
   $V.R. = 5$
   Also, $\varepsilon = 80\%$

$$M.A. = \frac{5 \times 80}{100}$$

$$M.A. = 4$$

$$M.A. = \frac{L}{E}$$

So, $4 = \frac{400}{E}$

$$E = 100N$$

The inclined plane

Heavy loads such as drums of oil and engine blocks can be raised with the aid of a sloping plank with little applied effort. This arrangement is called an inclined plane and it is said to be a machine.

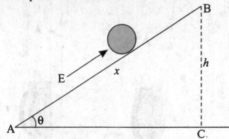

Fig. 18.10 Inclined plane

Suppose a load, L, is moved by an effort, E, which move a distance $AB = x$, the angle of inclination of the plane being θ (Fig. 18: 10), the effort moves a distance, x, while load, L, moves a vertical distance $h = BC$. Then the velocity ratio

$$= \frac{\text{distance moved by } E}{\text{distance moved by } L}$$

$$i.e. V.R. = \frac{AB}{BC}$$

$$= \frac{x}{h}$$

$$V.R. = \frac{1}{\sin \theta}$$

In general, the $V.R.$ and hence the $M.A.$ increases when θ decreases.

Another practical form of the inclined plane is the wedge. This is a small triangular block which is driven between two objects to force them apart. It is similar in action to the chisel, another inclined plane.

Example 18.9
What is the velocity ratio of an inclined plane of length 6m, if the higher end is 2m above the ground? If the efficiency of this plane used as machine is 60%. Calculate the $M.A.$

$$V.R. = \frac{1}{\sin \theta}$$

$$= \frac{\text{length of plane}}{\text{height}}$$

$$= \frac{6}{2}$$

$$= 3$$

$$\varepsilon = \frac{M.A.}{V.R.} \times 100\%$$

$$\therefore 60 = \frac{M.A.}{3} \times 100$$

$$M.A. = \frac{180}{100}$$

$$= 1.8$$

The hydraulic press

The hydraulic press was described in Chapter 15. We saw that a small effort could lift a large load. If A_1 is the area of the small piston, and p is the pressure in the liquid inside the press,

$$E = p \times A_1$$

If A_2 is the area of the large piston, the load is large

$$L = p \times A_2$$

Therefore a small effort is required to lift a large load. If there is no friction (the liquid inside the press is usually an oil).

$$M.A. = \frac{L}{E}$$

$$= \frac{A_2}{A_1}$$

$$= \frac{R^2}{r^2}$$

where R and r are the radii of the large and small pistons respectively.

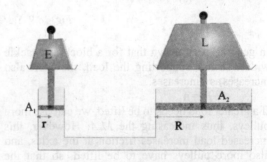

Fig. 18. 11 Hydraulic press

Also if x and y are the distances moved by E and L respectively, we have $A_1 x = A_2 y$

$$\therefore \quad \frac{x}{y} = \frac{A_2}{A_1} = V.R. = \frac{R^2}{r^2}$$

The screw

The screw can be thought of as an inclined plane wrapped round a cylinder to form a thread. The simplest example of a screw is a nut and bolt. As the nut is turned, it moves along the thread of the bolt as though travelling up an inclined plane (Fig. 18.12).

Fig. 18.12 The screw as an inclined plane

When a screw is turned through one complete revolution by the application of an effort, the load moves a distance equal to the pitch (Fig. 18.13(a)). The pitch p is the distance between consecutive threads.

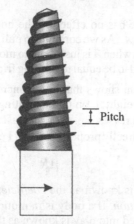

Fig. 18. 13 (a) The threads of a screw.

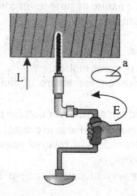

Fig. 18.13(b) Applying effort.

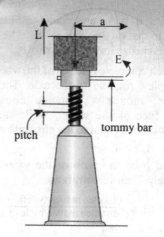

Fig. 18.13 (c) Screw jack

If the effort is applied by means of a handle, as for example, in the screw jack in fig. 18.13 (c), the velocity ratio can be worked out by finding the distances moved by the effort and the load in one complete revolution of the handle. If the length of the handle is a, distance moved by effort = $2\pi a$. The distance moved by the load is equal to the pitch p.

$$V.R. = \frac{2\pi a}{p}$$

Example 18.10

The pitch of the screw of a screw jack is 0.5cm. When used to raise a load, the handle turns through a circle of radius 40cm. What is the mechanical advantage of the jack if its efficiency is 25%? ($\pi = 3.14$)

Velocity ratio $(V.R) = \varepsilon = \dfrac{2\pi \times 40}{0.5}$

$\dfrac{M.A.}{V.R.} = \varepsilon = \dfrac{25}{100}$

$\therefore M.A. = \dfrac{25}{100} \times \dfrac{2\pi \times 40}{0.5}$

$= 125.6$

The wheel and axle

This machine, as shown in Fig. 18.14, consists of a large wheel P grooved to take a rope, and an axle Q also grooved.

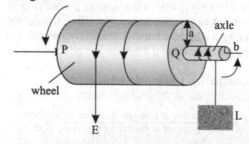

Fig. 18.14 The wheel and axle

The rope is fixed onto the wheel and wound round it, leaving a free end where an effort E is to be applied. The axle Q has a smaller diameter and the rope attached to it is wound round in the opposite direction to that on the large wheel. The load to be lifted is attached to its free end.

For each complete rotation of the wheel, there is one complete rotation of the axle. Therefore the effort, E, moves a distance equal to the circumference of the wheel, while the load, L, moves a distance equal to the circumference of the axle.

Let a and b be the radii of the wheel and axle respectively. Then velocity ratio

$$V.R. = \frac{\text{distance moved by effort}}{\text{distance moved by load}}$$

$$= \frac{2\pi a}{2\pi b}$$

$$= \frac{a}{b}$$

$\therefore$ Velocity ratio of the wheel and axle is given by:

$$V.R. = \frac{a}{b}$$

Example 18.11
A wheel and axle is used to raise a man of weight 700N by application of an effort 200N. If the radii of the wheel and axle are 400mm and 100mm respectively, determine the efficiency of the machine.

$$V.R. = \frac{a}{b}$$

$$= \frac{400}{100}$$

$$= 4$$

$$M.A. = \frac{L}{E}$$

$$= \frac{700}{200}$$

$$= \frac{7}{2}$$

$$\varepsilon = \frac{M.A.}{V.R.} \times 100\%$$

$$= \frac{7}{2} \times \frac{1}{4} \times 100\%$$

$$= 87.5\%$$

Gears
Gears work on the wheel and axle principle. The toothed wheels A drives the wheels B resulting in turning forces. If the number of teeth in the driven wheel B is x and the number in the driving wheel A is y, the velocity ratio of the system can be shown to be $\frac{x}{y}$.

For example if $x = 20$ and $y = 10$,
the velocity ratio of the gear system is:

$$V.R. = \frac{\text{Number of teeth ratio on the driven gear}}{\text{Number of teeth on the driving gear}}$$

$$= \frac{20}{10}$$

$$= 2$$

Other machines which work on wheel and axle principle are: the brace used by carpenters to bore holes on wood, screw driver, box spanner, etc.

18.4 Friction
Friction plays an important role in machines. Before we discuss the role, let us review friction briefly.

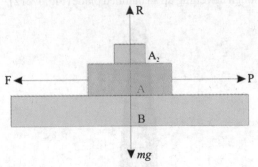

Fig. 18.15 Friction

Friction is defined as a force which acts at the surface of separation of two bodies in contact and tends to oppose the motion of one over the other.

If a body A is placed on another B, the normal reaction of B on A, R is equal and opposite the weight mg

$$\therefore R = mg$$

This force has no effect on the horizontal force P applied at A. As we continue to pull A with P, a stage will reach when A is just about to move and the value of P is said to be equal to limiting frictional force F.

Experiment shows that if A is increased by adding another weight A_2 on it, the limiting frictional force F or P increases, i.e. as R increases F increases so that F is directly proportional to R i.e. $F \propto R$.

$$F = \mu R$$

Where μ is known as the *coefficient of limiting or static friction*. If a body is in motion, the frictional force called into play is known as the coefficient of dynamic friction. It is found that in general, friction depends on the nature of surfaces in contact, and the normal reaction R.

To summarise:
(i) Friction opposes motion.
(ii) It depends on the nature of the surfaces in contact.
(iii) It depends on normal reaction $F = \mu R$.
(iv) It is independent of area in contact.
(v) It is independent of relative velocity between the surfaces.

The easiest way of determining μ is by use of inclined plane.

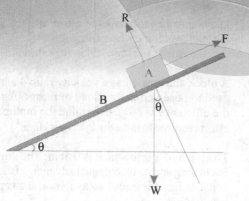

Fig. 18.16

A body *A* is placed on the inclined plane, *B* which is gradually increased until the body slips. It can be shown mathematically that the coefficient of static friction between *A* and *B* is $\mu = \tan\theta$ where θ is the inclination at the point of slip.

Proof: Let *R* be the normal reaction and *F* the limiting frictional force.

$$F = W\sin\theta$$
$$R = W\cos\theta$$
$$\therefore \frac{F}{R} = \mu$$
$$= \frac{W\sin\theta}{W\cos\theta}$$
$$= \tan\theta$$

Example 18.12

A body of mass 5kg is placed on a horizontal plane. It is found that a force of 10N applied horizontally to the body is just about to move it. Calculate the coefficient of friction between the body and the plane.

Limiting friction $F = 10$N
Normal reaction $R = 5$kg $= 50$N

$$\mu = \frac{F}{R}$$
$$= \frac{10}{50}$$
$$= 0.2$$

Example 18.13

A body of weight *W* is placed on a rough inclined plane of inclination. When the inclination is 30°, the body was about to slip. What is μ?

The coefficient of friction $\mu = \tan 30° = \frac{1}{\sqrt{3}} = 0.58$

Reducing friction in machines

We try to reduce friction in machines for two reasons:
(i) It causes wear.
(ii) It uses up energy and reduces the efficiency of the machine.

One way of reducing friction is to lubricate the surfaces which are sliding over each other with a liquid usually oil. Oil is less viscous as it gets hot, so it lubricates better when hot.

Another method of reducing friction is to use ball or roller bearing.

Summary

1. A machine is a contrivance by means of which an effort applied at one point can be used to overcome a load at some other point.
2. Examples of machine: pulley, screw, wheel and axle, inclined plane and lever.
3. Mechanical Advantage $M.A. = \frac{\text{Load}}{\text{Effort}}$.
4. Velocity Ratio $V.R. = \frac{\text{distance moved by effort}}{\text{distance moved by load}}$.
5. Efficiency $\varepsilon = \frac{\text{work output}}{\text{work input}} \times 100\%$
   $= \frac{M.A.}{V.R.} \times 100\%$
6. Velocity ratio of an inclined plane is $\frac{1}{\sin\theta}$. If there is no friction; θ is angle of inclination.
7. The *V.R.* of a screw $= \frac{2\pi a}{\text{pitch}}$.
8. Laws of solid friction:
   (i) Friction opposes motion.
   (ii) The limiting frictional force is independent of the area of contact of the given surfaces.
   (iii) The frictional force depends on the nature of the surfaces in contact.
   (iv) The limiting frictional force is proportional to the normal reaction for a given pair of surface,
   $F = \mu R$
   Where *F* = limiting frictional force.
   R = normal reaction.
   μ = coefficient of static friction, a constant.
9. Advantages of friction:
   (i) It makes walking and running on the ground possible without slipping.
   (ii) It enables vehicles to stop.
   (iii) It assists in gripping of belts in machines.
   (iv) It prevents ladders from sliding.
   (v) It is a means of converting mechanical energy to heat energy.
10. Disadvantages of friction:
    (i) It opposes motion.
    (ii) It reduces efficiency of machine.
    (iii) It causes wear and tear of moving parts.
    (iv) It causes unwanted heat in machines.
11. Methods of reducing friction:
    (i) Use of ball or roller bearings.
    (ii) By lubricating with oil.
    (iii) Smoothing/Polishing.
    (iv) Streamlining.
    (v) Road banking assists in reducing slide – ways friction.

1. A body of mass 40kg is given an acceleration of 10ms^2 on a horizontal ground for which μ=0.5. Calculate the force required to accelerate the body (take g = 10ms^{-2}).
   A. 200N   B. 300N   C. 400N   D. 600N

2. A body of mass 4kg is on the point of slipping down the plane inclined at 30°. What force, parallel to the plane will just move it up the plane?
   A. 100N   B. 80N   C. 40N   D. 20N

3. Which of the following is correct?
   A. Efficiency of a machine is always greater than 1.
   B. Mechanical advantage increases with increase in friction.
   C. Velocity ratio depends on friction.
   D. Efficiency decreases with increase in friction.

4. Which of the following is not correct? Simple examples of first order levers are:
   A. crowbar   B. claw hammer
   C. pliers   D. wheel barrow

5. What is the velocity ratio of the machine shown in Fig. 18.17?
   A 1.   B. 2   C. 3   D. 4

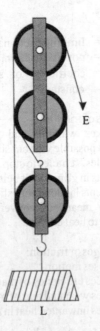

Fig. 18.17

6. Draw sketches to show the effort applied and the load overcome when using:
   (a) the arm (b) a hinged door (c) a shovel.

7. A block and tackle has a velocity ratio 4 and is used to raise vertically a load of mass 50kg. If the efficiency is 80%, determine the minimum effort required to raise the load (g = 10ms^{-2}).

8. The pitch of a screw jack is 0.5cm. The arm is 50cm long and its mechanical advantage is 250. What is its efficiency? (leave your answer in terms of π).

9. A screw jack of pitch 2.5cm is turned by a handle having a lever arm 40.5cm long. Neglecting friction, calculate its M.A.

10. An inclined plane of angle 30° is used as a simple machine. What is its velocity ratio?

11. In a hydraulic press, the areas of the small and the large pistons are 4cm^2 and 600cm^2 respectively. Find the velocity ratio of the machine. Assuming there is no friction, find the mechanical advantage.

HEAT ENERGY: MEASUREMENT OF TEMPERATURE

Chapter 19

19.1 Heat and temperature

Heat reminds us of a sensation of hotness.

Heat is a form of energy, called **thermal energy** that is normally transferred from one body to another as a result of temperature difference between the two bodies.

Heat is referred to as a form of energy because it can do some work. What work can heat do? It can cook our food, dry our clothes, warm our homes. Heat can also be used in industry to separate metals from ore, for shaping, softening, hardening, cutting, coating metals and removing tight lids from main bodies. Heat produced by burning fuel in engines causes vehicles to move. On the other hand,

temperature is the measure of degree of hotness or coldness of a body.

Table 19.1 Differences between heat and temperature

	Heat	Temperature
(i)	Heat is a form of energy.	Temperature is measure of degree of coldness or hotness of a body.
(ii)	Heat flows from a body at higher temperature to that at lower temperature.	Temperature does not flow.
(iii)	Heat can not be directly measured with any instrument, rather it can be calculated.	Temperature is measured by an instrument, called thermometer.
(iv)	Unit of heat is in Joule (J).	Units of temperature is in kelvin (K), degree centigrade (°C) and degree Farenheit (°F).
(v)	Heat can do some Work.	Temperature can do no work.

Heat produced by the sun which is received on earth, is referred to as **solar heat**. Heat could also be produced during chemical reaction. It could also be produced by rubbing two bodies.

Heat affects objects in various ways:
(i)   Heat can change both physical and chemical properties of an object.
(ii) It can alter (increase) the temperature of a body.
(iii) It can change the state a body (from solid to liquid and liquid to vapour).
(iv) It can cause the emission of electrons from the surface of a metal.
(v)   Addition of heat increases the pressure as well as volume of a gas.
(vi) It can also cause expansion of a conductive body.

Measurement of temperature

Temperature is measured by an instrument called **thermometer**. The various thermometers make use of thermometric substances which change with the change in temperature.

Table 19.2 Thermometer and their thermometric substances

Thermometers	Thermometric substance used	Physical property of the thermometric substance
(i) Mercury/ in-glass thermometer	Mercury	Increase in volume of mercury with increase in temperature.
(ii) Gas Thermometers	Gas	Pressure of gas at constant volume or volume of gas at constant pressure.
(iii) Thermo-electric thermometer	Current flowing	One junction of two dissimilar metals is heated.
(iv) Resistance thermometers	Resistance of a metal	Increase in the resistance of a metal wire when the the wire is heated.

Fixed points of thermometer

Two reference temperatures are important and should be noted before constructing the liquid-in-glass thermometers, these are called the fixed points.

The upper fixed point is the temperature of steam from pure water boiling at normal atmospheric pressure.

The lower fixed point is the temperature of a mixture of pure ice and water at normal pressure.

Scales of temperature

The temperature scale used globally in most scientific work is the Celsius or centigrade scale, in which the upper fixed point is chosen as 100°C and the lower fixed point is 0°C.

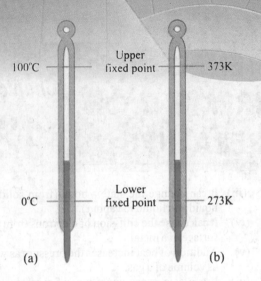

Fig. 19.1   Scales on a thermometer.

Fundamental interval is the interval between the lower and upper fixed points. On a celsius scale, this interval is divided into 100 equal parts and each defines one degree on this scale. On the other hand, on a Kelvin or absolute scale, which is used in *SI*, there exist a lowest possible temperature (absolute zero), below which nothing can be cooled. This absolute zero temperature is found to be at −273°C. Kelvin scale has no negative temperatures, here absolute zero is taken as its fixed point for zero. The upper fixed point (steam point) and the lower fixed point (ice point) are 373K and 273K respectively. Kelvin and Celsius temperatures, T and θ respectively are related by the equation $T = 273 + \theta$.

Example 19.1
Calculate the equivalent of 30°C and 50°C on a Kelvin scale.

Solution
Using $T = 273 + \theta$ and substituting yields;
   $T = 273 + 30 = 303K$
and $T = 273 + 50 = 323K$

Example 19.2
What is the equivalent of 300K on Celsius scale.

Solution
Using $T = 273 + \theta$ and substituting we get,
   $300 = 273 + \theta$
   $\therefore \ \theta = 300 - 273 = 27°C$

19.2. Construction and graduation of liquid-in-glass thermometer

The first step in constructing and graduating of a liquid-in-glass thermometer is to get a capillary tube of the same cross-sectional area throughout its length. One end of the tube is then sealed, and a bulb is blown at same end. Thereafter, the tube is left to cool, and using a funnel, mercury is poured into the

tube kept vertical. Trapped air in the tube is expelled by gently warming the bulb, after which the same procedure is repeated until more mercury is poured into the bulb. Finally, all air is expelled out of the glass tubing by boiling the mercury. The glass is then maintained at a temperature a little above the highest at which it will be used, and the top is sealed.

The icepoint is determined by placing the thermometer with its bulb in funnel of melting ice (Fig. 19.2(a)), and the steady level of mercury is marked *A*, *as the ice point*.

Next, the thermometer T is placed in a hyposometer, that contains water, a manometer M which measures the pressure of the steam obtained when water is boiled. T is placed with its bulb well above the water so that the mercury in the tube is all at the temperature of the steam. When the mercury level becomes steady, its position C is marked on the glass tube with a sharp file. The steam pressure is read from the manometer M.

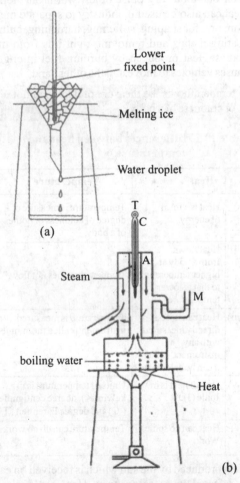

Fig. 19.2(a) and (b) Lower and upper fixed points.

Having determined both steam and ice points, then the distance between the two points is divided into 100 or 180 equal divisions according to the scale being used. These divisions are then graduated and calibrated, this is ready to be used as a liquid (mercury)-in-glass thermometer.

Precautions

(i)   The thermometer must be placed vertically both in the hypsometer and funnel of ice, to ensure accurate marking of the two points.

(ii) The thermometer must be placed well above water, this is to ensure that the temperature of water is not recorded which depends on temperature of impurities contained in water.

(iii) The pressure of steam must be 76cmHg otherwise the marking of *C* would require a minor correction since steam point is the temperature of steam at pressure of the mercury.

19.3   Types of thermometers and thermometric substances

There are many types of thermometers, each using a physical property which changes with change in temperature.

Examples

(a) The liquid-in-glass thermometer; uses liquid (mercury) as thermometric substance, in which the change in volume of the liquid measures the change in temperature.

(b) The gas thermometer; uses gas as thermometric substance, here, variation in gas pressure or volume causes change in temperature.

(c) The platinum resistance thermometer; change in resistance causes the change in temperature.

(d) The thermoelectric thermometer; here, change in current flow measures the change in temperature.

(e) The bimetallic strip thermometer; here, difference in expansion of two metals causes bending in the strip, which indicates change in temperature.

19.4   Working principles of various thermometers

Liquid-in-glass-thermometers

Most widely used is the mercury-in-glass thermometers; examples are the clinical thermometer and maximum and minimum thermometers. Clinical thermometer is used in determining the temperature of the human body.

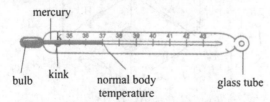

Fig. 19.3 A clinical thermometer

The range of clinical thermometer lies between 35°C to 45°C as the normal body temperature of human being ranges between the above range. It consists of a short tube with a narrow bore, which makes it possible for a small change in temperature to cause a large change in the length of the mercury column. There is a kink or constriction just above the bulb in the capillary tube. To record the temperature of a person, the thermometer is placed beneath the tongue or under the armpit or in the anus for some time. The mercury thread expands due to heat and passes the kink to the right, and indicates the body temperature when the thermometer is removed from the person's body, the mercury thread to the left of the kink recedes, but the column to the right remains in position owing to the constriction, by this means, the thermometer can still be read. Before the thermometer is used again, it is jerked vigorously to allow the mercury on the right of the constriction get into the tube.

Maximum and minimum thermometers

The maximum and minimum thermometers record the maximum and minimum temperatures over a period of time.

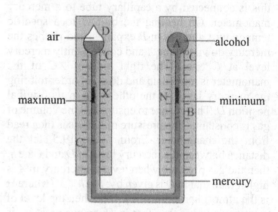

Fig.19.4 Combined maximum and minimum thermometer.

This consists of a large bulb *A* which is filled with alcohol, and is connected to a bent capillary tube which contains mercury along the part *BC*. Above *C* is alcohol, and *D* contains a little air. A steel index, *X* kept in position by a light spring is above C, and another index *N*, is above *B*. Since alcohol expands much more than mercury for the same temperature change, hence when temperature rises, the alcohol in *A* expands and flows past *N*, and the mercury at *C* rises and pushes *X* in front of it. At fall of temperature, alcohol in *A* contracts, and mercury column at *B* rises and pushes *N* in front of it. The maximum temperature on the scale shown is read from the lower end of *X*. Similarly, the lower end of *N* indicates the minimum temperature. After reading the temperatures, a magnet is used to reset each index above the mercury columns. The thermometer is ready for use, for the next day recording.

Gas thermometer

Constant-volume gas thermometer is a typical example of the above thermometer (Fig. 19.5).

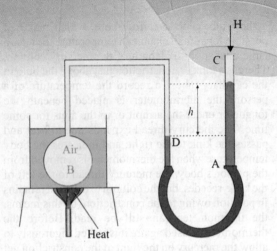

Fig. 19.5 Simple gas thermometer

Gas thermometers are basically used for very accurate temperature measurements. The operation utilises the fact that its temperature changes for a large volume change of gas. This thermometer is made up of a large glass bulb B containing air and this is connected by a capillary tube to a mercury manometer. On heating the bulb B to a specific temperature, the gas in B expands, and pushes the mercury down to tube A and consequently mercury level at C rises. The right side of AC of the manometer is moved up and down in order to bring the mercury level on the other side to its original position D. This is done to ensure that the volume of gas is constant. The pressure of the gas is then read from the manometer. From figure 19.5, let the distance between the mercury level in D and C be h, then the gas pressure when level of mercury in A is higher than that in D is given by; $P = h + H$ (where H is the atmospheric pressure). But when the level of mercury is lower than that in D the gas pressure is given by; $P = H - h$.

The thermometer is calibrated by first measuring the gas pressure at 0°C, when the bulb containing the gas is placed in pure melting ice. Its pressure at 100°C, is measured by placing it over steam. Then, finally a graph of pressure plotted against temperature, using these two measured points gives a straight line graph (Fig. 19.6).

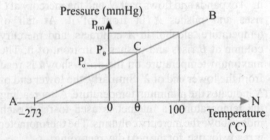

Fig. 19.6 Graph of pressure against temperature at constant volume.

The graph above could be employed in determining the temperature of a body at known pressure.

Example 19.3
Determine the temperature of a body from the graph of Fig. 19.6, when the pressure reads P.

Solution
Let the temperature be θ, and the pressure be P_θ. One immediately goes to the graph and marks the pressure P_θ, and draws a horizontal line which touches the line AB at C, then, a vertical line from C to horizontal line AN touches AN at the required temperature θ°C.

Example 19.4
A constant volume gas thermometer records pressure of a body as 300mm of Hg at 0°C and 400 mmHg at 100°C. Calculate the temperature of the body when the gas pressure reads 350mmHg.

Solution
Let the temperature be θ°C, then using

$$\theta°C = \frac{P_\theta - P_o}{P_{100} - P_o} \times \frac{100}{1} \qquad 19.1$$

Where P_o = pressure at 0°C = 300mmHg
P_{100} = pressure at 100°C = 400mmHg
P_θ = pressure at θ°C = 350mmHg

Using equation 19.1 above and substituting we get,

$$\theta°C = \frac{350-300}{400-300} \times \frac{100}{1}$$

$$= \frac{50}{100} \times 100$$

$$= 50°C$$

The temperature of the body is 50°C.

Resistance thermometer

One example of resistance thermometer is the platinum resistance thermometer. The thermometric property used in this thermometer is the resistance of a coil of the platinum wire. The working principle is based on the fact that for a metallic conductor, the electrical resistance changes proportionally with its temperature.

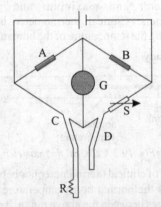

Fig.19.7 Resistance thermometer

The resistance R of the platinum coil is measured employing wheatstone bridge circuit. Measurement at 0°C, 100°C and at required temperature (θ°C) are taken and recorded as R_0, R_{100} and R_θ respectively.

The temperature scale for this resistance is defined as;

$$\theta\,°C = \frac{R_\theta - R_0}{R_{100} - R_0}$$

R_0 = resistance of the platinum coil at 0°C (ice point)

R_{100} = resistance of the platinum coil at 100°C (steam point)

R_θ = resistance of the platinum coil at temperature of θ°C (unknown temperature)

Example 19.5

A platinum resistance thermometer measures a resistance of 3 ohms at 0°C, 4.5 ohms at 100°C. Calculate the temperature when the resistance is 3.5 ohms.

Solution

using $\theta\,°C = \dfrac{R_\theta - R_0}{R_{100} - R_0}$ 19.2

Where R_θ is the resistance (3.5 ohms) at temperature θ°C.

Substituting yields; $\theta\,°C = \dfrac{3.5-3.0}{4.5-3.0} \times \dfrac{100}{1}$

$$= \frac{0.5}{1.5} \times \frac{100}{1}$$

$$\theta = 33.3\,°C$$

Thermoelectric thermometer

This thermometer utilises the principle of thermocouple. Thermocouple consists of two dissimilar metals, copper and constantan, or copper and iron or iron and constantan, joined together at one end A, (fig 19.8 (a), 19.8(b)) and connected to a galvanometer (G) which measures current flow. This current depends on the temperature difference between the cold and the hot junction.

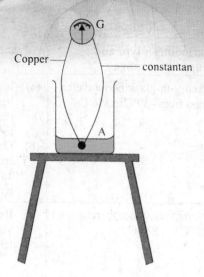

Fig. 19.8 (a) Thermocouple

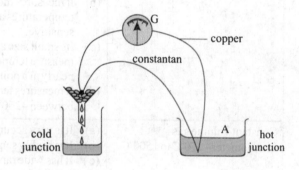

Fig. 19.8 (b) Thermoelectric thermometer

Thermoelectric thermometers are usually employed in industry for measuring very high temperatures. The G measures the temperature of the hot junction directly.

Pyrometer is another type of thermometer, that utilizes the laws governing radiation from a hot body.

19.5   Comparison of types of thermometers

Table 19.3 Advantages and disadvantages of some thermometers

Thermometer type and Temperature range	Advantages	Disadvantages
Mercury-in-glass thermometer, ranges from −39°C to 356°C	(a) It's silvery colour, makes it opaque, therefore easily seen, and temperature easily read. (b) Does not evaporate easily. (c) Its conductivity allows it to respond more rapidly to temperature changes.	(a) Freezes at −39°C, therefore can not be used for measuring lower temperature. (b) Very fragile, needs to be handle with great care. (c) Not very accurate.
Platinum resistance thermometer −180°C to 1520°C	(a) It measures accurately very low and high temperatures.	(a) Because of the time involved in its attaining thermal equilibrium with its surrounding, it is not suitable for measurement of rapid changes in temperature.
Thermoelectric thermometer −250°C to 1155°C	(a) It has a wide range of temperature. (b) It measures momentary temperatures and is very sensitive. (c) Its small size allows it to measure temperatures nearly at a point. (d) It measures temperatures between −250°C to 1100°C.	(a) Anytime the flow of current is affected by sensitivity of the galvanometer, the temperature measurement is affected.
Constant volume gas thermometer −270°C to 1500°C	(a) It is very accurate. (b) It is highly sensitive. (c) It has wide range. (d) It is used in calibrations of other types of thermometers.	(a) It is cumbersome, and therefore cannot be used in measurement of small volumes of liquids etc. (b) The knowledge of the pressure of the gas at the fixed points must be known any time the instrument is to be used.

Table 19.4 Comparison of mercury and alcohol as thermometric substance

	Mercury		Alcohol	
Property	Disadvantages	Advantages	Advantages	Disadvantages
Freezing	Freezes at −39°C therefore cannot be used for measuring very low temperatures.		Freezes at −115°C, can be used for measuring low temperatures.	
Expansivity	Low expansivity		Expansivity of about six times that of mercury.	
Evaporation		Not easily vaporised		Vaporises easily.
Opacity		Its silvery colour makes it opaque therefore, easily seen.		Not easily seen, it has to be coloured.
Conductivity		Has much greater conductivity than alcohol, therefore responds more rapidly to temperature changes.		Has poor conductivity therefore, responds slowly to change in temperature.

19.6 Temperature scales of thermometers and conversion from one temperature scale to another

The temperature scales have been discussed in section 19.1, what remains now is to convert from one temperature scale to another. The relationship between any temperature on one scale and another could easily be established by simply remembering the fixed points of each scale. For example, the relationship between centigrade ($^{\circ}$C), Farenheit ($^{\circ}$F) and Kelvin (K) scales could be got as follows:

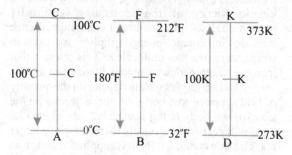

Fig. 19.9 Conversion from one temperature scale to another.

From fig. 19.9, above, the interval AC on the centigrade temperature scale is equal to that of BF, and DK on Farenheit and Kelvin scales respectively. This means that:

$$\frac{C-0}{100-0} = \frac{F-32}{212-32}$$

$$= \frac{K-273}{373-273}$$

i.e. $\quad \frac{C}{100} = \frac{F-32}{180} = \frac{K-273}{100} \qquad 19.3$

we can derive standard formulae between $^{\circ}$C and $^{\circ}$F using equation (19.3)

i.e. $180C = 100(F-32)$,

$$\therefore C = \frac{100}{180}(F-32)$$

$$\therefore C = \frac{5}{9}(F-32)$$

Similarly; $100F = 180C + 3200$

$$\therefore F = \frac{9}{5}C + 32$$

Also $100^{\circ}C = 100K - 27300$

$$\therefore C = K - 273 \text{ or}$$
$$K = C + 273$$

Rather than trying to remember the conversion formula, it is best to remember the fixed points of each scale and hence the relative size of the degrees. The following worked examples illustrate the steps.

Example 19.6

Convert 20°C, - 40°C to Farenheit scale and **Kelvin** scale.

Solution (a)

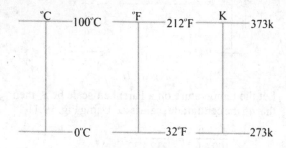

Fig. 19.10

Using $\quad \frac{C}{100} = \frac{F-32}{180}$ and substituting yields;

$$\frac{20}{100} = \frac{F-32}{180} \; ;$$

$$100(F-32) = 3600$$
$$F - 32 = 36,$$
$$\therefore F = 36 + 32 = 68^{\circ}F$$

(b) Also $\quad \frac{-40}{100} = \frac{F-32}{180}$,

i.e. $100(F-32) = -7200$
$\quad F - 32 = -72$
$\therefore F = -72 + 32 = -40^{\circ}F$

Therefore $20^{\circ}C \equiv 68^{\circ}F$ and $-40^{\circ}F \equiv -40^{\circ}C$.

Alternatively using $F = \frac{9}{5}C + 32$ and substituting yields

$$F = \left(\frac{9}{5}\right)20 + 32 = 68^{\circ}F,$$

and $F = \left(\frac{9}{5}\right)(-40) + 32 = -40^{\circ}F.$

Converting to Kelvin scale we use

$$\frac{C}{100} = \frac{K-273}{100},$$

i.e. $\quad \frac{20}{100} = \frac{K-273}{100}$

i.e. $100(K - 273) = 2000$
$K = 20 + 273 = 293K$

Similarly for -40°C, we have;

$$\frac{-40}{100} = \frac{K-273}{100},$$

i.e. $100(K - 273) = -4000$
$\therefore K = 273 - 40 = 233K$

Example 19.7

At what temperature on a Farenheit scale will the temperature on a Centigrade scale be doubled of that on a Farenheit scale?

Solution

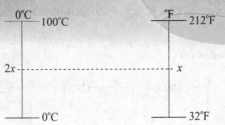

Fig. 19.11

Let the temperature on a Farenheit scale be x, then that on the centigrade scale is $2x$. Using Fig. 19.11,

$$\frac{2x-0}{100-0} = \frac{x-32}{212-32}$$

i.e. $\dfrac{2x}{100} = \dfrac{x-32}{180}$

i.e. $100(x-32) = 360x$

$100x - 3200 = 360x$

$\therefore -3200 = 260x$

$\therefore x = \dfrac{3200}{260}$

$= -12.3°F$

Thus, $2x = -24.6°C$

On a farenheit scale, the temperature is $-12.3°F$.
On a centigrade scale, the temperature is $-24.6°C$.

Example 19.7

The upper fixed and lower fixed point of a certain thermometer are marked $110°$ and $-10°$ respectively. What temperature on a centigrade thermometer will be four times that on this thermometer?

Solution

Let the temperature on this thermometer be y, then on a °C scale, it is $4y$.

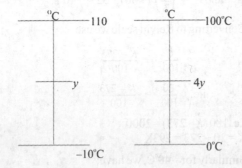

Fig. 19.12

From Fig. 19.12,

$$\frac{y-(-10)}{110-(-10)} = \frac{4y-0}{100-0}$$

i.e. $\dfrac{y+10}{110+10} = \dfrac{4y}{100}$,

$\dfrac{y+10}{120} = \dfrac{4y}{100}$

$100y + 1000 = 480y$

$380y = 1000$

$\therefore y = 2.63°C, 4y = 10.53°C$

Temperature on a °C scale $= 10.5°C$.

19.7 Molecular explanation of temperature

The molecules that make up a solid vibrate about a fixed position. When heat is applied to the solid, the amplitude of vibration of these molecules become larger, and invariably their kinetic energy (*K.E.*) increases. From kinetic theory, the total translational kinetic energy of the molecules is directly proportional to the absolute temperature, hence increase in kinetic energy implies increase in temperature of the molecules. This means that increase in temperatures means increase in kinetic energy and verse versa. Both depend on the quantity of heat supplied to a body. All these depend on the mass of the body being heated, a body of smaller mass will get heated up easily than that with a larger mass if same quantity of heat is supplied. This is true because the number of molecules contained in the former is less than that contained in the latter.

Summary

1. Temperature is the measure of degree of hotness or coldness of a body while heat is a form of energy called thermal energy.

2. Thermometric substances are substances that different types of thermometers make use of, which change with change in temperature.

3. The lower and upper fixed points are the temperature of mixture of pure ice and water, and steam from pure boiling water at normal atmospheric pressures respectively.

4. Conversion of temperature from one scale to another requires the knowledge of the fixed points.

5. Most liquid-in-glass thermometers use mercury as thermometric substance, gas thermometer uses gas, resistance thermometer uses change in resistance that causes change in temperature, while thermoelectric thermometer uses change in current flow with change in temperature.

6. In molecular explanation of temperature; increase in temperatures implies increase in kinetic energy of the molecules and vice versa.

Exercise 19

1. Mercury is preferred to water as a thermometric liquid because:
   A. mercury has a lower boiling point than water.
   B. mercury has uniform thermal expansion.
   C. mercury has a lower coefficient of expansion in relation to glass than water.
   D. mercury does not wet glass.

138

2. Thermoelectric thermometers are used in industry because
   A. they measure very high temperatures.
   B. other types of thermometers are not convenient in use in industry.
   C. they are very responsive to temperature variations.
   D. A and C only.

3. Convert $-10°C$ to $°F$.
   A. $40°F$ B. $50°F$ C. $14°F$ D. $28°F$

4. A thermometer has its stem marked in millimetre instead of degree celsius. The lower fixed point is 30mm and the upper fixed point is 180mm. Calculate the temperature in degree Celsius when the thermometer reads 45mm. (SC/GCE)
   A. $67.5°C$ B. $30.0°C$
   C. $10.0°C$ D. $15.0°C$

5. Which of the following features does not increase the sensitivity of a liquid in-glass thermometer?

   A. A thick-walled tube.
   B. A capillary tube with a narrow bore.
   C. A thin-walled bulb.
   D. A liquid with a high expansivity. (SSCE/GCE)

6. Distinguish between heat and temperature. A mercury-in-glass thermometer reads $-20°C$ at the ice point and $100°C$ at steam point. Calculate the Celsius temperature corresponding to $70°$ on the thermometer. (SSCE/GCE)

(a) State at least three precautions needed in construction and graduation of liquid-in-glass thermometer.

(b) List at least four types of thermometers and state the physical property on which the thermometric substance each is using is based upon.

7. A constant volume gas thermometer records pressure of a body as 250mm of Hg at $0°C$ and 350mmHg at $100°C$. Calculate the temperature of the body when the gas pressure reads 300mmHg.

8. What are advantages of mercury over alcohol as a thermometric substance?
   (b) State advantages and disadvantages of constant volume gas thermometer over other types of thermometer.

9. Convert:
   (a) $80°C, -30°C$ to $°F$ and Kelvin.
   (b) $-40°F, 70°F$ to $°C$ and Kelvin.
   (c) When is the temperature on a centigrade scale thermometer will be five times that on a Farenheit scale?

10. Describe briefly the working of thermoelectric thermometer. State some of its advantages and disadvantages.

MEASUREMENT OF HEAT ENERGY

Chapter 20

20.1 Specific heat and thermal capacity of a body

Heat is a form of energy called thermal energy that flows due to temperature difference. Heat can be used to do some work, and could also be transformed from one form to another. The unit of heat is **Joule**. Addition of heat to a body causes the temperature to rise, but as the heat is removed the temperature falls.

Specific heat capacity of material

It has long been discovered that the quantity of heat (Q) received by a body is directly proportional to its mass (m), change in temperature ($\theta_2 - \theta_1$) and also on nature of the material of which the body is made up of. Stating this mathematically we can write;

$$Q \propto m\,(\theta_2 - \theta_1)$$

$$\text{or } Q = mc\,(\theta_2 - \theta_1) \qquad 20.1$$

Where c is the proportionality constant which depends on the material of which the body is made up of, c is called the specific heat capacity of the body.

From equation 20.1, we can define c as;

$$\frac{Q}{m(\theta_2 - \theta_1)} \qquad 20.2$$

Unit of c is J $kg^{-1}K^{-1}$. (Because unit of mass is kilogram (kg), temperature in kelvin(K)).

> The specific heat capacity of a substance is the quantity of heat required to raise the temperature of unit mass (1kg) of a substance through a degree rise in temperature (i.e. 1°C or 1K).

Specific heat capacity of water is 4200$Jkg^{-1}K^{-1}$ (or 4.2 $Jg^{-1}K^{-1}$ when the mass is in grams), it is observed that the specific heat capacity of water is higher than that of most other substances.

Specific heat capacities of some substances are given in table 20.1.

Table 20.1 Specific heat capacities of some substances

Substance	c in $Jkg^{-1}K^{-1}$
Lead	130
Mercury	140
Brass	380
Zinc	380
Copper	400
Iron	450
Glass	670
Aluminium	900
Ice	2 100
Methylated spirit	2 400
Sea-water	3 900
Water	4 200

The Heat Capacity (C)

When an entire mass of a body is taken into consideration instead of a unit mass, we talk of heat capacity. When the temperature is raised by 1K that is $\theta_2 - \theta_1$ is unit, then quantity of heat C is given by $C = mc$, this is called the heat capacity C.

> The heat capacity of a body is the quantity of heat required to raise the temperature of the entire body through one degree rise in temperature (1K).

Unit of C is in Joule per Kelvin (JK^{-1}).

Example 20.1

Calculate the mass of iron with heat capacity of 900 $Jkg^{-1}K^{-1}$.

Solution

Specific heat capacity of iron = 450$Jkg^{-1}K^{-1}$ using heat capacity $C = mc$ and substituting yields:

$$900 = m \times 450$$

$$m = \frac{900}{450}$$

$$= 2.0 kg$$

Example 20.2
What quantity of heat is needed to raise the temperature of 20kg of aluminium through 10K?

Solution
Specific heat capacity of aluminium is $900\,Jkg^{-1}K^{-1}$
Using $Q = mc(\theta_2 - \theta_1)$ and substituting we get,
$Q = 20 \times 900 \times 10 = 180000\,J$ or $18 \times 10^4\,J$.

Example 20.3
What is the heat capacity of 20kg of brass?

Solution
Specific heat capacity of brass is $380\,Jkg^{-1}K^{-1}$
$C = mc = 20 \times 380 = 7600\,JK^{-1}$.

20.2 Measurement of specific heat capacity
Quantity of heat Q is usually obtained using a calorimeter. The most common method used in calorimeter experiment is known as the method of mixtures, another method usually employed is electrical method.

Transfer of heat
When a hot metallic object is dropped into a copper vessel containing known mass of water at lower temperature, heat continues to pass from the metallic object to the copper vessel and water, until the temperature of the three items (hot metallic object, copper vessel and water) are the same. The hot metallic object loses heat, while the copper vessel and water gain heat. When they finally come to a steady temperature (same temperature), then we can equate heat lost by hot metallic object to be equal to the heat gained by the copper vessel and water. This is referred to as *heat transfer*.

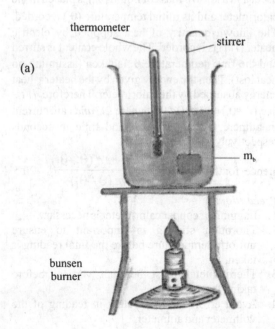

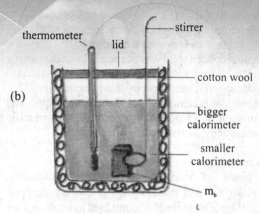

Fig. 20.1 (a) and (b) Determination of specific heat capacity of a solid by method of mixtures.

Measurement of specific heat capacity of a solid by method of mixtures

The apparatus is as seen in figure 20.1. The calorimeter and the stirrer are weighted empty and the weight recorded. Then, the weight of the calorimeter which is then two-thirds filled with water and the stirrer are weighed and recorded, too. The metal block is weighed (m_b), the initial temperature of cold water say θ_1 is taken. The metal block is put inside a boiling water and the temperature of boiling water is recorded, which is the temperature of the hot metal block say θ_2 (fig. 20.1 (a)). The metal block is quickly transferred to the lagged calorimeter containing water, (fig. 20.1 (b)). The whole content is stirred until all the content come to a final steady temperature. The final temperature of the mixture is taken, say θ_f. At this final steady temperature, heat lost by hot metal = heat gained by water and calorimeter.

Hence $m_b c(\theta_2 - \theta_f) = M_c c_c(\theta_f - \theta_1) + M_w c_w(\theta_f - \theta_1)$

$$\therefore C = \frac{M_c c_c(\theta_f - \theta_1) + M_w c_w(\theta_f - \theta_1)}{m_b(\theta_2 - \theta_f)} \quad 20.3$$

Where c is specific heat capacity of the metal block and $M_w c_w$ and $M_c c_c$ are the mass and specific capacity of water and calorimeter respectively.
Consequently heat capacity is *mc*.

Precautions that need to be taken during the experiment
1. Lagging of calorimeter is necessary.
2. Thorough stirring of mixtures before taking readings must be ensured.
3. There must be quick transfer of heated metal to calorimeter.
4. Shake off surplus water from hot metal before transferring to calorimeter.
5. Use sufficient water in calorimeter to ensure hot metal is completely covered by water after transfer.

Specific heat capacity of a liquid

In determining the specific heat capacity of a liquid the experiment so described above may be employed, but a solid whose specific heat capacity is known is used and water is replaced by the liquid whose specific heat capacity is to be determined. Alternative method involves heating the liquid and pouring it in a lagged container of known specific heat capacity, here no solid is required.

Example 20.4

A piece of iron, of specific heat capacity, $0.04 Jkg^{-1}K^{-1}$ and mass 400kg, is quickly dropped into 30kg of water at $10^\circ C$ contained in a calorimeter of 120kg mass and c of $0.1 J kg^{-1}K^{-1}$. If the temperature of the mixture is $30^\circ C$, calculate the initial temperature of the hot iron.

Solution

Using heat lost by iron = heat gained by water and calorimeter.

Let the temperature of the hot iron be θ_3, steady temperature be θ_2

We have; $m_i c_i (\theta_3 - \theta_2) = m_w c_w (\theta_2 - \theta_1) + m_c c_c (\theta_2 - \theta_1)$.

i.e.

$400 \times 0.04 \times (\theta_3 - 30) = 30 \times 4200 \times 20 + 120 \times 0.1 \times 20$

$16\theta_3 - 480 = 2520000 + 240$

$$\therefore \theta_3 = \frac{2520720}{16}$$

$$= 157545 K$$

Determination of specific heat capacity of a solid by electrical method

The apparatus is as shown in fig. 20.2.

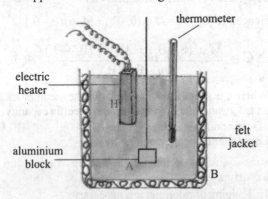

Fig. 20.2 Determination of specific heat capacity of a solid by electrical method.

The heat capacity and specific heat capacity of a solid (e.g. metal block) can be found by electrical method, as shown in fig. 20.2.

A metal block of known mass is thermally insulated from its surrounding and a certain quantity of energy is given to it by electric heater, placed in a hole in the metal block. The temperature difference

$(\theta_2 - \theta_1)$ inside a second hole bored in the metal block (assuming no heat lost) is recorded. Then energy given by electrical heater is IVt (where V is voltage supply, I is the current that passed in time t seconds). Energy gained (absorbed) by the metal block is $mc(\theta_2 - \theta_1)$, therefore, energy given by the electric heater = energy gained by metal, hence,

$$c = \frac{IVt}{m(\theta_2 - \theta_1)} \quad Jkg^{-1}K^{-1} \qquad 20.4$$

Precautions

1. Lagging of metal is necessary.
2. Accurate reading of the current, voltage and time must be taken.

Determination of specific capacity of a liquid by electrical method

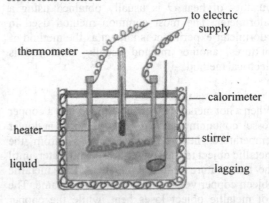

Fig. 20.3 The specific heat capacity of a liquid by the electrical method

The specific capacity of a liquid can be found by passing a current through a heating coil immersed in the liquid. A calorimeter of known heat capacity is used, and a known mass of liquid (m_l) is placed in the calorimeter and its initial temperature (θ_1) recorded. The known quantity of heat supplied by electric heater (IVt) is recorded. The whole content is stirred and the final temperature θ_2 is taken (assuming no heat lost). Then the energy given by the heater = heat energy absorbed by the calorimeter. Therefore, $IVt = m_l c_l (\theta_2 - \theta_1) + m_c c_c (\theta_2 - \theta_1)$, where $I, V,$ and t are current in ampere, voltage in volt and time in seconds respectively.

Hence, for the liquid $c = \dfrac{IVt - m_c c_c (\theta_2 - \theta_1)}{m_l (\theta_2 - \theta_1)}$ 20.5

Precautions

1. Lagging of copper calorimeter is necessary.
2. Thorough stirring is important to ensure uniform temperature before the final reading is taken.
3. Thermometer must be kept vertical before taking the reading.
4. Avoid error due to parallax in reading of the voltmeter and ammeter.

Example 20.5

A liquid of specific heat capacity $3Jg^{-1}K^{-1}$ or $3000Jkg^{-1}$ rises from 15°C to 65°C in one minute when an electric heater is used. If the heater generates 63kJ per minutes, calculate the mass of the liquid.

Solution

Heat gained by liquid = heat supplied by heater
i.e. mct (for liquid) = IVt (for heater)
$63kJ = 63 \times 10^3 J$
$IVt = 63 \times 10^3 J$
$\therefore m \times 300 \times (65 - 15) = 63 \times 10^3$
$\therefore m = \dfrac{63 \times 10^3}{3 \times 5 \times 10^4}$

$= 0.42kg$
Hence, $m = 0.42kg$

Example 20.6

A certain metal of mass 1.5kg at initial temperature of 27°C, absorbed heat from electric heater of 75W rating for 4 minutes. If the final temperature was 47°C, calculate the specific heat capacity of the metal, hence its heat capacity.

Solution

Heat supplied by electric heater = heat gained by the metal.

Hence, $IVt = mc(\theta_2 - \theta_1)$
i.e. Power = $IV = 75 W$
time = 4mins = $60 \times 4 = 240$ seconds
$\therefore 75 \times 240 = 1.5 \times 20 \times c$
$\therefore c = \dfrac{75 \times 240}{1.5 \times 20}$

$= 600 Jkg^{-1}K^{-1}$
mc = heat capacity = $1.5 \times 600 = 900JK^{-1}$.

20.3 Latent heat

When heat is supplied to a solid (e.g. Ice), its temperature rises steadily until a certain temperature is reached, then the solid begins to melt. During the course of melting, the temperature of the substance remains steady even though the heat is being supplied to it. This heat, which is not visible even as the rise in the temperature of the body occurs, but remains hidden, is known as **latent heat of fusion** or **hidden heat.**

Latent heat of fusion is the heat energy required to convert a substance from its solid form to its liquid form without change in temperature.

When water is heated from a known temperature to its boiling point, (100°C), when more heat is supplied at this boiling temperature, it continues to boil without change in temperature.

This hidden heat is known as **Latent heat of vaporisation.** This heat is used in changing the liquid to vapour, this latent heat depends on the mass of the liquid and the nature of liquid.

The specific latent heat of fusion of a substance is the quantity of heat required to change unit mass of a substance from solid to liquid without change of temperature.

The symbol for specific latent heat of fusion is l. Its unit is derived as follows:
If Q = quantity of heat (in joules)
m = mass of substance (in kg)
$$Q = m \times l$$
$$\therefore l = \frac{Q}{m}$$

The unit of specific latent heat is joules per kilogram Jkg^{-1}.

The specific latent heat of vaporisation of a substance is the quantity of heat required to change unit mass of substance from liquid to vapour without change of temperature.

Example 20.7

How much heat energy is required to change 10kg of ice to water at 0°C? Specific latent heat of fusion of ice = $336kJkg^{-1}$.
$$Q = m \times l$$
$$= 10 \times 336000$$
$$= 3.36 \times 10^6 J.$$

Example 20.8

If $1.13 \times 10^6 J$ of heat energy is required to convert 15kg of steam to water, calculate the specific latent heat of vaporization of steam.
$$Q = m \times l$$
$$1.13 \times 10^6 = 15\,l$$
$$\therefore l = \frac{1.13 \times 10^6}{15}$$
$$= 75333.3 = 7.53 \times 10^4 Jkg^{-1}$$

20.4 Determination of specific latent heat of fusion of ice

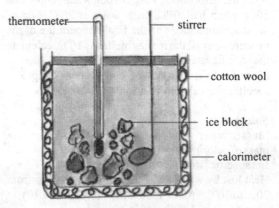

Fig. 20.4 Latent heat of fusion.

Pieces of ice are dried with blotting paper and dropped in weighed calorimeter, containing water of known mass and known temperature (θ_1). The mixture is stirred throughout the experiment. More pieces of ice are added until the temperature of the mixture falls to about 10°C below the room temperature, say θ_2. The whole content is reweighed to find the mass of the ice. The specific latent heat of fusion of ice is calculated as follows.

Let:

m_1 = mass of empty calorimeter

m_2 = mass of calorimeter and water

m_3 = mass of calorimeter + water + ice

θ_1 = temperature of warm water

θ_2 = temperature of water after all the ice has melted

c_c = specific heat capacity of calorimeter

c_w = specific heat capacity of water

l = specific latent heat of ice

Mass of water = $m_2 - m_1$

Mass of ice = $m_3 - m_2$

Heat lost by calorimeter and water in cooling from θ_1 to $\theta_2 = [(m_1 c_c + (m_2 - m_1)c_w \times (\theta_1 - \theta_2)]$

Heat gained by ice in melting to water at 0°C
$= (m_3 - m_2)l$

Heat gained by melted ice when its temperature rises from 0°C to $\theta_2 = (m_3 - m_2) c_w \theta_2$

Total heat gained = heat lost

$(m_3 - m_2)l + (m_3 - m_2) c_w \theta_2.$

$= [m_1 c_c + (m_2 - m_1)c_w](\theta_1 - \theta_2)$

$$l = \frac{[m_1 c_c + (m_2 - m_1)c_w](\theta_1 - \theta_2) - (m_3 - m_2)c_w \theta_2}{(m_3 - m_2)} (Jkg^{-1})$$

Precautions

(a) Each piece of ice must be dried before it is put into the calorimeter.

(b) The ice should be added in small quantities.

(c) The calorimeter should be lagged.

(d) Stirring is important to ensure uniformity in temperature.

Example 20.9

A copper calorimeter weighs 100g when empty and 500g when half filled with water at 20°C. 50g of dried ice are added and the final temperature of the mixture after all the ice has melted is 10°C. calculate the specific latent heat of fusion of ice.

(Specific heat capacity of copper is 400Jkg⁻¹K⁻¹, specific heat capacity of water = 4200Jkg⁻¹K⁻¹).

Solution

Mass of water = 500g – 100g = 400g = 0.4kg

mass of calorimeter = 0.1kg

Let specific latent heat of fusion of ice be l

Heat lost by water and calorimeter in cooling from 20°C to 10°C = (0.4 x 4200 x 10) + (0.1 x 400 x 10)

$= 16800 + 400$

$= 17200J$

Heat gained by ice in melting at 0°C
$= 0.05 \times l = 0.05 l$

Heat gained by melted ice when its temperature rises from 0°C to 10°C = 0.05 x 4200 x 10 = 2100J.

Total heat gained = heat lost

$0.05l + 2100 = 17200$

$\therefore 0.05l = 17200 - 2100$

$$l = \frac{15100}{0.05}$$

$= 302000$

$= 302 \times 10^3 Jkg^{-1}$

Determination of specific latent heat of vaporisation of steam

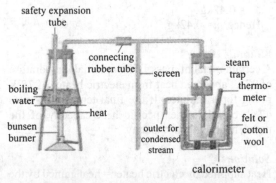

Fig. 20.5 Latent heat of steam.

The experiment is carried out using the set up in fig. 20.5. The calorimeter is weighed empty and mass recorded. Dry steam is passed into the lagged calorimeter containing water, the temperature of water rises by about 25°C. When the steam is removed, then, the content is stirred continuously until a final steady temperature is reached. Then, the whole content is reweighed in order to obtain the mass of the steam. The specific latent heat of steam is thus calculated as follows:

m_1 = mass of calorimeter empty

m_2 = mass of calorimeter + water

m_3 = mass of calorimeter + water + steam

θ_1 = initial temperature of calorimeter and contents

θ_2 = final temperature of calorimeter and contents

c = specific heat capacity of calorimeter

c_w = specific heat capacity of water

l = specific latent heat of steam

Temperature of steam is assumed to be 100°C

Mass of water = $m_2 - m_1$

Mass of steam = $m_3 - m_2$

Heat lost by steam in condensing = $(m_3 - m_2)l$

Heat lost by condensed steam in cooling from 100°C to $\theta_2 = (m_3 - m_2)(100 - \theta_2)c_w$

Heat gained by water and calorimeter during the experiment = $[(m_2 - m_1)c_w + m_1 c)](\theta_2 - \theta_1)$

Heat lost = heat gained

$(m_3 - m_2)[l + (100 - \theta_2)c_w] = [(m_2 - m_1)c_w + m_1 c](\theta_2 - \theta_1)$

Hence l is given by:

$$l = \frac{[(m_2-m_1)\,c_w + m_1 c](\theta_2 - \theta_1) - (m_3 - m_2)(100 - \theta_2)c_w}{(m_3 - m_2)}$$

Precautions

1. The calorimeter should be lagged.
2. Steam must be dried.
3. The temperature of water in the calorimeter must be below room temperature before steam is added. After the steam has been added, the temperature of the mixture must be the same number of degrees above room temperature.

Example 20.10

What quantity of heat is needed to melt 120g of ice at -20°C to water at 30°C? (Take c of water to be $4200 \text{Jkg}^{-1}\text{K}^{-1}$, c for ice = $2100 \text{ Jkg}^{-1}\text{k}^{-1}$, l for ice = $3.36 \times 10^5 \text{JK}^{-1}$).

Solution

(i) Quantity of heat required to change 0.12kg of ice from -20°C to 0°C

$= mc\,(\theta_2 - \theta_1) = 0.12 \times 2100 \times (0 - (-20)$
$= 0.12 \times 2100 \times 20 = 5040 \text{ J}$

(ii) Heat required to melt 0.12kg of ice at 0°C to water at 0°C is

$ml = 0.12 \times 3.36 \times 10^5 = 40.32 \times 10^3 \text{J}$

(iii) Heat required to change 0.12 kg of water at 0°C to water at 30°C =

$mc\theta = 0.12 \times 4200 \times (30 - 0) = 15.120 \times 10^3 \text{J}$

Total quantity of heat is that in (i) + (ii) + (iii)

$= (5.040 + 40.32 + 15.12) \times 10^3 \text{J}$

Hence, total heat needed is; $Q = 60.48 \times 10^3 \text{J}$

Example 20.11

A 30V electric heater is used to supply a current of 10A for 1200 seconds to a (solid) mass of 1kg, the body melts and rises through a temperature of 50°C, at an extra one minute. Determine latent heat of fusion l and specific heat capacity of the solid.

Solution

Heat supplied by electric heater in the first 1200s when the body melts is $IVt = ml$

$$\therefore l = \frac{IVt}{m} = \frac{10 \times 30 \times 1200}{1} = 36 \times 10^4 \text{ Jkg}^{-1}$$

For another 1 minute = 60 seconds,

$Ivt = 10 \times 30 \times 1260 = ml + mc\theta$
$37.8 \times 10^4 - 36 \times 10^4 = mc\,(\theta_2 - \theta_1)$, (but $\theta_2 - \theta_1 = 50^\circ$C)

$$\therefore c = \frac{37.8 \times 10^4 - 36 \times 10^4}{1 \times 50}$$

$$= \frac{1.8 \times 10^4}{50}$$

$$= 3.6 \times 10^2 \text{ J kg}^{-1}\text{K}^{-1}$$

$l = 3.6 \times 10^5 \text{Jkg}^{-1}$
$c = 3.6 \times 10^2 \text{ J kg}^{-1}\text{K}^{-1}$

20.5 Newton's law of cooling and the cooling curve

Newton's law of cooling states that for a small difference of temperature between a body and the surroundings, the rate of gain or loss of heat by the body is proportional to the difference in temperature between the body and the surroundings.

This law holds only within small range of temperature. It is important to note that the rate of cooling of liquid depends on:

(i) its temperature,
(ii) the temperature of the enclosure,
(iii) the area of the exposed surface,
(iv) the nature and extent of the surface of the containing vessel.

Finding the specific heat capacity of a liquid using cooling curve method

The mass of a copper calorimeter, weighed when empty is recorded. It is then half filled with the liquid and heated to about 20°C above room temperature. (Fig. 20.6)

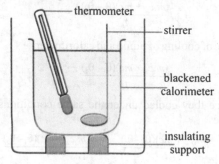

Fig. 20.6 The specific heat capacity using a cooling curve.

A stopwatch and a thermometer are used in measuring the temperature of the liquid at regular intervals of about half a minute.

The liquid is continuously stirred during the period of cooling. The calorimeter and the contents is reweighed at the end of the experiment. A graph of temperature is plotted against time for the liquid, and this represents the cooling curve of the liquid (Fig. 20.7).

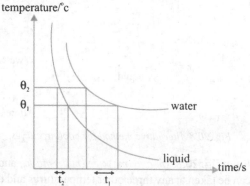

Fig. 20.7 Cooling curve graphs

An equal volume of water is used in place of the liquid and the experiment is repeated using the same temperature range. A cooling curve is also plotted for the water.

From the time intervals taken by the two liquids to cool through the same range of temperatures, the specific heat capacity of the liquid can be calculated from the following;

Let the mass of calorimeter be m

Let the mass of water be m_1

Let the time taken by the water to cool from θ_1 to θ_2 be t_1

Let the mass of the liquid used be m_2

Let the time taken by the liquid to cool from θ_1 to θ_2 be t_2

Let the specific heat capacity of water be c_w

Let the specific heat capacity of the liquid be c_2

Let the specific heat capacity of the calorimeter be c

Heat lost by water in cooling from θ_1 to θ_2

$$= m_1 c_w (\theta_1 - \theta_2)$$

Rate of cooling of water and calorimeter

$$= \frac{(m_1 c_w + mc)(\theta_1 - \theta_2)}{t_1}$$

Rate of cooling of liquid and calorimeter

$$= \frac{(m_2 c_2 + mc)(\theta_1 - \theta_2)}{t_2}$$

Since they cooled under the same conditions, we have

$$\frac{(m_1 c_w + mc)(\theta_1 - \theta_2)}{t_1} = \frac{(m_2 c_2 + mc)(\theta_1 - \theta_2)}{t_2}$$

$$\frac{(m_1 c_w + mc)}{t_1} = \frac{(m_2 c_2 + mc)}{t_2}$$

$$\therefore c_2 = [\frac{(m_1 c_w + mc)}{t_1} t_2 - mc] \frac{1}{m_2}$$

Alternative calculation

Drawing tangents to the cooling curves at a specific temperature θ, leads to finding respective rates of cooling k_1 and k_2 for the water and liquid as shown below.

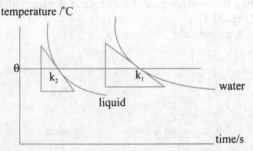

Fig. 20.8 Alternative method for cooling curves.

From fig. 20.8, $(m_1 c_w + mc)k_1 = (m_2 c_2 + mc)k_2$, and c can be taken at any three other temperatures and the average c_2, can be found.

20.6 Melting and freezing points

If heat is added to a solid, its temperature rises until at a peculiar temperature, the solid begins to melt into its liquid form. This temperature is the melting point of the solid. The melting point of a solid (e.g. ice) is found to be the same as the freezing point of its liquid state, that is, the temperature at which its liquid changes to a solid.

Some solids do not melt or freeze at a definite temperature. Examples of such solids with no definite melting or freezing point are candle wax, glass and wrought iron. This property is used in the blowing of molten glass to any desired shape.

Experimental determination of melting point by cooling curve

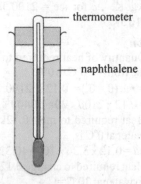

Fig. 20.9 The melting point of naphthalene.

A quantity of a suitable substance such as naphthalene is heated in a test tube immersed in a water bath, until the whole solid has liquidified. Thermometer is inserted in the naphthalene and the heating is continued until a temperature of about 100°C is reached. The molten naphthalene is allowed to cool slowly in the bath and its temperature is recorded at intervals of about one minute.

The temperature is plotted against the time, to obtain a cooling curve (see Fig. 20.10).

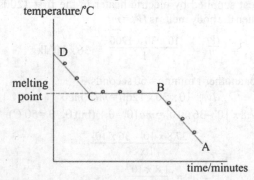

Fig. 20.10 The cooling curve

Between the point D and C the temperature falls with time. Between C and B the curve is paralled to the time axis, showing that the temperature remains steady during that interval of time. This steady temperature is the melting point of the substance. The flat portion of the curve is an indication that heat lost to the surroundings is balanced by the heat which is given out as the substance changes from liquid to solid state. Between B and A temperature falls with time.

20.7 Evaporation

When a volatile liquid, i.e. one that evaporates easily such as alcohol or ether, is exposed to the atmosphere, molecules of the liquid gradually escape from the surface of the liquid causing the liquid to change to its vapour form. This process is known as **evaporation**. It takes place at all temperatures and from the surface.

Factors which influence the rate of evaporation include:

(i) **Temperature**: The rate of evaporation increases with temperature increase.

(ii) **Pressure**: The rate of evaporation decreases with increasing pressure.

(iii) **Area of liquid surface exposed**: The greater the surface area of liquid exposed, the more rapid will be the evaporation.

(iv) **The nature of the liquid**: Different liquids evaporate at different rates; the lower the boiling point of a liquid, the greater will be the rate of evaporation.

(v) **Wind and dryness of air**: It is a common observation that clothes hung out on a dry windy harmattan day dry out very quickly. The dryness of the air around the clothes causes rapid evaporation of the water from the wet material. Wind blows away the water vapour around the material and causes more evaporation to take place.

Cooling by evaporation

Usually, water stored in earthen pots is cooler than that stored in glass bottles. Evaporation takes place through the pores on the earthen pots causing the water to cool.

If a few drops of methylated spirit is placed on the back of one's hand, it feels cold as the spirit evaporates. These two observations demonstrate the cooling effect of evaporation. Whenever a liquid is converted into vapour, heat is absorbed from the liquid or any object in contact with it. This heat is the latent heat used in causing the transformation from liquid to vapour. The absorption of this latent heat from the liquid brings about a fall in its temperature. The faster the evaporation, the greater is the fall in temperature. Thus on dry, hot or windy days, the fall in the temperature of the liquid due to evaporation is greater than on moist, cold, still days.

The human body utilises the process of evaporation for cooling. If we become too hot through exercises or due to our hot surroundings, we sweat and the evaporation of the liquid from the skin cools us. Before an injection is given, volatile ether is rubbed on the skin, as the ether evaporates, it cools the skin and numbs it, so that the pain of injection is not felt much.

Application of cooling effect of evaporation

The refrigerator

The cooling effect of evaporation is used in a refrigerator, (Fig. 20.11). The volatile liquid used is usually liquid ammonia or Freon. Ammonia evaporates inside coiled copper tubes surrounding the freezing compartment, assisted by a pump which reduces the pressure. As it evaporates in these coils, the ammonia absorbs heat from the surrounding air, thus cooling the inside of the refrigerator and its contents. The vapour produced is pumped away and compressed in a condenser where it condenses to liquid ammonia. The heat released during this condensation is quickly dissipated by an arrangement of cooling fins at the back of the refrigerator. The liquid is recycled through the evaporator coil and the process is repeated, thus setting up continuous circulation of liquid and vapour.

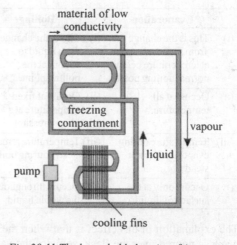

Fig. 20.11 The household electric refrigerator

20.8 Boiling

If we heat a beaker containing some liquid, the liquid evaporates due to increases in temperature. As the temperature of the liquid is steadily increased, bubbles of vapour appear in the liquid which rise to the surface. This process is known as boiling. Boiling occurs at a particular temperature, called the **boiling point**.

Effect of pressure and dissolved substances on boiling and freezing points

(i) We can observe the effect of pressure on the boiling point of a liquid by a simple experiment. A round-bottomed flask which is about half full of water is heated until the water boils, and it is allowed to boil for about five minutes, during which time all the air is driven out by the steam. The flask is corked and inverted over the sink as shown in Fig. 20.12.

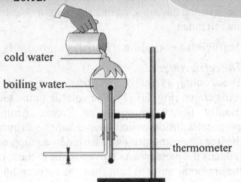

cold water

boiling water

thermometer

Fig. 20.12 Boiling under reduced pressure

The flask is allowed to cool until the water stops boiling. When a cup of cold water is now poured over the bottom of the flask, boiling is observed to resume and to stop when we cease pouring the cold water over the flask.

Table 20.2 Difference between boiling and evaporation

Evaporation	Boiling
(i) This is the change from liquid to vapour at temperature below normal boiling point.	(i) This is the change from liquid to vapour at the boiling point.
(ii) Occurs at all temperature.	(ii) Occurs at fixed temperature at a given pressure.
(iii) Temperature during evaporation is not steady.	(iii) Temperature remains steady during boiling.
(iv) Occurs only at the surface of liquid.	(iv) Occurs throughout the whole liquid.

The explanation of this effect is that when the cold water is poured over the flask, some of the vapour inside the flask condenses, thus reducing the pressure on the water surface. This reduced pressure lowers the boiling point of the liquid and it boils once more. Thus we see that reduced pressure lowers the boiling point of a liquid.

(ii) Aircraft flying at high altitude where the air is at a much lower pressure than normal, needs to be pressurised so that the people in the cabin are at their normal pressure. The reason being that reduced pressure has disastrous effects on the human body, which is used to an external pressure of 100k Pa and has a normal internal pressure which is the same. For this reason astronauts need to wear space suits, not only to contain air for them to breathe but to keep them at the right pressure. If an astronaut stepped into space without his suit, his blood

and the water in his body would tend to boil. In fact this would not happen immediately because his skin would contain the liquids, but the effect would be quite unpleasant.

(iii) Conversely increased pressure raises the boiling point. This has a practical application in the pressure cooker, which is a strong cooking pot with a lid that can be held down. Food is cooked faster in a pressure cooker. The increased pressure of the trapped gas above the liquid raises the boiling point of the liquid inside the cooker. Thus a high cooking temperature is reached very fast thereby reducing the cooking time and saving gas.

(iv) The effect of increased pressure could be observed on the freezing point by the following experiment. A thin wire with heavy weights attached to both ends is hung over a block of ice resting on two supports (Fig. 20.13(a). After some time, it is seen that the wire cuts its way through the ice block, but the block remains solid behind it. The explanation is as follows. The pressure on the wire lowers the freezing point of the ice beneath it. The ice therefore melts, allowing the wire to pass through the ice, the pressure above the wire decreases thus raising the freezing point of the melted ice above it. The water therefore freezes again and close up the surface. This process is referred to as **regelation**.

Note: Increase in pressure lowers the melting point of all substances that expand on solidifying, but for substance that contracts on solidifying (e.g. Paraffin) their melting point is raised by increase in pressure.

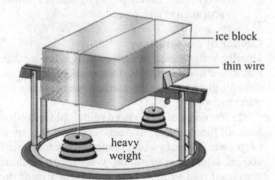

ice block

thin wire

heavy weight

Fig. 20.13(a) Regelation

Dissolved impurities lowers the melting point of a pure solid (ice) or the freezing point of its pure liquid (water). Hence, if water and common salts are mixed, the mixture will freeze at a temperature lower than 0°C. Salt poured on ice formed on road lowers the freezing point, and has effect of melting the ice. In cooler climates the sea (a solution containing salt) will not freeze, even when fresh water rivers are covered with ice. Also the presence of impurities raise the boiling point of a pure liquid.

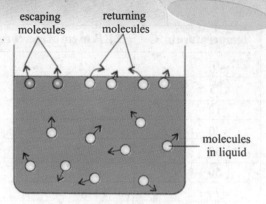

Fig.20.13(b) Evaporation explained by the kinetic theory.

According to the kinetic theory, a liquid is made up of molecules which are in random motion with different speeds. Molecules with high speeds near the liquid surface have enough kinetic energy to overcome the attraction of other molecules. They stay outside the liquid surface as molecules of vapour. Thus evaporation involves the escape of molecules from the liquid surface. A few molecules, however, return to the liquid.

High temperature increases the speeds of all the molecules, thus allowing more molecules to escape from the surface, and increasing the rate of evaporation. The presence of wind also increases the rate of evaporation by sweeping away the molecules of vapour above the liquid surface, thus making way for a fresh supply of escaping molecules.

As molecules with high kinetic energy escape from the liquid, the average kinetic energy of the remaining molecules of the liquid is reduced, hence the reduction in the temperature of the liquid. Therefore evaporation brings about cooling. As a liquid is heated, a temperature is reached at which the average speed of all the molecules is high enough for them all to escape from the surface. Thus at this temperature, the liquid boils and turns rapidly to vapour. Further heating does not raise the temperature more, but simply makes the liquid turn to vapour more quickly.

In a solid, the molecules, which are held together by intermolecular forces, vibrate about a mean position. As the temperature of the solid increases, the vibration of the molecules increases, and at a certain temperature the molecules have enough energy to overcome the forces binding them together. They are now free to move about in a random motion as in a liquid, and the solid is said to have melted.

Sublimation

This is a process whereby a substance changes from the solid to vapour state without going through the liquid state.

A solid first melts into a liquid state before it changes into the vapour state at high temperature. Under certain conditions, some substances will go from the solid to the vapour state without passing through the liquid phase, for example, iodine crystals, when placed in a test-tube at room temperature and pressure, will change directly into iodine vapour without going first into a liquid phase. Such a process is called **sublimation**. Another example is provided by dry ice (CO_2) which, when standing in the open air, evaporates directly without first liquefying.

20.9 Vapour pressure

Vapour and vapour pressure

Molecules escape from the surface of a liquid exposed to the atmosphere during the process of evaporation. These molecules accumulate above the liquid and form a vapour.

The vapour above any liquid surface consists of molecules which, according to the kinetic theory of gases, are in a state of constant motion and will hence exert pressure, just like the molecules of a gas. As they move and strike the walls of the container, they exert pressure on them and also exert pressure on the liquid surface. The pressure the molecules exert on the liquid's surface is called vapour pressure of the liquid.

Saturated and unsaturated vapour

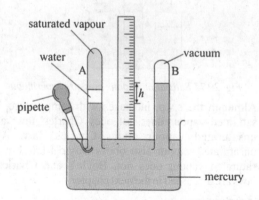

Fig. 20.14 Saturation vapour pressure

Fig. 20.14 shows the apparatus set up for studying the pressure exerted by a vapour. Two barometer tubes are filled with mercury and inverted over a trough of mercury. They are clamped vertically and the mercury levels in both tubes are the same. A pipette is used in introducing a few drops of water into the space above the mercury in tube A. This water evaporates immediately, causing a slight depression of the mercury column, which is due to the vapour pressure. As more water is introduced, a stage is reached when no further evaporation is observed and the water remains on top of the mercury column. We say that a state of dynamic equilibrium is reached, when the rate at which molecules leave the liquid is equal to the rate at which others return to it. At this stage, the space above the liquid is said to be saturated with vapour and pressure exerted is called **saturated vapour pressure** (*S.V.P.*). Before this stage, the space is unsaturated, i.e. it could take in more vapour.

> A saturated vapour is a vapour that is in contact with its own liquid within a confined space.

The pressure exerted by the saturated vapour is known as the **saturation vapour pressure** (*S.V.P.*) at that temperature. It corresponds to the maximum pressure exerted by the vapour when it is in contact with its own liquid, and it is obtained by taking the difference (h) between the mercury levels in the two tubes.

If we vary the temperature of the vapour, for example by surrounding tube A with a water bath containing water of which the temperature can be varied (Fig.20.15). It would be observed that the saturation vapour pressure increases as the temperature increases. Above 100°C, there is a very rapid increase of s.v.p. with temperature.

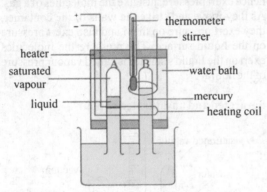

Fig. 20.15 Saturation vapour pressure experiment

Although the s.v.p. increases with temperature, a saturated vapour does not obey Charles' law; an unsaturated vapour obeys Charles' law. An unsaturated vapour also obeys Boyle's law but a saturated vapour does not. Boyle's and Charles' laws are discussed in the next chapter.

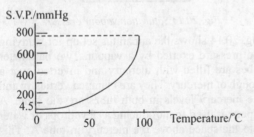

Fig. 20.16 Variation of s.v.p. with temperature

Typical figures for water are shown in the table.

Table 20.3

Temperature in °C	S.V.P. in cm of mercury
0	0.45
5	0.7
10	0.9
20	1.8
30	3.2
50	9.3
70	234.0
100	76.0
150	356.9
200	1164.7

Saturated vapour pressure (s.v.p.) is defined as one which is in state of dynamic equilibrium with its own liquid or solid.

(i) *Using kinetic theory to explain saturation vapour pressure*

At any temperature, molecules with enough kinetic energy escape from the liquid surface to the space above the liquid and form vapour. Some molecules return to the liquid while others remain outside. In an unsaturated state, the number of molecules leaving the liquid is greater than the number returning to the liquid, in unit time. In a saturated condition, the number leaving is equal to the number coming back in unit time, thus, saturated vapour is thus said to be in a state of dynamic equilibrium with its own liquid. If the temperature is increased, the kinetic energy of every molecules is increased. More molecules therefore gain enough energy to leave the liquid surface and the space above the liquid is occupied by more molecules which are also moving more quickly. The saturation vapour pressure thus increases.

(ii) *Using kinetic energy to explain boiling*

The kinetic energy of molecules increases when the liquid is heated. This increases the number of the fast moving molecules and leads to fast evaporation. The vapour pressure therefore increases when the vapour pressure of liquid equals to atmospheric pressure at that particular time, bubbles of vapour move freely and rise to the surface of the liquid where they explode. The liquid is said to be boiling, and the temperature at which this happens is called the boiling point.

(iii) The particles that make up a solid are constantly vibrating and therefore possess kinetic energy. If the solid is heated, kinetic energy increases and the vibrations increase after some time, the vibrations become so violent that the binding forces are overcome and the particles begin to move, at this time the solid turns into liquid and the particles move freely.

Saturation vapour pressure and boiling point

The saturation vapour pressure of a liquid at its boiling point is equal to the atmospheric pressure. This can be demonstrated with the apparatus shown in Fig. 20.17. A long barometeric tube is filled with mercury and inverted over a mercury trough. The mercury level falls leaving a vacuum above it.

Water is introduced into the tube by means of a bent pipette until the space above the mercury is saturated with water vapour, leaving some liquid on top of the mercury. Steam is now passed through the steam jacket. As the temperature rises, the mercury level in the tube begins to decrease showing that the vapour pressure is increasing. This depression of the mercury level continues until the level inside the tube is equal to the level in the trough outside the tube. At this stage, the thermometer is observed to read 100°C, the boiling point of water. Water boils at 100°C when the atmospheric pressure is 760mm of mercury.

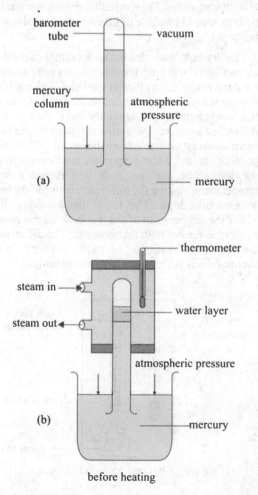

(a)

(b)

before heating

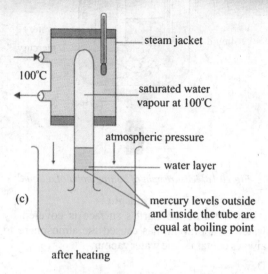

(c)

after heating

Fig 20.17 Saturation vapour pressure and boiling point

Determination of boiling point

The boiling point of water could be determined using a small quantity, using the fact that liquid boils when its saturation vapour pressure equals to the external atmospheric pressure.

The apparatus is shown in fig. 20.18.

The liquid is introduced into the space on top of the mercury in the shorter arm of the tube using a bent pipette. The liquid evaporates and the pressure of the vapour depresses the mercury slightly. The whole tube is immersed in a water bath which is gently heated. As the temperature of the bath rises, the saturation vapour pressure of the liquid rises. When the mercury levels in both arms of the tube become equal, the temperature is read from the thermometer. At this temperature, the vapour pressure is equal to the atmospheric pressure since the longer arm of the tube is open to the atmosphere, and the liquid is seen to be boiling.

Precaution

(a)   The water bath must be continuously stirred during heating.

(b)   Mean temperature of thermometer readings while the temperature are rising and falling are taken and recorded for more accurate results.

(c)   A pure sample of the liquid must be used.

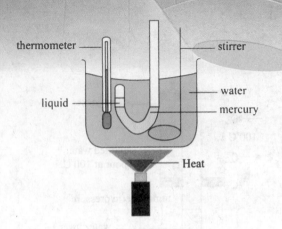

thermometer

stirrer

liquid

water

mercury

Heat

Fig.20.18Measurement of boiling point of a liquid.

Water vapour in the atmosphere

About 70% of the Earth's surface is covered by water. Evaporation, has caused the atmosphere to always contain some water vapour.

Dew

If air containing water vapour is cooled, it may be possible to reach a temperature at which the water present in the air just saturates it. If this air is cooled further, droplets of water will condense on cold surface. This condensed water is called **dew.**

Dew point: It is the temperature at which the water present in the air is just enough to saturate the air.

NB: Anytime air is cooled below its dew point, dew will be formed.

Mist

When moist air near the Earth's surface and few distance above it is cooled, the water vapour in it condenses and forms tiny droplets which are suspended in the air. These suspended water droplets are known as **mist.** For mist to form, the air must be cooled below its dew point.

Mist can also be formed when wind blows warm moist air over a cold surface. The sudden lowering of temperature causes the moisture to condense. Mist is closer to the ground and it restricts visibility, such that one cannot see very far when there is a mist. Whenever there is mist, vehicle drivers have to put on their head lamps and drive slowly, to avoid accidents.

Cloud

Cloud is a mass of small water droplets that float in the air. Cloud is high up in the atmosphere.

Humidity

In hot climates, or after vigorous exercise, our bodies sweat to maintain a stable temperature. When the sweat evaporates, we feel cool. If the air around us is dry, the sweat from our bodies evaporates faster than when the air is damp and contains plenty of water vapour. We describe the air that is moist as **humid air. Relative humidity** is a term used to describe how humid the air is.

Relative humidity is the ratio of the mass of water vapour present in a certain volume of air to the mass of water vapour required to saturate the same volume of air at the same temperature.

Relative humidity (R.H.)

$$= \frac{\text{Mass of water vapour in a given volume of air}}{\text{mass of water vapour required to saturate the same volume of air at the same temperature}}$$

OR

Relative humidity

$$= \frac{\text{S.V.P. of water at dew point}}{\text{S.V.P. of water at original air temperature}}$$

It is usually expressed as a percentage.
Relative humidity values are used by weathermen for making weather forecasts.

The wet and dry bulb hygrometer

A hygrometer is an instrument used for measuring humidity. One simple type is the wet and dry bulb hygrometer. (Fig.20.19). It consists of two thermometers, the wet bulb thermometer and the dry bulb thermometer. The wet bulb thermometer has its bulb wrapped in a piece of moist cloth dipped into a water pot.

The dry bulb indicates the temperature of the dry air, while the wet bulb records a lower temperature because evaporation of water from the cloth cools it. If there is much water in the atmosphere, water from the wet cloth evaporates only very slowly, the difference in the temperatures recorded by the two thermometers will therefore be small. When the humidity is low, water evaporates at a fast rate from the wet cloth, the wet bulb will record a low temperature, making the difference between the two temperatures high. The lower the humidity, the lower the temperature of the wet bulb thermometer relative to the dry bulb thermometer. The difference between the readings of wet and dry bulb thermometers is a measure of relative humidity.

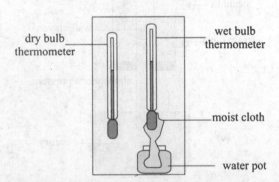

dry bulb thermometer

wet bulb thermometer

moist cloth

water pot

Fig. 20.19 Wet and dry bulb hygrometer.

The dew point hygrometer

Regnault's dew hygrometer can be used to measure dew point, and also used to work out the humidity of the air using standard tables. (See fig. 20.20).

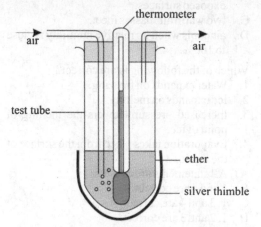

Fig. 20.20 The dewpoint hygrometer

This is made up of a large test tube containing ether, through which air is blown by means of either a bulb or a small pump. On the outside of the tube is tight fitting silver thimble and as the ether cools by forced evaporation, dew forms on the silver surface. A thermometer in the ether reads the temperature at which this happens, and it is the dew point.

Control of humidity

People can tolerate a range of humidities from ranging from 0 to 100% for short periods, but for long periods, very high and very low humidities are uncomfortable and can have adverse effects on people.

When the humidity is high and the weather is hot, the body tries to cool itself by sweating but cannot dispose of the moisture. The skin thus feels continually damp and unpleasant, difficulty in breathing is also experienced. This is the case in some tropical countries, and can be overcome by air-conditioning and fans circulate the air, so that there is a continual change of air around the body and evaporation can take place.

If the humidity is low and the air is very dry, there is excessive evaporation from the body. The throat can become uncomfortably dry and the skin generally dry and rough. This is also overcome by air-conditioning which takes air into the house through special humidifiers which dampen the air. However, it is almost as effective to keep bowls of water, or well-watered plants in the rooms.

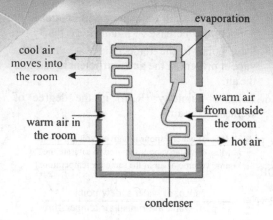

Fig. 20.21 Air conditioner

Summary

1. Specific heat capacity of a substance is the heat required to raise a unit mass of the substance through 1° temperature rise, its unit is in $Jkg^{-1}K^{-1}$.

2. Heat capacity is the heat required to raise the entire mass of a substance through one degree rise in temperature.

3. Quantity of heat is given by $Q = mc\theta$.

4. Specific latent heat of fusion of a substance is the quantity of heat required to convert a unit mass from solid to liquid without change in temperature.

5. Specific latent heat of vaporisation of a substance is the quanity of heat required to change unit mass from liquid to vapour without change in temperature.

6. Newton's law of cooling states that for a small difference of temperature between a body and the surroundings, the rate of loss or gain of heat by body is proportional to the difference in temperature between the body and the surroundings.

7. Gradual escape of molecules from the surfaces of the liquid causing the liquid to change to its vapour form is referred to as evaporation, and evaporation causes cooling.

8. Boiling is caused by steady rising of bubbles of vapours from the bottom of the liquid to the surface.

9. Boiling and evaporation differs in many ways.

10. Increase in pressure raises boiling point of water and lowers the freezing point of water.

11. The pressure the molecules exert on the liquid surface is called vapour pressure of the liquid.

12. At a state of dynamic equilibrium, the space above the liquid is said to be saturated with vapour and the pressure exerted is called saturated vapour pressure.

13. The saturated vapour pressure (s.v.p.) of a liquid at its boiling point is equal to atmospheric pressure.

14. S.V.P. varies with temperature i.e. increase in temperature increase s.v.p. and vice versa.

15. Dew point is the temperature at which the vapour present in the air is sufficient to saturate the air.

16. Relative humidity (R.H.) is the degree of wetness in the air.

$$R.H. = \frac{\text{Mass of water vapour in a given volume of air}}{\text{Mass of water vapour required to saturate the same volume of air at the same air temperature}}$$

OR

$$R.H. = \frac{\text{s.v.p. of water at dew point}}{\text{s.v.p. of water at original air temperature}}$$

17. We can measure R.H. by an instrument called hygrometer.

Exercises 20

1. How much heat is required to convert 20g of ice at $0^{\circ}C$ to water at the same temperature? (Specific latent heat of ice = 335 Jg⁻¹).
   A. $1.35 \times 10^3 J$ B. $5.38 \times 10^3 J$
   C. $6.70 \times 10^3 J$ D. $7.06 \times 10^3 J$

2. Which of the following statements is NOT correct?
   A. Evaporation takes place only at the surface of a liquid.
   B. Boiling takes place throughout the volume of a liquid.
   C. Evaporation takes place at all temperatures.
   D. The boiling point of a liquid is not affected by impurities.

3. Water in an open container boils at a lower temperature when heated at the top of a mountain than at sea-level because at the top of a mountain the
   A. relative humidity is higher than at sea-level.
   B. rays of the sun add more heat to the water.
   C. temperature is lower than that at sea-level.
   D. pressure is lower than that at sea-level.

4. An electric current of 3A flowing through an electric heating element of resistance 20Ω embedded in 1000g of an oil, raises the temperature of the oil by $10^{\circ}C$ in 10 seconds, then the specific heat capacity of the oil is
   A. $1.8\,Jg^{-1}$ B. $0.6\,Jg^{-1}$
   C. $0.18Jg^{-1}\,^{\circ}C^{-1}$ D. $1.8\,Jg^{-1}\,^{\circ}C^{-1}$

5. Which of the following processes does not reduce heat lost from a liquid in a calorimeter?
   A. Lagging the calorimeter.
   B. Using an insulating lids.
   C. Shielding the calorimeter from draughts.
   D. Constantly stirring the liquid.

6. Calculate the heat energy required to convert 0.500kg of ice at $0^{\circ}C$ to ice-cold water at $0^{\circ}C$ if the specific latent heat of fussion of ice is $3.34 \times 10^5 kg^{-1}$.
   A. 1670J   B. 6680J

C. 167000J   D. 66800J

7. Mist is formed when
   A. clouds mix up.
   B. water evaporates from oceans and exposed surfaces.
   C. two warm air masses meet.
   D. air cools when its relative humidity is close to 100%.

8. Which of the following is/are correct?
   1. Water expands on freezing.
   2. Ice expands on melting.
   3. Increased pressure lowers the melting of point of ice.
   4. Evaporation takes place from the surface of the liquid.
   A. All statements are correct.
   B. 1 and 4 are correct.
   C. 1, 3 and 4 are correct.
   D. 1, 2 and 3 are correct.

9. Explain what is meant by the
   (i) specific heat capacity of water is $4200Jkg^{-1}\,k^{-1}$.
   (ii) specific latent heat of fussion of ice $3.36 \times 105Jkg^{-1}$.
   (b) What quantity of heat is required to bring 20g of ice at $-10^{\circ}C$ to water at $80^{\circ}C$? (Take specific heat capacity of ice to be $2.2 \times 10^3\,Jkg^{-1}\,K^{-1}$ and specific latent heat of fusion of ice $336Jkg^{-1}$, specific heat capacity of water = $4.2 \times 10^2\,Jkg^{-1}\,K^{-1}$).

10. (a) Define specific latent heat of vaporization of water.
    (b) Describe an experiment you will use in determining the specific latent heat of water.
    (c) A copper calorimeter of mass 150g, was half-filled with water of mass 300g and temperature $0^{\circ}C$. 5g of ice at $0^{\circ}C$ was added to the content, later some quantity of steam was passed into the mixture and the temperature rose by $20^{\circ}C$. Calculate the quantity of steam added. (specific latent heat of vaporisation of steam = $2.26 \times 10^6 Jkg^{-1}$ specific heat of copper = 400 $Jkg^{-1}\,K^{-1}$).

11. (a) Define the following:
    (i) dew point   (ii) relative humidity
    (iii) saturation vapour pressure   (iv) cloud
    (B) Use kinetic theory to explain:
    (i) boiling;
    (ii) saturation in vapour pressure.

12. (a) Differentiate between boiling and evaporation.
    (b) Describe a simple experiment you would use in determining the boiling point of a small quantity of a liquid.
    (c) State precautions you would take while performing the experiment.

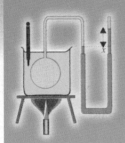

GAS LAWS

Chapter 21

To study in details the behaviour of a gas, three quantities of the gas that must be taken into consideration include, *pressure*, *volume* and *temperature*. When these three related quantities are being studied, one is normally kept constant, while the remaining two vary. For example; in studying relationship between:

(i) volume and pressure, temperature is kept constant (Boyle's law);

(ii) volume and temperature, pressure is kept constant (Charles' law); and

(iii) pressure and temperature, volume is kept constant (Pressure law).

21.1 Measurement of gas pressure

Gas pressure is usually measured with an instrument called **manometer**. This instrument has been described in earlier chapters under mechanics.

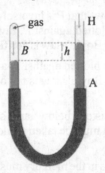

Fig. 21.1 Measurement of gas pressure.

In measuring the gas pressure using a manometer, the tap from the gas supply is turned on, as the gas rushes out, it exerts pressure on gas B which force the level of mercury in A, (the open tube) to rise. From Fig. 21.1, it is seen that the mercury level at A rises above that in B by height h(cm). When the levels in both A and B are steady, then the pressure P of the gas at B is $(H+h)$cm. This is true because, since pressure increases with depth, pressure at B will be greater than that at A by a value of $h$cm. The pressure acting on A is atmospheric pressure given by H, since it is opened to atmosphere. Hence the pressure of gas at $B = H + h$.

(Note: Atmospheric pressure H is taken to be 76cm of mercury).

Deriving standard atmospheric pressure (one atmosphere)

It is important to recall that pressure (P) is defined as force per unit area, and its unit is in Newton per metre squared (Nm^{-2}). Hence;

$$P = \frac{F}{A}$$
$$= \frac{mg}{A}$$
$$= \frac{\rho vg}{A}$$
$$= \frac{\rho Ahg}{A} = \rho gh$$

$$\boxed{P = \rho gh} \quad (Nm^{-2}) \qquad\qquad 21.1$$

Here, H = 76cm Hg = 0.76mHg

Density (ρ) of mercury = 13 600 kgm^{-3} and g = 9.8ms^{-2}.

Putting these values in equation 21.1 above gives,
P = 13600 x 9.8 x 0.76 = 1.013 x 10^5 Nm^{-2}.

This means that a standard atmospheric pressure is given by $1.013 \times 10^5 Nm^{-2}$.

1 Pascal (pa) = $1Nm^{-2}$ is another unit of pressure

1 bar = 10^5 Nm^{-2} or 10^5 Pascal is other unit of pressure

Example 21.1

(i) Calculate the mass as well as the height of mercury contained in a narrow tube of uniform cross-sectional area of 100m^2 that will support one atmosphere when a force of F is exerted on it by a gas.

(ii) Calculate also the F.

Solution

Using $P = \dfrac{F}{A}$

$\qquad = \dfrac{mg}{A}$

$\qquad = \rho gh$ and as substituting yields,

$$P = \frac{F}{A} \quad \text{(For finding force } F\text{)}$$

P = 1.013 x 10^5 Nm^{-3}

and A = $10^2 m^2$ we have F = P x A

$\qquad F = 1.013 \times 10^5 \times 10^2$

$\qquad = 1.013 \times 10^7 N$

For mass, m, $F = mg$

$$\therefore m = \frac{F}{g}$$

$$= \frac{1.013 \times 10^7}{10} = 1.013 \times 10^6 kg$$

For height $h, p = \rho g h$

$$1.013 \times 10^5 = 13600 \times 10 \times h$$

$$\therefore h = \frac{1.013 \times 10^5}{136 \times 10^3} = 0.745m$$

21.2 Boyle's law and its applications

Boyle's involves change in volume of gas with pressure at constant temperature.

> Boyle's law states that the volume of a fixed mass of gas varies inversely as its pressure, provided the temperature remains constant.

Stating this mathematically, this implies that:

$V \propto 1/P$ i.e. $V = k/P$, where k is a constant,

or $PV = K$ or $P_1V_1 = P_2V_2$ where P_1V_1 are the initial pressure and volume before changes occurred and P_2V_2 are that final pressure and volume after changes occurred.

$$P_1V_1 = P_2V_2 \qquad\qquad 21.2$$

Experimental verification of Boyle's law

A simple form of apparatus used for verification of Boyle's law is shown in fig 21.2. The atmospheric pressure of the gas is recorded (H) after dry air has been introduced into the tube B. B is kept steady, while A is raised or lowered, then the positions of mercury levels in A and B on the scale are noted and recorded (i.e. height (h)). The corresponding length (l) which is proportional to volume of air (since the tube is of uniform cross-sectional area), are measured and recorded. The procedure is repeated for four or five more times, then the values of $1/l$, ($H + h$) are tabulated for all the readings taken (see table 21.1)

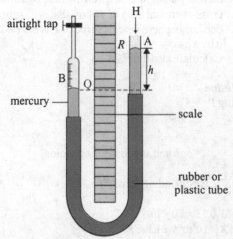

Fig. 21.2 Boyle's law verification

Table 21.1

h(cm)	P = h + H (cm Hg)	l(cm)	1/l (cm⁻¹)

Then, a graph of P is plotted against $\frac{1}{l}$ (or $\frac{1}{V}$),

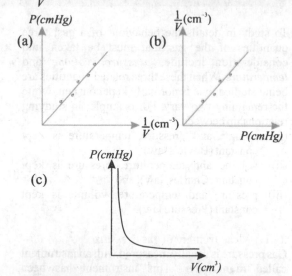

Fig. 21.3 (a) (b) (c) graphs of verification of Boyle's law.

Fig. 21.3(a) shows that P is inversely proportional to volume, $\frac{1}{V}$ is plotted against P. Fig. 21.3(b) shows the same, hence Boyle's law is verified.

Note that if P is plotted against V, a parabolic curve is obtained and Boyle's law is not obeyed (Fig.21.3 (c)).

Precaution: Listed below are some necessary precautions that must be taken while performing the experiment.

(i) Air bubbles in the mercury must be eliminated.
(ii) Readings are taken only when mercury levels are steady.
(iii) Ensure that the air we use is dry.
(iv) Read top of meniscus of mercury level.
(v) Allow time to keep temperature of air constant before taking readings.

Example 21.2

Calculate the volume fraction change of a fixed mass of gas whose pressure is tripled at constant temperature.

Solution

Using Boyle's law;

$$P_1V_1 = P_2V_2 \text{ or } \frac{P_1}{P_2} = \frac{P_2}{V_1}$$

But $P_2 = 3P_1$

$$\therefore \frac{P_1}{V_2} = \frac{3P_1}{V_1} \Rightarrow 3V_2 = V_1$$

$$\therefore \frac{V_1}{V_2} = 3 \text{ and } V_2 = \frac{V_1}{3}$$

Hence, the final volume becomes one-third of the original volume.

Example 21.3

The pressure of a fixed mass of gas is given as 850cmHg when its volume is 20cm^3. Calculate the volume of the gas when its pressure is 600cmHg.

Solution

Using Boyle's law; $P_1V_1 = P_2V_2$

Hence, $850 \times 20 = 600 \times V_2$

$$\therefore V_2 = \frac{850 \times 20}{600}$$
$$= 28.33 \text{ cm Hg}$$

Application of Boyle's law

(i) It is employed in determining the volume of a given mass of gas at constant temperature when the pressure is known.

(ii) It is also used in finding the pressure of a given mass of gas at constant temperature when the volume is known.

21.3 Charles' law and its applications

Charles' law deals with change in volume and temperature at constants pressure.

> Charles' law states that the volume of a fixed (given) mass of gas is directly proportional to its absolute temperature (T), provided the pressure remains constant.

Stating Charles' law mathematically;

$V \propto T$, i.e. $V = kT$ where k is a constant

OR $\quad \dfrac{V_1}{T_1} = \dfrac{V_2}{T_2}$ $\qquad\qquad$ 21.3

where V_1 and V_2 are the initial and final volumes of the gas before and after changes, respectively, while T_1 and T_2 are the initial and final temperatures before and after changes, respectively.

Experimental verification of Charles' law

Charles' law could be verified using the apparatus set as shown in fig 21.4

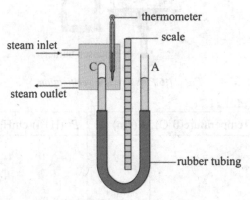

Fig. 21.4 Verification of Charles' law.

Air is trapped by mercury in the closed limb of the tube C of uniform bore, the volume of the gas at any temperature is proportional to the length of gas. Steam is passed, and a steady temperature is got. Then, the mercury level is adjusted in both limbs. This is done by raising or lowering the limb A, so that pressure on both arms of the tube is atmospheric pressure, which is taken to be constant, that is when the level of mercury on both arms are equal. Length (l) of gas column at that temperature is recorded, series of readings are taken at different temperatures and recorded as in table 21.1.

A graph of volume (length) is plotted against temperature, a straight line graph AB is obtained as seen in Fig 21.5. This shows that the volume of a gas at constant pressure increases linearly with absolute temperature. This proves that Charles' law is verified.

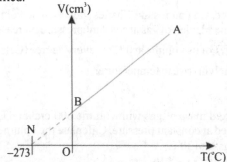

Fig. 21. 5 Graph of volume against temperature at constant pressure.

Precautions: Some precautions taken to ensure accurate results include the following:

(i)   Ensure the air is dry.

(ii) Take readings when mercury levels are steady.

(iii) Eliminate air bubbles in the mercury.

(iv) Read top of meniscus of mercury.

(v)   The bore of the tube must be clean and dry.

(vi) The thermometer must be kept vertical.

Applications of Charles' law

(i) Absolute zero of temperature

Charles' law shows that, if we plot the volume of a given mass of any gas at constant pressure against its temperature, graph as seen in fig. 21.5 is obtained. If AB is produced backwards it meets the temperature axis at N, (–273°C). This temperature is called absolute zero. This shows that as the temperature is reduced, the volume continues to diminish. Theoretically, the volume of the gas becomes zero at –273°C, but practically it is not so, for the gas liquifies before it gets to that temperature. Unit of absolute temperature is kelvin (K). Therefore, absolute zero temperature can be taken to be the lowest temperature attainable by the gas i.e. (theoretically).

(ii) The Kelvin temperature scale

The temperature on a Celsius scale can be converted

to Kelvin simply by adding 273, thus,
0°C = 0 +273K = 273K. The lowest temperature possible here is –273°C. Another temperature scale with its zero coinciding with –273°C is called the *Kelvin temperature scale* which sometimes is referred to as *absolute temperatures* or *thermodynamic temperatures*.

Hence the conversion of Celsius temperature to absolute temperature and vice versa are as a result of the knowledge of above.

(iii) *Cubic expansivity of a gas*, γ is as a result of Charles' law. Hence the cubic expansivity of a gas at constant pressure is defined as; γ

$$\gamma = \frac{\text{Increase in volume}}{\text{original volume at } 0°\text{C} \times \text{change in temperature}}$$

(Referred to expansion in chapter four)

Hence, we can restate Charles' law as; The volume of a fixed mass of gas at constant pressure increases by $\frac{1}{273}$ of its volume at 0°C for every degree (Celsius or Kelvin) rise in temperature.

Example 21.4
A fixed mass of gas with volume 600 cm³ at 0°C is heated at constant pressure. Calculate the volume of the gas at 130°C.

Solution: Using Charles' law;

$$\frac{V_1}{T_1} = \frac{V_2}{T_2}$$

$$T_2 = 273 + 130 = 403\text{k}$$

$$\text{Thus, } \frac{600}{273} = \frac{V_2}{403}$$

$$\therefore V_2 = \frac{600 \times 403}{273}$$

$$V_2 = 885.71 \text{cm}^3$$

Example 21.5
A fixed mass of gas is held at a constant pressure and its volume at 0°C is 150cm³. Calculate the temperature when the volume will be 250cm³ (Take cubic expansivity of gas at constant pressure to be $\frac{1}{273}\text{K}^{-1}$)

Solution:
Using $V_\theta = V_o(1+\gamma\theta)$

$$\therefore V_\theta = V_o(1+ \frac{1}{273} \theta)$$

$$\text{i.e. } 250 = 150 \{1 + \frac{\theta}{273}\}$$

$$250 = 150 \left(\frac{273 + \theta}{273} \right)$$

$$\therefore \theta = \frac{250 \times 273}{150} - 273$$

θ = 455 – 273
 = 182°C
Hence, the temperature, θ, is 182°C

21.4 Pressure law or Gay Lussac's law
This deals with change in pressure and absolute temperature of a gas when the volume is kept constant.

> Pressure law or Gay Lussac's law states that the pressure of a fixed (given) mass of a gas is directly proportional to its absolute temperature provided the volume is kept constant.

Mathematically stated we have;
$P \propto T, P = kT$

$$\text{or } \frac{P}{T} = k$$

$$\text{or } \frac{P_1}{T_1} = \frac{P_2}{T_2} \qquad 21.4$$

Where the symbols P_1, P_2 and T_1, T_2 retain their usual meanings.

Experimental proof of pressure law
The set up in fig 21.6 is employed in verification of pressure law. The bulb *A* which is totally immersed in water in a large beaker, contains dry air. Pieces of ice block are added to the water in the beaker until the temperature is 0°C. The manometer is adjusted until the mercury surface coincides with the fixed mark *x*. This position of *x* is used to ensure that the volume of gas is the same throughout the experiment. The pressure of gas at 0°C is obtained by reading the difference *h* between the mercury levels *y* and *x*. The temperature of water is raised and readings are taken at different higher temperatures and at temperature of 100°C.

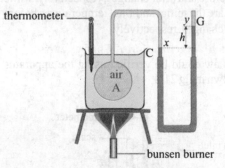

Fig. 21.6 Pressure law verification

Table 21.2

Temperature(θ°C)	h (cm)	P=(H+h)(cmHg)

The pressure of the gas is ($H+h$) (cmHg) where H is atmospheric pressure.
Note that if y is below x, the pressure of the gas is ($H-h$) cmHg.

A graph of pressure against temperature plotted (Fig 21.7) gives a straight line graph proving that pressure increases linearly with temperature.

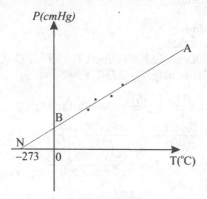

Fig. 21.7 Graph of pressure versus temperature at constant volume.

When the graph AB is produced to meet the temperature axis at N, it cuts it at $-273^\circ C$ which is the absolute zero temperature. It is important to note that from results obtained for all permanent gases and dry air, the pressure is found to increase by about 1/273 of its pressure at $0^\circ C$ for each degree Celsius rise in temperature. This value is the same as that obtained for volume expansivity of all gases, hence pressure expansivity of gas (γ) could be defined as increase in pressure per the product of original pressure and change in temperature .

Precautions
The following precautions are taken in verifying the pressure law.
(i)   The bulb must be dried and we ensure the air it contains is dry.
(ii) We must ensure that the position of fixed mark must not shift throughout the period of the experiment.
(iii) The thermometer must be kept vertical before taking the temperature reading.
(iv) The metre rule must be kept vertical.
(v)   The reading of the mercury level must be taken from the top of meniscus only when the mercury level is steady.

Absolute temperature and pressure
If we let P_o be the gas pressure at temperature $0^\circ C$ and P_θ be the gas pressure at temperature $\theta^\circ C$. The pressure law states mathematically that;

$$P_\theta = P_o(1+\gamma\theta) \qquad 21.5$$

Where $\gamma = \dfrac{1}{273}K^{-1}$, is pressure expansivity at constant volume

So $\gamma = \dfrac{P_\theta - P_o}{P_o\theta} = \dfrac{1}{273} K^{-1}$ \qquad 21.6

Rearranging the above equation yields

$$\frac{P_\theta}{P_o\theta} - \frac{1}{\theta} = \frac{1}{273} K^{-1}$$

i.e $\quad \dfrac{P_\theta}{P_o\theta} = \dfrac{1}{\theta} + \dfrac{1}{273}$

Multiply both sides by θ

$$\therefore \frac{P_\theta}{P_o} = 1 + \frac{\theta}{273} = \frac{273+\theta}{273}$$

{but $273+\theta$ is absolute temperature, T.}

$$\therefore \frac{P_\theta}{P_o} = \frac{T}{273},$$

Hence, $\quad P_\theta = \dfrac{P_oT}{273}$ \qquad 21.7

But $\dfrac{P_o}{273}$ is a constant, therefore $P \propto T$,

hence, $\dfrac{P}{T} = $ constant.

Therefore, the pressure P of a gas at constant volume is directly proportional to its absolute temperature T. For any given gas with pressure P_1, at temperature T_1, and pressure P_2, at temperature T_2, at constant volume, then,

$$\frac{P_1}{T_1} = \frac{P_2}{T_2}$$

Example 21.6
The pressure of a gas at constant volume is 100 cmHg at $27^\circ C$. Calculate the pressure at $87^\circ C$.

Solution
$T_1 = 27 + 273 = 300K$
$T_2 = 87 + 273 = 360K$
$P_1 = 100cmHg$,
Using pressure law and substituting yields

$$\frac{100}{300} = \frac{P_2}{360}$$

$$\therefore P_2 = \frac{100 \times 360}{300} = 120cmHg$$

Hence, $P_2 = 120cmHg$

Example 21.7
The pressures of a gas at constant volume registered 150cmHg at $0^\circ C$ and 300cmHg at higher temperature of $50^\circ C$. Calculate the absolute temperature (T).

Solution

Using $\dfrac{P_\theta}{P_o} = \dfrac{T}{273}$ yields

$$\frac{300}{150} = \frac{T}{273}$$

$$\therefore T = \frac{273 \times 300}{150}$$

$$T = 546K$$

21.5 General gas law

The general gas law is derived from the combination of these three laws, the Boyle's law, Charles' law and Pressure law

from Boyle's law: $PV = k$ at constant temperature

from Charles' law; $\frac{V}{T} = k$ at constant pressure

Pressure law or Gay-Lussac's law; $\frac{P}{T} = k$, at constant volume

These three equations from the above laws can be combined to obtain the general gas law as;

$$\frac{PV}{T} = \text{constant or}$$

$$\frac{P_1 V_1}{T_1} = \frac{P_2 V_2}{T_2} \qquad 21.7$$

where the symbols $P_1 V_1 T_1$ and $P_2 V_2 T_2$ retain their usual meanings.

Example 21.8

The temperature of gas of volume $50cm^3$ is $32°C$ at pressure of $300mHg$. Calculate the temperature when the volume is $80cm^3$ at pressure $360mmHg$.

Solution: Using the general gas law equation we have;

$$\frac{P_1 V_1}{T_1} = \frac{P_2 V_2}{T_2}$$

i.e. $\dfrac{300 \times 50}{305} = \dfrac{360 \times 80}{T_2}$

$T_2 = \dfrac{305 \times 360 \times 80}{300 \times 50} = 585.6K$

$$\therefore T_2 = 585.6 - 273$$
$$= 312.6°C$$

Example 21.9

Some quantity of dry air has a volume of $500cm^3$ at $40°C$ and under a pressure of $76cmHg$. At a temperature of $120°C$ its volume becomes $600cm^3$, calculate the pressure of the gas at this temperature.

Solution

Using the ideal gas equation.

$$\frac{P_1 V_1}{T_1} = \frac{P_2 V_2}{T_2}$$

$P_1 = 76cmHg, \ V_1 = 500cm^3, \ T_1 = 40 + 273 = 313K$
$P_2 = ?, \ V_2 = 600cm^3, \ T_2 = 120 + 273 = 393K$

$$P_2 = \frac{P_1 V_1 T_2}{V_2 T_1}$$

$$P_2 = \frac{76 \times 500 \times 393}{600 \times 313}$$

$$= \frac{149440}{1878} = 79.5cm\,Hg$$

$P_2 = 79.5cmHg$

Standard temperature and pressure (s.t.p)

The temperatures and pressures of volume of gases can be converted to a standard temperature and pressure, this conversion makes for easy and possible comparisons. The standard temperature is taken as $0°C$ or $273K$ while the standard pressure is taken as $760mm$ of mercury.

Example 21.9

$800cm^3$ of gas was collected at temperature of $33°C$ and pressure of $500mmHg$. Convert the volume of gas to s.t.p.

Solution

We note that;

$P_1 = 500mmHg \ V_1 = 800cm^3, \ T_1 = 33 + 273 = 306K$
$P_2 = 760mmHg, \ T_2 = 273K, \ V_2 = ?$

Using $\dfrac{P_1 V_1}{T_1} = \dfrac{P_2 V_2}{T_2}$ and substituting;

$$\frac{500 \times 800}{306} = \frac{760 \times V_2}{273}$$

$$V_2 = \frac{500 \times 800 \times 273}{306 \times 760}$$

$$= 469.56\,cm^3$$

21.6 Van der Waals' equation for real gas

Van der Waals, after studying the behaviour of real gases at low temperatures and high pressures found the existence of weak but short-range forces (**Vander Waals' forces**) between non-polar molecules.

These forces of attraction between the molecules of a gas, Van der Waals assumed not negligible as the kinetic theory did. He also assume the volume of the molecules of a gas not negligible when compared with the volume of the container. He considered molecules of gas in a container surrounded by other molecules and discovered that they have zero resultant attractive force on them, but molecules closer to the walls of the container have resultant attractive force away from the walls because of the attraction on them by the molecules surrounding them. This reduces the rate of change of momentum of the molecules and hence decrease in pressure. Consequently, the observed pressure, P_o is less than the ideal gas pressure by a pressure, P_i.

Therefore, for an ideal gas, the pressure is given by $(P_o + P_i)$. He also noted that this difference in pressure P_i is proportional to the product of the number of molecules striking with area of the container per second and the number per unit volume around them. But for a given volume of a gas, each of the above is proportional to density, ρ, hence, the product is proportional to ρ^2, for a given mass of gas, $\rho \propto \dfrac{1}{V}$, then $P_i \propto \rho^2 = \dfrac{a}{V^2}$, where a is a constant.

Hence, for ideal gas equation, pressure $= (P + \dfrac{a}{V^2})$.

If we take the volume of the molecules as b, then the volume of the space inside the container is $(V - b)$. Note, b is not the actual volume of the molecules, but a factor that depends on the actual volume (this is because they are in constant motion). Finally, Van der Waals' equation for real gases is given as;

$$\left(P + \frac{a}{V^2}\right)(V - b) = RT. \qquad 21.8$$

This equation is for gases at high pressure and molelcules relatively closer to each other and many. On the other hand, at low pressure when the molecules are further away from each other and are few, we can use,

$$PV = RT.$$

21.7 Kinetic molecular theory and gas laws

Kinetic theory states that:

(i)   All matters are made of atoms and molecules.
(ii)   These molecules are in a constant state of motion.
(iii)   Because of their motion, the molecules possess kinetic energy (*K.E.*).
(iv)   The molecules exert attractive force on one another.
(v)   The nearer the molecules are to one another, the greater the attraction force.

Explanation of gas laws using kinetic theory (*K. T.*)

(i)   *Using kinetic theory to explain pressure exerted by a gas:* The kinetic theory considers gas as made up of large number of molecules which behave like elastic spheres. They move about in their containers with random velocities, colliding with one another and with the walls of the container. As the gas molecules hit the walls of the containing vessel and rebound, they experience a change in velocity and therefore change in momentum. The walls therefore experience some force due to the changing momentum of the molecules of the gas. Since pressure is defined as force per unit area, some pressure is exerted on the walls of the vessel by the pestering of these molecules. This explains pressure exerted by a gas using kinetic theory.

(ii)   *Using kinetic theory to explain Boyle's law:* When the volume of the vessel containing the gas is reduced at constant temperature, the gas molecules have less space to occupy. They therefore take less time to hit the vessels walls. More bombardments are made on the walls per unit time. The pressure exerted by the gas therefore increases. On the other hand, if the volume of gas is increased, the molecules take more time to reach the walls and hence there are less impact per unit time. This leads to decrease in pressure. The pressure of the gas is therefore inversely proportional to the volume at a constant temperature. This is statement of Boyle's law.

(iii)   *Using kinetic theory to explain Charles' law:* When the temperature of the gas molecules is increased, at constant pressure, they gain kinetic energy and their velocities increase. With this increase in velocities, they hit the walls of the vessel more frequently, this brings about the increase in pressure, but to keep the pressure constant, the volume must increase so that the molecules could travel further before hitting the walls.

Therefore an increase in temperature at constant pressure would lead to an increase in volume, this is statement of Charles' law.

(iv)   *Using kinetic theory to explain pressure law or Gay Lussac's law*: When the temperature of a given mass of gas is increased at constant volume, the average kinetic energy of the molecules increases. This results in the increase in speed and hence they hit the walls of the containing vessel more frequently and stronger, in a second. Consequently the pressure of this given mass of gas increases with increase in temperature, at constant volume.

Summary

1. Three quantities are important in the study of gas behaviour, they are; pressure, volume and temperature.

2. Boyle's law states that volume of a fixed mass of gas is inversely proportional to its pressure, at constant temperature ($V \propto \frac{1}{p}$, $V = \frac{K}{p}$, $PV = k$).

3. Charles' law states that the volume of a fixed mass of gas is directly proportional to its absolute temperature, at constant pressure ($V \propto T$, $V = kT$, $\frac{V}{T} = k$).

4. Pressure law or Gay Lussac's law states that the pressure of a fixed mass of gas is directly proportional to its absolute temperature, at constant volume ($P \propto T$, $P = kT$, $\frac{P}{T} = k$).

5. General gas equation or ideal gas equation comprises of the above laws: Boyle's law, Charles' law and pressure law. It is given by $\frac{P_1 V_1}{T_1} = \frac{P_2 V_2}{T_2}$ or $\frac{PV}{T}$ = constant.

6. The volume coefficient of a gas is the increase in volume per unit volume at 0°C for 1°C rise in temperature. While, the pressure coefficient is the increase in pressure per unit pressure at 0°C for 1°C temperature rise.

7. Absolute zero of temperature is the temperature −273°C, then absolute temperature $T = 273 + \theta$, (where θ is the temperature in °C). The standard temperature and pressure (s.t.p.) are 0°C or 273K and 760mmHg or 76cmHg respectively.

8. In kinetic theory of gases, pressure is built up due to constant collision and bombardment of the molecules on the walls of the container. There is change in velocity and hence change in momentum. It is important to note that increasing the temperature at constant volume will increase the speed of the molecules, hence, increase in number of collisions per second and momentum change at respective collisions, therefore the pressure increases. But at constant pressure, they gain kinetic energy and their velocities will increase which will lead to pressure increase. In order to avoid the pressure increase, volume has to be increased so as to keep pressure constant.

9. Van der Waals' equation for real gas is given by
$(P + \frac{a}{V^2})(V - b) = RT$.

Exercises 21

1. The absolute zero of temperature is
   A. $-273°C$ B. $100°C$ C. $0°C$ D. $100°C$

2. Which of the following quantities will increase if a light-fitting piston is pushed into a cylinder closed at one end?
   I. The number of collision per second between the air molecules.
   II. The average distance between the air molecules.
   III. Pressure of the molecules.

   A. I and II only   B. I and III only
   C. I, II and III only   D. II and III only

3. The volume of a given mass of gas is $273cm^3$ at $0°C$. What is its volume at $273°C$ if its pressure remains constant?
   A. $272cm^3$ B. $273cm^3$
   C. $274cm^3$ D. $546cm^3$

4. A fixed mass of gas of volume $600cm^3$ at a temperature of $27°C$ is cooled at constant pressure to a temperature of $0°C$. What is the change in volume?
   A. $54cm^3$ B. $273cm^3$ C. $300cm^3$ D. $546cm^3$

5. A given mass of gas at $30°C$ is trapped in a tube, if its volume is reduced to two-thirds of its initial value by applying a pressure twice the original value, calculate the new temperature of the gas.
   A. $404°C$ B. $313°C$ C. $131°C$ D. $101°C$

6. Which of the following is **NOT** correct? According to the kinetic theory, an increase in the temperature of a gas at constant volume causes
   A. an increase in the mean speed of the molecules.

B. an increase in the number of collisions per second.
C. an increase in the momentum change at each collision.
D. a decrease in the mean kinetic energy of the molecules.

7. The pressure of a given mass of gas changes from $200Nm^{-2}$ to $100Nm^{-2}$, while its temperature drops from $127°C$ to $73°C$. Calculate the ratio of the final volume of the gas to its initial volume.
   A. 2:4:1   B. 2:0:1   C. 1:2:1   D. 1.73:1.00

8. The pressure of a fixed mass of gas is $2.0 \times 10^5 Nm^{-2}$ at a known temperature. Assuming that the temperature remains constant, what will be the pressure of the gas if its volume is halved?
   A. $1.0 \times 10^5 Nm^{-2}$ B. $2.0 \times 10^5 Nm^{-2}$
   C. $3.0 \times 10^5 Nm^{-2}$ D. $4 \times 10^5 Nm^{-2}$

9. Which of the following precautions are common in verification of Boyle's law, Charles' law and pressure law?
   (i) Air use must be dry.
   (ii) Thermometer must be kept vertical.
   (iii) Top of the mercury meniscus is read.
   A. 1 only   B. II only
   C. I and II only   D. I, II and III only

10. (a) State Boyle's law.
    (b) Describe briefly the verification of Boyle's law, stating all precautions needed to be taken during the course of the experiment.
    (c) Calculate the volume of a given mass of gas when its pressure changes from 900cmHg to 650cmHg at initial volume of $25cm^3$, at constant temperature.

11. (a) State Charles' law.
    (b) What precautions are taken in verifying this law in the laboratory?
    (c) A given mass of gas of volume $500cm^3$ at $0°C$ is heated at constant pressure.
    Calculate the volume of the gas at $120°C$.

12. (a) What is the statement of Gay-Lussac's Law?
    (b) Describe briefly how this law could be verified.
    (c) The pressure of a gas at constant volume registered 180cmHg at $0°C$ and 360cmHg at higher temperature of $60°C$. Calculate the absolute temperature (T).

13. Use general gas law to solve the following:
    (a) Some mass of dry air has volume of

300cm³ at 20°C and under a pressure of 76cmHg, at a temperature of 110°C its volume became 500cm³. Calculate the pressure of the gas at this temperature.

(b) 700cm³ of gas was collected at a temperature of 30°C and pressure of 450mmHg. Convert volume of this gas to s.t.p.

14. (a) Define:
    (i) absolute zero of temperature;
    (ii) absolute temperature (T);
    (iii) the standard temperature and pressure (s.t.p.);
    (iv) cubic expansivity (γ) of a gas.

(b) Use a diagram to describe briefly what happens when volume (V) of a gas is plotted against its temperature at constant pressure, particularly with the volume as the temperature becomes zero.

15. (a) State the assumptions of kinetic theory.
(b) Use this theory to explain:
    (i) Boyle's law;
    (ii) Charles' law; and
    (iii) Pressure law.

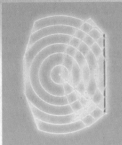

WAVES

Chapter

22

22.1   What is a wave?

A wave is a disturbance which travels through a medium and transfers energy from one point to another without causing any permanent displacement of the medium itself.

If a stone is dropped into a pond or swimming pool, ripples or waves are seen spreading on the surface of the water from the point where the stone was dropped. The water itself does not move in the direction of the ripples, but the wave transfers energy from one point to another.

Waves are also encountered in other branches of physics. For example, we can generate a wave along a string fixed at both ends by plucking the string (i.e. pulling it vertically and releasing it). Light and sound waves can also be shown to be wave motions.

There are two major classes of waves: *mechanical* and *electromagnetic* waves.

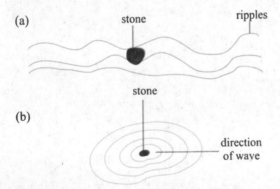

Fig. 22.1 Waves propagated along water.

Mechanical waves are waves that require a material medium for their propagation, such as water waves, waves generated in a spring or rope and sound waves.

Electromagnetic waves are waves that do not require a material medium for propagation. Examples are light rays, radiowaves, *X*-rays and gamma-rays.

22.2   Wave motion

The particles of the medium which transfer energy move to and fro, or vibrate, about a mean position as the wave passes. The vibrations are passed on from one particle of the medium to the next. The direction in which this vibration takes place is significant in classifying the type of wave, as we shall soon see.

Not all waves require a medium to carry them. Light, radiant heat and radio waves appear not to require any material medium for propagation. For example, light from the sun reaches us after passing through a vacuum. If light required a medium to carry it, then light from the sun would not be able to reach us. Light, radiant heat and radio waves are forms of electromagnetic waves and all travel through empty space at the same speed .

22.3   Transverse and longitudinal waves

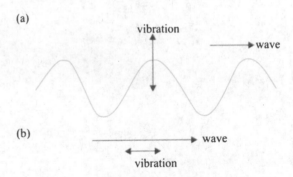

Fig. 22.2(a) Transverse and (b) Longitudinal wave

Depending on the direction of particle vibration with respect to the direction of travel of the wave, we can distinguish two types of wave.

A wave is said to be a transverse wave if the direction of travel of the wave is perpendicular to the direction of vibration of the medium.

For example, water waves and waves generated by plucking a string are transverse waves. Fig. 22.2(a).

A wave is said to be longitudinal if the direction of travel of the wave is the same as the direction of vibration of the medium.

For example, sound waves are longitudinal waves Fig. 22.2(b).

22.4   Propagation of waves
Mode of propagation of transverse waves
We have mentioned that a water wave is a typical example of a transverse wave. One can understand clearly the properties of transverse waves by studying water waves in greater detail.

Suppose a wave is generated by dropping a stone in water, and a small piece of light wood or cork is floating in the path of the wave. The cork will be seen to move up and down, that is, vibrate, or oscillate, in one spot as the wave travels past. This means that all the particles of water vibrate up and down as the wave passes. This up and down motion is perpendicular to the direction of the wave along the surface.

Similarly the particles of a plucked string vibrate up and down or from side to side, perpendicular to the direction of wave propagation, which is along the string. Water and string waves are therefore transverse waves.

It can be shown that light and electromagnetic waves are also transverse waves but since no medium is required for their propagation, the vibrations cannot be particle vibrations. In these cases the waves are made up of electric and magnetic vibrations of very high frequency. The theory involved in showing this is beyond the scope of this book.

A transverse wave can be represented pictorially by a series of up and down movements; that is, some portions of the waves are displaced upwards while adjacent portions are displaced downwards. The region of maximum upward displacement is called a **crest**. The region of maximum downward displacement is called a **trough** (see Fig 22.3).

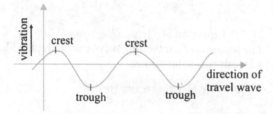

Fig. 22.3 Transverse wave showing crests and troughs.

Mode of propagation of longitudinal waves

We stated earlier that if a wave motion is such that the particles vibrate in the same direction as the wave travels, it is called a **longitudinal wave**. The vibrating particles behave like a spiral spring that has a series of compressed regions and spaced out regions travelling along it. These are referred to as **compressions** and **rarefactions**. Thus particles of the medium can be represented by a spiral spring in longitudinal wave motion, as in Fig 22.4.

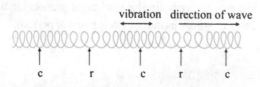

c = compression, r = rarefaction
Fig. 22.4 Mode of vibration of longitudinal waves

As a typical example, consider a sound wave (a longitudinal wave) being propagated in air, Fig 22.5(a) shows the original undisturbed position of the air. As the sound wave travels, some layers crowd together as shown. These are compression regions. Here, the air pressure has a pressure a little above normal. Between are rarefaction regions, where the layers are further apart than normal. The pressure here is less than normal (Fig. 22.5(b)).

Fig. 22.5 (a) and (b) Sound waves in compression and rarefaction.

22.5 General representation of a wave

A transverse wave as we have seen can be represented by a series of crests and troughs. We obtain a similar picture if we plot the wave as a graph, where y represents the direction of vibration of particles, while x represents the direction of propagation of the wave.

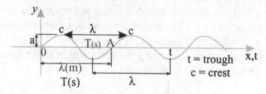

Fig.22.6 General representation of a wave.

In contrast, a longitudinal wave is made up of a series of compressions and rarefactions. If we plot a graph where y represents compression and x represents distance travelled by the wave, we obtain a graph similar to that for the transverse wave above. The compressions and rarefactions in a longitudinal wave represent the crests and troughs in a transverse wave. Hence it is convenient to represent any wave by the same diagram (Fig. 22.6). Thus, graphical representation of a longitudinal wave is not a true representation of the actual physical form.

22.6 Terms used in describing a wave and relationship between them

Amplitude (a)

As the wave progresses, the particles of the medium vibrate about a mean position. The maximum displacement of particles from their mean (or rest) position is called the amplitude a of the wave. It is measured in metres.

Period (T)

The time required for a particle to perform one complete cycle or to complete an oscillation is called the period T of the wave. It is measured in seconds.

The period is also the time for the wave to travel one wave length, .i.e. from O to A or c to c.

Frequency (f)
The number of cycles which the wave completes in one second is called the frequency, f. The *SI* unit of frequency is the hertz (Hz). Larger units are kilohertz (kHz) and megahertz (MHz). ($1kHz = 10^3$ Hz, $1 MHz = 10^6 Hz$).

Wavelength (λ)
The distance along the x-axis between successive crests or successive troughs is called the wavelength λ. It is the distance covered by the wave after one complete cycle. It is measured in metres. In longitudinal waves the wavelength is the distance between successive compressions or rarefactions.

Wave speed (v)
The distance which the wave travels in one second, is called the wave speed, v. It is measured in metres per second (ms^{-1}). If the wave covers a distance x metres in t seconds the speed of the wave is given by:

$$v = \frac{x}{t} \quad ms^{-1} \qquad 22.1$$

Relation between T, f, λ and v
From the definition of frequency (f) and period (T), it follows that the two quantities are related by the equation $f = \frac{1}{T}$. The argument leading to the formula is simple. In T seconds (i.e. one period) 1 cycle is performed. In 1 second, $1/T$ cycles will be described. This number is the frequency f.

$$\therefore \quad f = \frac{1}{T} \qquad 22.2$$

The speed v, the wavelength λ and frequency f are related by a very important equation.

$$v = f \lambda \qquad 22.3$$

Proof: In general the speed of the wave is given by this expression.

$$v = \frac{\text{distance travelled by the wave}}{\text{the corresponding time taken}}$$

In one period (T, in seconds), the wave covers a corresponding distance equal to the wavelength (λ).

$$v = \frac{\lambda}{T}$$

But $f = \frac{1}{T}$

$$\therefore v = f \lambda$$

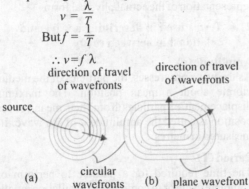

direction of travel of wavefronts

direction of travel of wavefronts

source

(a)

circular wavefronts

(b) plane wavefront

Fig. 22.7 Waves produced in a ripple tank (a) by point source (b) by a horizontal rod.

We illustrate the use of these important relations with the two examples below.

Example 22.1
A wave travels a distance of 80m in 4s. The distance between successive crests of the wave is 50cm. Calculate the frequency of the wave.

Speed of the wave $v = \frac{80}{4} = 20 ms^{-1}$

$$\lambda = 50cm = 0.5m$$
$$f = \frac{v}{\lambda} = \frac{20}{0.5} = 40Hz$$

Hence, $f = 40Hz$

Example 22.2
A radio station broadcasts at a frequency of 200kHz. If the speed of the wave is $3 \times 10^8 ms^{-1}$, calculate:
(a) the period;
(b) the wavelength of the wave.

Solution
frequency $f = 200kHz = 2 \times 10^5 Hz$

(a) Period, $T = \frac{1}{f}$

$$f = \frac{1}{2 \times 10^5} = 0.50 \times 10^5 s$$

(b) Wave length $\lambda = \frac{v}{f}$

$$\lambda = \frac{3 \times 10^8}{2 \times 10^5}$$
$$= 1.5 \times 10^3 m$$
$$= 1.5km$$

22.7 Equation of a travelling wave
The equation of a travelling wave can be written like a Sine or cosine functions:

$$y = \sin \theta \quad \text{or} \quad y = \cos \theta \qquad 22.4$$

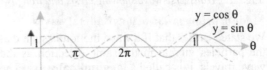

$y = \cos \theta$

$y = \sin \theta$

Fig. 22.8 sine and cosine functions

Both sine θ and cosine θ are periodic functions with amplitudes equal to one and period equals 2π rad, i.e. it repeats after 2π rad. Since angular velocity ω, is defined as $\omega = \frac{\theta}{t}$ radians per second or $\theta = \omega t$ rad, => (just very similar to circular motion i.e. $\theta = 2\pi$ rad. $= 360^0$ is one complete cycle or period).

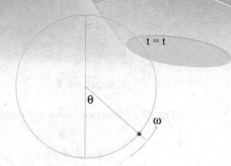

Fig. 22.9 Radians

The sin and cos equations can be written as

$$y = \sin \omega t \text{ or } y = \cos \omega t \qquad 22.5$$

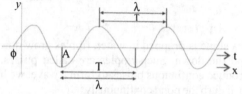

Fig. 22.10 Wave parameters

In general, a travelling wave whose amplitude is A and constant angular velocity is ω can be written as

$$y = A \sin (\omega t - \phi). \qquad 22.6$$

Or in Cosine form, where ϕ is a constant for a wave which did not start from origin.

The constant angular distance ϕ which is known as *phase constant* can be related to the linear distance x by

$$\phi = \frac{2\pi x}{\lambda} \qquad 22.7$$

Where λ is the wavelength of the wave, the quantity $\frac{2\pi}{\lambda}$ is called wave number k. Then we can write equation 22.6 as

$$y = A \sin (\omega t - kx) \qquad 22.8$$

or substituting $\omega = \frac{2\pi}{T}$; $k = \frac{2\pi}{\lambda}$ we get

$$y = A \sin \left(\frac{2\pi t}{T} - \frac{2\pi x}{\lambda} \right)$$

or $y = A \sin 2\pi \left(\frac{t}{T} - \frac{x}{\lambda} \right) \qquad 22.9$

or $y = A \sin \frac{2\pi}{\lambda} \left(\frac{\lambda t}{T} - x \right) \qquad 22.10$

Since $v = f\lambda$ and $v = \frac{\lambda}{T}$

We can further write equation 22.10 as

$$y = A \sin \frac{2\pi}{\lambda} (vt - x) \qquad 22.11$$

Any of the equation above can be used to represent a plane progressive wave.

Example 22.3

A travelling wave in a string is given by $y = 0.03 \sin (2.2x - 3.5t)$ where y and x are in metres, and t is in seconds. Find the amplitude, the wavelength, the frequency, the period and the speed of the wave.

Solution

Compare this function with equation 22.8, i.e.
$y = A \sin (\omega t - kx)$.
We can see that the amplitude $A = 0.03$m.
The wave number $k = 2.2$m^{-1} and the angular frequency $\omega = 3.5$ rad s^{-1}. Then, the wavelength
$\lambda = \frac{2\pi}{k} = 2.86$m and period $T = \frac{2\pi}{\omega} = 1.80$ s. The speed of the wave is therefore:

$$v = f\lambda = \frac{\lambda}{T}$$
$$= \frac{2.86}{1.80}$$
$$= 1.59 \text{ms}^{-1}$$

Example 22.4

The wavelength of a travelling wave is 5m at a frequency of 12 Hz.
(i) What is the wave velocity?
(ii) If there is a crest at $x = 3$m at time t, find three other positions of the crest at that instant.
(iii) What time later will there be another crest at $x = 3$m?
(iv) If the amplitude of the wave is 1.5m, write the equation of the wave.

Solution

(i) Velocity, $v = f\lambda = 12 \times 5 = 60$ms^{-1}.
(ii) The crests are at one wavelength apart, so there are crests at $x = 3, 3 + 5, 8 + 5, 13 + 5$ i.e. $x = 3, 8$m, 13m and 18m.
(iii) A crest will arrive again at $x = 3$m after one period i.e $T = \frac{1}{f}$
$$= \frac{1}{12}$$
$$= 0.083s$$

(iv) In general the wave equation may be written as
$$y = a \sin \frac{2\pi}{\lambda} (vt - x)$$

But $a = 15$m, $v = 60$ms^{-1}, $\lambda = 5$m

$\therefore y = 15 \sin \frac{2\pi}{5} (60t - x)$ or $y = 15 \sin 2\pi (12t - \frac{x}{5})$

22.8 Wavefronts

Consider a water wave generated by dropping a spherical object in water. Circular patterns are observed emerging from the centre of disturbance. All particles on the circumference of a given circle are at the same distance from the source. They are also in the same state of disturbance. They are said to be in phase. The common circle of all particles which vibrate in phase constitutes what is called a wavefront as in Fig 22.7(a).

A plane wavefront can also be generated in water by dropping a straight rod into water. Near the edges of the rod, the wavefront is curved. Fig 22.7(b).

22.9 Progressive and stationary waves

All waves, both transverse and longitudinal, which spread out continuously are called travelling or progressive waves. The graph of displacement against time is as shown in fig. 22.10.

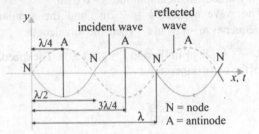

Fig. 22.11 General shape of a stationary wave

A stationary wave is a wave obtained when two progressive waves of equal amplitude and frequency are travelling in opposite directions and combined together

Most stationary waves are obtained as a result of reflection of the incident waves. Any wave can be reflection of the incident waves. Any wave can be reflected just like light in such a way that the laws of reflection are obeyed. Hence when a wave travels along a given path and it is reflected perpendicularly on striking an obstacle, the wave returns along the same path. The two waves form a stationary wave.

In a stationary wave, some points are permanently at rest. These are called **nodes** (N). Some other points vibrate with maximum amplitude. These are called **antinodes** (A).

Distances between nodes and antinodes are shown in Fig. 22.11. Note that the wavelength of the wave is twice the distance between two successive nodes.

A node is a point on a stationary wave where there is no movement of the medium.

An antinode is a point on a stationary wave where there is maximum movement of the medium.

Examples of stationary waves

(a) Waves obtained by plucking a string fixed at both ends. The transverse wave travels both ways along the string; and is reflected at the fixed ends. The waves travel in opposite ways then combine together, and the process continues until vibrations die down due to friction. This applies to all stringed instruments.

(b) Waves set up in open and closed pipes are longitudinal stationary waves in air. They are formed in a similar way to stationary waves in strings.

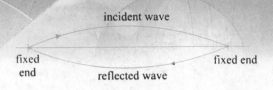

Fig. 22.12 Stationary wave in strings

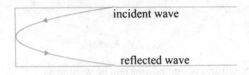

Fig. 22.13 Stationary wave in a pipe

The Ripple tank

If a stone is dropped in water, ripples grow quickly and die down. Such ripples are called **pulses**. To produce continuous pulses to form a wave, we have to disturb the pond continuously.

In the laboratory water waves can be studied using an apparatus called a **ripple tank**, (Fig 22.14). It is a shallow glass trough or a shallow container with a transparent bottom. When in use the tank is placed between a light source and a screen. Its transparent bottom enables us to project the images of the waves on a screen placed below it. The wave is produced by means of a dipper either in the form of a strip of metal or wood, or a small sphere. A small electric motor is attached to the dipper and this acts as a vibrator which generates continuous pulses, or a wave, in the water.

A stroboscope can be used to make the wave appear stationary or steady. It consists of a circular wooden disc with evenly spaced slits round it and an axle in the centre. As the stroboscope rotates the waves in the water can be viewed through the slits. As the speed of stroboscope is increased, a stage will be reached when, on viewing the wave through the slits, the waves will appear stationary and hence can be studied in greater detail.

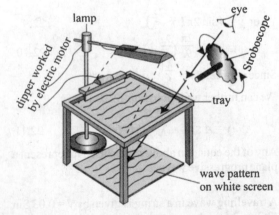

Fig. 22.14 A ripple tank

22.10 Properties or characteristics of waves

Waves have the following characteristic properties which can be examined using the ripple tank. They can be reflected, in the same way as a ball can be bounced off a surface. They also show the properties of *refraction, diffraction, interference,* and *polarization,* which are properties of waves alone.

(a)

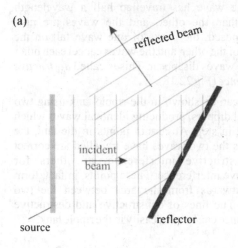

(b)

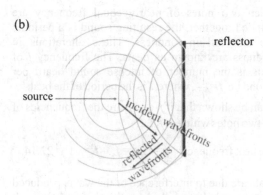

Fig. 22.15(a) and (b) Reflection of light waves.

Reflection

The reflection of waves can be shown in a ripple tank by directing plane waves from a wide dipper at a flat barrier placed in their path (Fig 22.15(a)). If a curved, concave reflector is used, the waves are brought to a single point, called a *focus* (Fig 22.15 (b)).

Refraction

The plane waves in the ripple tank can be refracted by placing a sheet of glass in the water to make it shallower. Where the water is shallower the waves travel more slowly. If they cross the edge of the glass at an angle, they are bent, or refracted, and travel in a different direction (see Fig 22.16(a)). Refraction in light is the result of a wave slowing down as it enters a more dense medium, or speeding up as it enters a less dense medium. To see how refraction in a ripple tank happens, look at the diagram of a wave being refracted in Fig. 22.16(b).

The lines across the direction of the wave are wavefronts showing what points the wave has reached after successive time periods. Notice that over the glass sheet the wavefronts are closer together, because the wave does not travel as far in each time period. The distance travelled in each time period is one wavelength, and this is shorter in the denser medium (λ_2) than in the less dense medium (λ_1).

When the wave front is at AB the edge of the wave is just reaching the boundary at A. In the next time period this edge travels to C, a distance $AC = \lambda_2$, while the other edge B travels to D, a longer distance $BD = \lambda_1$. Because one edge travels further than the other, the wave has to bend. The new wavefront CD is travelling in a different direction.

(a)

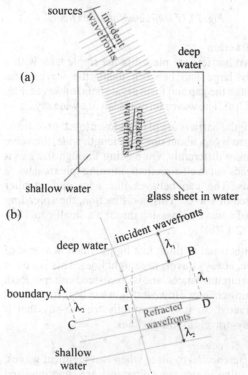

(b)

Fig. 22.16(a) and (b) Refraction of waves

The refractive index, $_Bn_A$ of medium A with respect to B is related to the speeds in the two media as follows.

$$_Bn_A = \frac{sped\ of\ wave\ in\ B}{speed\ of\ wave\ in\ A} \qquad 22.12$$

During refraction, the frequency of the wave remains the same but the wavelength, which is related to the path travelled, changes. Therefore, we can write $_Bn_A$ as

$$_Bn_A = \frac{f\lambda_B}{f\lambda_A} = \frac{\lambda_B}{\lambda_A} \qquad 22.13$$

That is, the refractive index is simply the ratio of the wavelengths of the wave in the two media.

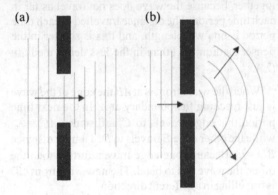

Fig. 22.17 Diffraction of waves fronts

Diffraction

If two barriers are placed in the ripple tank with a fairly large gap between them, the waves pass through the gap and form a wide band of waves, Fig. 22.17(a). The waves form a beam or a wide ray.

If the barriers are placed closer together to leave a narrow gap, about one wavelength wide, the wave behaves differently. On passing through the gap it spreads out in all directions, forming spherical wave fronts. The gap behaves like a second, smaller source of waves. This is diffraction, the spreading out of a wave on passing through a small gap. (See Fig 22.17(b)).

It is usual to think that light, which is a type of wave, always travels in straight lines. This is true in most circumstances, and is discussed further in forth coming chapter. However, light can be refracted and diffracted, so it is not strictly true to say that it always travels in straight lines.

Interference

Interference takes place when two identical waves, travelling in the same direction, are superimposed (or placed one on top of the other).

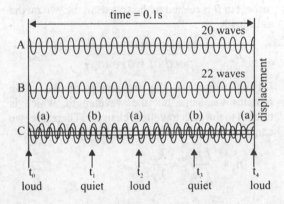

Fig 22.18 Interference

If the two waves have travelled the same distance, or if one wave has travelled a whole number of wavelengths further than the other, so that they are in step, then the waves will combine. The resulting wave has twice the amplitude of the others. This is called *constructive* or *additive interference* (Fig 22.18).

If one wave has travelled half a wavelength further than the other, and the waves are now superimposed, the peaks of one wave fall on the troughs of the other, and the waves cancel each other out. The waves disappear. This is called *destructive interference* (Fig 22.18).

This can be shown in the ripple tank using two spherical dippers, producing identical waves which start out in step. At certain points in the tank the distances the two waves have travelled are correct for constructive interference, at others for destructive interference. These points, in fact, form lines outwards from the area between the two dippers. The lines of constructive and destructive interference can be seen easily in the ripple tank.

Beats

When two notes of nearly equal frequency are sounded together, the resulting sound is a periodic rise and fall in loudness. These alterations in loudness are known as beats. The frequency f of beats is the number of intense sound heard per second i.e. $f = \frac{1}{T}$, where T is the period of the beat.

It can be shown that if f_1 and f_2 are the frequencies of the two notes with $f_1 > f_2$.

The beat frequency $\quad f = \frac{1}{T} = f_1 - f_2 \qquad 22.14$

Beats are due to interference of the wave, produced by two notes. Let us illustrate the phenomenon with two given notes A and B of frequencies 25Hz and 30Hz respectively.

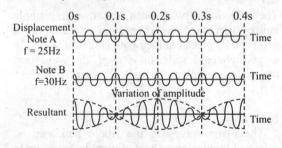

Fig. 22.19 Beats

As in Fig. 22.19, at 0, 0.2, 0.4, 0.6, 0.8s; the waves are in phases. We have maximum amplitude of vibration and hence highest loudness. But at 0.1, 0.3, 0.5, 0.7, 0.9s, we have minimum amplitude of vibration and least loudness. So a loud sound is heard every 0.2s.
The beat frequency $f = \frac{1}{T}$ and this is equal to $f_1 - f_2 = 30 - 25 = 5$Hz as stated above.

Uses of beats

Beats are found very useful. For example it can be used to determine the frequency of a known tuning fork. A tuning fork of unknown frequency, f_1 is sounded together with a fork of known frequency, f_2 to produce beats and the beat frequency f is noted. Then the f_1 can be calculated from $f_1 - f_2 = f$.

Also beats can be used to tune an instrument (e.g. piano) to the pitch of a given note. When two instruments are played and beats are heard, it shows that the pitch of the piano string is not equal to that of the tuning fork. The tension of the string of the piano is adjusted until the beats disappear, when the two instruments are played together. This shows that the two notes have equal pitches.

22.11 Polarization of waves

We have seen earlier that a transverse wave is one in which the vibration is perpendicular to the direction of propagation of the wave. For example, in a string wave the elements of the string move in a plane perpendicular to the string. Similarly it can be shown that light and other electromagnetic waves are transverse waves made up of electric, (E) and magnetic, (B) vibrations which are perpendicular to each other and to the direction of propagation.

The word 'polarization' comes from Latin word '*polus*' which means *axis* or *direction*. Therefore, if the vibrations of a transverse wave remains parallel to a fixed line in space, the wave is said to be linearly polarized. We thus define polarization of light as the direction of its electric field vector. For a plane polarized light, the electric field vector always remains in a given plane called the plane of polarization. It is the general agreement to speak of the polarization of electric field vector E and not magnetic field B because vision and other types of detection of *e-m* waves depend primarily on the sensitivity of the eye and the vast majority of other detection equipment, to the oscillations of E, rather than those of B.

In contrast to plane-polarized light, ordinary light produced by an incandescent source. (e.g. a tungsten filament lamp) is unpolarized, i.e. electric fields although still transverse to the direction of travel, are otherwise oriented at random and have no common direction.

We can visualize polarization most easily by considering mechanical waves on a string.

Mechanical analogue of polarization

We can demonstrate the mechanical analogue of polarization by a simple experiment using a horizontal rope, one of whose ends (R) is fixed to a wall and the other end (O) is free to move. (See Fig. 22.20). We can set up (along OR) many different transverse waves due to vibrations in various planes. This is done by holding O in the hand and moving it up and down in all directions transversely (or perpendicular) to the length of the rope; or, as shown by arrow in the plane A. We place two parallel slits P and Q between O and R as shown. Along OP there are transverse waves in all directions, but along PQ only the transverse wave that has passed through the slit emerges. This wave is said to be plane-polarized because its vibrations are only in one plane (the plane of the slit). This plane polarized wave also passes through Q when the slits P and Q are parallel. When Q is however turned so that it is no long parallel but perpendicular to P, no wave is obtained beyond Q.

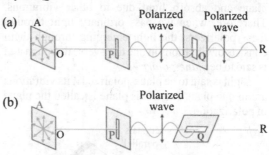

Fig. 22.20 Transverse waves and polarization.

The phenomenon of producing transverse vibrations which are only in one plane is known as polarization.

Polarization of light

Light is a form of wave motion as illustrated by the phenomenon of diffraction and interference. Polarization of light shows that light is a transverse wave motion, in contrast to the longitudinal wave motion of sound.

We consider each light wave as a transverse wave whose vibrations are along straight lines at right angles to the direction of propagation of the wave motion. An ordinary beam of light consists of several such waves each with its own plane of vibration. Looking at each light beam end-on, we have a picture as shown in Fig. 22.21.

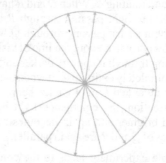

Fig. 22.21 End view of a beam of unpolarized light.

Production of polarized light

To obtain a polarized light we pass an ordinary (or un-polarized) light through a light polarizing filter.

Examples of such filters or polarizers are crystals such as tourmaline, calcite and quartz. Another polarizer is a manufactured material known as *polaroid*. This artifical crystalline material is made in the form of very thin films, which have the general appearance of the more common substance, cellophane, and is made from small needle shaped crystals of an organic compound iodosulphate of quinine.

These polarizers, because of their internal molecular structures, have the property of allowing light vibrations in only a particular direction. They transmit only those vibrations of light in a particular plane and absorb light due to other vibrations. Therefore, when we pass ordinary light through these polarizers, the light emerging through them consists of vibrations in one transverse direction and is said to be *plane-polarized*.

Light is said to be plane-polarized if its vibrations are in one plane only. This plane is called the plane of polarization.

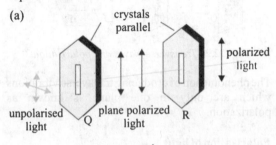

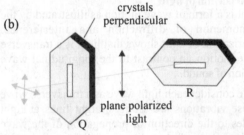

Fig. 22.22 Polarization of light by tourmaline crystals.

We can demonstrate that the light emerging from the crystal *Q* is polarized by putting a second crystal *R* behind *Q* and rotating *R*. When *Q* and *R* have their axes parallel, the light passing through *R* appears almost as bright as that passing through *Q*. When *R* is further slowly rotated about the line of vision, the light emerging through it appears darker and darker and this is completely extinguished when the axis of R is perpendicular to that of *Q*. On further rotation in the same direction, the emergence light becomes brighter and brighter and again becomes brightest when the axes of *Q* and *R* are again parallel.

This simple experiment leads to the conclusion that light consists of transverse waves, otherwise the light emerging from *Q* could never be extinguished by simply rotating the crystal *R*.

Thus we can establish whether some light is polarized or not, by simple rotating a polarizer (or polaroid) through which the light is passing. If the transmitted light

(i)   shows no change in intensity, the incident light was not polarized.

(ii)   varies slightly in intensity twice per revolution, the incident light was partly plane polarized.

(iii) is cut off completely twice per revolution, the incident light was plane-polarized

Polarization by reflection

It was discovered in 1808 by the French physicist, *Etienne Malus*, that when an ordinary, unpolarized light is incident at an angle of about 57° on the polished surface of a glass plate, the reflected light is plane-polarized.

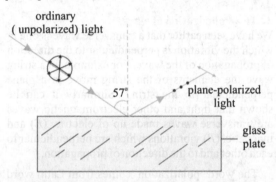

Fig. 22.23 Production of plane-polarized light by reflection.

This can be confirmed by viewing the reflected light through a polaroid or polarizer as already discussed.

Practical applications of polaroids

The polaroid finds practical applications particularly in areas where light glare is not desirable. Light glare is reflected, for example, from the window panes, the road ahead of a driver, on a sunny day, a polished table top or an open book. This reflected light is polarized, and the glaring can thus be eliminated by the use of a polaroid.

The polaroid is therefore used in a sunglasses to reduce the intensity of incident sunlight and to eliminate reflected light or glare.

Summary

1. A wave is a disturbance through a medium that carries energy from one point to another.

2. There are two major classes of waves, mechanical and electromagnetic. Electromagnetic waves do not require a medium for their propagation.

3. A mechanical wave can be transverse or longitudinal, transverse if the direction of travel of wave is perpendicular to direction of vibration and longitudinal if they are in the same direction.

4. All electromagnetic waves are transverse which is due to electric and magnetic vibrations which are perpendicular to each other.

5. Note the following equations:
$$f = \frac{1}{T}, \quad v = f\lambda, \quad f = \frac{\omega}{2\pi}$$

6. The equation of a progressive wave is
$$y = A\sin\left(\omega t + \frac{2\pi x}{\lambda}\right) \text{ or } y = A\sin\frac{2\pi}{\lambda}(vt - x)$$

Exercise 22

1. Which of the following statements about wave motion is correct?
   A. Transverse waves do not require a medium for propagation.
   B. Longitudinal waves vibrate perpendicular to direction of travel.
   C. Electromagnetic waves are transverse waves.
   D. All mechanical waves are longitudinal waves.

2. Which of the following equations is correct? (Where the symbols have their usual meanings.)
   A. $\lambda = \frac{f}{v}$ B. $\omega = 2\pi f$ C. $v = \frac{T}{\lambda}$ D. $v = \frac{t}{x}$

3. Which of the following property is a consequence of superposition of waves?
   A. Reflection   B. Refraction
   C. Interference   D. Polarization

4. State the differences between light and sound waves.

5. What do you understand by transverse and longitudinal waves? Give two examples.

6. Define the terms frequency (f), wavelength (λ) and wave speed (v)

   If for a wave $v = 0.2\text{ms}^{-1}$ and $f = 100\text{Hz}$ what is the wavelength?

7. The wavelength of a water wave is 6cm when the frequency is 10Hz.

   (a) What is the distance between successive crests of the wave?
   (b) What is the speed of propagation?

   (c) What is the period of the wave?

8. What is the period of vibration of a wave of wavelength 0.5m moving at a speed of 6.0ms^{-1}?

9. A wave of frequency 400 Hz in air has a speed of 320ms^{-1}. Find its wavelength. What will be the new wavelength when it enters water in which its speed is 1600ms^{-1}?

10. Explain how a stationary wave is formed.

11. Explain what is meant by the statement that a beam of light is plane-polarized. How can a plane-polarized light be produced and detected?

12. Explain the difference between transverse and longitudinal waves. In which of these two can plane polarization occur?

13. How can you demonstrate a mechanical analogue of polarization? Explain the uses of polaroids.

14. A long rope is fixed at one end, and the free end is made to oscillate in one plane at right angles to the rope with frequency 5Hz. The successive crests are 60cm apart. What is the speed of the waves? For what frequency would the wavelength be 0.4m?

15. A slinky spring 3m long rests on a horizontal bench with one end fixed. When the free end is suddenly pushed forward, the compression pulse travels to the fixed end and back in 2 secs. What is the speed of the longitudinal waves along the spring? What is the wavelength of the longitudinal waves produced when the free end is moved to and fro with a frequency of 2.5Hz?

16. A plane wave has equation:
    $y = 25\sin(120t - 4x)$. Find the:
    (i) wavelength
    (ii) wave velocity
    (iii) frequency and period of the wave
    (iv) amplitude of the wave
    (where y and x are in metres, t is in seconds)

23.1 Nature and sources of light

Light is a wave, it is a visible form of energy. The light from the sun comes to us by radiation. Light as a wave does not require material medium for its propagation, it travels best and faster through a vacuum, unlike sound wave. Light makes it possible for us to see and study our environment. The light produces sensation of vision through our eyes and brain. Plants grow and produce the food that we eat. They store energy produced from the sunlight, which is later converted to fuels, gas and oil many years after they have died.

> Light is a visible form of energy which is radiated outwards from a source.

We are able to see objects because of the light they produce that is reflected back to us, or the light that falls on them from other sources that are also reflected back to us.

Luminous objects: These are objects that produce their own light; e.g. the sun, stars, fire flies, glow worms, lamps, candles, electric light bulbs, etc.

Non-luminous objects (opaque): These are objects that do not produce their own light, they are only seen when light from other sources falls on them and is reflected back into our eyes.

23.2 Transmission of light

Light is transmitted through a vacuum, it needs no material medium for its propagation. The direction or path along which the light travels is called a **light ray.** We have parallel rays (beam), convergent rays (beam) and divergent beam of light.

(a) divergent beam

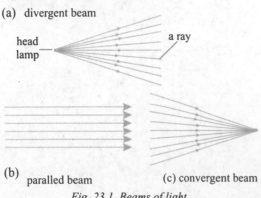

(b) paralled beam   (c) convergent beam

Fig. 23.1 Beams of light

These rays are referred to as beam of light.

23.3 Rectilinear propagation of light

It is an established fact that light travels in straight lines.

Experimental proofs of rectilinear propagation of light

This is seen from the sharpness of the shadow cast by an obstacle when placed in the path of light from a point source such as a burning candle.

Three cardboard screens, *A*, *B* and *C*, with holes in their centres, are arranged in a straight line, fig. 23.2. This is done by putting a string through the holes and drawing the string taut. Source of light is then placed behind the first screen *A*. As we look through the third screen *C*, we see the light from the source. If either screen is shifted, the light is cut off.

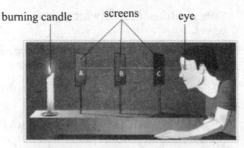

Fig. 23.2   Rectilinear propagation of light.

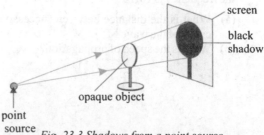

Fig. 23.3 Shadows from a point source.

> Rectilinear propagation of light is referred to as the phenomenon of light travelling in a straight line.

Formation of shadows and eclipses, are the two natural effects that result from the rectilinear propagation of light.

Shadows

Shadows are usually formed by opaque objects.

An opaque object is one which does not allow light to pass through it.

A shadow is that area to which light cannot reach because of the obstruction of an opaque object. Fig. 23.3 demonstrates how shadows formed by a tiny source of light, called a point source. A point source of light produces a sharp shadow. On the other hand, a large source of light (fig. 23.4) produces shadow that consists of the following, (i) umbra, i.e. inner shadow, which is a region of total shadow, not reached by any light and, (ii) penumbra, (a partial shadow), which receives only part of the light rays.

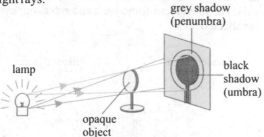

Fig. 23.4 Umbra and Penumbra

Eclipses

The sun produces its own light, and therefore, it is a luminous object. The earth and the moon are non-luminous, or opaque objects. The moon is seen by means of the sunlight reflected from the moon's surface.

Eclipse of the sun (solar eclipse)

This takes place when the moon comes between the earth and the sun. Then the moon's shadow is cast upon the earth (fig. 23.5). For people in the umbra region, it is total eclipse, while with people in penumbra region, it is partial eclipse.

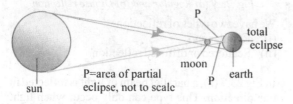

Fig. 23.5 Eclipse of the sun

Annular Eclipse of the Sun

This occurs when the sun and the moon are in positions where the end rays intersect before reaching the earth. The sun, is then covered, leaving a bright ring round the edge, (fig. 23.6).

One of the advantages of this annular eclipse is that it gives astronomers opportunity to study the properties of the outer part of the sun (corona) which have been obstructed by the moon and hence prevents such studies.

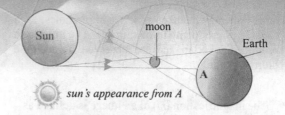

Fig. 23.6 Annular eclipse of the sun

Eclipse of the Moon (lunar eclipse)

This takes place when the earth is between the sun and the moon. As such, the shadow of the earth is thrown upon the moon, then a partial or total eclipse of the moon is observed (fig. 23.7). At B, no eclipse is observed, at C, partial eclipse is observed, while D total eclipse is observed because the entire moon is embedded in the umbra region.

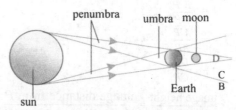

Fig. 23.7 Eclipse of the moon

The pin-hole camera

The pin-hole camera is made up of a light-tight box, painted black, a small hole is made at one end with a pin or needle point (Fig. 23.8). The opposite end has screen made of tracing paper or oil paper. In a dark room, an object placed a short distance from the hole forms a bright inverted image of the object on the screen. When the object is brought nearer to the hole, the image becomes larger. If the screen is replaced by a photographic plate, a picture can be taken with the pin-hole camera.

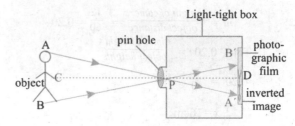

Fig. 23.8 The pin-hole camera

In fig. 23.8, an object AB, placed in front of the hole, forms an inverted image on the screen. Any time the object distance is greater than the image distance, then the image is diminished. In the contrary, when the object distance is less than the image distance, the image is enlarged. Light rays from various points on the object passes in straight line through the hole and strikes the screen as indicated in fig. 23.8. This is why the image is inverted. Making the hole large will mean production of brighter blurred image. A large hole may be taken as series of pin holes, each capable of producing its own image. The images so produced, overlap and are observed as a single blurred image.

Magnification

The magnification (m) of an image is defined as the ratio of the height of the image to the height of the object

From fig. 23.8 for the pin-hole camera,

$$m = \frac{B'A'}{BA}$$

It can be seen from similar triangles APB and $A'PB'$ that

$$m = \frac{B'A'}{BA}$$
$$= \frac{B'P}{BP}$$
$$= \frac{A'P}{AP}$$
$$= \frac{DP}{CP}$$

Thus, $\dfrac{\text{image height}}{\text{object height}} = \dfrac{\text{image distance from } P}{\text{object distance from } P}$

or $\quad m = \dfrac{\text{length of camera}}{\text{object distance from } P}$ \qquad 23.1

Example 23.1
The length of a pin-hole camera is 12cm. It is used to photograph an object 60cm away from the hole, and 80cm high. Calculate the height of the image and magnification produced.

Solution
Let the height of the image be x and magnification m, but by definition;

$$m = \frac{\text{length of camera}}{\text{object distance}} = \frac{12}{60} = 0.20$$

Thus, $0.20 = \dfrac{\text{image height}}{\text{object heights}}$

$$0.20 = \frac{x}{80}$$

$$\therefore x = 16 \text{cm}$$

Example 23.2
An object of height 40cm is placed 0.8m in front of a pin-hole camera of length 16cm. What is the magnification and height of image produced?

Solution
Let height of image be h, then using

$$m = \frac{\text{image height}}{\text{object height}}$$
$$= \frac{v}{u}$$

$$\frac{\text{image height}}{\text{object height}} = \frac{\text{length of camera}}{\text{object distance}}$$

$$\therefore m = \frac{h}{40} = \frac{16}{80},$$
$$h = 8.0 \text{cm},$$
$$m = 0.2 \text{cm}$$

23.4 Reflection of light from plane surfaces
When light strikes a surface it is absorbed, transmitted or reflected. The rays which strike the surface are referred to as **incident rays** while those that are thrown back from the surface are referred to as **reflected rays.** We are able to see the picture of ourselves behind the mirror when we look through the mirror because the incident rays from our face strike the mirror and come back and enters our eyes as reflected rays.

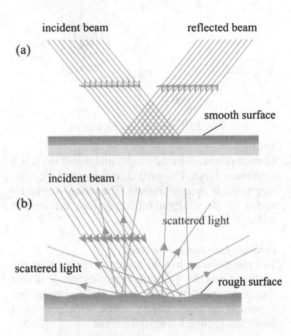

Fig. 23.9 (a) Regular and (b) Diffuse reflection

We have two types of reflection
(i)   Regular and
(ii) Scattered or diffused reflection.

In Fig 23.9 (a), a parallel beam of light is reflected in one direction. This type can only occur when light strikes a smooth, polished surface such as plane or flat mirror. Scattered or diffuse reflection takes place when light strikes a rough surface, such as paper surface, table etc, rays are reflected in different directions (fig. 23.9(b)).

Laws of reflection
The laws governing the regular reflection of light from a plane surface could be in investigated with the following experiment.
A piece of paper is placed firm on a drawing board with drawing pins. A plane mirror placed in a

176

wooden holder is placed in a vertical position on a line *AB* drawn on the paper, Fig. 23. 10 (a). *A* line *ON* (normal *AB*) is drawn to meet *AB* at right angles at *N*, the midpoint of *AB*. Lines are drawn making angles of 30°, 40°, 60°, and 80° with *ON*. With a ray box, a narrow beam of light is directed on to the mirror along the line making angle 30° with the normal (Fig. 23.10(b)).

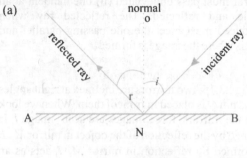

(a)

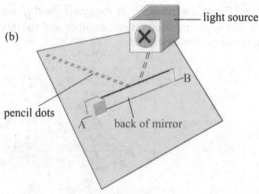

(b)

Fig. 23.10 Using a ray box to show the laws of reflection.

The position of the reflected ray is then marked by two dots. *A* line representing the reflected ray is drawn to these dots. The same procedure is repeated with the other angles. The angle of reflection is measured and compared with angle of incidence.

In each case, it is found that the angle of incidence is equal to the angle of reflection.

The experiment could also be carried out with optical pins rather than a ray box, Fig. 23.11.

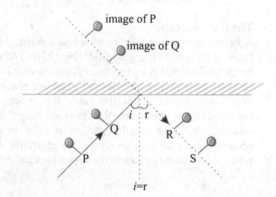

Fig. 23.11 Demonstration of laws of reflection.

Two pins are placed vertically at points *P* and *Q* along the incident ray. Two other pins *R* and *S* are used to determine the reflected ray by placing them in line with the images of *P* and *Q* as seen in the mirror. The angles of incidence and reflection are measured as before. In each case the angle of incidence is found to be equal to the angle of reflection.

The laws of reflection state:
(i) The incident ray, the reflected ray and the normal at the point of incidence all lie in the same plane.
(ii) The angle of incidence is equal to the angle of reflection.

Finding the image of an object using a plane mirror

An object pin is placed a few centimeters in front of the mirror. Looking past the object pin into the mirror, one sees an image of it.

A second pin, the search pin, (or image pin), is now placed behind the mirror, so that it appears to be in straight line with the image of the object pin, as the observer moves his/her head from side to side, as shown in fig. 23.12.

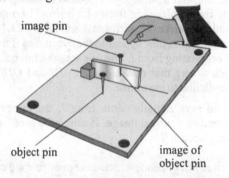

Fig. 23.12 Locating the image by the method of no parallax.

If the pins do not move together, but move relative to one another, there is parallax between them.

Parallax is the apparent relative movement of two aligned objects when they are not at the same distance from an observer. The image pin has to be adjusted until there is no relative movement as the observer moves his head from side to side. There is then no parallax between the image pin and the image of the object pin.

The position of the second pin is marked and a line is drawn from this position to that of the object pin. The measured angle between this line and the mirror is be found to 90°. It is also found that object distance in front of the mirror equals the image distance behind the mirror.

Lateral inversion

Lateral inversion stems from the fact that an object is perpendicularly opposite its image behind the mirror. We can demonstrate this by writing a letter L on a paper in front of the mirror, as our object. Then pins are placed at various points of L (fig. 23.12), corresponding image is located by the method of no-parallax. The position of the image in each case is marked by a dot. In this way we join the position of the image of the letter L as a set of dots. On joining the dots, we observe that the L has been turned around, as shown in Fig.23.13. We say that the image in a plane mirror is laterally inverted. Because of lateral inversion, you will observe that, in placing your right palm in front of a plane mirror, that its image appears in the mirror as a left palm.

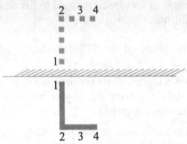

Fig. 23.13 Lateral inversion

How the image is formed by plane mirror

Let us consider a point object O, such as the tip of a candle flame, placed in front of a mirror. Two rays OA and OB, strike the mirror at A and B (Fig 23.14). After reflection, they appear to the eye at E as if they were originating from I. The eye sees the image at I in such a way that ON is equal to IN and ONI is perpendicular to the mirror.

As no rays actually come from I, the image is described as a virtual image. It cannot be seen on a screen placed at I.

A virtual image is one which can not be formed on the screen.

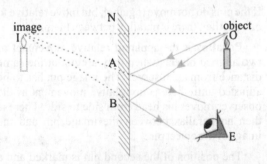

Fig. 23.14 Image of an object in a plane mirror

A real image is one which can be formed on the screen

The image in a plane mirror has the following characteristics: it is
(i)   the same size as the object;
(ii)   as far behind the mirror as the object is in front;
(iii) laterally inverted;
(iv)   virtual; and
(v)   upright.

It is very important to note that for images formed by plane mirror, two most important incident rays must be considered (i) one falling perpendicular to the mirror must pass undeviated (ii) one incident at an angle and reflected. The reflected ray when produced must meet the one passing parallel and that is where the image is formed.

Images formed by inclined mirrors

In Fig.23.15, two mirrors are inclined at right angles and a pin O is placed in front of them. When we look into the mirrors, three images are seen. Image I_1 is formed by the reflection of the object in mirror M_1. I_2 is formed by reflection in mirror M_2. I_1 acts as an object for M_1 and image $I_{2,1}$ is formed. $I_{1,2}$ and $I_{2,1}$ are actually superimposed on one another and so only three images are observed.

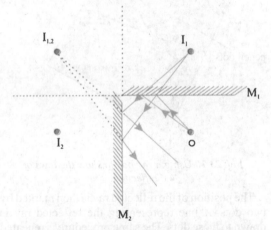

Fig. 23.15 Image formed by inclined mirror

If the mirrors are inclined at angles other than 90°, a different number of images will be seen. When mirrors are placed parallel to one another, an infinite number of images is formed.

$$\text{Number of images} = \frac{360°}{n} - 1$$

The Kaleidoscope

A kaleidoscope is a tube in which two mirrors are fixed, inclined at an angle of 60° (Fig. 23.16) At the bottom of the tube is a window of glass, on which are several loose pieces of coloured glass are placed . When one looks down the tube, the pieces of coloured glass between the mirrors form five images, so that a regular pattern is seen in six sectors. The tube can be shaken to rearrange the pieces of coloured glass and obtain various patterns.

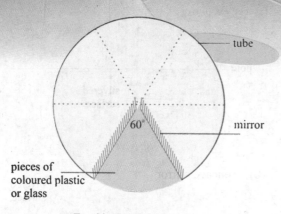

Fig. 23.16 A Kaleidoscope

Practical application of plane mirror reflection

One of the applications is in the construction of a periscope. Two mirrors are used in the construction of a periscope that enables one to see over walls and other obstacles. Periscopes are also used in tanks to see out above the armour plating.

In a simple periscope, two parallel plane mirrors are fixed facing one another and inclined at 45° to the line joining them (Fig. 23.17)

A ray *OA* striking mirror M_1 at 45° at *A* is reflected downwards along *AB* and strikes mirror M_2 at 45° at *B*. The ray is then reflected along *BE*. The object hidden from view by the obstacle is thus brought to the eye of the observer by the reflection of the two mirrors. The periscope will not function properly if the mirrors are not adjusted so that the ray from the object meets both mirrors at 45° to the normal.

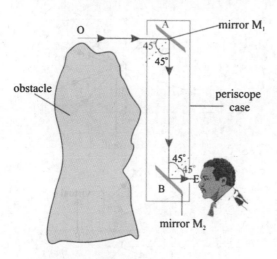

Fig. 23.17 A simple periscope

Effect of mirror rotation on a reflected ray

Let a ray be incident at angle *i* to the mirror *MNL* (Fig. 23.18). The angle of reflection is also equal to *i*. The angle between the incident and reflected ray (angle *ONR)* is the sum of angle of incidence and angle of reflection, i.e. 2*i*. If the mirror is rotated through an angle θ, the normal is also moved through θ. If the incident ray is fixed at the same direction as before the rotation, the angle of incidence in the new situation is equal to *i*+θ. The angle between the incident ray and the reflected ray equals

$(i+\theta)+(i+\theta)= 2i +2\theta$. So angle $ONR_2 = 2i + 2\theta$.

Therefore, the angle of rotation of the reflected ray when the mirror is turned through θ is :

$$(2i + 2\theta) - 2i = 2\theta. \qquad 23.2$$

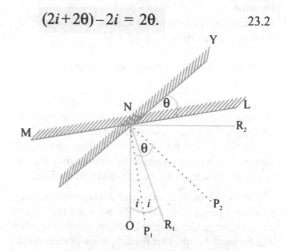

Fig. 23.18 Rotation of a mirror

The reflected ray always turns through twice the angle of rotation of the mirror each time the mirror is rotated. Its application is seen in some of the scientific instruments such as mirror galvonometer and navigator's sextant.

Example 23.1

A ray of light is incident at 50° to a plane mirror. Calculate the angle between the incident and reflected rays.

Solution

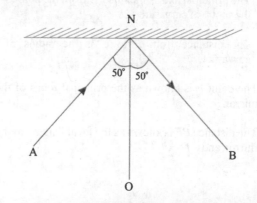

Fig. 23.19

From fig. 23.19,
    AN = incident ray
    NB = reflected ray

incident angle $(i) = 50°$
reflected angle $(r) = 50°$

Angle $ANB = <ANO + <ONB = 50° + 50° = 100°$
This means that the angle between the incident and
reflected ray is normally $2i$.

Example 23.2
The angle of incidence of a plane mirror is 30°, if the
mirror is rotated through 40°, calculate the degree of
rotation of reflected ray.

Solution
The angle of rotation of the mirror is 40°, therefore
the reflected ray rotates 2 x 40° = 80°.

23.5 Reflection of light by curved mirrors
Definitions
A curved surface could be produced by cutting out a
part of a spherical shell. If light is reflected from the
outside of this surface, a **convex** or **diverging** mirror
is produced. If light is reflected from the inside
surface, we have a **concave** or **converging** mirror.
Such curved mirrors are called spherical mirrors.

Due to the curved nature of these mirrors, they
produce images in a way different from that of the
plane mirrors. Concave mirrors are used in torches
and car head-lamps, in reflecting telescopes and also
as shaving mirrors. Convex mirrors are often used as
driving mirrors and to see round corners in
supermarkets.

In studying the images formed by curved mirrors,
it is necessary that we define some terms related to
these mirrors, see fig. 23. 20.

The pole of the mirror is the mid point (P) of the
mirror.

The centre of curvature (C) is the centre of the
sphere of which the mirror is a part.

The principal axis is the line PC from the pole to
the centre of curvature.

The distance from P to C is the radius of
curvature, r.

The point F is known as the principal focus of the
mirror,

The distance PF is known as the focal length f of the
mirror, and $f = \frac{r}{2}$

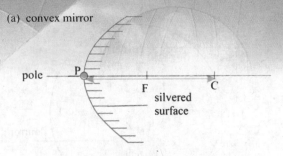

(a) convex mirror

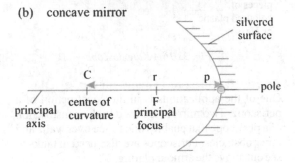

(b) concave mirror

Fig. 23.20 Reflection in curved mirrors.

The effect of curved mirrors on rays
When a beam of light is incident on a concave
mirror, the rays are reflected to converge or come
together at a point, F, called a **focus**.

The principal focus of a concave mirror is the
point where rays that are parallel and close to the
principal axis converge after reflection (fig.
23.21).

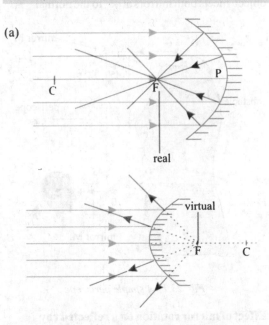

Fig 23.21 Reflection of parallel beams.

With a convex mirror, the rays appear to diverge or
come from the point F behind the mirror after
reflection.

The principal focus of a convex mirror is the point from which rays parallel and close to the principal axis appear to diverge from after reflection.

In a concave mirror, the rays converge to a point which we can obtain on a screen placed in front of the mirror as a bright spot of light, therefore, its focus is a real one. But for a convex mirror, the reflected rays do not actually pass through the focus but only appear to do so. If a screen is placed behind the convex mirror, no bright spot of light is seen on the screen, focus of a convex mirror is thus a virtual focus.

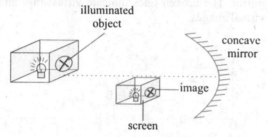

Fig. 23.22 Images from a concave mirror

23.6 Formation of images and mirror formulae (in curved mirrors).

The nature and position of images formed by a concave mirror for different positions of an object could be investigated using a raybox (fig. 23.22).
The mirror is placed on a wooden stand, and light from the object (crosswire) is made to fall on the centre of the concave mirror.

Images are formed differently when object is placed in front of a concave mirror, depending on their positions in front of the concave mirror. We now consider the following:

(i)   When object is placed farther away from the mirror, the image formed is real, smaller than the object and inverted.

(ii)   Object placed closer to the mirror, the image size gets bigger, real and inverted.

(iii) Object placed at centre of curvature of the mirror; the image is same size as the object, inverted and real.

(iv)   Object placed between the centre of curvature and the principal focus; the image is larger than the object, real and inverted.

(v)   Object placed at the principal focus; the image is no longer formed on the screen.

(vi)   Object placed between the principal focus and the pole; the image is larger, erect but virtual.

It is important to note that with a convex mirror, the image is always erect, smaller than the object and virtual no matter where the object is placed.

The above results help us in distinguishing a convex mirror from a concave mirror.

Mirror formulae

(a)   A concave mirror has a real principal focus, hence the focal length (f) is positive. It forms real or virtual image depending on the position of the object. If it forms real image, then the object distance, u, and image distance, v, from the mirror are both positive. If on the other hand the image is virtual, then v is negative.

For the former where v is positive (+ve) u is positive (+ve) then f is also +ve, therefore the mirror formula is given by;

$$\frac{1}{f} = \frac{1}{u} + \frac{1}{v} \quad \text{and} \qquad 23.3$$

Magnification m is given by

$$m = \frac{\text{height of image}}{\text{height of object}}$$
$$= \frac{\text{image distance from the mirror}}{\text{object distance from the mirror}}$$
$$= \frac{v}{u}$$

For the same concave mirror, if v is negative (–ve), and u is positive and f is (+ve) then

$$\frac{1}{f} = \frac{1}{u} - \frac{1}{v} . \qquad 23.4$$

If we multiply the mirror formula in 23.3 by v we get;

$$\frac{v}{f} = \frac{v}{u} + 1 ,$$
$$\text{i.e. } m + 1 = \frac{v}{f}$$

(b)   For convex mirror, principal focus is virtual, therefore its focal length (f) is negative, but u is positive, therefore we have;

$$\frac{1}{(-f)} = \frac{1}{u} + \frac{1}{(-v)} \quad \text{i.e. } \frac{1}{u} - \frac{1}{v} = \frac{-1}{f}$$

Simple ray construction of image positions

The nature and position of the images formed by curved mirrors could also be found with the aid of ray diagrams drawn to scale, employing the facts below.

(i)   A ray parallel to the principal axis passess through the principal focus after reflection.

(ii)   A ray through the centre of curvature is reflected back along the same path.

(iii) A ray passing through the principal focus must be reflected parallel to the principal axis.

The point at which the reflected rays meet is where the image is formed.

We can represent the object as a straight line perpendicular to the principal axis with an arrow to represent its head. We can also represent the mirror by a curved line, shaded on the back.

Fig. 23.23 represents the ray diagrams for the various positions of the object as have been earlier discussed.

OA represents the object, *IB* the image. The point *B* of the image represents point *A* of the object. *B* is the point of intersection of the rays.

In Fig. 23.23(a-d) *AM* is the ray which is parallel and close to the principal axis. It is reflected as *MF* to pass through the principal focus. Ray *AC* is the ray that passes through the centre of curvature, and must be reflected back on its path as indicated by the arrows.

(a)

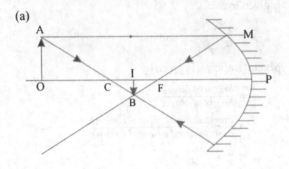

(b)

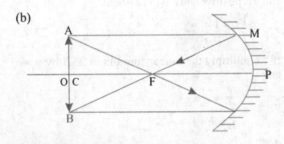

(c)

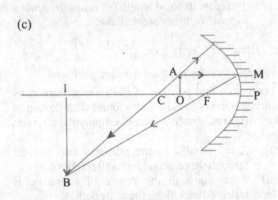

(d)

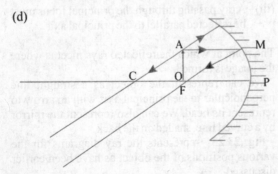

(e)

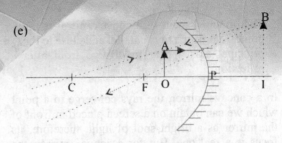

Figure 23.23 Position and nature of the image produced by a concave mirror.

In Fig.23.23 (e) the object is between *F* and *P*, we note that the rays appear to meet at a point behind the mirror. The broken lines indicate virtual rays and virtual images.

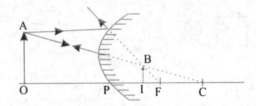

Fig. 23.24 Formation of an image by a convex mirror.

Fig. 23.24 illustrates the formation of an image by a convex mirror. We have already noted that only virtual images are formed in convex mirrors. This is because rays diverging from any point of the object, after reflection, appear to diverge from a point situated behind the mirror, whatever the position of the object.

23.7   Use of convex driving mirrors

The driving mirror of a motor car is a convex mirror, because this mirror always gives an erect image of an object behind the driver. Convex mirrors also provide a wide field of view. Therefore objects within a large angle can be seen with the help of the mirror. (Fig 23.25).

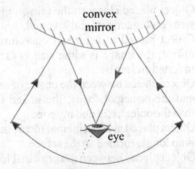

Fig. 23.25 Use of a convex driving mirror.

Finding the position and nature of image by a curved mirror by scale drawing. This could be done using the example on the next page as illustration.

Example 23.3

An object of height 2.0cm high is placed 8.0cm in front of a concave mirror of radius of curvature 10.0cm. Use scale drawing to determine the:
(i) position (ii) height (iii) nature of magnification of image produced.

Solution

We first choose the most convenient scale; we let 2.0cm represent 1.0cm on the drawing, so that 2.0cm, 8.0cm and 5.0cm are represented by 1.0cm, 4.0m ad 2.5cm respectively. Since $r = 10.0$cm, $f =$ focal length $= 5.0$cm.

Let MNP represent the curved mirror and we draw CFP to cut MNP at right angle, AO (object) 1cm high, is drawn at right angle to CFP and is 4.0cm from P. The incident ray AN drawn parallel to CFP must pass through F after reflection. Another important ray, CA, which passes through C must return through its path as shown in fig. 23.26.

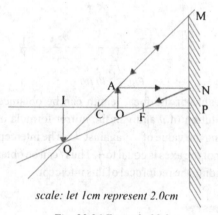

scale: let 1cm represent 2.0cm

Fig. 23.26 Example 23.3

The image (IQ) is formed at the point of intersection of CM and QN. From our scale:
(i) the image is 6.5cm x 2 = 13.0cm in front of the mirror,
(ii) height = 1.7 x 2 = 3.4cm
(iii) nature; it is inverted and real and magnification
$$= \frac{3.4}{2} = 1.7$$

Magnification

We define magnification (m) of an object in mirror as the number of times the image is bigger than the object.

$$m = \frac{height\ of\ image}{height\ of\ object}$$

$$or\ m = \frac{image\ distance\ from\ mirror}{object\ distance\ from\ mirror}$$

Use of parabolic mirrors in car headlamps

It has been observed that, for a mirror of wide aperture, rays from the point source of light at the focus do not all emerge as parallel rays after reflection. Rather, rays that are reflected from the outer parts of the mirror are divergent rays while those reflected from the central portion are parallel rays. The intensity or brightness of the emergent light therefore decreases from the central area of the mirror to the outer area. For this reason, spherical concave mirrors are not used as car head-lamps or as searchlights. For production of parallel rays of constant intensity from all parts of the surface, a mirror has to be of parabolic shape. Parabolic mirrors are therefore used as car head-lamps and as search lights (Fig. 23.7). Spherical mirrors are often used as car headlamps because they are readily available and cheaper to produce.

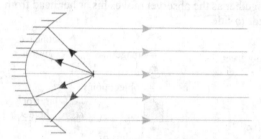

Fig. 23.27 A parabolic reflector

Experimental determination of the focal length of a concave mirror

Quick and approximate method

A quick and approximate method of determining the focal length of a concave mirror involves holding the mirror on a metre rule near the wall. Then face the mirror to target a far distant object, when the bright image of the object is obtained on the wall or screen, the mirror is adjusted until the sharpest image of object is obtained. The distance between the wall (screen) and mirror is measured and recorded as the approximate focal length.

Focal length from measurement of the radius of curvature

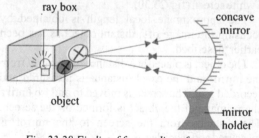

Fig. 23.28 Finding f from radius of curvature.

Fig.23.28 illustrates the apparatus used for determining radius of curvature. A ray box is used, and the cross-wires in the front surface of it is used as the object. The height of the concave mirror is adjusted until it is at same level as the object. The mirror is moved backwards and forward until a sharp image of the object is seen near the cross-wires on the front surface of the ray box which serves as a screen. The distance between the cross-wires and the mirror is measured and recorded. This procedure is repeated for three more times and the average value taken and recorded, this is the radius of curvature of the mirror. Since $f = r/2$, the average value is divided by two, this is the focal length (f) of the mirror.

Focal length by the no-parallax method

The apparatus is set up as in Fig 23.29. The pin, mounted vertically on a cork is moved to and fro in front of the concave mirror until a position is found where there is no parallax between the pin and its inverted image as seen in the mirror. At the point of no-parallax, the object and its image appear to move together as the observer moves his or her head from side to side.

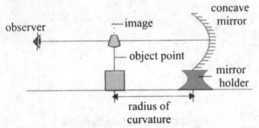

Fig. 23.29 Finding r for a concave mirror.

The distance between the pin and the mirror is measured and this is the radius of curvature of the mirror. The experiment is repeated for four more times and an average value is obtained. Half of the radius of curvature gives the focal length.

Focal length by use of the mirror formula

It has been ascertained that the image distance (v), the object distance (u) and the focal length (f) of a mirror are related by this formula.

$$\frac{1}{v} + \frac{1}{u} = \frac{1}{f}$$

The apparatus consists of a ray box with a cross-wire to act as an illuminated object, a concave mirror and a white screen (fig. 23.30).

The approximate focal length is obtained by focusing the image of a distant object as has been earlier described.

The object is placed at a distance of about $3f$ from the mirror and the exact distance is measured and recorded as u. The screen is moved to and fro until a sharp image of the object is formed on the screen. The distance from the screen to the mirror is measured and recorded as v.

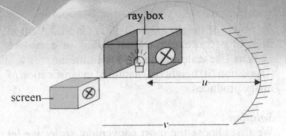

Fig. 23.30 (a) finding the focal length (f) of a mirror.

The procedure is repeated for various object distances (u) and the corresponding image distance (v) are measured and recorded.

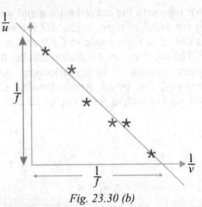

Fig. 23.30 (b)

The value of the focal length can be obtained by substitution of u and v in the mirror formula or by plotting the value of $\frac{1}{v}$ against $\frac{1}{u}$. The intercept on either of the axes is equal to $\frac{1}{f}$. Thus f can be obtained by finding the reciprocal of this intercept.

Summary

1. Light is a visible form of energy, which travels in a straight line.
2. Umbra is area of total darkness whereas penumbra is area of partial darkness.
3. A real image is one that is formed on the screen, while virtual image cannot be formed on the screen.
4. Mirror formular is given by;

$$\frac{1}{v} + \frac{1}{u} = \frac{1}{f}$$

$$f = \frac{r}{2}$$

5. Magnification = $\dfrac{height\ of\ image}{height\ of\ object}$

   = $\dfrac{image\ distance\ from\ mirror}{object\ distance\ from\ mirror}$

6. For concave (converging) mirror:
(i) the focus is real.
(Ii) the image is real and inverted, when the distance of the object from the mirror is greater than the focal length.
(iii) the image is virtual, erect and magnified when

the distance of the object from the mirror is less than its focal length.

7. For a convex (diverging) mirror, the image is always erect, diminished and virtual.

8. A concave mirror has a positive focal length and a convex mirror has a negative focal length (sign convention).

Exercise 23

1. The image of any real object formed by a diverging mirror is not
   A. inverted.   B. erect.
   C. diminished.   D. virtual.

2. Which of the following is not self-luminous?
   A. Incadescent electric bulb.
   B. Lighted candle.
   C. The moon.
   D. The sun.

3. Light travels in a straight lines. In which of the following is this principle manifested?
   I. Pinhole camera II. Formation of shadows
   III Diffraction of light IV. Occurrence of eclipse
   A. I and III only   B. I, II and IV and
   C. II and III only   D. I, II & III only

4. An object is placed on the principal axis and at the centre of curvature of a concave mirror. The image of the object formed by the mirror is
   A. at the centre of curvature.
   B. erect and virtual.
   C. real and diminished.
   D. real, inverted and magnified.

5. Which of the following is/are not correct about image formed by a plane mirror?
   I. Erect II. Virtual III. Magnified IV. Farther from the mirror than the object.
   A. I only   B. III only
   C. III and IV only   D. IV only

6. A ray of light is incident on a plane mirror at an angle of 30°. Calculate the angle which the reflected ray makes with the surface of the mirror.
   A. 120° B. 60° C. 90° D. 180°

7. The image in a pin-hole camera is always
   A. enlarged.   B. upright.
   C. inverted.   D. blurred.

8. An object is placed 15cm from the pole of a concave mirror of radius of curvature 20cm, calculate the magnification of the image formed.
   A. 0.35 B. 0.75 C. 4.00 D. 2.00

9. An object is placed between two mirrors which are inclined at an angle of 90° while facing each other. The number of images formed by the two mirrors are
   A. 6 B. 2 C. 3 D. 4

10. An object is placed 20cm in front of a concave mirror of radius of curvature 30cm. Calculate the position and nature of image formed.
    A. 60 real,   B. 8.6 real
    C. 8.6 virtual   D. 30 virtual

11 (a) Describe how a pin-hole camera works.
   (b) What is umbra and penumbra?
   (c) The distance between the pin-hole and screen of a pin-hole camera is 5cm, and the plate is 8cm long. Calculate the minimum distance from the pin-hole where a man of height, 6m must stand to get a full-length of his photograph.

12 (a) Name three applications of the plane mirror.
   (b) State the laws of reflection of light.
   (c) An image that is half the size of the object is produced when the object is placed in front of a concave mirror of radius of curvature 20cm, determine the position of both the object and image.

13 (a) Prove that the image in a plane mirror and the object are at equal distances from the mirror.
   (b) An object of height 4.0cm is placed 2.0cm, from a plane mirror. An observer taller than the object observes the image, draw to scale the rays entering the observer's eye.
   (c) Explain why the image of a right hand formed by a plane mirror looks like a left hand.

14 (a) Distinguish between real and virtual images.
   (b) Define principal focus of a concave mirror.
   (c) An object 4.0cm high is placed 10cm, on and perpendicular to the axis of a concave mirror of radius of curvature 30cm. Determine the position and size of the image and illustrate using diagram the paths of three rays from points on the object to an observer's eye.

15 (a) Describe (i) kaleidoscope (ii) periscope
   (b) Explain a quick method of determining the radius of curvature of a spherical concave mirror. How would you use a concave mirror, of radius of curvature 24.0cm to get a three times magnified erect image of an object? Use a ray diagram to illustrate the formation of the image.

REFRACTION OF LIGHT WAVES AT PLANE SURFACES

24.1 Definitions

Refraction is change in direction of light rays. Refraction occurs whenever light rays travel from a transparent medium to another transparent medium of different density. The abrupt change in direction at the surface of the two media is referred to as **refraction.** Refraction occurs when light travels from air to glass or from air to liquid and vice versa. The difference in speed of light in two different media is responsible for refraction or bending of light rays. It is important to define some of the parameters associated with refraction of light.

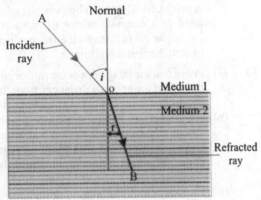

Fig. 24.1 Refraction of light ray

Consider a ray of light travelling from medium 1 to medium 2, we make the following definitions (see fig. 24.1)

The incident ray *(AO)* is the path along which the light travels in the first medium.

The refracted ray *(OB)* is the path along which the light travels in the second medium.

The angle of incidence, *i*, is the angle between the incident ray and the normal to the surface at *O*.

The angle of refraction, *r*, is the angle between the refracted ray and the normal to the surface at *O*.

If medium 2 is denser than medium 1, the ray is bent towards the normal as it travels from the first to the second medium. Conversely, a ray travelling from the denser to the less dense medium bends away from the normal, as it crosses the surface of separation of the two media.

24.2 Refraction of light through a rectangular glass block

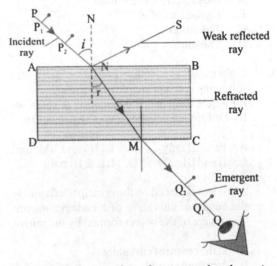

Fig. 24.2 Refraction through a rectangular glass prism.

In studying the refraction of light through a rectangular glass block *ABCD* (fig. 24.2), we have to consider an incident ray of light *PN* which passes from air into a rectangular glass block. The light travels in a new direction *NM* in the glass, and emerges along a direction *MQ* which is parallel to *PN*. At this point, we say that a ray of light *PN* has been refracted in the glass at *N*. It is good to note that at this stage, reflection as well as refraction, of light takes place at the air-glass boundary. Also, the energy of weak reflected ray (*NS*) from the glass boundary plus the light energy of the refracted ray equals the energy of the light in the incident ray. The refracted ray *NM*, is much brighter than the weak reflected ray *NS*, as most of the incident light energy passes into the glass.

Real depth, apparent depth and refractive index
We can explain why an object placed underneath a glass block appears nearer the top when viewed from above. The apparent depth of the swimming pool or the glass block is therefore less than its real depth.

It can be shown mathematically that the real depth, the apparent depth and the refractive index of the medium are related by this formula:

$$\frac{\text{real depth}}{\text{apparent depth}} = \text{refractive index}$$

If the real depth of a pond is 12 metres and its apparent depth is 9.0 metres. The refractive index of the water of the pond is given by:

$$n = \frac{12}{9} = \frac{4}{3} = 1.33$$

Experimental determination of refractive index by real and apparent depth method

(a)   Refractive index of a glass block
A straight line is ruled on a sheet of paper and the glass block is placed vertically over a portion of this line (Fig. 24.3) using a search pin attached to a piece of cork and held in a clamp, the apparent height of the line is found by a no parallax method. The pin is moved up and down until it coincides with the image of the line seen through the glass block. The real and apparent depth are thereby measured and refractive index is hence calculated using the above relationship.

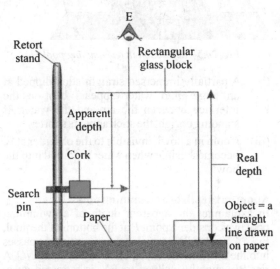

Fig. 24.3 Finding the refractive index of glass.

(b)   Refractive index of a liquid, e.g. water
An optical pin is placed on the bottom of a clean tall beaker standing on a piece of white paper (Fig. 24.4(a)). Water is poured into the beaker until it is about three-quarters full. The pin is viewed through the liquid from above.

A search pin attached to a piece of cork clamped on a stand is moved up and down until it coincides with the apparent position of the pin as seen from above the liquid.

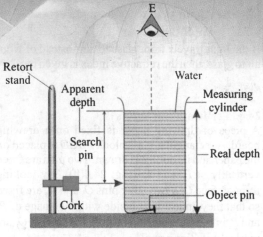

Fig. 24.4(a) Finding the refractive index (n) of a liquid.

Marks are made on the beaker corresponding to the position of the surface of the liquid and the position of the image of the pin. The beaker is then emptied and the real and apparent depths of the pin are measured using a metre rule.

$$n = \frac{\text{real depth}}{\text{apparent depth}}$$

24.3 Laws of refraction

(a) The incident ray, the refracted ray and the normal at the point of incidence, all lie in the same plane.

(b) The ratio of the sine of the angle of incidence to the sine of the angle of refraction is a constant for a given pair of media, i.e. $\frac{\sin i}{\sin r} = n$, a constant, known as refractive index of the second medium with respect to the first.

The second law is known as **Snell's law**

It is important to note that if light travels from air to glass, the refractive index is given by;

$$_a n_g = \frac{\sin i \ (\text{in air})}{\sin r \ (\text{in glass})} \qquad 24.1$$

Sometimes, it is simply written as $n = \frac{\sin i}{\sin r}$
Equation 24.1 above could be expressed as;

$$_A n_g = \frac{\text{velocity of light in air}}{\text{velocity of light in glass}} \qquad 24.2$$

This is infact the main definition of refractive index.

Example 24.1
If the refractive index of air to glass is 1.5, calculate the angle of refraction for which the incident angle is 30°.

Using $_a n_g = \frac{\sin i}{\sin r}$,

i.e. $1.5 = \frac{\sin 30}{\sin r}$

$\sin r = \frac{0.5}{1.5}$

$\quad = \frac{1}{3}$

$\sin r = 0.333$

$r = \sin^{-1} 0.333$

$r = 19.5°$

If the light travels from glass to air, instead of from air to glass, then the refractive index is given by:

$$_gn_a = \frac{1}{_an_g}$$

24.4 Verification of Snell's law

A piece of drawing paper is fixed on a drawing board. A rectangular glass block *ABCD* is placed on the paper and its outline is drawn. Two pins are fixed vertically at P_1 and P_2 (Fig. 24.4(b)). By looking through face *CD*, two other pins Q_1 and Q_2 are fixed so that they appear to coincide with the image of P_1 and P_2 in the glass block. The points P_1, P_2, Q_1, Q_2 are marked with fine pencil.

The glass block is removed and the incident ray is drawn through P_1 and P_2 to the point *N*. The emergent ray is drawn through Q_1 and Q_2 to point *M*. The refracted ray is drawn by joining the points. This is repeated for several other rays. The angles of incidence and the corresponding angles of refraction are measured and recorded.

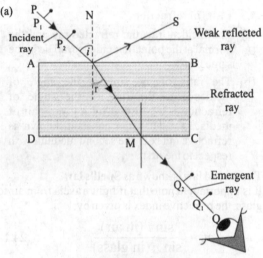

Fig. 24.4(b)   Snell's law

When the sines of the angles of incidence are plotted against the sines of the angles of refraction, a straight line graph passing through the origin is obtained (fig. 24.4(c)). This proves that the ratio:

$$\frac{\text{sine of angle of incidence } (i)}{\text{sine of angle of refraction } (r)} = \text{constant}.$$

The slope of this graph gives the refractive index for glass. We could use a ray box for this experiment instead of pins as an alternative.

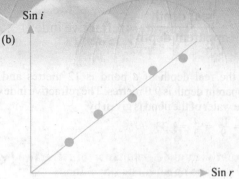

Fig. 24.4(c) Graph of sin i versus sin r

Effects of refraction at a plane surface

The effects of refraction at plane surfaces help us to explain several everyday observations.

(i)   A swimming pool appears shallower when we look down into it than it actually is.

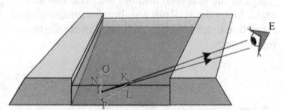

Fig. 24.5   Refraction in a swimming pool.

(ii)   A partially immersed straight stick dipped at an angle into water appears bent at the interface between the air and the water. If standing upright the stick appears shorter.

(iii) A coin in a bowl, invisible to the observer at E, becomes visible when water is poured into the bowl.

Apparent depth of a swimming pool

In explaining the apparent depth of a swimming pool, we consider a point *P* at the bottom of the pool, Fig. 24.5, a ray *PN* normal to the water surface passes into the air from the water, undeviated, along *NO*. A ray *PL*, slightly inclined to *PN*, is refracted away from the normal on emerging into the air. It travels along *LE*. Another ray *PK* is refracted along *KE*.

To an observer at *E*, the two emerging rays appear to originate from *I*, their point of intersection. Since *I* is nearer the surface than *P*, the bottom of the pool appears to be raised to the level of *I*. The pool therefore appears shallower than it actually is.

Apparent bending of stick partially immersed in water

The part of the stick immersed in water appears broken and bent upwards. This is because rays from different points on the object below the water surface are bent away from the normal on emerging from the denser medium (water) to the less dense medium (air). For example, rays of light from end *T* of the stick, on crossing the water-air-interface, bend away from the normal and appear, to an observer at

E to be coming from T_i (Fig. 24.6 (b)). The same reasoning applies to all points between *O* and *T*. The image of *TO* is thus T_iO, and the stick appears bent upwards.

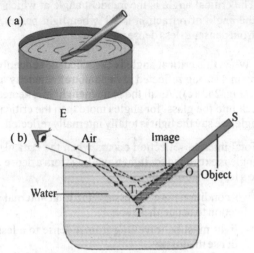

Fig. 24.6 Real and apparent depth.

Bringing objects into view

A coin in a bowl not visible to an observer at *E* can be brought into view by pouring sufficient water into the bowl (Fig. 24.7). With no water in the bowl rays from the coin *C* are blocked by the edge of the bowl (fig. 24.7(a)) and thus the coin is hidden from *E*. When sufficient water is poured into the bowl, refraction occurs. The rays from *C*, on leaving the water surface, are refracted away from the normal and appear to be coming from C_1, which is visible to *E* (Fig. 24.7 (b)).

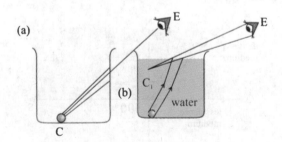

Fig. 24.7 A coin brought into view by refraction.

24.5 Refraction of light through a triangular prism and minimum deviation

A ray of light is refracted along *XY* is incident on the face *AB* at *Y*, of the glass prism, the light is refracted along *YR* in the glass and emerges on the face *AC* after refraction at the two faces (Fig. 24.8) along *RS* in the air.

> The refracting angle of the prism is the angle A between the refracting faces *AB* and *AC*.

Angles *i*, *r*, *d* and *e* are the angles of incidence, refraction, deviation and emergence respectively.

If a ray *XY* is incident on the face *AB*, it is observed that the emergent ray *RS* is not parallel to *XY*, rather, the prism bends rays of light incident on *AB* towards the base and away from the edge at *A*. The angle between the original direction and the final direction of the ray is called the angle of deviation, *d*. We then determine the refractive index of the material of a triangular prism by the following experiment.

Two object pins are placed on *XY*, which define the incident ray, are viewed from *S*, through the prism. Two image pins are then placed on *RS* to appear in line with the images of the other two in the glass prism. The angles *i* and *r* are measured and recorded. Fig. 24.8.

Then, the ratio $\frac{\sin i}{\sin r}$ gives the refractive index (*n*).

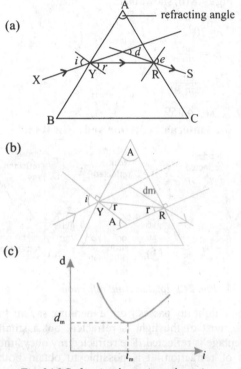

Fig. 24.8 Refraction by a triangular prism.

The angles of deviation (*d*) produced for different angles of incidence are measured and recorded. A graph of these angles of deviation (*d*) against angle of incidence (*i*) obtained (fig. 24.8(c)) reveals that at an angle of incidence i_m there exists a minimum angle of deviation d_m, which is the smallest angle of deviation produced by the prism. It is important to note that at minimum deviation, the light ray passes symmetrically through the prism. Hence, the refracted ray inside the prism makes equal angles with the prism surface at *Y* and at *R*.

Hence, it could be proved that $n = \dfrac{\sin \frac{1}{2}(d_m + A)}{\sin \frac{1}{2}A}$

where *A* is the refracting angle of the prism.

Example 24.2

A 60° prism is of refractive index 1.5. Calculate: (a) the angle of minimum deviation, (b) the angle of refraction of the light passing through the prism at minimum deviation, and (c) the angle of incidence at minimum deviation.

(a) $$n = \frac{\sin\frac{1}{2}(d_m + 60)}{\sin\frac{1}{2}(60)}$$

$$1.5 = \frac{\sin\frac{1}{2}(d_m + 60)}{0.5}$$

$$0.75 = \sin\frac{1}{2}(d_m + 60)$$

$$\therefore d_m = 37.18°$$

(b) At minimum deviation, the geometry of Fig 24.8 (b) shows that

$$2r = A = 60°$$
$$r = 30°$$

(c) $$n = \frac{\sin i}{\sin r}$$

$$1.5 = \frac{\sin i}{\sin 30}$$

$$i = 48.59°.$$

24.6 Total internal reflection and critical angle

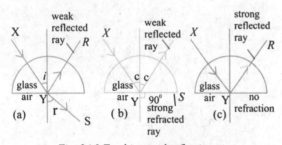

Fig. 24.9 Total internal reflection

When a light ray passes from a medium, say air to glass, most of the light is refracted, but a small percentage is reflected. The refracted ray obeys the laws of refraction. It is possible to obtain both refraction and reflection for all angles of incidence.

This is not the case when light travels from a denser to a less dense medium. Consider an incident ray *XY* emerging from a semi-circular glass prism into air at *Y* (Fig. 24.9 (a)). It is convenient to use a semi-circular glass prism because a ray such as *XY* travelling along the radius enters the prism normally and is not refracted on entering.

The refracted ray *YS* is bent away from the normal. The angle of incidence is therefore smaller than the angle of refraction. There is also a weak reflected ray *YR*. If we increase the angle of incidence *i*, the refracted ray is further bent away from the normal and the angle of refraction *r* is increased. Again there is a strong refracted ray and a weak reflected ray. As the incidence angle is further increased, then the refracted ray passes along the glass air boundary and angle of refraction is 90°, this particular angle of incidence at which the angle of refraction is 90° is

called the **critical angle c,** Fig. 24.9(b), the value of which depends on the two media. For crown glass, the most common type of optical glass, the critical angle is about 42°.

> The critical angle is the incident angle at which the angle of refraction is 90° when light passes from denser to less dense medium.

When this critical angle is exceeded we suddenly obtain a strong reflected ray and no refracted ray at all (Fig. 24.9(c)). As all the incident light is reflected back into the glass, for angles more than the critical angle, we say the light is totally internally reflected.

> Total internal reflection occurs when the critical angle is exceeded for light travelling from a dense to a less dense medium.

Two conditions are necessary for total internal reflection to occur, these are:

(i)   light must be travelling from a dense to a less dense medium.

(ii) the angle of incidence in the denser medium must be greater than the critical angle.

Relation between critical angle and refractive index

At critical angle as in Fig. 24.10, the angle of refraction is 90°. For light travelling from air to glass, Snell's law states that $\frac{\sin i}{\sin r} = {}_a n_g$.

For light traveling from glass to air,

$$\frac{\sin i}{\sin r} = {}_g n_a = \frac{1}{{}_a n_g}$$

$$\sin c = \frac{1}{{}_a n_g} \quad \text{(since } \sin 90° = 1\text{)}$$

$$\text{or } {}_a n_g = \frac{1}{\sin c}$$

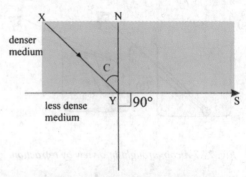

Fig. 24.10 The relation between critical angle and refractive index .

Hence, the refractive index of the denser medium with respect to the less dense medium is the reciprocal of the sine of the critical angle.

Example 24.3

Calculate the critical angle for light travelling from glass to air. (Take ${}_a n_g = \frac{3}{2} = 1.5$)

$$\frac{\sin c}{\sin 90°} = \frac{1}{1.5} = 0.67$$

Thus, $\sin c = 0.67 \quad \therefore c = 42.07°$

Field of view of a fish under water

A fish under water can see objects above the water surface only within a certain range, provided the water surface is unruffled.

Rays of light such as *AB* and *CD* reach the eye *E* of the fish after refraction in the water in the direction *BE* and *DE* (Fig. 24.11). The extreme rays that can enter the eye of the fish by refraction are such rays as *FG* and *LM* which just graze the surface of the water. The angle of incidence here is 90°. The angle of refraction *r* is given by:

$$\frac{\sin 90°}{\sin c} = \frac{4}{3}$$

$$\frac{1}{\sin c} = \frac{4}{3}$$

$$\sin r = \frac{3}{4} = 0.75$$

r is approximately 49°.

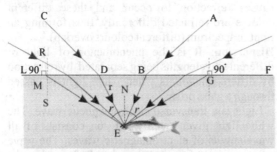

Fig. 24.11 A fish-eye view.

From Fig. 24.11, because *RS* is parallel to *NE*, angle *NEM* is also equal to 49°. The fish can therefore see everything above the water by rays which fall within a cone with half angle *r* = 49° inside the water.

Outside this cone the fish sees objects within the water by total internal reflection at the water-air boundary.

The mirage

As one drives along a tarmac road on a hot day, he often seems to see pools of water in front of him. These pools disappear as one approaches them, and reappear further ahead of him. Such an optical illusion, by which inverted images of palm trees or other distant objects are often seen, sometimes as if reflected in the ground, is called a **mirage**. It is a phenomenon that can be explained by total internal reflection.

The sun heats the ground which in turn heats the air in contact with it. The heated air expands and rises. As it rises, it gets cooler, the air in contact with

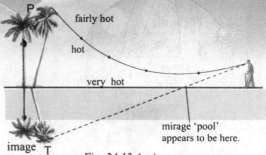

Fig. 24.12 A mirage

the ground is hotter and less dense than the air above.

The density of the air thus increases as we go up (Fig. 24.12).

A ray of light from the top of a palm tree proceeding downwards, travels through air of different densities, from denser air to less dense air. The angle of incidence of this oblique ray increases from layer above to layer below until at a particular layer, it exceeds the critical angle. Total internal reflection occurs and the ray moves upwards into the dense layers of air again.

As the reflected ray is now travelling from less dense to more dense layers, it gradually bends in the opposite side and ultimately enters the eye of an observer. This observer sees the image of the top of the palm tree in this direction from which the ray seems to be coming. To him the top of the palm tree appears to be at the point *T*. This gives an impression that there is a pool of water in the road in front of him which is reflecting the palm tree into his eyes.

24.7 Applications of totally reflecting prisms

An ordinary plane mirror forms an image of an object in front of it by reflection from the silvered surface on the back of the mirror and also by reflection from the front of the glass. One bright image and another weak image are seen. These weak secondary images introduce problems when plane mirrors are used in certain optical instruments, such as a submarine periscope. Here the problem is greater at night, when the object is often a bright light on a distant ship, and the secondary image can appear almost as bright as the main image. To avoid this problem, periscope binoculars and totally reflecting prisms are used instead of mirrors.

In submarine periscopes, glass prisms are arranged as shown in Fig. 24.14. A ray incident normally on the face *XY* passes through to face *XZ* where it is incident at an angle of 45° which is greater than the critical angle for glass (42°). It is totally internally reflected at *M* with angle of reflection equal to 45°. It therefore travels downwards at right angles to its original direction.

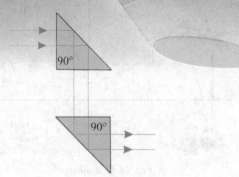

Fig. 24.13 Totally reflecting prisms

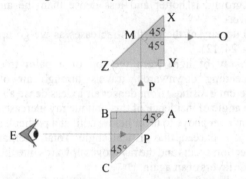

Fig. 24.14 Totally reflecting prisms used in periscopes.

Only one bright image of the object is thus obtained. The ray travelling downwards from the prism meets another right-angled isosceles prism placed parallel to *XYZ* as shown, and total internal reflection again occurs on face *AC*. The ray emerges along *PE*, a direction parallel to *OM*. An eye at *E* sees a bright image of the object at *O*.

In prism binoculars, used for example by spectators to watch sports in a far off field, totally reflecting prisms are also employed. A simplified diagram of the way they are arranged is shown in Fig. 24.15.

Parallel rays from a distant object strike the face *XZ* normally and continue undeviated.

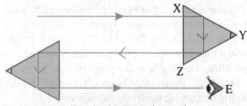

Fig. 24.15 Prism binoculars

They are incident on face *XY* at angle 45° which is more than the critical angle for glass. Total internal reflection takes place on the faces *XY* and *YZ* and the rays emerge parallel to their original direction. The second prism is employed to reverse the rays again. Prisms have the advantage that they do not tarnish and deteriorate as mirrors do. Also mirrors absorb more light and give a fainter image.

24.8 Dispersion of white light and colour

Dispersion of light by a prism.

When white light (light from sun) passes through a prism, an elongated coloured patch (spectrum) of light is obtained on a screen placed behind the prism. The colours of the spectrum are red, orange, yellow, green, blue, indigo and violet (ROYGBIV).

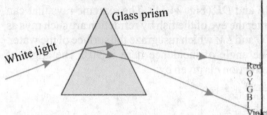

Fig. 24.16 Production of an impure spectrum.

Impure spectrum

White light is a mixture of seven colours (as named above) when it passes through a prism. The prism causes refraction to occur and these different colours are refracted differently, thus forming an impure spectrum (different colours overlap).

Dispersion: It is the phenomenon of light of different wavelengths being separated by refraction by different amounts when white light is passed through a glass prism.

Light is a transverse electromagnetic wave. The white light given out by the sun consists of all wavelengths of electromagnetic waves. The wave we see as light form a narrow band of wavelengths and we see the different wavelengths as different colours of light.

Monochromatic light

This is a light of one wavelength and colour. When such light passes through a prism, refraction occurs without dispersion.

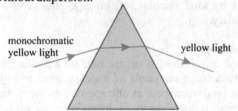

Fig. 24.17 Refraction of monochromatic light

Formation of pure spectrum

The following are needed for the production of a pure spectrum:

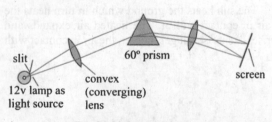

Fig. 24.18 Pure spectrum

(i) A narrow slit through which rays from source of light passes that produces a series of narrow, coloured images which minimises the chances of overlapping colours.

(ii) A converging lens with the slit placed at its focus so that a beam of parallel light is produced.

(iii) A 60° prism for dispersion of the parallel beam.

(iv) A second lens for collecting the parallel beams of different colours, but this is not essential.

(v) A screen at the focus of the second lens on which the pure spectrum can be projected.

Continuous and line spectra

The spectra produced by solids or liquids when they are incandescent (glowing) are called continuous spectra and contain all colours. For example; white light from the sun produces a *continuous spectrum*.

When light emitted from glowing vapour is passed through a prism a particular spectrum containing distinct bright lines is obtained. The spectrum so produced is called a **line spectrum**. For example, the spectrum of sodium obtained from a sodium flame consists of a very bright yellow line, made up of two bright lines very close together and several other faint lines. The spectrum of both mercury and hydrogen are referred to as *emission spectra*.

Emission and absorption spectra

It has been noted that the spectrum of sodium that is obtained from a sodium flame has a very bright yellow line and several other faint lines. While mercury vapour has a line spectrum of mainly green and blue lines, hydrogen gas has spectrum consisting of many bands, all the above spectra are referred to *emission spectra*. On the other hand, when white light is passed through a sodium flame, the spectrum obtained is a continuous spectrum with a number of dark lines on it, which correspond to the bright lines of the line spectrum of sodium. This spectrum which is obtained in this way is called *absorption spectrum*.

Colour

Red, blue and green are called *primary colours*. Other colours got by mixing any of the primary colours are regarded as *secondary colours*. But if primary and secondary colours are mixed to give white light, they are called *complementary colours*.

e.g. yellow + blue = white
    cyan + red = white
    magenta + green = white

Summary of colour mixing

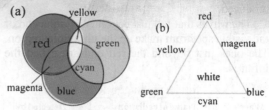

Fig. 24.19 Triangle of colour mixing.

red + green = yellow
red + blue = magenta
green + blue = cyan

Mixing pigments

Here, we have colour mixing by subtraction unlike mixing of colours in light of which colour mixing is by addition or additive colour mixing or additive combination.

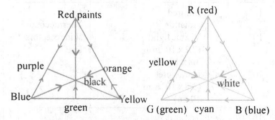

Fig. 24.20 (a) Substractive colour mixing
Fig. 24. 20 (b) Additive colour triangle

In colour mixing by subtraction, it is observed that when different paints or pigments are mixed, for example; when yellow and blue paints are mixed the resulting paint is green in colour. What happens is that yellow paint absorbs blue and violet and the blue absorbs red and yellow, leaving green as the only colour that the mixture could reflect.

Objects appear to be a certain colour because they reflect light of that colour only. We use fig. 24.19 to illustrate this fact as summarized in the table below.

Table 24.1

Colour of object on which light is incident	Reflected ray which one sees	Absorbed rays
Red	Red	Green, blue
Blue	Blue	Red, green
Green	Green	Red, blue
Cyan	Green, blue	Red
Magneta	Red, blue	Green
Yellow	Red, green	Blue

The electromagnetic spectrum

The human eye can see only light of which the wavelength lies between 3.8×10^{-7}m and 7.2×10^{-7}m. Other waves of similar nature to visible light exist, some with shorter wavelengths and others with longer wavelengths. They differ from light only in wavelength and in the ways by which they are produced.

The waves that fall just beyond the violet end of the visible spectrum make up the ultraviolet region. The ones just beyond the red end are called the infrared.

Table 24.2: The electromagnetic spectrum

Wavelength (in m)	Name of radiation		Detected by
10^5			
10^4	Long		
10^3	Medium		
10^2	Short	Radio	Radio
10		Waves	Receiving
1	T.V.	(1 mm to	Circuits
10^{-1}	Microwaves	100km)	Microwaves
10^{-2}	and Radar		Receiver
10^{-3}			
10^{-4}			
10^{-5}	Infrared radiation		Thermocouple
10^{-6}	Visible light (7.2×10^{-7}m to 3.8×10^{-7}m)		skin receptors Eye
10^{-7}	Ultraviolet (3.8×10^{-7}m to 10^{-8}m)		
10^{-8}			
10^{-9}			
10^{-10}	X-rays (less than 10^{-8}m)		Phosphorescene ionisation effects
10^{-11}	γ-rays (10^{-11}m)		
10^{-12}			
10^{-13}			

Each is present in sunlight. X-rays are even shorter in wavelength than the ultraviolet, and of still shorter wavelength, and more penetrating than X-rays, are gamma rays produced by radioactive substances.

On the long-wave side the infrared are followed by the microwave band and the radio band. A summary of the electromagnetic spectrum is shown in Table 24.2. The associated wavelengths and the instruments used for detecting the waves are included. It can be seen that visible light forms only a small part of the whole electromagnetic spectrum.

24.9 Refraction of light through lenses

Lenses

Refraction through lenses involves change in the direction of light rays as they travel from one medium to another i.e. from less dense medium to denser medium or vice versa.

A lens is a portion of a transparent medium bounded by two spherical surfaces or by a plane and a spherical surface

Types of lenses

There exist two kinds of lenses:
(a) Convex or converging lens; and
(b) Concave or diverging lens.

(a) **Convex lens:** These are thicker at the middle than at the edges. The different types are shown in Fig. 24.21 below.

A converging lens makes rays of light originating from a point come together at another point, called a focus.

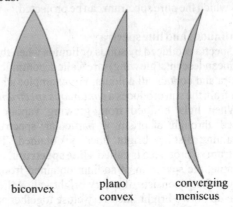

biconvex   plano convex   converging meniscus

Fig. 24.21 Converging lenses

It makes the rays converge at focus. When we look through a converging lens a magnified upright image, is observed. A magnified inverted image or a diminished inverted image, could also be observed, depending on the distance the object is from the other side of the lens.

(b) Diverging lenses

These are thinner at the middle than at the edges. The different types of diverging lens are shown in Fig. 24.22.

A diverging lens makes rays of light which pass through it, spread out or diverge.

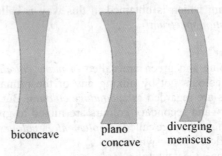

biconcave   plano concave   diverging meniscus

Fig. 24.22 Diverging lenses

When we look through a diverging lens, we always see a diminished, upright image.

Definitions of terms

The principal axis of a lens is an imaginary line joining the centres of curvature of its surfaces.

Optical center (C) is a point through which rays of light pass without being deviated by the lens.

The principal focus (F) of a converging lens is the point to which all rays parallel and close to the principal axis converge after refraction through the lens (Fig. 24.3(c)).

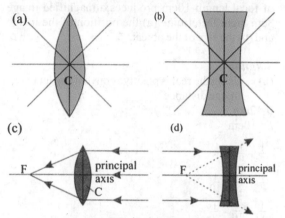

Fig. 24.23 Definitions of terms.

The principal focus (F) of a diverging lens is the point from which all rays parallel and close to the principal axis appear to diverge after refraction through the lens (Fig. 24.3(d)).

The focal length (f) is the distance between the optical centre and the principal focus of the lens.

Note: The principal focus of a converging lens is on the far side from the incident rays (Fig. 24.23 (c)). The principal focus of a diverging lens is on the same side as the incident rays, and the rays do not actually pass through it (Fig. 24.3(d)).

Ray diagrams and their construction for lenses

Three classes of rays are used to obtain the position and nature of images formed by lenses. These are:

(i) rays parallel to the principal axis and close to it, which pass through the principal focus after refraction.

(ii) rays through the principal focus which emerge parallel to the principal axis after refraction.

(iii) rays through the optical centre which pass through the lens undeviated, i.e. their direction is unchanged.

When constructing ray diagrams for images formed by a lens, for convenience, we represent the two refractions produced by the lens surfaces as a single deviation at a line passing through the length of the lens, normal to the principal axis. We represent the object by another line with an arrow at its head.

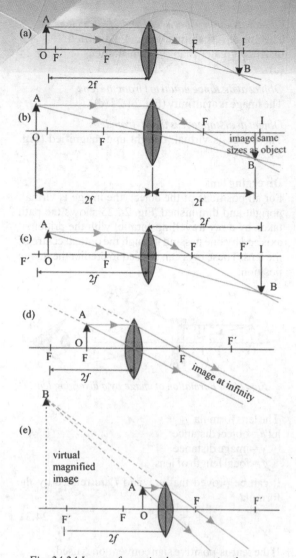

Fig. 24.24 Images formation by converging lenses.

For curved mirrors we distinguish between real and virtual images. A real image is one that can be formed on a screen. Actual light rays pass through it. A virtual image is one through which the light rays forming it only appear to pass, without actually doing so. A virtual image cannot therefore be formed on a screen.

A converging lens has a real focus but a diverging lens has a virtual focus.

Drawing ray diagrams to find the position and nature of the image when the object is in different positions.

Converging lens

Object at a distance greater than 2f from the lens
The image is real, inverted and diminished in size. It is found at a point which is at a distance between f and 2f from the lens (Fig. 24.24(a)).

Object at distance 2f from lens
The image is real, inverted and the same size as the object. It is also at a distance *2f* from the lens (Fig. 24.24(b)).

Object at distance between f and 2f from lens
The image is real, inverted and magnified. It is at a distance greater than 2f from the lens (Fig. 24.24 (c)).

Object at distance equal to f from the lens
The image is at infinity (Fig. 24.24 (d)).

Object at distance less than f from lens
The image is virtual, upright and magnified (Fig. 24.24(e)).

Diverging lens

For all positions of the object, the image is virtual, upright and diminished. Fig. 24.25 shows the path taken by a ray travelling parallel with the principal axis and by one passing through the optical centre of the lens. These rays can be used to predict the image position.

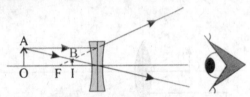

Fig. 24.25 Formation of image by a diverging lens.

The lens formula
let u = object distance
v = image distance
f = focal length of lens

It can be proved that u, v and f are related by the formula

$$\frac{1}{v} + \frac{1}{u} = \frac{1}{f} \qquad 24.3$$

If the real-is-positive sign convention is used,
(a) all distances are measured from the optical centre of the lens.
(b) distances of real images, objects and foci are positive, those of virtual images, objects and foci are negative.
(c) the focal length of a converging lens is positive.
(d) the focal length of a diverging lens is negative.

The magnification *(m)* is defined as:
$$m = \frac{\text{image height}}{\text{object height}}$$

By considering ray diagrams in Fig. 24.26 and using the principles of similar triangles, it can be seen that:
$$\frac{\text{image height}}{\text{object height}} = \frac{\text{image distance}}{\text{object distance}}$$
$$= \frac{v}{u}$$

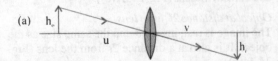

(a)

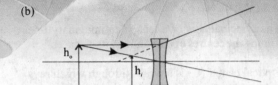

(b)

Fig. 24.26 The lens formula

Example 24.4

An object placed 2cm in front of a converging lens of focal length 10cm produces a magnified image 8cm high. Determine (a) the position of the image and (b) the size of the object.

Solution

(a) Using the real is positive convention, let v = image distance
u = 2cm
f = 10cm

$$\frac{1}{v} + \frac{1}{u} = \frac{1}{f}$$
$$\frac{1}{v} + \frac{1}{2} = \frac{1}{10}$$
$$\frac{1}{v} = \frac{1}{10} - \frac{1}{2}$$
$$\frac{1}{v} = \frac{-4}{10}$$
$$\therefore v = \frac{-10}{4}\text{cm} = -2.5\text{cm (The image is virtual)}$$

(b) Let size of the object be x
$$m = \frac{\text{image height}}{\text{object height}}$$
$$\frac{\text{image height}}{\text{object height}} = \frac{\text{image distance}}{\text{object distance}}$$
$$\frac{8}{x} = \frac{2.5}{2}$$
$$\therefore x = \frac{8.2}{2.5}$$
$$= 6.4\text{cm}$$

Example 24.5

Determine the nature and position of the image of an objects 2cm from a diverging lens of focal length 10cm.

Solution

u = 2cm
f = -10cm
but
$$\frac{1}{v} + \frac{1}{u} = \frac{1}{f}$$
$$\therefore \frac{1}{v} + \frac{1}{2} = -\frac{1}{10}$$
$$\frac{1}{v} = \frac{-1}{10} - \frac{1}{2}$$
$$= -\frac{6}{10}$$
$$= -\frac{10}{6}$$

Hence, $v = -1.67$cm

The image is virtual and 1.67cm in front of the lens, on the same side as the object.

Example 24.6
An object 10cm high is placed 10cm from a diverging lens of focal length 15cm. Determine the position and nature of the image using graphical method.

Solution
In fig 24.27, *TS* represents the diverging lens, choose the scale such that 1 cm = 5cm.
$u = OC = 2$ cm
$OA = 2$cm, *A* is the top of the object.

Example 24.6

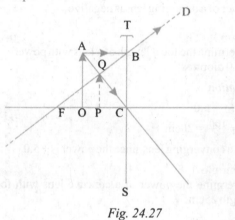

Fig. 24.27

Draw *AB* parallel to *OC*. It emerges as *BD*, coming from the focus *F*.

Draw *AC* through the optical centre, it passes undeviated. The point of intersection (*Q*) of *AC* and *BF* gives the top point of the image. *QP* is drawn as a normal to the principal axis. From our construction, the image is virtual, 6.0cm in front of the lens and of height 6.0cm.

Experimental determination of focal length of a converging lens

(a) Quick but approximate method
We could obtain an approximate value of the focal length of a converging lens by holding it well away from a window and moving a screen towards the lens or away from it until a sharp clear image of the window-panes is obtained on the screen. It is assumed that the rays from the window are parallel rays. They are therefore brought into focus at a point which corresponds to the principal focus. The distance from this point to the lens gives the focal length.

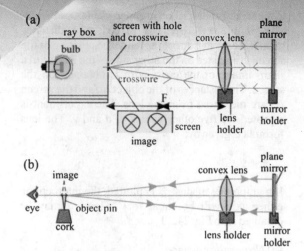

(a)

(b)

Fig. 24.28 Finding focal length of a converging lens,

This is an approximate value for the focal length as the rays from the window are not perfectly parallel.

(b) Using an illuminated object and a plane mirror
The apparatus used is as seen in Fig. 24.29. The object is the cross-wire of a ray box. It is illuminated by the electric bulb. The lens is mounted on a lens holder and placed in front of a mounted plane mirror in such away that the planes of both the mirror and the lens are vertical. The position of the lens holder is adjusted until a sharp image of the cross-wire is formed on the screen near the object. The distance between the lens and the screen is measured.

The procedure is repeated, and the average distance between the screen and the lens gives the focal length of the lens.

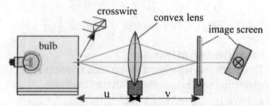

Fig. 24.29 Finding the focal length using u and v.

(c) Using a pin and plane mirror
An optical pin is stuck in a cork and placed in front of the lens and mirror arranged as in Fig. 24.28. The pin is adjusted until there is no parallax between it and its image formed by the combination of the lens and mirror. The distance between the pin and the lens gives the focal length. The experiment is repeated thrice and the average obtained.

(d) Using the lens formula
(i) Illuminated object method
The apparatus consists of an illuminated object (e.g. a ray box with cross-wires), a white screen, and a converging lens mounted in a holder.
The approximate focal length *f* of the lens is first obtained by focusing the image of a distant object on

to the screen as described in experiment (a).

The illuminated object is placed at a distance greater than f in front of the lens. The position of the screen is adjusted on the other side of the lens until a sharp image of the cross-wire is obtained on the screen. The distances of the object (u) and the screen (v) are measured from the lens. The experiment is repeated for five other values of u and v. The lens formula is given by:

$$\frac{1}{u} + \frac{1}{v} = \frac{1}{f}$$

If a graph of $\frac{1}{v}$ against $\frac{1}{u}$ is plotted, the intercept on either axis will be equal to $\frac{1}{f}$. Hence f may be obtained as in Fig. 24.30.

(ii) No parallax method
In the absence of a ray box, two pins may be used to obtain the focal length of the lens by the "no parallax method". The object pin is placed before the lens and its image is located using the search pin placed on the other side of the lens. u and v are measured as usual and a graph like Fig. 24.30 is drawn; the value of f is obtained as before.

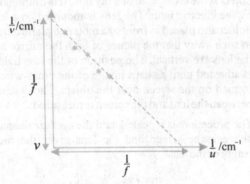

Fig. 24.30 Graph of $\frac{1}{v}$ against $\frac{1}{u}$

Identification of lenses
To determine whether a given lens is converging or diverging we can use the following methods.

(i) When we feel the lens with finger and it is thinner or thicker at the centre, then it is diverging and converging lens respectively.

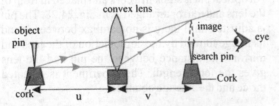

Fig. 24.31 No parallax method

(ii) We could bring a candle from a great distance towards the lens, looking at it through the lens, if the image is always erect and smaller than the candle, the lens is a diverging lens, and if the image is inverted and gradually, increases in size as the candle is brought nearer the lens, then disappears, and reappears as an enlarged upright image, then the lens is converging.

(iii) We could point the lens towards a distant object, if the image of the distant object appears on a screen, the lens is converging.

Power of a lens
We define the power of a lens as the reciprocal of the focal length expressed in metres.

When the focal length is 1 metre, the power of the lens is 1 dioptre. (A dioptre is not an *SI* unit). The power of a lens in dioptres is given by

$$\frac{100}{f \text{ in cm}}$$

The power of a converging lens is positive, the power of a diverging lens is negative.

Example 24.7
Determine the focal length of a lens with power + 5.0 dioptres

Solution
$$\frac{100}{f} = 5.0$$
$$f = \frac{100}{5} = 20 cm$$

it is a converging lens since the power is + 5.0.

Example 24.8
Determine the power of a concave lens with focal length 25cm.

$$\frac{100}{f} = \frac{-100}{25}$$
$$f = -4 \text{ dioptres}$$

Summary

1. Rays of light travelling from less dense to a denser medium are refracted towards the normal, the reverse is the case when it travels from denser to a less dense medium.

2. Refractive index (n) of a medium is defined as

   the ratio: $n = \dfrac{\sin i \text{ (in air or vacuum)}}{\sin r \text{ (in the medium)}}$

3. Laws of refraction states that:
   (i) the incident ray, the refracted ray and the normal at the point of incidence, all lie in the same plane; and
   (ii) the ratio of $\frac{\sin i}{\sin r}$ is constant for given media,
   it is referred to as Snell's law.

4. (i) Refractive index n of a medium is the ratio of velocity of light in vaccum to that in the medium.
   (ii) Refractive index $n = \sin i / \sin r$.
   (iii) It could also be shown to be equal to real depth/apparent depth.

5. Two conditions necessary for total internal reflection to occur are (i) light must travel from denser to a lense dense medium (ii) critical angle *(c)* must be exceeded.

6. The critical angle *(c)* can be defined as $\sin c = 1/n$.

7. The angle between the incident ray and emergent ray is referred to as angle of deviation *(d)*.

8. Spectrum of white light consists of red, orange, yellow, green, blue, indigo and violet colours.

9. A prism produces dispersion and deviation of colours at its first face and further deviation of colours at its second face.

10. A pure spectrum of white light can be formed using a narrow slit, two lenses and a prism.

11. Additive colour mixing is a process of mixing coloured lights on a white surface, while colour mixing by subtraction entails mixing of different colours of paint or pigments. The latter absorb, or subtracts out, certain wavelengths from white light and reflects the rest.

12. Primary colours of white light are red, green and blue; colours obtained by additive mixing of any of the two primary colours are referred to as secondary colours, these include; yellow, cyan and magenta.

13. Principal focus of a lens is the point on the principal axis to which rays parallel and close to the principal axis converge or diverge after refraction through a converging or diverging lens respectively.

14. Image formed by a convex (converging) lens may be real or virtual depending on the position of the object, while image formed by a concave(diverging) lens is always virtual, erect and diminished no matter the position of the object.

15. Focal length (f) of a lens is the distance from the lens to the principal focus, while power of a lens is $\frac{100}{f}$ (unit is in dioptres).

16. Lens formular for real-is-positive convention
Is: $\frac{1}{v} + \frac{1}{u} = \frac{1}{f}$
$m = \frac{v}{u}$

17. For convex lens f = positive and for a concave lens f = negative.

Exercise 24

1. Which of the following instruments makes use of the principle of total internal reflection?
   A. Periscope   B. Microscopes
   C. Sextants   D. Telescopes

2. The power of a lens is measured in
   A. Newton.   B. kilogram.
   C. dioptres.   D. Watt.

3. A pure spectrum may be produced from an impure spectrum by
   I. using an additional source of light.
   II. decreasing the size of illuminated slit.
   III. increasing the size of illuminated slit.
   IV. using a converging lens to produce a parallel beam of light incident on the prism.
   A. I and II   B. II and IV
   C. III & IV   D. II, III and IV

4. *ON* is a ray of light incident at an angle of 60° on a rectangular glass block *ABCD*. If the length of the refracted ray *NM* is 9cm, calculate the length *KM*. (Refractive index of glass = 1.5).

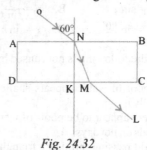

Fig. 24.32

A. $\sqrt{\frac{2}{9}}$ cm   B. $\frac{\sqrt{3}}{3}$ cm

C. $3\sqrt{3}$ cm   D. $3\sqrt{6}$ cm

5. Which of the following is the correct illustration for the passage of monochromatic light through a glass prism?

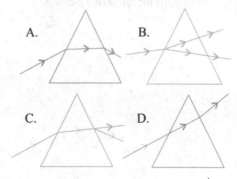

Fig. 24.33

6. An object 1.00cm high is placed 18.0cm from a converging lens forms a real image 2.00cm high. Calculate the focal length of the lens.
   A. 36.0cm   B. 18.0cm
   C. 12.0cm   D. 9.0cm

7. A white screen illuminated by red and green light appears
   A. red.   B. green.
   C. purple.   D. yellow.

8. Which of the following colours of light is primary?

A. white   B. black
C. yellow   D. Red

9. Which of the following best describes the image formed by a concave lens?
A. Virtual, erect and magnified.
B. Real, inverted and diminished.
C. Virtual erect and diminished.
D. Magnified inverted and virtual.

10. Which of the following is the correct relationship between the relative refractive index n of glass and the critical angle x?

A. $n = \sin x$ B. $n = \dfrac{1}{\sin x}$

C. $n = \sin \dfrac{90^{\circ}}{x}$ D. $x = \sin n$

11. One of the following is not caused by refraction alone.
A. A pool of water appears shallower than it really is.
B. There appear to be pools of water on tarred roads on hot days.
C. Light passing through a triangular prism is bent towards the box.
D. A parallel beam of light is made to converge to a point by a convex lens.

12. (a) State the laws of refraction.
(b) If the refractive index of air to glass is 1.5, calculate the angle of refraction for which the incident angle is 30°.
(c) If the light travels from glass to air, determine the refractive index.

13. (a) The velocities of light in air and glass are 3×10^{8} ms^{-1} and 2×10^{8} ms^{-1} respectively, calculate the refractive index.
(b) State conditions necessary for total internal reflection to occur.
(c) Calculate the refractive index of a glass for which the critical angle is 42°.

14. An object is placed 4cm in front of a converging lens of focal length 12cm, the magnified image of 8cm high was produced, determine:
(a) the position of the image
(b) the size of the object
(c) where an image of an object placed:
   (i) at a distance greater than $2F$ from the lens will be formed
   (ii) at a distance $2F$ from the lens will be formed

15. (a) Describe briefly a method for determination of focal length of a convex lens.
(b) Show using diagram, the image of an object as formed by a diverging lens.
(c) An object 10cm high is placed 30cm from a diverging lens of focal length 60cm. Determine the nature and size of the image.

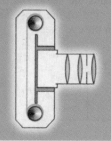

OPTICAL INSTRUMENTS: APPLICATIONS

Chapter 25

25.1 Microscopes

One of the applications of light wave is seen in the operation of a simple microscope or magnifying glass. It is also seen in the compound microscope.

The simple microscope or magnifying glass.

A converging lens acts as a simple microscope or magnifying glass (fig. 25.1) when an object is placed between the principal focus and the optical centre of same lens. The image formed is enlarged, erect and virtual. The magnifying glass is used for reading tiny points and for studying other tiny scientific specimens.

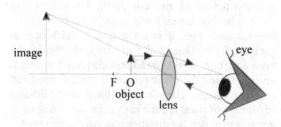

Fig. 25.1 The magnifying glass

The compound microscope

A compound microscope consists of combination of two converging lenses, the objective lens and the eye-piece, both lenses having short focal lengths (Fig. 25.2).

The objective lens produces a magnified, inverted and real image of an object *OA*, which must be strongly illuminated. The eye-piece is moved until *IB* is nearer to it than its principal focus.

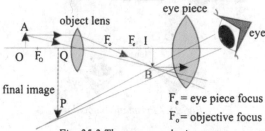

F_e = eye piece focus
F_o = objective focus

Fig. 25.2 The compound microscope

A magnified but virtual image *PQ* of *IB* is thus formed at *Q* with the eye-piece lens acting as a magnifying glass for an object at *I*.

Hence the object *OA* is enlarged by the action of the two lenses. Relative to the object, the final image is inverted. This however, is not a problem in the use of the instrument for studying tiny objects. The observer adjusts the eye-piece so that the final image is at his near point (about 25cm from the normal eye).

Magnifying power

The magnifying power *m* of the compound microscope is a product of the magnifications due to the two lenses. Thus if m_1 is the magnification produced by the objective and m_2 is that of the eye-piece, then $m = m_1 \times m_2 = PQ/AO$.

25.2 Telescopes

The astronomical telescope

Astronomical telescope is the simplest type of telescope, it is used in viewing distant objects, such as stars and planets. The astronomical telescope consists of two converging lenses mounted so that they have a common axis. The objective lens has a long focal length and the eye-piece has a short focal length. This ensures that the telescope has a high magnifying power.

The ray diagram is shown in Fig. 25.3. The rays coming to the objective lens from a distant object arrive as parallel rays, inclined at a small angle to the principal axis. A real image is therefore formed at the principal focus F_o of the objective. The eye-piece is moved so that this image lies within a distance of one focal length. It thus acts as a magnifying glass and produces a magnified image P_1Q_1 of the distant object. As in the compound microscope, this final image is inverted.

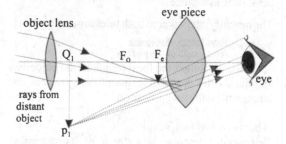

Fig. 25.3 The astronomical telescope

The lenses can be arranged so that the final image is at infinity. In such an arrangement the principal focus of the objective must coincide with that of the eye-piece (Fig. 25.4).

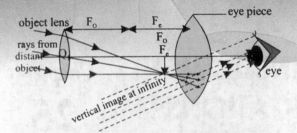

Fig. 25.4 The astronomical telescope in normal adjustment.

In this arrangement, the telescope is said to be in normal adjustment. The astronomical telescope gives an inverted image, which can be tolerated when looking at stars, but is a disadvantage on the Earth.

The Galilean telescope

The Galilean telescope consists of two lenses; a converging lens of long focal length as objective lens and a diverging lens of short focal length as eye-piece. The two lenses are mounted so that they have a common axis with the distances between them, equal to the difference between their focal lengths. (Fig 25.5)

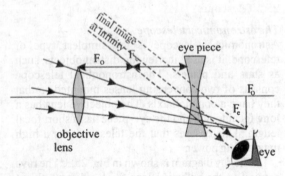

Fig. 25.5 The galilean telescope in normal adjustment.

Parallel rays from a distant object pass through the objective lens which forms a real inverted image at its principal focus. Before the rays actually converge to a focus, they are intercepted by the diverging lens which causes the rays to diverge and emerge as a parallel beam. A virtual, erect and magnified image is therefore seen at infinity by the eye, placed close behind the eye-piece.

The magnifying power of both telescopes is given

$$by\ m = \frac{\text{focal length of objective}}{\text{focal length of eye piece}}$$

Thus, the longer the focal length of the objective and the shorter the focal length of the eye-piece the larger will be the magnification.

The terrestrial telescope

Terrestrial telescope is a form of astronomical telescope with an additional lens in the centre, to re-invert the image so that it is upright (Fig 25..6). The objective lens forms an image of the distant object at its principal focus. The inverting lens is placed so that the image is at $2f$ from it, and hence, forms

another image that is real and the same size but inverted at $2f$ on the other side of the lens. This image is taken as an object for the eye-piece.

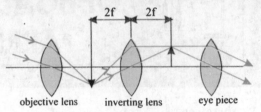

Fig. 25.6 The terrestrial telescope

The inverting lens extends the length of the telescope, by $4f$, so the lens now has a small focal length as much as possible, that is consistent with good quality.

The problem of length is overcome in prism binoculars, where the prisms re-invert the image.

Prism binoculars

This works on the same principle as the astronomical telescope. Totally reflecting prisms in combination with converging lenses are employed in construction of modern prism binoculars (fig 25.7). The instruments are usually made in pairs, one for each eye, it is astronomical telescope in compact form. One of the prisms turns the image from a distant object round and corrects for lateral inversion, and the other prism inverts the image as an erect image. They equally have an additional advantage of bringing the rays from two telescopes inwards to match the distance apart of the two eyes.

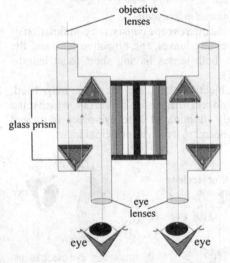

Fig. 25.7 Prismatic binoculars

25.3 Simple camera

The simple camera is similar in principle to the human eye, as we shall soon see in fig. 25.8. The camera is employed in taking photographs of an object or a view. It is made up of a light-proof box with a converging lens in front and a light sensitive film at the back. A provision is made for adjusting the distance between the lens and the film, so that objects in front of the lens can always be focused on the film by the converging lens. A better image could be obtained by replacing the converging lens by system of lenses.

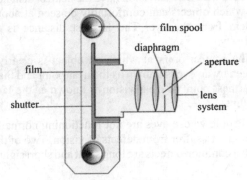

Fig. 25.8 The simple camera

A shutter, of variable speed, between the lens and the film admits or shuts off light from the film, and a diaphragm regulates the size of an aperture which controls the amount of light energy sensitizing the film.

In taking a photograph, the camera lens is pointed at the object and the focusing ring is used to adjust the distance of the lens from the film, until a sharp image is seen on the film. When a button is pressed, the shutter quickly opens and closes, exposing the film, for a brief period to light from the object. After the photograph is taken, the film is wound on between the spools.

In practice, it is important to adjust the aperture size before taking a photograph using another ring control, so that the correct amount of light enters. This setting depends on the brightness of the conditions, which can be measured using a light meter. Some cameras do all this automatically and on simple cameras there are just settings for sunny days, cloudy days, dull days and so on.

25.4 Projectors (the slide projector)

Projector is an instrument employed in projecting the image of a transparent slide or other object on to a screen (fig. 25.9). The essential parts and their functions are described below.

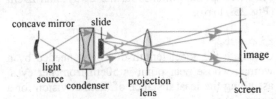

Fig. 25.9 The slide projector

(i) A small but powerful source of light with a converging mirror placed behind it, which directs the light rays towards the slide. The powerful source of light is essential since the object is non-luminous.

(ii) A condenser which is usually a combination of two plano-convex lenses. Its function is to collect the rays from the light source and to concentrate them onto the slide and illuminate every part of it strongly. In this way every part of the image is bright on the screen. Between the two lenses is usually an infrared filter to prevent the passage of heat to the slide, which might otherwise melt.

(iii) The slide carrier is a framework in which the slide or the object to be projected is placed upside down, so that it will appear erect on the screen.

(iv) The focusing lens is placed near the slide. The position of the lens with respect to the slide can be adjusted. The lens produces an enlarged, inverted image of the slide on the screen. The lens is at a distance of between f and $2f$ from the object, (where f is its focal length).

(v) The white screen receives the image which is the right way up if the object is inserted upside down in the slide carrier. The principle of the slide projector is used also in cine-projectors, photographic enlargers and several other devices.

25.5 The human eye

The eye is one of the most sensitive instruments devised by nature. The vertical section through the human eye is as seen in fig 25.10. The essential parts of the eye and their various functions are described below.

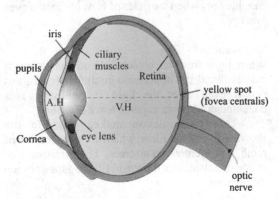

Fig. 25.10 Optical features of the eye

(i) The *cornea* is the transparent front part of the eye, that serves as a protective covering and also partly focuses light entering the eye.

(ii) The *iris* acts as a stop or diaphragm of variable size. The pupil is a circular aperture in the iris.

(iii) The *eye lens* is supported by the ciliary muscles and its function is to focus light entering the eye onto the retina. The action of the ciliary muscles alters the focal length of the lens, by changing its shape.

(iv) The *retina* is the light-sensitive surface at the back of the eye. The optic nerves to the brain begin at the retina from which they transmit messages to the brain. The most sensitive spot of the retina is known as the **yellow spot** and its least sensitive portion is the **blind** spot, which is where the optics nerve leaves the eye for the brain.

(v) The *aqueous humour* is the transparent liquid between the lens and the cornea and the vitreous humour is a jelly- like liquid between the lens and the rest of the eye ball.

How we see with the eye

The optical system of the eye consists of the cornea, the aqueous and vitreous humour and the lens. They form a real, diminished and inverted image of an external object on the retina. The retina transmits the impression created on it by this image through the optic nerve to the brain. The brain then interprets the impression. The amount of light entering the eye through the pupil is regulated by the iris.

Binoculars vision

Because our eyes are some distance apart, the images of an external object falling on the retinas are not exactly alike. The right eye tends to see more of the right side of the object while the left eye sees more of the left side of the object. When the two images are combined by the brain, the proper impression is obtained. The combination of the two perspectives is known as *binoculars vision* and is possible only when the fields of view of the two eyes overlap.

Persistence of vision

When light from an object falls on the retina, it excites it and the impression continues for a short period even after the light is removed. This phenomena is known as *persistence of vision*.

This phenomenon makes possible the showing of cinema films, which are a succession of rapid, still pictures on a screen. The persistence of vision effect enables the eye to fill the gaps between the pictures.

Accommodation

When a normal eye is at rest, parallel rays from a distant object are focused on the retina. For a relaxed eye, the principal focus of the lens is at the retina. When the eye looks at a near object, the light rays are diverging. The action of ciliary muscles increases the thickness of the eye lens, and consequently changes its focal length, so that the image of the object can form again at the retina.

Thus the focal length of the eye lens is not constant. It is altered by the action of the ciliary muscles in such a way that both far and near objects can be focused at the retina. These both far and near objects can be focused at the retina. This action of the human eye is known as *accommodation*.

Normal vision and defects of vision and corrections

People with normal vision have the nearest distance at which objects can comfortably be seen at about 25cm from the eye. The farthest distance is at infinity.

> The nearest point at which an object is clearly seen by an eye is known as the near point and the farthest point of clear vision is known as the far point.

People whose eyes are not functioning normally are said to suffer from defects of vision. Two of the most common defects are long sight and short sight.

Long sight (or hypermetropia)

A long sighted person can see objects at a far distance but cannot see close objects clearly. Its near point is farther away than the normal near point which is 25cm.

This is caused by the eyeball being too short or the eye lens not being sufficiently convergent so that rays from an object at 25cm from the eye are brought to focus behind the retina (Fig. 25.11 (a)).

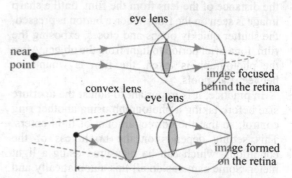

Fig. 25.11 (a) and (b) Long sight and its correction.

It is corrected by a suitable converging lens being placed in front of the eye for near vision. The converging lens used in spectacles reduces the divergence of the rays entering the eye from an object so that they appear to come from the defective eye's near point which is farther away than 25cm (Fig. 25.11 (b)).

Example 25.1

Calculate the focal length of a lens needed by a woman whose near point is 50cm from her eyes, assuming the least distance of distinct vision for a normal eye is 25cm.

Solution

For the woman to see an object clearly at 25cm from the eye, the image must be formed at 50cm on the same side of the lens, at her near point.

$u = 25$cm and $v = -50$cm (virtual image)

But, $\frac{1}{f} = \frac{1}{v} + \frac{1}{u}$ i.e. $\frac{1}{f} = \frac{-1}{50} + \frac{1}{25}$

$\therefore \quad f = 50.0cm$

This implies that a converging lens of focal length 50.0cm is required.

Short sight (myopia)

A short-sighted person cannot see distant objects clearly as rays from such objects are focused in front of the retina instead of at the retina. Such a person has eyeballs that are too long, or lenses that are too convergent. His far point is thus less than the normal far point which is at infinity. Only near objects can be seen distinctly (Fig. 25.12 (a).

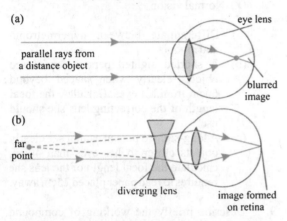

(a)

eye lens

parallel rays from a distance object

blurred image

(b)

far point

diverging lens

image formed on retina

Fig. 25.12(a) and (b) Short sight and its correction.

This defect of vision is corrected by the use of suitable diverging lenses. The diverging lens makes objects at infinity appear to be at the person's far point (fig. 24. 12 (b).

Example 25.2

A short-sighted person cannot see distinctly objects beyond 80cm from his eye. What is the focal length of the correcting lens he needs to see distant objects clearly?

Solution

For the short-sighted person, an object at infinity must be made to appear to be at his far point which 80cm away. The image of the distant object must be formed on the same side of the lens as the objects.

$\therefore v = -80cm$

$u = \infty, \quad \frac{1}{f} = \frac{1}{v} + \frac{1}{u}$

$\frac{1}{f} = \frac{-1}{80} + \frac{1}{\infty} \; (\frac{1}{\infty} = 0)$

$f = -80cm$

Therefore a concave lens of focal length 80cm is required.

Comparison of the human eye with the camera

In comparing the human eye with the camera, we have to look at the similarities and differences between them.

Similarities
(i) The human eye is impregnated with black pigment within, and the camera consists of a light-tight box painted black inside.
(ii) The human eye has the retina which is light-sensitive and the camera has a film which is also light-sensitive.
(iii) Both have converging lens systems to focus light from an external object.
(iv) The iris in human eye performs the same function as diaphragm in camera; that is regulating the amount of light entering the eye/camera respectively.
(v) The pupil in human eye performs the same function as aperture in camera.

Differences
(i) The eye is a biological organ while the camera is a mechanical device, leading to other differences.
(ii) The human eye has a variable focal length, while that of the camera is fixed.
(iii) The distance between the lens and the retina in the human eye is fixed, while the distance between the lens and the film in a camera can be varied.
(iv) The eye suffers defects of vision while camera does not suffer any of such defects.

Summary

1. A converging lens acts as a simple microscope or magnifying glass when an object is placed between the principal focus and the optical centre of the same lens, forming enlarged, erect and virtual image.

2. Compound microscope consists of a combination of two converging lenses; the objective lens and the eye-piece, both having short focal lengths.

3. The magnifying power of a compound microscope is the product of the magnification of the two lenses.

4. The astronomical telescope has two converging lenses, the objective lens has a long focal length and the eye-piece has a short focal length. This instrument gives an inverted image.

5. The Galilean telescope has two lenses; a converging lens of long focal length as objective lens, and a diverging lens of short focal length as eye-piece. A virtual, erect and magnified image is seen at infinity by the eye placed close behind the eye-piece. The magnifying power of the tele-scope is given by, $m = \dfrac{focal\ length\ of\ objective}{focal\ length\ of\ the\ eye\text{-}piece}$

6. Prism binoculars work on the same principles as the astronomical telescope.

7. Simple camera is similar in principl to the human eye, in various ways. There exist some similarities as well as differences between the human eye and a camera.

8. Defects of eye include long sight (hypermetropia) and short sight (myopia). The former is corrected by a suitable converging lens, while the latter is corrected by use of suitable diverging lens.

Exercise 25

1. In a compound microscope, the image formed by the objective lens is at a distance of 3.0 cm from the eye lens. If the final image is at 25.0cm from the eye lens, calculate the focal length of the eye lens.
   A. 28.0cm   B. 22.0cm
   C. 8.3cm   D. 3.4cm

2. The image of object on the retina of a human eye is
   A. virtual and diminished.
   B. inverted and real.
   C. erect and real.
   D. inverted and virtual.

3. A document is to be reproduced using a duplicating camera, where should the document be placed in order to obtain an exact copy?
   A. At the optical centre of the lens of the camera.
   B. At the principal focus of the length of the camera.
   C. At the point which is twice the focal length of the lens of the camera.
   D. Between the principal focus and a point twice the focal length of the lens of the camera.
   E. Beyond a point twice the focal length of the lens of the camera.

4. What part of the human eye corresponds to the diaphragm of a camera?
   A. Cornea   B. Pupil

   C. Iris   D. Retina

5. The magnifying power of Galilean telescope is 10.0, calculate the focal length of the eye piece, if that of the objective is 100.00cm
   A. 1000cm   B. 0.1cm
   C. 50cm   D. 10cm

6. Long sight is corrected by one of the following:
   A. Diverging lens   B. Bi-concave lens
   C. Bi-convex lens   D. Converging lens

7. Explain the following:
   A. Binocular vision
   B. Persistence of vision
   C. Accommodation
   D. Normal vision

8. (a) Differentiate between hypermetropia and myopia.
   (b) A shorted sighted person cannot see objects clearly when placed beyond 60cm from her eyes. Calculate the focal length of the correcting lens she should use.
   (c) A long-sighted person cannot see clearly objects closer to her eyes than 40cm. calculate the focal length of the lens she requires to read paper placed 25cm away.

9. Describe briefly the working of compound microscope. If a compound microscope has lenses of focal length 1.0cm and 5.0cm, and an object is placed 1.2cm from objective lens, and a virtual image is formed 25cm from the eye-piece, calculate the distance between the two lenses. (GCE).

10. (a) Describe briefly with a diagram the working of a simple camera.
    (b) Compare and contrast the human eye and the simple camera.

11. (a) Describe the prism binoculars, what advantages, does it have over other telescopes.
    (b) Draw a well-labelled slide projector, discuss at least 4 of its essential parts.

12. (a) Use well-labelled diagram to describe the working principles of a human eye.
    A magnifying glass forms an enlarged image that is 10 times the object at a distance 25cm from the lens. Calculate the focal length of the lens.

PROPAGATION OF SOUND WAVES

Chapter 26

Sound is a form of wave motion which is conveyed through an elastic medium from a vibrating body to a listener.

Gases, liquids and solids can all transmit sound waves, but a vacuum cannot. Sound produced by sources is a longitudinal wave; that is, it is a form of energy which moves in such a way that its direction of motion is parallel to the direction of oscillation of the molecules of the medium. The study of sound waves is important because sound is made use of in our everyday life, for example, when we talk, listen or play musical instruments.

26.1 Transmission of sound waves

We saw in Chapter 22 that sound waves travel as a series of compressions and rarefactions. Air being highly elastic expands and in doing so compresses the layer of air next to it. In this way the state of compression is passed on and spreads rapidly outwards in much the same way as ripples spread out over the surface of water in water waves. Sound is therefore a compression wave. The sensation of hearing results when such waves strike the ear. Sound waves can travel through solids and liquids as well as gases such as air.

Experiment shows that a material medium is always required to propagate sound. Sound waves do not travel through a vacuum.

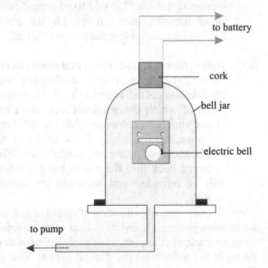

Experiment to show that sound does not travel through a vacuum

An electric bell is suspended inside an airtight jar as shown in Fig 26.1. The jar is connected to a vacuum pump. The electric bell is then operated and set ringing.

As air is gradually pumped out from the jar, it is observed that the sound from the bell gets fainter and fainter though the hammer is still striking the bell. No sound is heard when all the air in the jar is evacuated although the hammer is still striking the bell. Sound is again heard when air is re-introduced.

This shows that sound cannot be propagated in a vacuum but requires a material medium for transmission.

26.2 The speed of sound waves

The speed of sound is found to depend on the density and elasticity of the medium, which means that the speed varies from medium to medium. The speed of sound in air is about 332ms-1 at 0°C, and in water it is about 1500ms-1. In a steel rod the speed of sound may be as high as 500ms-1. It is also found to vary with the temperature of the transmitting medium. In air the speed increases by about 0.6ms^{-1} for every 1°C rise in temperature. In solids and liquids the rise with temperature is much less.

Wind will also affect the speed of sound in relation to a listener. For example the speed is increased if sound travels in the same direction as the wind and decreases if the sound travels in the opposite direction.

26.3 Some phenomena in sound wave

(a) Reflection of sound (echoes)

In chapter 22, we stated that all waves can be reflected. Therefore if a sound wave strikes a smooth surface the sound will be thrown back, so that one hears the sound a second time.

A sound heard after the reflection of sound waves from a plane surface is called an echo.

An echo can sometimes be a nuisance, but in other cases echoes are very useful and have important applications. Listening to speech or music outdoors is not very satisfactory because the loudness falls off rapidly with distance, and in particular the sounds seem uninteresting. In an auditorium, the reflection from the walls and ceiling make the loudness more uniform all over the audience. If however the room is not properly designed, the loudness may not be uniform all over. If the walls and ceiling are made of hard smooth materials, the sound wave will be reflected back and forth many times, so several echoes will be heard in the room and this makes the room reverberate for a long time. This leads to bad listening conditions in which it is difficult to distinguish separate notes. In an auditorium it is therefore advisable to cover the ceiling and walls with soft perforated boards, which can minimize the reflection of sound waves by absorbing them quickly.

Applications of echoes

Determination of speed of sound in air

We can use an echo to determine the speed of sound in air, by directing a sound signal to a wall and measuring the time taken by the echo produced to reach us. Standing in front of a vertical wall, someone claps two hinged boards together to produce a loud sound and listens for the echo produced.

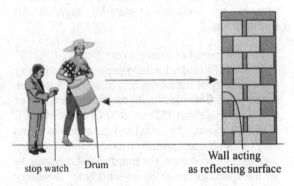

Fig. 26.2 Measuring the speed of sound.

As the clapping is continuously repeated, it is possible to arrange the next clap to coincide with the echo. By means of a stopwatch held by a second person, a number of successive claps are timed and hence, the time between successive claps is found. Let this be t seconds. The distance, x, between the observer and the wall is found, in metres. The sound wave takes t seconds to cover twice this distance. Therefore the speed of the sound wave is

$$v = \frac{2x}{t} \ \text{ms}^{-1}.$$

Echo sounding devices

Echo sounding devices, sometimes called **sonar**, can be used on a ship for measuring the depth of the sea. The principle involves sending a wave down to the sea bed. The wave is reflected back after striking the sea bed. Knowing the speed, v, of the wave in water, and the time, t, to receive the echo the depth (x) of the sea is calculated.

$$x = \frac{vt}{2}$$

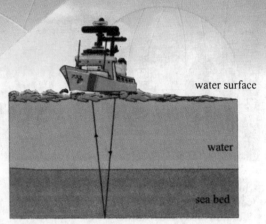

Fig. 26.3 Echo sounding

(a) Exploration for gas

Use of echoes in the exploration for gas and oil.

Echoes are used in oil and gas exploration. To do this, a small explosion is set off on or just below the earth's surface. The resulting sound wave is reflected by underground layers of rock. The nature of each echo and the time it takes to reach the surface reveal to the geophysicist the type and thickness of each rock layer present. Interpretation of the echo can indicate the location of possible mineral or oil-bearing rock formation.

(b) Reverberation

Reverberation is an effect observed in very large halls. Sound takes a very long time to die away after being made, this effect is as a result of multiple reflections of sound from walls, roof and floor of the hall.

Excessive reverberation causes music sound to be indistinct and confused. However, it is good to have some little reverberation otherwise the music sound becomes much weaker and the hall is said to be acoustically 'dead'. Reverberation is reduced by using soft furnishing and padding the walls of the hall.

(c) Refraction of sound waves and some effects

Sound, being a wave, undergoes the phenomenon of refraction. If a person inside a room of which the windows and doors are closed shouts, someone outside can still hear his voice, though faintly. Some of the sound will be absorbed by the walls and some will be reflected back into the room, but a fraction will be refracted and so reach the person outside.

There is one effect of refraction of sound which we sometimes notice: it is easier to hear sound coming from a distance in the evening or at night than at day. At night the air nearest the ground is cool. The air above is warm. Sound travels faster in the warmer upper air, and as the sound travels into the warmer layers, it is continuously refracted from the normal, gradually changing direction. The wavefronts are refracted towards the ground, instead of spreading away higher and higher. Sounds coming from a distance are brought down towards the ground and so are heard clearly. During the day, the air nearer the ground is usually warmer than the air above, the reverse effect occurs and sounds from a distance are less easily heard.

We have seen in chapter 22 that waves are refracted if they travel from one medium to another in which the speed of the waves differs. Refraction of sound can be demonstrated as shown in Fig. 26.4.

Sound travels more slowly in carbon dioxide than it does in air. If a balloon is filled with carbon dioxide and held in front of a small source of sound (such as a small loudspeaker) the sound is refracted by the balloon and can be brought to a point, or focus, on the far side of the balloon.

The converse occurs with a balloon filled with helium, in which the speed of sound is greater than in air. An helium filled balloon causes the sound waves to diverge. This may be compared with the effect on light waves of converging and diverging lenses.

Example 26.1

A hunter at a distance x from a cliff fires a gun. He hears the echo from the cliff after 2.4s. If the speed of sound in air is 340ms^{-1}, calculate x.

$$\text{The velocity of sound } v = \frac{2x}{t}$$

$$\text{i.e. } x = \frac{vt}{2}$$

$$= \frac{340 \times 2.4}{2} = 408\text{m}.$$

Example 26.2

A sound wave emitted from the bottom of a ship travels at 1500ms^{-1} vertically downwards through water to an ocean bed 1000m below, and is reflected upwards. What is the time interval between the instant the sound is emitted and the instant the echo is received?

$$\text{Time interval, } t = \frac{2x}{v} = \frac{2 \times 1000}{1500} = \frac{4}{3} \text{ s}$$

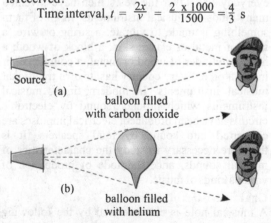

Fig 26.4 The refraction of sound waves.

26.9 Limit of audibility

These are ranges of frequencies of sound that can be comfortably heard by human beings, although it differs with individuals. Generally, we have a range of 4000Hz to about 20kHz.

(d) **Beat**

Beat is a phenomenon obtained when two notes of nearly equal frequency are sounded together. There after, there is a rise and fall of intensity of sound. It is as a result of constructive interference. The beat frequency is the difference in the frequencies.

(e) **Doppler effect in sound**

Doppler effect is the change in frequency (pitch) of a source when there is a relative motion between the source and the observer. It occurs in both sound and light waves.

For example when a train sounding its whistle or an ambulance with a siren just passes an observer a sudden drop in pitch is heard. On the other hand when the train is approaching the observer the pitch heightens. The same effect is noticed if the source is stationary and the observer is moving.

Derivation of expression for apparent frequencies

Case 1: Source S is moving towards a stationary observer O.

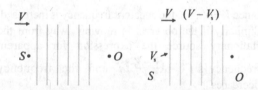

(Both S and O stationary)   (S moving, O stationary)

Fig 26.5(a)

If both S and O were stationary, the associated wavelength of sound of velocity V will be given by:

$$\lambda = \frac{V}{f}$$

Let S move with velocity V_s and therefore $V-V_s$ relative to sound toward O, then the wave length will be:

$$\lambda' = \frac{V-V_s}{f}$$

$\therefore$ apparent frequency, f' is:

$$f' = \frac{V}{\lambda'} = \left(\frac{V}{\frac{V-V_s}{f}}\right) = \left(\frac{V}{V-V_s}\right)f$$

Since $(V-V_s) < V$ the apparent frequency f' will be increased when the source is moving towards a stationary observer. It is easy to see that if on the other hand the source is moving away from a stationary observer.

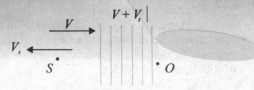

Fig. 26.5(b)

The relative velocity between S and O is $V + V_s$ and the corresponding expression for the apparent change

in frequency is $f' = (\frac{V}{V+V_s})f$

In which case the frequency decreases when the source is moving away from an observer.

Case 2: Source S, is stationary and observer O moving towards it

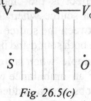

Fig. 26.5(c)

If V_o is the velocity of the observer then the relative velocity in this case between sound and observer is $V+V_o$.

The associated wavelength of sound still remains

$$\lambda = \frac{V}{f}$$

The apparent frequency, $f' = \frac{V+V_o}{\frac{V}{f}} = (\frac{V+V_o}{V})f$

Since $V + V_o > V$, the apparent frequency is increased. Similarly if the observer is moving away from the stationary source the expression for apparent

frequency is $f' = (\frac{V-V_o}{V})f$ and the frequency decreases.

Finally, it is easy to see that if both observer and source are moving say in the same direction the apparent frequency takes the form of

$$f' = (\frac{V+V_o}{V-V_s})f$$

Example 26.3
Suppose a stationary siren emits a note of frequency 440Hz as a train approaches it at 30ms⁻¹. What frequency will be received on the train? (Speed of wave is 331ms⁻¹).

Solution
This is a case of source stationary and observer moving towards it. The apparent frequency f' is

given by $f' = (\frac{V+V_o}{V})f$.

substituting $f = 440$Hz, $V_o = 30$ms⁻¹, $V = 331$ms⁻¹ we get $f' = 480$Hz.

Example 26.4
The whistle of a train emits a tone of frequency 440Hz as the train approaches a stationary observer at 30ms⁻¹. What frequency does the observer hear? (Speed of wave is 331ms⁻¹).

Solution
In this case $f' = (\frac{V}{V-V_s})f$

$f = 440$ Hz, $V = 331$ms⁻¹, $V_s = 30$ms⁻¹
$f' = (\frac{331}{331-30})$ x $440 = 484$Hz
$\therefore f' = 484$Hz

Example 26.5
A sounding tuning fork of frequency 384Hz is moved away from an observer and towards a flat wall with a velocity of 2ms⁻¹.

(i)   What is the apparent frequency of the unreflected sound waves coming directly to the observer?

(ii) What is the apparent frequency of sound received by the observer after reflection.

(iii) How many beats per second are heard? (Speed of sound in air is 341ms⁻¹).

Solution
When the fork is receding from observer, the

apparent frequency $f_1 = (\frac{V}{V+V_s})f = \frac{384 \times 341}{(341+2)}$

$= 381.8$Hz

Fork approaching wall, the apparent frequency

$f_2 = (\frac{V}{V-V_s})f = \frac{384 \times 341}{(341-2)} = 386.3$Hz

Beat frequency $= f_2 - f_1 = 386 - 382 = 4$Hz.

26.4 Musical sound and their characteristics
A musical note is a sound which originates from a source that is vibrating at certain set frequencies. Noise is produced by sources vibrating with no fixed frequency, or by several sources producing an unpleasant mixture of sounds.

The analysis of musical sound is important because of the important role which music plays in everyday life. Over the years men have invented many kinds of musical instruments. In all of them something is made to vibrate: a string or wire; a sheet of metal or elastic skin, a block of wood; a hollow cylinder of wood or metal; a column of air inside a pipe. Every country has its own traditional musical instruments. In modern times, musical instruments which produce sound by electronic circuits have been produced, electrical impulses are converted into sound by loud speakers. It is therefore necessary to study the characteristics of musical sounds, and the mode of production of various kinds of music.

Characteristics of sounds
A musical note is characterized by the following three sensations in the ear: **pitch**, **quality** and **loudness**.

Pitch

Pitch is the characteristic of a note which enables us to differentiate a high note from a low one.

As judged by musicians, the pitch of a note is its position on a musical scale, but strictly, the pitch of a note depends on the frequency of the sound wave. The pitch becomes higher as the frequency increases. A tight string produces a high pitched (or high frequency) sound when plucked but a loose string produces a low pitched sound when plucked.

Quality

The quality of a note is the characteristic that distinguishes it from another note of the same pitch and loudness when played on musical instruments.

Thus the quality of the note 'middle C' played on a piano is different from that of the 'middle C' played on a violin or an organ. It will show later that instruments do not give tones which are pure because their notes do not consist of sound of single frequencies but of several different frequencies blended together. The strongest audible frequency present is called the **fundamental frequency, f_o**. The other frequencies that might be present are integral multiples of f_o; that is $2f_o$, $3f_o$, $4f_o$, etc.

These are called **overtones** or **harmonics**. Thus the harmonics present in a given note determine the quality of the note.

Intensity and loudness

The intensity of sound at a certain place is the rate of flow of energy per unit area perpendicular to the direction of the sound wave.

Loudness, in contrast, is a sensation in the mind of the individual observer, depending on the intensity of sound.

Different observers react differently to similar sound intensities. Clearly, the greater the intensity the greater the loudness. The larger the vibration energy of the air carrying the sound, the larger the intensity and the loudness. For example, loudspeakers producing very loud notes have large cones attached to them, to create very large air vibrations. Large drums produce greater sounds than small drums.

Intensity depends, among other factors, on the amplitude of vibration, the frequency of the sound and the distance away of the sounding body. Loudness depends on all these and also on the characteristics of the individual ear.

Ultrasonic sound

Not all sound waves can be heard by the human ear. The normal human ear can respond to frequencies ranging from about 20Hz to 16000Hz. Frequencies above hearing range, especially those of several hundred thousand hertz, are called *ultrasonics*. These sound waves are useful in some ways because of their high frequency. They can destroy bacteria in water and are used, for example, in cleaning metals, drying papers, removing smoke from air.

Resonance

Resonance is a phenomenon which occurs in many branches of physics. When a vibration of a particular frequency takes place, a nearby object may start to vibrate in sympathy. The vibrations then combine to produce a large vibration. This is called resonance.

If a body is set into vibration and left to vibrate by itself, the body will vibrate with its own natural frequency. On the other hand, it can be made to vibrate at any frequency by an imposed external frequency. When the imposed frequency is the same as the natural frequency, the vibrations build up to a large amplitude. This is what we call **resonance.**

Resonance is an effect caused by a vibrating body setting another body vibrating, both having the same natural frequency.

When studying sound it is found that when a vibrating tuning fork is placed over a column of air and the volume of air is gradually varied, a stage will be reached when the natural frequency of air in the tube is equal to the frequency of the tuning fork. At this particular stage resonance occurs and a very loud sound is heard, so loud that it will be noticed by everyone around.

In the study of mechanics, we find that a diver who jumps repeatedly at one end of a diving board will achieve resonance when his rate of jumping has the same frequency as the natural frequency of the vibrating board. He will be suddenly lifted up to a maximum height at this stage. It is also found that the body of a car sometimes vibrates loudly when the engine speed is of a particular value. The frequency of the engine is then roughly equal to the natural frequency of vibration of the body of the car.

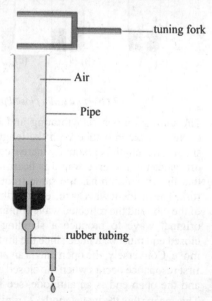

Fig. 26.6 Resonance tube

When studying electricity, we find that a radio receiver is tuned to a station when the current in the aerial circuit inside is in resonance with the incoming radio waves.

26.5 Vibrations of air column in pipes

The study of modes of vibrations in pipes is of importance because musical instruments such as flutes, drums, etc, are either open or closed pipes. A closed pipe is one which is closed at one end only but an open pipe is one which is open at both ends.

It is found experimentally that the frequency of vibration of air in these pipes (or that of stationary waves set up in these pipes) increases as the length of air column decreases. If f is frequency and l is length of air column, then $f \propto 1/l$.

Usually we can vary the length of air column either by shortening the tube or by filling it with water and gradually running off water to create more space for air.

Vibrations in a closed pipe

A tall tube is filled with water and the volume or length of air can be varied by gradually letting out the water. A column of air in the tube will have its own natural frequency of vibration. If a tuning fork of the same frequency as the air column is made to vibrate above it, we can expect that the fork will set the column into resonant vibration. Suppose we are provided with a tuning fork of frequency f_o.

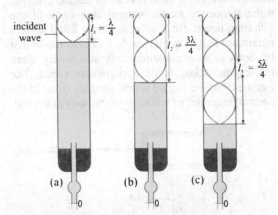

Fig. 26.7 Overtones of a closed pipe.

The tuning fork is set vibrating and held over a column of air in a tube with the length l initially small. The length is gradually increased by running off water until a large sound is heard. This means that the air column has the same frequency as the fork. The incident wave is reflected at the closed end of the tube and the reflected wave combines with the original wave to produce a standing wave. The closed end must be a node since the air there cannot move. Conversely, the open end is an antinode. The first resonance occurs when the closed end is a node and the open end is an antinode, see Fig. 26.7(a). This means that the wavelength, λ, is given by:

$l = \frac{\lambda}{4}$ or $\lambda = 4l$

Therefore, the associated frequency of vibration is
$f_o = \frac{v}{\lambda} = \frac{v}{4l}$

where v is the speed of sound in air.
$f_o = \frac{v}{4l}$ is called the **fundamental frequency** of the closed pipe.

By varying the length of air column in the tube, i.e. increasing the length further by running off more water, a second position will be reached when a large sound will once again be heard. In this position a second node will be formed such that the wavelength of the vibrating air is now $l = \frac{3}{4}\lambda$ or $\lambda = \frac{4l}{3}$.

Therefore the frequency of vibration is:
$f_1 = v \div \frac{4l}{3} = \frac{3v}{4l} = 3f_o$.

A harmonic is a note with frequency equal to an integral multiple of that of the fundamental note.

The frequency $f_1 = 3f_o$ is called the **third harmonic** or first overtone of a closed pipe (f_o is the first harmonic). By further increasing the length we can find the next overtone frequency with three nodes, and so on. These are $5f_o$, $7f_o$..... Hence the possible harmonics of a closed pipe are f_o, $3f_o$, $5f_o$, $7f_o$,..Note that only odd harmonics are present.

Vibrations in an open pipe

In an open pipe, since the two ends of the pipe must end in an antinode, the fundamental or the simplest note of the vibration (first harmonic) is that in which the mid-point is a node.

Therefore $l = \frac{\lambda}{2}$ or $\lambda = 2l$
The fundamental frequency in this case is therefore
$f_o = \frac{v}{2l}$.

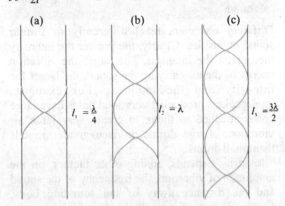

Fig. 26.8 Vibrations in an open pipe.

From Fig. 26.8 (b) and (c) it can be seen that the second harmonic has frequency
$f_1 = \frac{v}{\lambda} = \frac{v}{l} = \frac{2v}{2l} = 2f_o$

The third harmonic is $f_2 = \frac{v}{\lambda} = \frac{3v}{2l} = 3f_o$
Hence, the harmonics present in an open pipe are f_o, $2f_o$, $3f_o$, $4f_o$,....
Thus, all harmonics are possible.

Determination of the speed of sound in air using a resonance tube

A set of tuning forks is required. Starting with the tube filled with water, the fork of the highest frequency is set into vibration and placed as shown in fig. 26.9.

Water is then gradually run off by means of tap T, and hence the length of the air column l is varied until resonance occurs. The experiment is then repeated with the fork of next highest frequency by running out more water, and so on with the remaining forks.

If the frequency of the tuning fork is f, $f = \frac{v}{4l}$,

this means that the graph of f against $\frac{1}{l}$ will be a straight line through the origin. The slope of this graph is equal to $\frac{v}{4}$ and thus v can be calculated. The experiment also verifies the relation of $f \propto \frac{1}{l}$

If we are provided with only one tuning fork and a long pipe, it is possible to determine v by obtaining both the first and second positions of resonance with the same fork.

For the first position:

$$l_1 + c = \frac{\lambda}{4} \text{(see Fig. 26.9)}$$

Where c is the *end correction* which arises from the fact that the antinode at the top does not exactly coincide with the top of the tube.

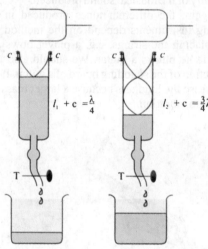

$$l_1 + c = \frac{\lambda}{4}$$ $$l_2 + c = \frac{3}{4}\lambda$$

Fig. 26.9 Resonance tube experiment: determination of velocity of sound in air.

For the second position:

$$l_2 + c = \frac{3\lambda}{4}$$

Eliminating c from both equations we have

$$l_2 - l_1 = \lambda/2$$
i.e. $\lambda = 2(l_2 - l_1)$
$\therefore v = f\lambda = 2f(l_2 - l_1)$

The velocity v can then be calculated. Note that two lengths l_1 and l_2 are obtained instead of just one. This is because in practice the standing wave extends beyond the top of the tube, so that l_1 and l_2 are each inaccurate to measure. However, their difference $l_2 - l_1$, is quite accurate.

Example 26.6

In a resonance tube experiment, a tuning fork of frequency 256Hz gave resonance when the water level was 32.5cm below the open end of the tube. If the next position of resonance was 100cm, what is the speed of sound in air?

First position: $l_1 = \frac{\lambda}{4}$

Second position: $l_2 = \frac{3}{4}\lambda$

$$l_2 - l_1 = \frac{\lambda}{2}$$

$$f = \frac{v}{2(l_2 - l_1)}$$

$$v = 2f(l_2 - l_1)$$

Using $f = 256$Hz, $l_1 = 32.5$cm $= 0.325$m,
$l_2 = 100$cm $= 1.00$m, we have
$v = 2 \times 256(1.00 - 0.325) = 345.6$ms^{-1}.

Example 26.7

The length of air column at which the first resonance was observed, when a vibrating fork was placed on a resonance tube, was 30cm. Calculate the wavelength of the air column and the frequency of the fork. (Take speed of sound as 330ms^{-1}.)

Since the fork is sounding its fundamental frequency,

$l = \lambda/4$
$\lambda = 4l = 4 \times 30 = 120$cm
or $\lambda = 1.20m$

The frequency of the fork is

$$f = \frac{v}{\lambda} = \frac{330}{1.20} = 275\text{Hz}$$

26.6 Modes of vibration of a stretched string (the sonometer)

A sonometer is a hollow box on which a string or wire is stretched as shown. The ends of the string are determined by the two movable knife edges or bridges.

If the string is pulled and released (plucked) a

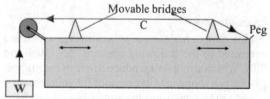

Fig. 26.10 Sonometer box

transverse stationary wave is generated. The wave travels to each knife edge and is reflected back. These ends cannot move and are therefore nodes. The simplest mode of vibration (fundamental) is the case where the midpoint is an antinode while the ends are nodes. This is obtained when the string is plucked at the midpoint. The vibrating length, l, is:
$l = \frac{\lambda}{2}$

So that, $\lambda = 2l$.

The fundamental frequency, $f_o = \frac{v}{\lambda} = \frac{v}{2l}$.

It can be shown that, as with an open pipe, we can obtain all possible harmonics, f_o, $2f_o$, $3f_o$, ..., (see Fig. 26.11).

It can be shown that the velocity of a wave propagated along a fixed wire or string is given by: $v = \sqrt{\frac{T}{m}}$, where T is tension in the wire or string, and m is mass per unit length of the wire or string. The fundamental frequency can therefore be written as:

$f_o = \frac{1}{2l}\sqrt{\frac{T}{m}}$.

This means that the frequency of a vibrating string depends on its length, mass per unit length and the force applied to keep the string stretched. You will notice that a long, thick and loose guitar string produces a low frequency note, while a thin, short and taut string produces a high frequency note.

We can therefore say that:

$f_o \propto \sqrt{T}$ (if m and l are constant)

$f_o \propto \frac{1}{l}$ (if m and T are constant)

$f_o \propto \sqrt{\frac{1}{m}}$ (if l and T are constant)

These laws can easily be verified experimentally. The experiments are fully discussed in *Certificate Practical Physics* by Okeke and Ndupu.

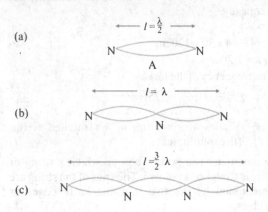

(a) $\quad l = \frac{\lambda}{2}$

(b) $\quad l = \lambda$

(c) $\quad l = \frac{3}{2}\lambda$

Fig. 26.11 Vibration in stretched string.

Example 26.8

An instrument has three identical strings which are subjected to the following tensions: 5N, 10N and 20N. Which string will produce a note of the highest pitch when sounded? Give reasons for your answer.

The string which has tension 20N will have the highest frequency (pitch), because the frequency is proportional to the square root of the tension.

26.7 Musical instruments

Most musical instruments which we are familiar with can be classified as follows:

(i) String instruments
(ii) Wind instruments
(iii) Percussion instruments

Fig. 26.12 Stringed instrument

String instruments

Typical examples of string instruments include: the sonometer, the guitar, the piano and the violin. The physical principles involved in the operation of these instruments are based on the fact that the frequency of the emitted sound depends on equation

$f = \frac{1}{2}\sqrt{\frac{T}{m}}$

That is, the frequency is inversely proportional to the vibrating length, l, directly proportional to the square root of the tension in the string, T, and inversely proportional to the square root of the mass per unit length of the string, m. For example, vibrating length, l, of a thick and loose guital string produces a low frequency note, while thin, short and taut strings produced high frequency notes. The strings of a musical instrument can vibrate not only as a whole, but also in loops. Thus, both fundamental and various harmonics can be produced. The combination of the fundamental harmonic and the other harmonics determine the quality of the musical sound produced.

Again, the different tones produced in various string instruments depend on the method used in displacing the strings. e.g. a player bows a violin while he plucks a guitar. We should also note the function of the sounding board of a guitar. It helps to increase the loudness because a larger mass of air is set into vibration.

Fig. 26.13 Wind instrument

Wind Instruments

Typical examples of wind instruments include: flutes, clarinets, saxophones, trumpet, etc. These instruments produce sound because of vibrating air columns. Whether it is in the form of a closed pipe or an open pipe, the column determines the quality of the note produced, while the frequency of the note produced depends mainly on the length of the vibrating air column according to $f \propto \frac{1}{l}$ i.e. it is inversely proportional to the vibrating length, l.

A player blowing through any such instrument causes a column of air to be set into vibration. A short column of air produces a high pitched note, but a long column of air produces a low pitched note.

Fig. 26.14 Percussion instruments

Percussion instruments

Typical examples of percussion instruments include: bells, drums and tuning forks. In these instruments, sound is produced when they are struck or hit. They contain rods, plates or membranes which vibrate when struck.

In the case of drums, the chords around the rim of the drum enables the player to alter the pitch of the note emitted by the drum.

Summary

1. Sound is a form of energy.

2. Sound waves require some medium for their propagation.

3. The sound wave is a longitudinal wave. It is produced as a result of the compression and rarefaction of the medium.

4. The speed of sound in air is directly proportional to the square root of the absolute temperature.

5. Sound waves can be reflected, and the sound obtained after the reflection of a sound wave is called an **echo.**

6. Echoes can be used in determining the velocity of sound in air, finding the depth of a sea, and in oil prospecting.

7. A musical sound is characterised by three factors: pitch, quality and loudness. Pitch depends on the frequency, quality on the number of harmonics present while loudness is directly proportional to intensity.

8. One vibrating source can induce vibrations in another body which has the same natural frequency. This phenomenon is called **resonance.**

9. The fundamental frequency of a musical instrument is the lowest note produced by the instrument. Notes of higher frequencies are called the overtones. The frequencies of the overtones are integral multiples of the fundamental frequency. The fundamental, together with the overtones, constitute the harmonics.

10. The length of the air column in a closed pipe vibrating at its fundamental frequency is $l = \frac{\lambda}{4}$ and the frequency is $f = \frac{v}{4l}$.

11. The length of the air column in an open pipe vibrating with its fundamental is $l = \frac{\lambda}{2}$ and the corresponding frequency is $f = \frac{v}{2l}$.

12. The fundamental frequency of a vibrating string is given by $f = \frac{1}{2l}\sqrt{(T/m)}$ where l is length of string, T is tension and m is the mass per unit length of the string.

13. When two notes whose frequencies f_1 and f_2 are nearly equal, are sounded together, the combined sound gives a periodic rise and fall in the intensity (or loudness) of the tone heard. These alterations in loudness are known as beats. The frequency of the beats is the number of intense (or loud) sounds heard per second, i.e. $f_1 - f_2$.

14. The horning of a car appears to increase in pitch as the car approaches a stationary observer, but, as it passes the observer, the pitch changes and becomes lowered. This phenomenon is known as the Doppler effect, after the scientist who first explained it.

15. Musical instruments can be classified as wind, stringed, and percussion instruments.

16. A wind instrument makes a sound because of a vibrating air column. Examples of wind instruments include clarinets, saxophones, flutes and trumpets.

17. Examples of stringed instruments include the piano, the violin and the guitar, and the physical Principle is that $f = \frac{1}{2l}\sqrt{(T/m)}$.

18. Percussion instruments include drums, bells and the tuning fork.

Exercise 26

1. The quality of a note depends on
   A. frequency.   B. tension.
   C. harmonics.   D. Intensity.

2. The speed of sound in air is
   A. $20\,ms^{-1}$.   B. $332\,ms^{-1}$.
   C. $1500\,ms^{-1}$.   D. $5,000\,ms^{-1}$.

3. Doppler effect is as a result of
   A. reflection.   B. refraction.
   C. relative motion.   D. beat effect.

4. Calculate the frequency of fundamental of a closed pipe of length 20cm, if the speed of sound waves in air is $340\,ms^{-1}$.
   A. 40Hz   B. 200Hz
   C. 350Hz   D. 425Hz

5. Loudness of sound depends on
   A. frequency.   B. intensity.
   C. overtones.   D. Harmonics.

6. In which of the following is the speed of sound greatest?
   A. Air at 100°C   B.   Water
   C. Wood   D.   Steel

7. Which of the following is not true of sound?
   A. Sound is a form of energy.
   B. Sound is due to vibrations.
   C. Sound requires a medium for propagation.
   D. Sound is transverse wave.

8. A man standing 99m from the foot of a tall cliff claps his hands and hears an echo 0.6 s later. Calculate the velocity of sound in air in ms^{-1}.
   A. 59.4   B.   82.5
   C. 330   D.   430

9. The frequency of a vibrating string depends on length, tension and mass per unit length. The frequency decreases when
   A. the mass per unit length is decreased.
   B. the length is decreased.
   C. the tension is decreased.
   D. both mass per unit length and length are decreased.

10. The resonating air column of a tube closed at one end emits its fundamental frequency when the effective length of the tube is 55.0 cm. Calculate the frequency of the vibrating air column if the speed of sound in air is 330 ms^{-1}.
   A. 1.5Hz   B.   6.0Hz
   C. 150.0Hz   D.   300.0Hz

11. If the length of the air column in a closed pipe is 45cm when it emits its first overtone, the wave length of the note produced is
   A. 60cm.   B. 180cm.
   C. 90cm.   D. 45cm.

12. Why do recording studios and concert auditoriums sometimes have their ceilings and walls covered with soft perforated boards?

13. What do you understand by the term echo?

14. State two practical uses of echoes.

15. Give three examples of your native string or wind instruments and two examples of modern musical instruments.

16. What is resonance? Give one example.

17. What is the shortest length of a closed tube which resonates with a tuning fork of frequency 320 Hz? (Take the speed of sound in air as 330ms^{-1}).

18. Describe how you would use a resonance tube to determine the frequency of the note emitted by a tunning fork, showing how the result would be obtained from the observations. (Velocity of sound in air = 330ms^{-1}).

19. The length of the vibrating air column of a simple resonance tube can be altered by adjusting a water level. Resonance is found for a fork of frequency 440 Hz when the length of the air column is 18.8cm and again when it is 57.3cm. Explain how each of these positions occurs; calculate the speed of sound in the air in the tube.

20. A horn is sounded at regular intervals in front of a high wall 1320m away. If the echo from the wall is heard simultaneously with the next hoot, how many hoots are made every two minutes? (Speed of sound in air is 330ms^{-1})

21. State:
   (a) one disadvantage of echoes
   (b) two applications of echoes

22. How can the speed of sound be measured?
   Two people Emeka and Ngozi are 165m apart along a line at right angles to a wall which is 165m behind Ngozi and Emeka fires a shot. What is the interval:
   (a) between the two reports heard by Emeka and;
   (b) the two reports heard by Ngozi?
   Take the speed of sound as 330ms^{-1}.

23. What is a mechanical wave?
   Describe with the aid of a diagram, an experiment to show that sound needs a material medium for transmission. State three characteristics of sound and mention the factor on which each depends.

24. A boy standing some distance from the foot of a tall cliff claps his hands and hears an echo 0.5 sec later. If the speed of sound is 340 ms^{-1}, how far is he from the cliff?

25. A source of sound produces waves in air of wavelength 1.65m. If the speed of sound in air is 330ms^{-1}, what is the period of vibration? (SSCE).

BOOK
3

Chapter 27

ELECTROMAGNETIC WAVES (E. M. WAVES)

27.1 Nature of E.M. Waves

Electromagnetic waves are members of a family of waves which are produced by electromagnetic vibrations. Electromagnetic waves have electrical origin and the ability to travel in vacuum, for instance, from the sun to the earth. So, electromagnetic waves are regarded as a combination of travelling electric and magnetic forces which vary in value and are directed at right angles to each other and to the direction of travel. In other words, they are transverse waves.

By definition, electromagnetic waves are those that do not require a medium for their propagation. The electromagnemtic waves consist of:

(i) radio waves with wavelengths 10^{-3} m to 1000m;
(ii) infrared waves with average wavelength of 10^{-6}m;
(iii) visible spectrum, known as light waves, with wavelength of 7×10^{-7}m for red rays;
(iv) ultraviolet rays with wavelength of 10^{-8} m;
(v) X-rays with wavelength of 10^{-10}m;
(vi) gamma-rays with wavelength of 10^{-11} m.

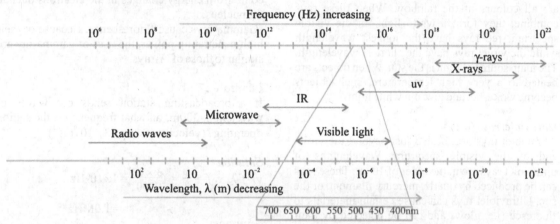

Fig. 27.1 Electromagnetic waves

All the electromagnetic waves have the same velocity of about $3 \times 10^8 ms^{-1}$ but, as shown in Fig. 27.1, they differ in their wavelengths. Since the velocity of a wave v is given by the equation $v = f\lambda$, it means that the frequencies of the different waves also differ. Therefore, the waves can be distinguished by either their wavelengths or by their frequencies.

In addition to their travelling at the same velocity of $3 \times 10^8 ms^{-1}$ in air, all members of the electromagnetic spectrum carry energy and exhibit interference and diffraction. Although each wave is produced differently, most of them result from electrons suffering some kind of energy change. For example, when electrons are accelerated in an aerial, radio waves are emitted.

27.2 Types of electromagnetic waves, sources, and uses

Examples of *e-m* waves arranged in order of decreasing wave lengths are: radio waves, infrared rays, visible light, ultraviolet rays, X-rays and Gamma-rays. We now discuss the sources, detection techniques and uses of each of these rays.

Radio waves

Radio waves have the longest wavelengths. The wavelengths vary from a few millimetres to several kilometres. Radio waves are emitted from transmitters and carry radio signals to radio sets.

The shortest radio waves are called microwaves. Microwaves are used in radar, and in heating, hence, they are used in cooking. The long wavelength radio waves travel by reflection through the **ionosphere**. The ionosphere consists of electrically-charged gases which are very high above the earth.

Infrared waves (I.R. Waves)

Infrared waves are found just beyond the red end of the visible spectrum. They are present in the radiation from the sun or from the filament of an electric lamp. Infrared waves are easily detected by their sensation of heat. A non-glowing hot body, that is a body with a temperature below 500°C, emits infrared rays alone. At above 500°C, the body becomes red-hot, and emits red light and infrared rays. When a body becomes white-hot, white light (that is, all the colours of the visible spectrum) and infrared radiation are emitted.

Infrared rays have wavelengths of around 10^{-6}m, and they can be reflected by polished surfaces, just like light. Infrared rays, in addition to being detected by their sensation of heat, can also be detected by special photographic films. Pictures can be taken in the dark with infrared rays.

Many manufacturing industries use infrared lamps to dry paints on painted items. They are also used for the treatment of muscular complaints.

Visible spectrum or light waves

The visible spectrum is made up of red, orange, yellow, green, blue, indigo, and violet-rays. These are all colours of the rainbow. When these rays combine, they form a white light. In the visible spectrum, red rays have the longest wavelength while the violet rays have the shortest wavelength. The main source of light is the sun. When objects are heated to a very high temperature, such objects become white-hot and give out white light.

Ultraviolet rays (u-v)

Ultraviolet rays are located just beyond the violet end of the visible spectrum. Wavelengths of ultraviolet rays are in the order of 10^{-8}m. These rays can be produced by quartz, mercury filament, or the sun. Ultraviolet rays can cause certain materials to fluoresce (i.e. glow) and can be detected by their action on fluorescent papers. They also affect photographic plates, by reacting with the chemicals which coat the photographic plates.

Ultraviolet rays cannot pass through smoky atmosphere or ordinary window glass. They cause sunburn when they fall on the human body.

X-rays

The wavelengths of X-rays are in the order of 10^{-10}m. Thus, X-rays have shorter wavelengths than the ultraviolet rays. X-ray wavelengths are about a thousand times shorter than those of light waves. X-rays are produced when fast-moving electrons strike a metal target, which reduces their velocity.

X-rays are used in hospitals to destroy malignant growths in the body, and to produce X-ray photographs which can locate broken bones. Much of X-ray in the human body is harmful and can lead to sterility and adverse change in the blood. X-rays are used in industry to locate cracks in metal castings and flaws in pipes.

X-rays ionize gases and have a penetrating effect such that they pass through substances opaque to white light, are diffracted by crystals, and unaffected by either electric or magnetic fields. They also affect photographic plates.

Gamma-rays

The gamma (γ) rays are similar to X-rays. The wavelengths of γ-rays are in the order of 10^{-11}m, clearly shorter than the wavelengths of X-rays. Gamma-rays are emitted by radioactive substances such as cobalt –60 and can be detected by the Geiger Muller tube.

Like X-rays, gamma-rays ionize gases and darken photographic plates. Because of their shorter wavelengths, gamma-rays have a greater penetrating power than X-rays. Like X-rays, they have no electric charge, and so are not affected by either electric or magnetic fields.

Apart from the difference in their wavelengths, gamma-rays and X-rays differ in their origin. Gamma-rays arise in atomic nuclei whereas X-rays come from energy changes in the electrons outside the nucleus.

Gamma-rays cause fluorescence. Because of their high penetrating power, the uses of gamma-ray are similar to those of X-rays.

Example 27.1

If a broadcasting station sends out waves of wavelength 300m, on what frequency is the station operating? (velocity of wave: 3×10^{-8}ms^{-1}).

Solution

$$v = f\lambda, \therefore f = \frac{v}{\lambda} = \frac{3 \times 10^8}{300} = 1 \times 10^6\,\text{Hz}$$

$$= 1.0\,\text{MHz}$$

Summary

1. Electromagnetic waves are combinations of electric and magnetic forces, and are transverse waves which travel in vacuum.

2. Electromagnetic waves consist of the following waves: radio waves, infrared waves, visible spectrum, ultraviolet rays, X-rays, and gamma-rays.

3. All electromagnetic waves have the same velocity, about 3×10^8 ms^{-1} in air but differ in wavelengths and frequencies.

4. In addition to having the same velocity; all electromagnetic waves carry energy and exhibit interference and diffraction.

5. Of all electromagnetic waves mentioned, radio waves have the longest wavelengths. The shortest radio waves, called microwaves, are used in radar, and in very fast cooking.

6. Infrared rays are found in the radiation from the sun or from the filament of an electric lamp. Infrared rays are easily detected by the sensation of heat, and by special photographic films. Infrared rays are used for taking pictures in the dark, to dry paints, and for treating muscular complaints.

7. The visible spectrum is what is called the "white light", made up of red, orange, yellow, green, blue, indigo and violet. The main source of white light is the sun.

8. Ultraviolet radiations are produced by quartz, mercury filament lamp, and the sun. Ultraviolet radiations are detected by their action on fluorescent paper; that is, they cause certain materials to fluoresce. They also affect photographic plates. They cause sunburn.

9. X-rays are produced when fast-moving electrons strike a metal target. X-rays are used in hospitals to destroy malignant growths in the body, and to produce X-ray photographs which can help locate broken bones, etc. X-rays are used in some industries to locate cracks in metal castings and flaws in pipes. X-rays pass through substances opaque to white light, are diffracted by crystals, and unaffected by either electric or magnetic fields. They also affect photographic plates. When X-rays are beamed on photographic plates, the plates when developed are found to be darkened at the points the X-rays were beamed upon.

10. Gamma-rays are similar to X-rays but have shorter wavelengths. Gamma-rays have no charge like X-rays, but possess greater penetrating power than X-rays. Gamma-rays cause florescence. While gamma-rays arise in atomic nuclei, X-rays come from energy changes in the electrons outside the nucleus.

Exercise 27

1. Which of A-D below is/are true of all electromagnetic waves?
   (a) They have the same velocity.
   (b) They have different wavelengths.
   (c) They have the same frequency.
      A. (a) only   B. (a) and (b)
      C. (a) and (c)   D. (b) only

2. Which of the following types of radiation has the highest frequency?
   A. Infrared rays   B. Radio waves
   C. Visible light   D. X-rays

3. What type of electromagnetic radiation can be used to take photographs in the haze?
   A. Radio-waves   B. Infrared rays
   C. Visible light   D. Ultraviolet rays

4. Which of the electromagnetic radiations passes through a thin sheet of lead?
   A. Radio waves   B. Infrared rays
   C. Ultraviolet rays   D. Gamma-rays

5. The wavelength of X-rays is longer than the wave length of
   A. radio waves.   B. γ-rays.
   C. infra-red waves.   D. light waves.

6. The frequency of infra-red waves is more than the frequency of
   A. light waves.   B. X-rays.
   C. γ-rays.   D. radio waves.

7. Give three similarities of electromagnetic waves. Mention two distinguishing properties of infrared and ultraviolet rays.

8. What are the properties of X-rays? Mention and describe two important uses of X-rays.

9. What are the main differences between X-rays and gamma-rays? Mention two important similarities between the two types of rays.

10. What is the main source of light waves? List one similarity and two differences that light waves have with other electromagnetic waves.

11. A broadcasting station is operating at a frequency of 2.0 MHz. What is the wavelength of waves it sends out? (Velocity of waves = 3×10^8 ms^{-1}).

12. What are electromagnetic waves? Give four examples of them. For each, state its source, one of its properties, and one of its uses.

13. How many rays make up the visible spectrum of light waves? Name them in the ascending order of their wavelengths. Which one has a higher frequency, orange or green rays?

14. How are
   (a) X-rays and
   (b) Infra-red rays produced?
   How is each detected? Mention two uses of each.

GENERAL PROPERTIES OF FIELDS

Chapter 28

28.1 Concept of field

A field is a concept introduced to describe a region under the influence of some physical agency such as gravitation, electricity, magnetism, heat etc. There are two kinds of fields: **vector** and **scalar**. Examples of scalar fields include distribution of temperature, density, electric potential, etc. Examples of vector fields include: the distribution of velocity in a fluid, gravitational force field, magnetic and electric field.

The magnitude of scalar fields are usually mapped by lines such as lines of isothermals, lines of equidensity and lines of equipotential surfaces, while vector fields which require magnitude and direction to specify them are mapped by **lines of flux** or **lines of force**.

28.2 Gravitational field

As long ago as 1666, Newton discovered a universal law now known as the law of gravitation.

> The force of attraction between two given particles of masses, M and m is inversely proportional to the square of their distance, r, apart and directly proportional to the product of their masses.

$$F_g = \frac{GMm}{r^2} \qquad 28.1$$

where G is the gravitational constant expressed in Nm^2kg^{-2}.

At the surface of the earth, the force of attraction on a mass, m, is mg, where g is the acceleration of free fall. If we assume that the earth is a sphere of radius, r, so that the mass of the earth, M, is concentrated at the centre, then the force of attraction of the earth on the mass m at the surface is $\frac{GMm}{r^2}$

$$\therefore \quad \frac{GMm}{r^2} = mg \qquad 28.2$$

The interaction between masses described by the law of gravitation is an example of action at a distance. Today, we prefer to think in terms of the concept of fields in analyzing gravitational interactions. A gravitational field is said to exist near any body that possesses mass. That is, we imagine that one of the masses sets up a gravitational field which permeates all of space and is the agent that exerts a force on any other mass placed in it. We know that a gravitational field exists at a point because an object placed there experiences the gravitational force of the Earth's field.

With every point near the earth we can associate a gravitational field vector g. This is the gravitational acceleration that a test body of mass m placed at the point would experience. If F_g, is the gravitational force acting at a point where a test charge of mass m is placed then the field g is given by:

$$g = \frac{F_g}{m} \qquad 28.3$$

The direction of the field g is the same as the direction of F_g which is the direction in which the test mass m is urged. Thus a gravitational field is a vector field since it has magnitude and direction. For points near the surface of the earth, the field is often taken as uniform; g is the same for all points.

From the equations above, the magnitude of the gravitational field g at any point where a test mass m is placed at a distance, r, from mass, M, is given by

$$g = \frac{F_g}{r^2} = \frac{GMm}{mr^2} = \frac{GM}{r^2}$$

$$\therefore \quad g = \frac{GM}{r^2} \qquad 28.4$$

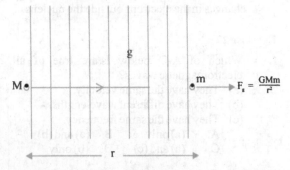

Fig. 28.1 M sets up a field g which exerts a force on m

Thus the gravitational field at a point due to an object of mass M placed a distance r from a test mass depends on the magnitude of M and r^2.

28.3 Electric force and field

In 1875 Coulomb studied the magnitude of the forces between two electrically charged bodies. He formulated the law governing the electrostatic forces of attraction, called **Coulomb's law**.

In a given medium the force of attraction or repulsion F_e between two bodies with charges of Q and q is directly proportional to the charges and inversely proportional to the square of their separation r.

$$F_e = \frac{1}{4\pi\varepsilon_0} \cdot \frac{Qq}{r^2} \qquad 28.5$$

The constant of proportionality $\frac{1}{4\pi\varepsilon_0}$ has been chosen to have the value $9.05 \times 10^9 \, mF^{-1}$.

Example 28.1

Calculate the magnitude of the force of repulsion between two equal charges of $2.0\mu C$, separated by a distance of 1m in a vacuum.

(Take $\frac{1}{4\pi\varepsilon_0} = 9 \times 10^9 mF^{-1}$)

$$F = \frac{Qq}{4\pi\varepsilon_0 r^2}$$

$$= \frac{9 \times 10^9 \times (2.0 \times 10^{-6})^2}{1^2}$$

$$= 0.036N$$

Electric field

Like the gravitational force, the force described by Coulomb's law is an action at a distance. The charge Q acts through a distance to exert an electric force F_e on the test charge q.

We imagine that the existence of Q changes the state of the space by producing an electric field in the space surrounding itself. If a test charge q is placed at some point distant r from the charge Q, the electric field E at that point is given by

$$E = \frac{F_e}{q} \qquad 28.6$$

The unit of E is Newton/coulomb (NC^{-1})

Since $F_e = \frac{1}{4\pi\varepsilon_0} \cdot \frac{Qq}{r^2}$, the magnitude of E is given by

$E = \frac{Q}{4\pi\varepsilon_0 r^2}$

Since F_e is a vector and q is a scalar, the direction of E is the same as that of F_e. i.e. the direction in which a test positive charge placed at the point would tend to move.

Thus electric field, like the gravitational field, is a vector field and the two are very similar. The only difference is that the charge of a test body, rather than the mass, is the property of interest.

Also from the last equation, we see that the electric field, like the gravitational field, varies inversely as the square of the distance but is directly proportional to charge Q and not mass. It is independent of test charge.

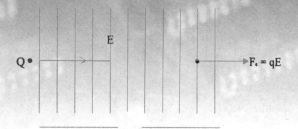

Fig. 28.2 *Q sets up a field E which exerts an electric force, F, on q.*

28.4 Magnetic field

The study of magnetism grew from the observation that certain stones, *magnetites*, would attract bits of certain metals, such as iron. Modern permanent magnets were eventually produced. The earth itself was also known to have magnetic properties. In 1820, Oersted discovered that a current-carrying conductor also produces magnetic effects. Like electric and gravitational fields, we can regard a space around a magnet and a current-carrying conductor as an area of magnetic field. The basic magnetic *vector B* which we now want to define is called *magnetic induction*.

The expression for the magnetic induction is more complex than either gravitational or electric field. As we did for the electric fields, let us consider a body with charge q_m as a test body. If this test charge is placed at rest near the magnetic field, we would find by experiment that no force acts on q_m. However, if we fire the test body with a velocity, v, we find that a force F_m at right angles to v acts on it, if the magnetic field is acting. We thus define B at a point in terms of F_m, v and q_m.

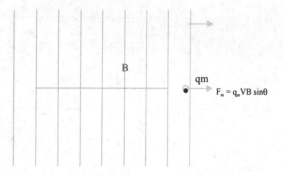

Fig. 28.3 *A current-carrying conductor or a magnet sets up a field B which exerts a force, F_m on q_m.*

The direction of B is given in such a way that F_m is always perpendicular to the plane of v and B. The field, B can be shown to be equal to

$$B = \frac{F_m}{q_m v \sin\theta}$$

where θ is the angle between v and B.

The *SI* unit of B is the *tesla*.

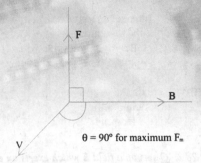

$\theta = 90°$ for maximum F_m

Fig. 28.4 F_m is always perpendicular to the v-B plane

28.5   Properties of electric lines of forces

The concept of lines of force was introduced by Faraday as an aid in visualising electric, magnetic and even gravitational fields. These fields are vector fields which, in general, vary from point to point in magnitude and direction. Thus lines of force are imaginary lines for representing field patterns. The direction of the line at any point (or the direction of the tangent at that point) is the same as the direction of the field at that point. The number of lines of force passing through a unit area perpendicular to the lines of force is proportional to the magnitude of the field at the point. That is, the density of field lines is an indication of the magnitude of the field.

Field lines may be parallel, radial or curved depending on the nature of the electric or magnetic field. This depends on the geometrical shape of the body carrying the charge or the statistical distribution of the electric charges in the electric field or, in the case of magnetic field, on the nature of the current element or magnet producing the field.

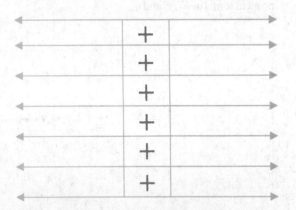

Fig 28.5   A positively charged sheet.

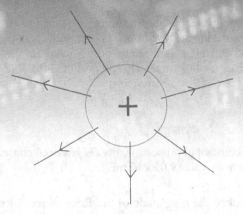

Fig. 28.6   A positively charged sphere.

Fig. 28.5 and Fig. 28.6 show the pattern of field lines for a positively charged sheet and sphere respectively. The lines of force are directed away from these positively charged bodies because they will repel a unit positive charge.

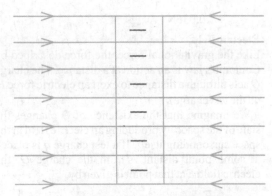

Fig. 28.7   A negatively charged sheet.

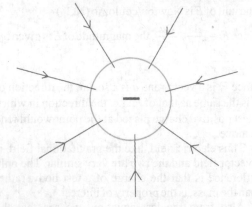

Fig. 28.8   A negatively charged sphere.

Fig. 28.7 and Fig. 28.8 show the pattern of lines of force for a negatively charged sheet and sphere respectively. The lines of force are directed towards these negatively charged bodies because they will attract a unit positive test charge. Fig 28.9 shows the pattern of lines of force of two charges of opposite sign close to each other.

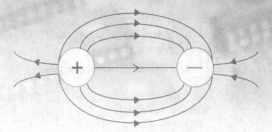

Fig. 28.9   Two unlike spherical charges

The magnetic field lines of a straight conductor carrying current are concentric circles.

Equipotential surfaces
While we use lines of force to represent magnetic and electric fields, we sometimes use lines known as equipotential surfaces to represent potentials.

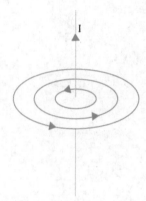

Fig. 28.10   The field around a conductor.

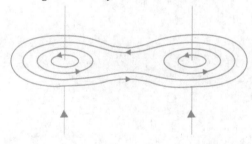

Fig. 28.11   The field of two parallel conductors.

> An equipotential surface is a surface on which all points are at the same potential.

It follows that no work is done in moving a charge from one point to another on an equipotential surface.

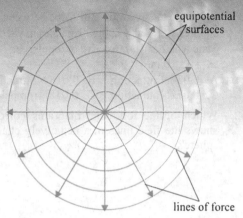

Fig. 28.12   Equipotentials and lines of force about a point charge.

This is true because the potential difference (which represents work) between any two points on such a surface is zero. Hence, electric field must be perpendicular to an equipotential surface, otherwise its component along the surface will do work on the charges placed on the surface.

Summary
1. A field is the region under the influence of some physical agents which can be scalar or vector such as density distribution, magnetic or electric field.

2. The force of attraction between two particles of mass m and M is inversely proportional to the square of distance r between them and directly proportional to the product M and m.

    $F_g = (GMm)/r^2$ where G is gravitational content.

3. Since $(GmM)/r^2 = mg$, $g = F_g/m$. Thus the gravitational intensity g is defined as the gravitational force F_g per unit mass m.

4. The force of attraction between two charged bodies of charges Q and q is also given by $F_e = \frac{1}{4\pi\varepsilon_0}\left(\frac{Qq}{r^2}\right)$, where $\frac{1}{4\pi\varepsilon_0}$ is the proportionality constant.

5. Lines of force are imaginary lines for representing field patterns. The direction of the field at any point is the direction of the tangent at that point.

Exercise 28
1. The following are examples of vector fields except:
    A. Gravitational force.   B.   Electric potential.
    C. Magnetic field.   D.   Electric field.

2. The following are scalar fields except:
    A. Density distribution.
    B. Temperature distribution.
    C. Electric field.
    D. Electric potential.

3. Calculate the magnitude of force between two charges 1.0μC and 2.0μC 1m apart in vaccum. State whether it is attractive or repulsive. ($K_e = 9 \times 10^9 mF^{-1}$)

A. 0.036N attraction.   B. 0.018 N attraction.
C. 0.072N attraction.   D. 0.018N repulsion.

4. Which of the following diagrams correctly shows the field lines of a negatively charged sphere?

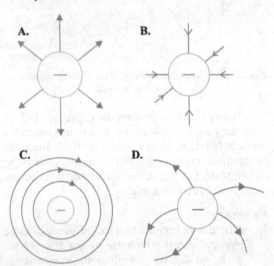

A.

B.

C.

D.

5. What is equipotential surface?

6. Do lines of force cross each other? Give reasons for your answer.

7. Define electric field intensity at a point

GRAVITATIONAL FIELD

29.1 Concept of gravitational field

In the previous chapter, we introduced the gravitational field. It was made clear that a gravitational field is a force field. This force always attracts every object on or near the earth's surface. The earth therefore, exerts an attractive force on every object on or near it. The force of attraction of the earth for a body is equal and opposite to the force of attraction of the body for the earth. Similarly, two objects of different masses exert equal and opposite forces of attraction on each other. The line of action of both forces lies along the line joining the centre of gravity of the two objects.

Fig. 29.1 Earth gravitational field

29.2 Newton's law of gravitation

This leads us to the statement of the law of universal gravitation.

This law states that every particle of matter in the universe attracts every other particle with a force that is directly proportional to the product of the masses of the particles and inversely proportional to the square of the distance between them.

In other words,

$$F = \frac{Gm_1m_2}{r^2} \qquad 29.1$$

where F is the gravitational force on either particle; m_1 and m_2 are their masses; r is the distance between the particles and G is the universal gravitational constant whose numerical value depends on the units in which the force, mass and length are expressed. The gravitational attraction holds the moon in its orbit about the earth and also the earth and its fellow planets in their orbits round the sun. The value of G is $6.67 \times 10^{-11} \mathrm{Nm^2kg^{-2}}$.

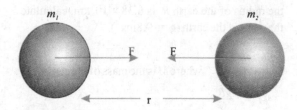

Fig. 29.2 Gravitational attraction between masses.

Example 29.1

Calculate the gravitational force of attraction between two planets of masses 10^{24}kg and 10^{27}kg separated by a distance of 10^{20} metres.

Solution

$$F = \frac{Gm_1m_2}{r^2}$$
$$= \frac{6.67 \times 10^{-11} \times 10^{24} \times 10^{27}}{(10^{20})^2}$$
$$= 6.67\,\mathrm{N}$$

29.3 Relationship between the acceleration due to gravity g and the gravitational constant G

Force of gravity

Have you ever watched a coconut falling from its tree? You should have wondered what caused the coconut to fall. An invisible force must have acted on the coconut to make it move. This force is called '**the force of gravity**' and is the pull of attraction between the earth itself and objects on or near it. All bodies attract each other with a force which depends on the product of their masses, m_1 and m_2 and which increases as the two bodies move nearer to each other. Most common objects are too small to cause a force of attraction large enough to be measured but the earth itself, having a very large mass, pulls any object with a measurable force known as its force of gravity. This force is the weight of the object. For an object on the earth's surface, its force of gravity, F is given by $F = (GMm)/R^2$ where M is mass of earth, m is mass of object and R is radius of earth and G is the gravitational constant, but we already know that force of gravity on a body of mass, m according to Newton's law is also given by $F = mg$.

Thus, $\dfrac{GMm}{R^2} = mg$

$\therefore g = \dfrac{GM}{R^2}$

Example 29.2

Given that $G = 6.67 \times 10^{-11}$ Nm^2 kg^{-2}. units and that the radius of the earth R is 6.38×10^6 km, calculate the mass of the earth ($g = 9.8$ ms^{-2}).

Solution

$g = \dfrac{GM}{R^2}$ where M is the mass of the earth

$M = \dfrac{gR^2}{G}$

$= \dfrac{9.8 \times (6.38 \times 10^6)^2}{6.67 \times 10^{-11}}$

$= 5.98 \times 10^{24}$ kg

29.4 Variation of g at different places on the earth's surface

Since $g = \dfrac{GM}{R^2}$, then if the earth is perfectly spherical and G and M are constant, the value of g will be the same all over the earth's surface. Since the earth is not a perfect sphere; the value of R, which is the distance between the centre of the earth and any point on the earth's surface, varies along the earth's surface. For this reason, the value of g varies from place to place along the earth's surface. The value of g is large where the value of R is small. In other words, the value of g increases as the radius of the earth decreases. This is why the value of g is greater at the poles than at the equator. The equatorial diameter is greater than polar diameter.

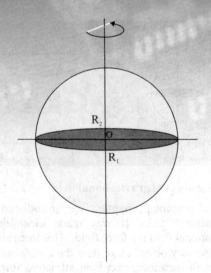

Fig. 29.3 *Variation of g with latitude.*

29.5 Variation of g with altitude

The acceleration due to gravity at sea level is given by:

$g = \dfrac{GM}{R^2}$,

The acceleration due to gravity g' at a height h above the surface of the earth is similarly given by:

$g' = \dfrac{GM}{(R + h)^2}$,

By division $\dfrac{g'}{g} = \dfrac{R^2}{(R + h)^2}$

Dividing the numerator ad denominator by R^2, we get:

$\dfrac{g'}{g} = \dfrac{1}{\left(1 + \dfrac{h}{R}\right)^2}$

If h is small compared with R, we can write:

$g' = g \left(1 + \dfrac{h}{R}\right)^{-2}$

$= g \left(1 - \dfrac{2h}{R}\right)$

Thus, the acceleration due to gravity decreases with increasing altitude.

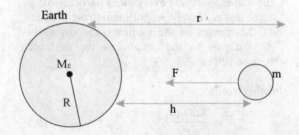

Fig. 29.4 *Variation of g with height.*

29.6 Weightlessness

Weightlessness is a feeling of having no weight. At that time the gravitational pull of the earth has no effect on the body.

Illustrations of weightlessness

1. A body experiences weightlessness at a certain height above the surface of the earth. As seen from equation $g' = g\left(1 - \frac{2h}{R}\right)$, the acceleration due to gravity decreases with increase in altitude. At a particular altitude 'h' which is equal to half of the radius R of the earth, the acceleration due to gravity on the body is zero. The gravitational pull of the earth on the body is zero. Hence the body will experience the sensation of weightlessness at that height.

2. Weightlessness is also experienced when a body is in a lift or an aeroplane descending. If a lift is descending with an acceleration 'a' the equation of motion is given by

$$W - R = ma$$

Where W = the weight of the man
R = the reaction on his feet
m = the mass of the man

$R = W - ma = mg - ma = m(g-a)$

Thus, $R = 0$, when $g = a$.

Therefore the body becomes weightless when the acceleration of the lift is equal to acceleration due to gravity.

29.7 Gravitational potential

The potential, V, at a point due to the gravitational field of the earth is defined as numerically equal to the work done in taking a unit mass from infinity to that point.

If the earth is spherical, it can be imagined that the whole mass M of the earth, is concentrated at its centre. The potential at a point distant r from the centre of the earth can be shown to be given by:

$$V = -\frac{GM}{r} \qquad 29.2$$

where V is the gravitational potential, and the potential at infinity is taken as zero by convention. The negative sign is an indication that the potential at infinity (zero) is higher than the potential close to the earth.

On the earth's surface of radius, R, gravitational potential $V = -\frac{GM}{r}$. Therefore, if a body of mass, m, is moved from infinity to the earth surface of radius, R, the work done on the body is gravitational potential, which is equal to $-\frac{GmM}{R}$

i.e. Work done $= -\frac{GmM}{R}$

29.8 Velocity of escape

Let a rocket of mass, m, be fired from the earth's surface X so that it just escapes from the gravitational influence of the earth. Then work done equals the product of mass of rocket and potential difference between infinity and X. In other words,

Work done $= m \times \dfrac{GM}{R}$

If the rocket moves with velocity, v, then its kinetic energy is

$$\frac{1}{2}mv^2 = \text{work done}$$

That is, $\frac{1}{2}mv^2 = m \times \dfrac{GM}{R}$

Therefore, $v = \sqrt{\left(\dfrac{2GM}{R}\right)}$

$\qquad\qquad$ = velocity of escape

now, $\dfrac{GM}{R^2} = g$

Therefore, $v = \sqrt{(2gR)}$

29.9 Satellites

These are bodies which move in orbits around the moon or planets. Some of them are natural, others are artificial, i.e. man-made.

To put an artificial satellite in orbit at a certain height above the earth, it must enter the orbit at the correct speed where the centripetal force needed to keep it in the orbit is equal to the force of gravity on it.

Let us consider a satellite of mass, m, which just circles the earth of mass, M, in an orbit, A, close to its surface.

If the earth is spherical and its radius, r, the centripetal force = the gravitational force.

$$\text{i.e. } \frac{mv^2}{r} = \frac{GMm}{r^2} = mg \qquad 29.3$$

where g = acceleration due to gravity, and v = the velocity of m in its orbit

$\therefore \quad v^2 = rg$

and $\quad v = \sqrt{rg} \qquad\qquad 29.4$

Assume $r = 6.4 \times 10^6 m$,

and $\quad g = 9.8 \text{ms}^{-2}$

$\therefore \quad v = \sqrt{rg}$

$\qquad = \sqrt{6.4 \times 10^6 \times 9.8}$

$\qquad \approx 8 \times 10^3 \text{ ms}^{-1}$

$\qquad = 8 \text{kms}^{-1}$

Parking orbits

If a satellite of mass m is circling the earth in a plane of the equator in an orbit B concentric with the earth, and if it moves at velocity, v, in the same direction of rotation as the earth at a distance, R, from the centre of the earth, then:

$$\frac{mv^2}{R} = \frac{GMm}{R^2} \qquad 29.5$$

But $GM = gr^2$ (from 1) where r = radius of the earth.

$$\therefore \quad \frac{mv^2}{R} = \frac{mgr^2}{R^2}$$

$$\therefore \quad v^2 = \frac{gr^2}{R}$$

and

$$v = \sqrt{\frac{gr^2}{R}} \qquad\qquad 29.6$$

If the period of the satellite in orbit B is T_1, then

$$v = \frac{2\pi R}{T_1}$$

$$\therefore \quad \frac{4\pi^2 R^2}{T_1^2} = v^2 = \frac{gr^2}{R}$$

$$\therefore \quad T_1^2 = \frac{4\pi^2 R^3}{gr^2} \qquad\qquad 29.7$$

and $T_1 = \sqrt{\dfrac{4\pi^2 R^3}{gr^2}} \quad \left(\text{or } 2\pi\sqrt{\dfrac{R^3}{gr^2}}\right)$

If the period of the satellite in its orbit equals the period of the earth as it turns about its axis which equals 24 hours, the satellite will stay at the same place above the earth as the earth rotates. This orbit is called "parking orbit". Satellites placed on parking orbits can be used to transmit television programmes continuously from one part of the world to another.

The radius, R, can be found as follows:

$$R = \sqrt[3]{\frac{T_1^2 g r^2}{4\pi^2}}$$

where $g = 9.8\,\text{ms}^{-2}$,
$\qquad\quad r = 6.4 \times 10^6\,\text{m}$

$$\therefore \quad R = \sqrt[3]{\frac{(24 \times 3600)^2 \times 9.8\,(6.4 \times 10^6)^2}{4\pi^2}}$$

$$= 42340\,\text{km}$$

$\therefore$ The height of the parking orbit above the surface of the earth

$$= R - r$$

$$= (42340 - 6400)\,\text{km}$$

$$= 35940\,\text{km}$$

also the velocity of the satellite in the parking orbit

$$= \frac{2\pi R}{T_1}$$

$$= \frac{2\pi \times 42340\,\text{km}}{24 \times 3600\,\text{s}}$$

$$= 3.1\,\text{kms}^{-1}$$

In reality, the orbit of a satellite, like that of a planet is not a circle but an eclipse. The earth's shape is not spherical. It is flat at the poles. So, the gravitational field acting on different parts of the satellite's orbit is not equal. Air which extends to great heights affects the velocity of a satellite. Because of all the above observations, there are variations in the satellites orbit. The direction of the satellite is changed by a small angle each time it moves round the earth. So, at intervals, small corrections to the direction of motion have to be made to keep the satellite in the correct orbit.

Example 29.3
The gravitational force on a mass of 10kg at the earth's surface is 100N. If the earth is a sphere of radius R, calculate the gravitational force on a satellite of mass 180kg in a circular orbit of radius $\frac{3R}{2}$ from the centre of the earth.

Solution
The gravitational force of the earth on the body is given by:

$$F = \frac{GMm}{R^2}$$

$$100 = \frac{GM \times 10}{R^2}$$

$$G = \frac{100 R^2}{M \times 10}$$

$$= \frac{10 R^2}{M}$$

The gravitational force of the earth on the satellite is:

$$F_2 = \frac{GM \times 180}{\left(\frac{3R}{2}\right)^2}$$

Substituting the value $G = \frac{10R^2}{M}$ in the equation above, we have

$$F_2 = 800\,\text{N}$$

Example 29.4
A satellite moves in a circular orbit of radius 2R round the earth. What is the acceleration of the satellite?

The gravitational pull of the earth on the satellite of mass m kg is given by

$$F = \frac{GMm}{(2R)^2} = ma$$

Thus, $a = \dfrac{GM}{4R^2}$

but $\dfrac{GM}{R^2} = g$

$$\therefore \quad a = \left(\tfrac{1}{4}g\right)\text{ms}^{-2}$$

Example 29.5
If the weight of an astronaut on the surface of the earth is 700 N, what will be his weight in a space station which is at a distance equal to the radius R of the earth, above the surface of the earth?

Solution
Let W' be the weight of the astronaut in space
g' be the acceleration due to gravity
m be the mass of the astronaut
M be the mass of the earth

$$W' = mg'$$

$$= \frac{GMm}{(R+R)^2}$$

$$= \frac{GMm}{4R^2}$$

$$= \frac{mg}{4} \text{ (since } \frac{GM}{R^2} = g)$$

$$= \frac{700}{4}$$

$$= 175N$$

Summary

1. The force of attraction F between a particle of matter and every other particle in the universe is given by $F = \frac{GM_1M_2}{r^2}$, where M_1 and M_2 are the masses of the two particles, r is the distance between the centres of the two particles, and G is the universal gravitational constant.

2. On the moon, a mass of 1kg will weigh about $\frac{1}{6}$ as much as on earth. The moon exerts a smaller gravitational attraction on objects than does the earth.

3. The value of acceleration due to gravity g varies from place to place along the earth's surface because the earth is not perfectly spherical. The value of R, which is the distance of the centre of the earth to any point on the earth's surface, varies along the earth's surface.

4. Weightlessness is a feeling of having no weight. It is experienced, for example, by a person descending in a lift, when the acceleration of the lift is equal to the acceleration due to gravity.

5. The potential at a point, distant r from the centre of the earth is given as $V = -\frac{GM}{r}$, where M is the mass of the earth and G is the universal gravitational constant.

6. The work done in moving a body of mass, m, from infinity to the earth's surface of radius R is $-\frac{GMm}{R}$.

7. The velocity at which a rocket just escapes from the gravitational influence of the earth (i.e. velocity of escape) is given by:
$$v = \sqrt{\frac{2GM}{R}} = \sqrt{2gR}$$

8. Satellites are bodies which move in orbits around the moon, or planets. There are natural and artificial satellites.

9. An artificial satellite must enter the orbit at the correct speed where the centripetal force needed to keep it in the orbit is equal to the gravitational force on it.

10. The period in the orbit close to the surface of the earth in a plane of the equator equals the circumference of the earth plus the velocity of the satellite in the orbit (i.e. v).

11. If the period of the satellite in its orbit equals the period of rotation of the earth about its axis, the orbit is called "parking orbit".

12. A satellite in a parking orbit will stay in the same place above the earth.

Exercise 29

1. Suppose a rocket is fired from the earth's surface, of radius r so that it just escapes from the gravitational influence of the earth with velocity, v, then v is given by:
A. $v = \frac{g}{r}$ B. $v - gr$ C. $\sqrt{\frac{r}{g}}$ D. $v = \sqrt{2gr}$

2. If F is the force of gravity on any object of mass, m, the gravitational field strength g is given by the following equation:
A. $g = mF$ B. $g = \frac{F}{m}$ C. $g = \frac{F}{m^2}$ D. $g = F\sqrt{m}$

3. The force with which the earth pulls any object is the
A. mass of the object.
B. gravity of the object.
C. density of the object
C. weight of the object.

4. If the mass of an object on the face of the earth is m, the mass of the earth is M, and the radius of the earth is R, the force of gravity on the object is
A. $\frac{Mm}{R}$.   B. $\frac{Mm}{R^2}$.   C. $\frac{MmG}{R^2}$.   D. $\frac{Mm}{GR^2}$.

5. Two bodies, of masses 50 kg and 100 kg, are 25cm apart. Calculate the universal gravitational force between them if the universal gravitational constant $G = 6.670 \times 10^{-11}$ Nm^{2}kg^{-2} and radius of the earth is $6.4 \times 10^6 m$.

6. What do you understand by the terms 'gravitational field strength' and 'gravitational potential' at a point in the earth's gravitational field? How are the two terms related?

7. A rocket of mass 150 kg is fired from the earth's surface so that it just escapes from the gravitational influence of the earth. Calculate the velocity with which it escapes. The universal gravitational constant G is 6.67×10^{-11} Nm^{2}kg^{-2}, radius of the earth is 6.4×10^6m and mass of the earth is 6.0×10^{34} kg.

8. Explain what is meant by the universal gravitational constant G. Derive its *S.I.* unit. Obtain an expression for the acceleration g, due

to gravity, on the surface of the earth, in terms of G, the radius of the earth R and its density ρ.

(Take volume $V = \dfrac{4\pi r^3}{3}$).

9. If the mass of proton is 1.67×10^{-27}kg and the mass of an electron is 9.11×10^{-31}kg, calculate the force of gravity between:
   (i) a proton and electron
   (ii) two electrons
   (iii) two protons
   (Assume the usual separation between two electrons and two protons).

10. Explain what is meant by weightlessness. Describe two examples to illustrate weightlessness.

11. Explain the conditions under which a satellite in orbit in an equatorial plane round the earth will stay at the same place above the earth. What use is made of this situation?

12. The radius of planet venus is nearly the same as that of the earth but its mass is only 80% that of the earth. If an object weighs w on the earth, what does it weigh on Venus? Calculate g on Venus.

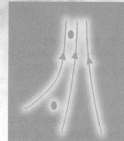

ELECTRIC FIELD I: CHARGES

Chapter 30

30.1 Electric force and Coulomb's law

The magnitude of the force between two electrically charged bodies was studied by Coulomb in 1785. He showed that if bodies were small compared with the distance between them, the magnitude of the electric force, F, between two point charges Q_1 and Q_2 separated by a distance, d, is (i) directly proportional to the product of the charges and (ii) inversely proportional to the square of the distance between them and acts along the line joining the charges.

i.e. $F = \dfrac{K_e Q_1 Q_2}{d^2}$

where K_e is a proportionality constant and is written as $\dfrac{1}{4\pi\varepsilon_0}$ where ε_0 is called permitivity of free space if the charges are situated in a vacuum.

$$F = \frac{Q_1 Q_2}{4\pi\varepsilon_0 d^2} \qquad 30.1$$

ε_0 has a numerical value $8.854 \times 10^{-12}\,\text{Fm}^{-1}$ and $K_e = \dfrac{1}{4\pi\varepsilon_0}$ is $9 \times 10^9\,(\text{Nm}^2\text{C}^{-2})$ approximately. The unit of charge is the coulomb (C). If charges are situated in other media such as water, then the force between the charges is reduced.

In general;

$$F = \frac{Q_1 Q_2}{4\pi\varepsilon r^2} \qquad 30.2$$

where $\varepsilon_r\varepsilon_0 = \varepsilon$ and ε_r is the relative permittivity.

Example 30.1

Two positive point charges of 12μc and 8μc respectively are 10cm apart in vacuum. Calculate the force between them.

Solution

From equation 30.2, $F = \dfrac{Q_1 Q_2}{4\pi\varepsilon_0 r^2}$

$$F = \frac{9 \times 10^9 \times 12 \times 8 \times 10^{-12}}{(10 \times 10^{-2})^2}$$

$$= \frac{9 \times 96 \times 10^{-3}}{(10 \times 10^{-2})^2}$$

$$= 86.4\text{N}.$$

Table (30.1) gives the relative permittivities (ε_r) of some common substances.

Table 30.1

Solid	ε_r
Amber	2.8
Ebonite	2.8
Glass	5-10
Mica	5.7-6.7
Wax	2-2.3

Liquid	ε_r
Glycerol	43
Paraffin	2.20
Turpentine	2.23
Water	80.4

Gas	ε_r
Air	1.0000536
Nitrogen	1.0000580
Oxygen	1.0005300
Hydrogen	1.0002700

Electrostatic and gravitational attraction

We wish to compare the electrostatic and gravitational forces for the electron circling a hydrogen atom.

The gravitational attraction to the nucleus is

$$F_g = \frac{GM_e M_p}{r^2}$$

$$= 4 \times 10^{-47}\,\text{N}$$

and the electrostatic attraction

$$F_e = \frac{1}{4\pi\varepsilon_0} \cdot \frac{e^2}{r^2}$$

$$= 9 \times 10^{-8}\text{N}$$

$M_e = 9.11 \times 10^{-31}\text{kg}$ $\qquad M_p = 1.67 \times 10^{-27}\,\text{kg}$

$e = 1.6 \times 10^{-19}\text{C}$ $\qquad G = 6.67 \times 10^{-11}\text{Nm}^2\text{kg}^{-2}$

$r = 5.04 \times 10^{-11}\text{m}$

This shows that the electrostatic force is about 10^{39} times stronger than the gravitational force and it is therefore the electrostatic force that is responsible for binding :

(a) electrons to nuclei to form atom;

(b) atoms to atoms to form molecules; and

(c) molecules to molecules to form solids and liquids.

For large bodies carrying a small charge, the gravitational force predominates.

The electric field

An "electric field" can be defined as a region where an electric force is experienced. An electric field may be described in terms of lines of force which represent the directions of motion of a small positive charge placed at that point in the field assuming that the charge is so small that the field is not changed appreciably by the presence of the charge.

Arrows on the lines of force indicate the direction of the forces on a positive charge: the forces on a negative charge are in opposite direction. Fig. 30.1 shows the lines of force also termed electric flux in some electrostatic fields.

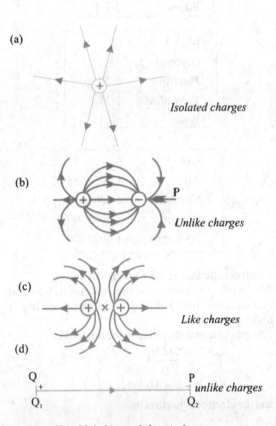

(a) Isolated charges

(b) Unlike charges

(c) Like charges

(d)

Q₁ unlike charges Q₂

Fig. 30.1 Lines of electric force:

30.2 Electric field intensity

The force exerted on a charged body in an electric field depends on the charge of the body and on the intensity or strength of the field.

> The intensity, E, of an electrostatic field at any point is defined as the force per unit charge which it exerts at that point. Its direction is that of the force exerted on a positive charge.

i.e. $E = \dfrac{F}{Q}$ 30.3

The units for E are NC^{-1} or volts per metre (Vm^{-1}). The electric field intensity can also be defined as the negative potential gradient at a point in the field, i.e.

$$E = -\frac{\delta v}{\delta x}$$

From the equation for the force, F, between two charges Q_1 and Q_2 separated by a distance, d, in a vacuum,

$$F = \frac{1}{4\pi\varepsilon_0} \cdot \frac{Q_1 Q_2}{d^2}$$

If the test charge Q_2 were situated at a point P as shown in fig 30.1(d), the electric field strength E at that point is given by:

$$E = \frac{F}{Q_2} = \frac{Q_1}{4\pi\varepsilon_0 d^2} \qquad 30.4$$

The direction of the field points outwards if Q_1 is positive and points inward if Q_1 is negative.

Example 30.2

Calculate the magnitude of the electric field at a field point 3.0m from a point charge $Q = 5.0nC$?

Solution

From equation 30.4,

$$E = \frac{1}{4\pi\varepsilon_0} \cdot \frac{Q}{d^2}$$

$$= \frac{9 \times 10^9 \times 5 \times 10^{-9}}{(3.0)^2}$$

$$= 5.0 NC^{-1}$$

Electric field flux

Suppose that the electric field intensity, E, makes an angle, θ, with a small surface area ΔA, then the electric field flux, $\Psi = E \cos\theta \Delta A$.

The flux through an area perpendicular to the lines of force is the product of $E \times$ area. For a sphere, the flux is

$$\Psi = E \times \text{area} = \frac{Q}{4\pi\varepsilon r^2} \times 4\pi r^2 = \frac{Q}{\varepsilon} \qquad 30.5$$

Example 30.3

Calculate the flux through a sphere produced by a charge of 5nC in a vacuum.

Solution

From equation 30.5,

$$\Psi = E \times \text{area of sphere}$$

$$= \frac{Q}{4\pi\varepsilon_0 r^2} \times 4\pi r^2 = \frac{Q}{\varepsilon_0}$$

$$= \frac{5 \times 10^{-9}}{8.85 \times 10^{-12}}$$

$$= 5.65 \times 10^2 CmF^{-1}$$

30.3 Electric potential

> The potential at a point is defined as the work done in bringing a unit positive charge from infinity to that point against the action of the field.

The units are volts (V) or joules per coulomb (JC^{-1}).

The potential difference between two points is therefore the work done (energy expended) when a unit positive charge is moved from one point to the other. We take the practical zero of potential to be the earth.

Potential due to a point charge

The expression for the potential, V, due to a charge, Q is given as:

$$V = \frac{Q}{4\pi\varepsilon r}$$

and for the potential difference V_{ab} which is the work done in taking a unit positive charge from b to a against the force as:

$$V_{ab} = \frac{Q}{4\pi\varepsilon}\left[\frac{1}{r_a} - \frac{1}{r_b}\right]$$

If $b \gg a$

$$V_a = \frac{Q}{4\pi\varepsilon r} \qquad\qquad 30.6$$

Example 30.4

Calculate the potential associated with a point charge of 5.0μc. if it is placed at 6cm from a point A.

Solution

From equation 30.6,

$$V = \frac{Q}{4\pi\varepsilon_o r_A}$$

$$= \frac{9 \times 10^9 \times 5 \times 10^{-6}}{6 \times 10^{-2}}$$

$$= 7.5 \times 10^5 V$$

30.4 Capacitors and capacitance

Any two conductors separated by an insulator are known as a capacitor. The two conductors usually carry an equal and opposite charge such that the net charge on the capacitor as a whole is zero. A capacitor is an electrical device that stores electric charge.

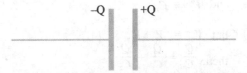

Fig. 30.2 *Circuit representation of a capacitor.*

Charging and discharging capacitor

When a capacitor is connected to a battery as shown in fig 30.3, electrons flow from the negative pole of the battery on to plate A of the capacitor. At the same rate, electrons flow from the plate B of the capacitor towards the positive terminal of the battery. Positive and negative charges thus appear on the plates. As the charges accumulate the potential difference between A and B increases and the charging current reduces to zero when the potential difference becomes equal to the battery voltage, V_o. When the battery is disconnected, the capacitor stays fully charged. To discharge the capacitor, the plates are joined with a thick wire and electrons flow from plate A to plate B until the positive charge on B is completely neutralized. A current thus flows for a time in the wire and at the end of time, the charges on the plates become zero.

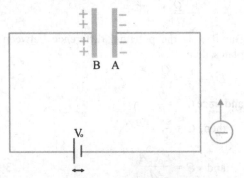

Fig. 30.3 *Charging of a capacitor.*

Capacitance

> The ability of the capacitor to store charge is called the *capacitance* of the capacitor.

If the potential across the capacitor changes by V when a charge, Q, is placed on it, then the capacitance, C, is given by the expression:

$$\text{Capacitance (C)} = \frac{\text{Charge } (Q)}{\text{Potential difference } (V)}$$

Therefore,

$$Q = CV \qquad\qquad 30.7$$

The capacitance of a capacitor is measured in farads (F).

A capacitor has a capacitance of 1 farad if the potential across it rises by 1 volt when a charge of 1 coulomb is placed on it.
From the formula:

$$C = \frac{Q}{V}$$
$$Q = CV$$
$$V = \frac{Q}{C}$$

The unit of 1F is the capacitance of a very huge capacitor. In practical circuits such as in radio receivers, the capacitance used are usually expressed in microfarads (μF), (1μF $= 10^{-6}$F). For smaller capacitors, the capacitance used are expressed in pico farad (pF); 1pF $= 10^{-12}$ F.

The parallel plate capacitor

We consider a simple capacitor in the form of two metal plates with a material of permittivity, ε (dielectric) filling the space between them. If the area of each plate is A and their separation is d, let one plate have a charge $+Q$ and the other $-Q$ with a capacitance, C.

We assume that the field E between the plates is uniform and that the charge density of the plates, σ is (Q/A) therefore, the electric field intensity E between the plates is given by :

$$E = \frac{\sigma}{\varepsilon_0}$$

$$= \frac{Q}{\varepsilon_0 A}$$

But if V is the potential difference between the plates, then

$$E = \frac{V}{d} = \frac{Q}{\varepsilon A}$$

and since $C = \dfrac{Q}{V}$

then, $C = \dfrac{\varepsilon A}{d}$

and

$$C = \frac{\varepsilon_0 \varepsilon_r A}{d} \qquad 30.8$$

Example 30.5

A parallel plate capacitor has an area 10cm^2, a plate of separation 2.0cm is charged initially to 100V in a vacuum. Calculate the:

(a) capacitance of the capacitor,
(b) charge of the plates,
(c) capacitance of the capacitor if the space between the plates is filled with mica wire, $\varepsilon_r = 5$.

Solution

From equation 30.8,

(a) $C = \dfrac{\varepsilon_0 \varepsilon_r A}{d}$, where $\varepsilon_r = 1$

$$C = \frac{8.85 \times 10^{-12} \times 10 \times 10^{-4}}{2 \times 10^{-2}}$$

$$= 4.43 \times 10^{-13}\text{F} \qquad (0.443\text{pF})$$

(b) From equation 30.7,
$$Q = CV$$
$$= 4.425 \times 10^{-13} \times 10^2$$
$$= 4.425 \times 10^{-11}\text{C}$$

(c) From equation 30.8,
$$C = \frac{\varepsilon_0 \varepsilon_r A}{d}$$

$$= \frac{8.85 \times 10^{-12} \times 5 \times 10 \times 10^{-4}}{2 \times 10^{-2}}$$

$$= 2.215\text{pF}$$

Thus, the capacitance increases if the area of the plates is increased or their separation decreased. An insertion of a dielectric material with a high permittivity, will also increase the capacitance. $\varepsilon_r = 1$ for air or vacuum.

Arrangement of capacitors

In some electronic circuits, capacitors often appear in arrangements whose resultant capacitance is required. Such arrangements may be in series (end-to-end connection) and in parallel.

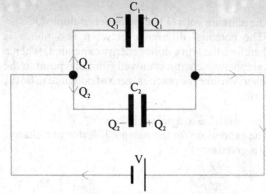

Fig. 30.4(a) Capacitors in parallel.

(a) **Capacitors in parallel**

Consider two capacitors connected in parallel as shown in figure 30.4 (a).
The potential, V across both capacitors is the same. Let the charges on the capacitors be Q_1 and Q_2 respectively.

Now $Q = CV$
so $Q_1 = C_1 V$
and $Q_2 = C_2 V$
But $Q = Q_1 + Q_2$
Therefore, $CV = V(C_1 + C_2)$
Giving

$$C = C_1 + C_2 \qquad 30.9$$

where C is the capacitance of the combination.

(b) **Capacitors in series**

The two capacitors in fig 30.4(b) are connected in series. The charge Q stored by each capacitor is the same. If V_1 and V_2 are the potentials across C_1 and C_2 respectively.

Then $V_1 = \dfrac{Q}{C_1}$

and $V_2 = \dfrac{Q}{C_2}$

but $V = V_1 + V_2$,

then, $\dfrac{Q}{C} = \dfrac{Q}{C_1} + \dfrac{Q}{C_2}$

Hence, dividing through by Q, then

$$\frac{1}{C} = \frac{1}{C_1} + \frac{1}{C_2} \qquad 30.10$$

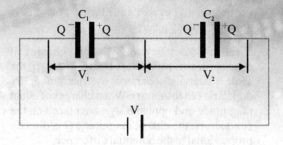

Fig. 30.4(b)   Capacitor in series

Example 30.6

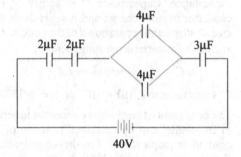

40V

Calculate the:
(a)   total capacitance in the circuit represented by the figure above.
(b)   charge on the 3µF capacitor.

Solution

The two 4µF capacitors are in parallel and the effective capacitance, using equation 30.9,
$$C_p = C_1 + C_2$$
$$= 8µF$$
Then, all capacitors are now connected in series with C_p and using equation 30.10,
$$\frac{1}{C_s} = \frac{1}{2} + \frac{1}{2} + \frac{1}{8} + \frac{1}{3}$$
$$= \frac{12 + 12 + 3 + 8}{24}$$
$$C_s = \frac{24}{35} µF$$
Total capacitance = $\frac{24}{35}$ = 0.686µF.

(b)   from $Q = CV$,
$$= \left(\frac{24}{35} \times 40\right)µC$$
$$= 27.43µC$$

30.5   Energy stored in a charged capacitor

Since capacitors have the ability to store charge, they are also a source of electrical energy. When a charge, Q is moved through a potential difference, V, the work done W is given by
$$W = \text{average potential difference x charge}$$
$$= \frac{1}{2} QV$$
but $V = \frac{Q}{C}$,

then $W = \frac{1}{2} \frac{QQ}{C}$
$$= \frac{Q^2}{2C}$$
or if $Q = CV$,
$$W = \frac{1}{2} CV^2$$
Energy stored $W = \frac{1}{2} QV$
$$= \frac{1}{2} CV^2$$
$$\therefore \quad W = \frac{1}{2} \frac{Q^2}{C} \qquad\qquad 30.11$$

Example 30.7
Calculate the energy stored in and the charge on the plates of the combined capacitor in the circuit below:

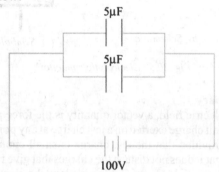

100V

Solution
Using $W = \frac{1}{2} CV^2$

Energy, $W = \frac{1}{2} C V^2$

Where $C = 10µF$ and $V = 100V$
$$W = \frac{1}{2} \times 10 \times 10^{-6} \times 10^4 J$$
$$= 5 \times 10^{-2} J$$
$$W = \frac{1}{2} QV$$
$$Q = \frac{2W}{V} = \frac{2 \times 5 \times 10^{-2}}{100}$$
$$Q = 10^{-3}C$$

Applications of capacitors
Capacitors have many applications in electrical circuits including the following:
(i)   Tuning in radio circuits.
(ii)   Smoothening rectified current from d.c. power supplies.
(iii) Elimination of sparking in switches.
(iv) Storing of large quantities of charge.
(v)   Blocking noise in a.c. amplifiers.

Some practical forms of capacitor
Variable air capacitors - used in radio tuning.

Paper capacitors - used for applied p.d. in the frequency 10^2–10^8Hz with capacitance range in the 10^{-9}–10^{-5}F.

Electrolytic capacitors - very thin 10^{-7}m but with very high insulation 10^9 Vm^{-1}; used in radio circuits and power supplies.

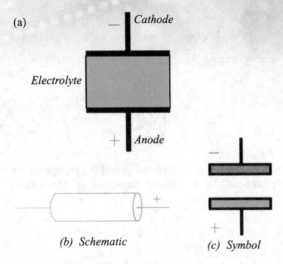

(a)

Cathode

Electrolyte

Anode

(b) Schematic

(c) Symbol

Fig. 30.5 Electrolytic capacitor

Summary

1. Electric field, a vector quantity is the force per unit charge exerted on a test charge at any point, provided that the test charge is small enough that it does not disturb the charges that give rise to the field. From Coulomb's law, the electric field produced by a point charge is:

$$E = \frac{1}{4\pi\varepsilon_0} \cdot \frac{Q}{d^2}.$$

2. Coulomb's law is the basic law of interaction for point electric charges. For charges q_1 and q_2 separated by a distance, d, the magnitude of the force on either charge $F = \frac{1}{4\pi\varepsilon_0}\frac{q_1 q_2}{d^2}$. The force on each charge is along the line joining the two charges; it is repulsive if q_1 and q_2 have the same sign but it is attractive if they have opposite signs. The force form an action-reaction pair and they obey Newton's third law and $\vec{F} = q\vec{E}$.

$$\frac{1}{4\pi\varepsilon_0} = 8.988 \times 10^9 \, \text{Nm}^2\text{C}^{-2}.$$

3. Field lines provide a graphical representation of electric fields. At any point on a field line, the tangent to the line is in the direction of E at that point`. Where the field lines are close together, E is larger, where the field lines are far apart, E is smaller.

4. Electric potential, a scalar quantity, is the potential energy per unit charge for the interaction of a charge with electric field.

$V = \frac{1}{4\pi\varepsilon_0} \cdot \frac{Q}{d}$ is the expression for the potential due to a point charge, where d is the distance from the point charge Q to the point at which the potential is evaluated. Electric potential is potential energy per unit charge.

5. A capacitor is a device for storing charges. It consists of two conductors (metal plates) of the same materials separated by vacuum or by dielectric (an insulator). When charges of equal magnitude and opposite sign are placed on the conductors, the charge magnitude Q is directly proportional to the potential difference.

That is $Q \propto V \Rightarrow Q = CV$.

The proportionality factor is called the capacitance. Capacitance C is ability of the capacitor to store charge and it depends on the size A, shape and separation d of the conductors and on the material separating them ε.

$$C = \frac{\varepsilon A}{d}, \text{ where } \varepsilon = \varepsilon_0 \varepsilon_r$$

C is measured in F, $1\mu F = 10^{-6}$, or $1pF = 10^{-12}$ F.

6. The behaviour of capacitors connected in series or in parallel can be described in terms of an equivalent capacitance for the combination. For capacitors with C_1, C_2, C_3:

Connected in series $\frac{1}{C_s} = \frac{1}{C_1} + \frac{1}{C_2} + \frac{1}{C_3}$

Connected in parallel $C_p = C_1 + C_2 + C_3$

7. The energy, W, stored in a charged capacitor is expressed as:

$$W = \left(\frac{QV}{2}\right) \text{J}$$

$$or \quad W = \left(\frac{1}{2}CV^2\right) \text{J}$$

$$or \quad W = \frac{1}{2}\left(\frac{Q^2}{C}\right) \text{J}$$

Placing a dielectric between the conductors of a capacitor increases the capacitance.

Exercise 30

Take $\varepsilon_o = 8.85 \times 10^{-12}$Fm^{-1}
and $k_e = 9 \times 10^9$ mF^{-1}

1. A device that stores electrical energy is called
   A. an inductor.   B. a capacitor.
   C. a leclanche cell.   D. a fuel cell.

2. Calculate the magnitude of the electric field intensity between two plates, 15cm apart, if the p.d. between the plates is 4.2V.
   A. 2.8 Vm^{-1} B. 7.2 Vm^{-1} C. 25.2 Vm^{-1}
   D. 28.0Vm^{-1}

3. The area of each plate of a parallel-plate air capacitor of permittivity ε_o is A. If the separation is r, the capacitance of the capacitor is expressed as :
   A. $\frac{\varepsilon_o r}{A}$ B. $\frac{\varepsilon_o A}{r}$ C. $\frac{A}{\varepsilon_o r}$ D $\frac{Ar}{\varepsilon_o}$

4. A point charge of magnitude 1μC is moved through a distance of 0.2m against a uniform field of 25Vm⁻¹. Calculate the work done on the charge.
   A. 5×10^{-6}J B. 1.0×10^{-5}J C. 5.0×10^{-5}J
   D. 1.0×10^{-2}J

5. The magnitude of the force on a charge of 0.4C is 2N. If the field is uniform, calculate the magnitude of electric field intensity.
   A. $20.0 NC^{-1}$ B. $8.0 NC^{-1}$
   C. $5.0 NC^{-1}$ D. $2.0 NC^{-1}$

6.
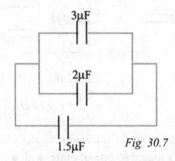

Fig 30.7

What is the effective capacitance in the diagram above?
A. 6μF B. 5μF C. $\frac{15}{13}$ μF D. $\frac{13}{15}$ μF

7. What is the electric potential at a point distance d of a point charge Q in a medium of permittivity ε_o?
   A. $4\pi\varepsilon_o Q^2 d$ B. $\frac{1}{4\pi\varepsilon_o} \cdot \frac{Q}{d}$
   C. $\frac{1}{4\pi\varepsilon_o}$ D. $\frac{1}{Q^2 4\pi\varepsilon_o d}$

8. Calculate the energy stored in a capacitor of capacitance 20μF, if the potential difference between the plates is 40V.
   A. 2×10^{-4}J   B. 4×10^{-4}J
   C. 8×10^{-4}J   D. 1.6×10^{-2}J

9.

I   II
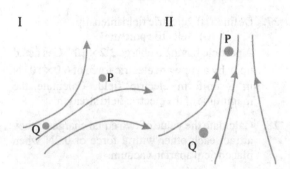

III
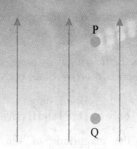

Fig 30.8

The diagrams above show lines of force in electric fields. In which of the diagrams would a test charge experience the least force as it moves from Q to P.
A. I only B. II only   C. III only
D. I and II only   E. II and III only

10. The effective capacitance of three capacitors each of capacitance 9μF connected in series is
    A. 54μF.   B. 27μF.
    C. 9μF.   D. 3μF.

11. Which of the following physical quantities is **not** a vector?
    A. Electric field intensity
    B. Magnetic flux intensity
    C. Electric potential
    D. Magnetic flux

12.
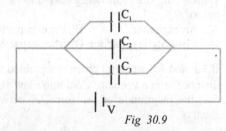

Fig 30.9

What is the total capacitance in the circuit represented by the diagram above?
A. $C_1 C_2 C_3$ B. $\frac{C_2 C_2 C_3}{C_1 + C_2 + C_3}$
C. $\frac{C_2}{C_1 + C_3}$ D. $C_1 + C_2 + C_3$

13.
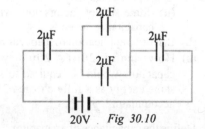

20V   Fig 30.10

What is the energy stored in the combined capacitor in the circuit represented in the diagram above?
A. $1.6 10^{-5}$J   B. 1.6×10^{-4}J
C. 1.6×10^{-3}J   D. 1.6×10^{-2}J

14. The force exerted on a charged body in an electric field depends on:
   I.   the charge on the body.
   II. the electric field intensity.
   III. the square of the mass of the body.

   A. I only   B. II only
   C. I and II only   D. I and II only

15. Calculate the magnitude of the force of repulsion between two equal charges of $6\mu C$ each and separated by a distance of 100cm. (Take $K_e = 9 \times 10^9 mF^{-1}$).
   A. 0.324N   B. 0.108N
   C. 0.060N   D. 0.048N

16. Calculate the capacitance of a parallel plate capacitor with area of plate $0.01m^2$, with a dielectric of $\varepsilon_r = 7$ and separated by 10mm. Take $\varepsilon_0 = 8.85 \times 10^{-12} Fm^{-1}$.
   A. $62.00 \times 10^{-12} F$ B. $6.205 \times 10^{-12} F$
   C. $0.62 \times 10^{-12} F$ D. $0.06 \times 10^{-12} F$
   E. $0.06 \times 10^{-13} F$

17. Which of the following is **not** an application for capacitor?
   A. Tuning radio circuits B. Smoothening
   C. Blocking noise   D. Rectification

18. Which of the following capacitors has polarity?
   A. Air capacitor   B. Paper capacitor
   C. Electrolytic capacitor D. Mica capacitor

19. If $+q_1$ and $-q_2$ are point charges separated by a distance, r, in a vacuum, Coulomb's law states that the magnitude of the force, F, between them is

   A. $\dfrac{q_1 q_2}{4\pi\varepsilon_0 r^2}$.   B. $\dfrac{q_1 q_2}{4\pi\varepsilon_0 r}$.

   C. $\dfrac{-q_1 q_2}{4\pi\varepsilon_0 r^2}$.   D. $\dfrac{-q_2}{4\pi\varepsilon_0 r q}$.

20. (a) (i) Explain what is meant by the statement "the capacitance of a parallel plate capacitor is $10\mu F$".
       (ii) State three factors on which its capacitance depends.
    (b) List three applications of capacitors.
    (c) How many $20\mu F$, 200V working capacitors would be required to store the same energy as a fully charged 2V, 60Ah accumulator?

21. Define the capacitance of a capacitor.
    The plates of a parallel-plate capacitor are 2mm apart and $0.1m^2$ in area. The plates are in vacuum and a potential difference of 200V is applied across the capacitor. Calculate the :
    (i) capacitance

(ii) charge on each plate
(iii) electric intensity in the space between them
(iv) energy stored in the capacitor

22. Calculate the equivalent capacitance of the combination shown in Fig. 30.11 below.

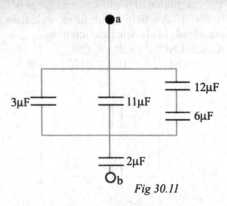

Fig 30.11

23. A capacitor of $10\mu F$ with a p.d. of 100V across it is joined to one of $50\mu F$ with a p.d. of 50V across it. Calculate the change in energy in the system.

24. A parallel plate capacitor has an area of $100cm^2$, a plate separation of 1.0cm and is charged initially to 100V in a vacuum. Calculate the:
    (a) capacitance of the capacitor
    (b) charge of the plates
    (c) electric field strength in the gap between the plates

25. Calculate the potential energy of an electron in a hydrogen atom if it is separated from the proton by a distance of $5 \times 10^{-11}m$, the charge on the electron and proton being equal and opposite and of magnitude $1.6 \times 10^{-19}C$.

26. Calculate the electrostatic force between two electrons separated a distance 10^{-10} m apart. Charge on the electron is $1.6 \times 10^{-19}C$.

27. Define: (i) electric field intensity
             (ii) electric potential
    A particle having a charge 3.2×10^{-19} C is acted upon by an upward electric force of $6.0 \times 10^{-6}N$ in a uniform electric field. Calculate the magnitude of the electric field strength.

28. Calculate the value of two equal charges if they attract each other with a force of 0.2N when placed 5cm apart in vacuum.

29. (a) Define electric field.
    (b) Sketch the electric lines of force around:
        (i) an isolated negative charge
        (ii) two unlike charges

240

(iii) two like charges

(c) Calculate the force on an electron of charge 1.6×10^{-19}C situated in a uniform electric field of intensity 120NC^{-1}.

30. Define the electron volt and deduce a value for 1eV. Two positive charges 10 and 6 microcoulombs respectively are 5cm apart in a vacuum. Find the work done in bringing them 2cm closer.

31. Define the electric potential, V, and electric field strength, E, at a point in an electrostatic field. Write down an expression to show their relationship.

32. Two horizontal parallel plates each of area 100cm^2 are mounted 1mm apart in vacuum. The lower plate is earthed and the upper plate is given a charge of 0.5µC. Neglecting edge effects, find the electric field between the plates and sketch the field lines between them.

33. (a) Define potential and capacitance.
(b) Deduce expressions for the capacitance of two capacitors when joined in:
(i) series and (ii) parallel.
(c) If they are connected across a p.d. of 1000V and each of the capacitors has a capacitance of 10µF. Calculate for each case:
(i) the charge on each capacitor; and
(ii) the difference in energy stored.

34. (a) List four types of capacitors and their corresponding applications.
(b) On what factors does the capacitance of a capacitor depend?
(c) Briefly describe how a capacitor can be charged.

ELECTRIC FIELD II: CURRENT ELECTRICITY

Chapter 31

This second part of our study of current electricity is a revision and extension of the course in current electricity presented in chapter 7. Students are advised to revise that section.

31.1 Electric current

A current is any motion of charge from one point to another in conducting materials. In an ordinary metal such as copper or aluminium some of the electrons are free to move within the material. These electrons move randomly in all directions with speeds of the order of $10^6 ms^{-1}$ and hence there is no net flow of charge in any direction and no current. With the introduction of a source of e.m.f., current flows.

The current, denoted by I, is in the direction in which there is flow of positive charge and thus, currents are described as if they consist entirely of positive charge flow. We define the current, I through the cross sectional area, A, to be the net charge, Q, flowing through the area per unit time. That is $I = Q/t$ (Cs^{-1}) or ampere (A).

It is possible to have a current that is steady, one that is constant in time in complete circuits in which the total charge in every segment of the conductor is constant. In many **simple** circuits, the direction of the current is always the same, this is called **direct current**. Here, we shall consider only direct current; alternating current, in which the current continuously changes direction will be considered later in chapter 34.

31.2 Electromotive force and circuits

For a conductor to have a steady current, it must be a part of a path that forms a closed loop or complete circuit. In such an electric circuit, there is a device somewhere in the loop that makes current flow from lower to higher potential. This is called a source of electromotive force. The SI unit is volts (V) for steady current circuits, examples of sources of e.m.f. are batteries, d.c. electric generator, solar cells, thermocouples and fuel cells. Such devices convert energy of some form (mechanical, chemical, thermal and so on) into electrical potential energy and transfer it into the circuit to which it is connected. These are dealt with in chapter 7.

> We define electromotive force (e.m.f.) as the magnitude of the potential difference of both the external circuit and the inside of the cell.

> The potential difference (p.d.) between any two points in a circuit is the work done when one coulomb of charge moves from one point to another.

The e.m.f. of a cell E in volts is the p.d. between the terminals of the cell when it is not delivering any current in the external circuit i.e. (p.d. across external circuit and internal resistor) $E = IR + Ir$ (IR = p.d. across external circuit and Ir = p.d. across internal circuit). The units of both p.d. and e.m.f. are volts and other large and small units of p.d. are kilovolts (kV) and millivolts (mV).

The e.m.f. is the work done in moving a unit of positive charge (in coulomb) through the external circuit and the inside of the cell.

An important part of an electric circuit is drawing the circuit diagram. Fig. 31.1 shows some symbols used in circuit diagrams. For a source in an open circuit as in Fig 31. 2(a), note that the wires to the left of a and to the right of ammeter (A) are not connected to anything. No current flows since there is no complete circuit.

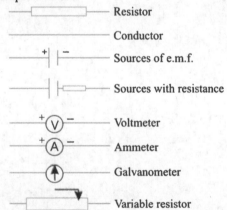

Fig. 31.1 Symbols of some electrical components.

For a source in a complete circuit there is no p.d. between aa' and bb' since the ammeter is assumed to have negligible resistance. See fig. 31.2(b).

Measuring instruments

1. **Current:** Electric current can be detected by the use of sensitive instruments called galvanometers, a centre zero galvanometer is shown in Fig. 31.1.

    When no current passes through it, the pointer is at zero mark. When current passes through it, the pointer will deflect right or left depending on the direction of current flow. In experiments, when we require detection of small current flow, such as in bridge experiments to be described later, this instrument is quite useful.

For measuring specific amount of current in the circuit, an ammeter (*A*) is used for large currents while a milliameter (*mA*) or microammeter (*μA*) is used for smaller values of current.

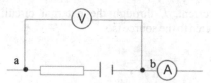

Fig. 31.2(a)   A source in open circuit.

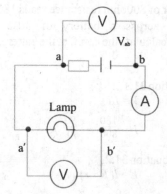

Fig. 31.2(b)   A source in complete circuit.

In a circuit, an ammeter is connected so that the current to be measured flows through it directly and it is said to be connected in series. In fig. 31.2(b), the ammeter records the current flowing through the lamp and the source of e.m.f. An idealized ammeter has zero resistance.

2. The instrument for measuring p.d. and e.m.f. is known as a voltmeter (*V*) and is graduated in volts or millivolts. The voltmeter is always connected across the two points where the potential difference is to be measured. i.e. it is connected in parallel as in Fig. 31.2(b) across the cell V_{ab}, and across the lamp $V_{a'b'}$. An idealized voltmeter has very large resistance and does not indicate any current diverted through it.

Resistivity and resistance

Different materials have different electrical conducting powers. The ability of a material to oppose the flow of electricity through it is its resistance.

The resistivity ρ(rho) of a material is the ratio of the magnitude of electric field *E* and current density J (current per unit area) $\left[\rho = \dfrac{E}{J}\right]$. It is also defined in terms of the resistance *R* of a wire of a unit length, *l*, and a unit cross-sectional area *A*.

$$\rho = \frac{AR}{l} \implies \boxed{R = \frac{\rho l}{A}} \qquad 31.1$$

The greater the resistivity, the greater the field needed to cause a given current density. A perfect conductor would have very low resistivity while a perfect insulator would have an infinite resistivity. Metals and alloys have the smallest restivities and are the best conductors. The resistivities of insulators are much greater than those of metals by a factor of the order of 10^{22}.

The reciprocal of resistivity, ρ, is the conductivity, σ; its units are siemens per metre (Sm^{-1}). Good conductors of electricity have larger conductivity than insulators. It is observed from experiments that electrical conductors, such as metals, are usually also good conductors of heat. Poor electrical conductors such as ceramic and plastic materials are also poor thermal conductors. Table 31.1 shows the resistivity values of some materials.

Example 31.1

A wire of 0.50m long and of diameter 0.80mm has a resistance of 2.5Ω. Calculate the resistivity of material of which it is made and (ii) determine its conductivity.

Solution

From equation 31.1,
$$R = \frac{\rho l}{A}$$

Where $R = 2.5\Omega$, $l = 0.5$m $A = \dfrac{\pi \times 0.64 \times 10^{-6}}{4}$

(i)   Restivity $\rho = \dfrac{RA}{l} = \dfrac{22}{7} \times \dfrac{0.64 \times 10^{-6} \times 2.5}{5 \times 10^{-1}}$

$$= 1.0 \times 10^{-5}\Omega\text{m}.$$

(ii)   Conductivity $\sigma = \dfrac{1}{\rho} = 10^{5}(\Omega\text{m})^{-1}$

Resistivity values of some materials.

Table 31.1

Conductors (Metals)	$\rho\,(\Omega\,\text{m} \times 10^{-8})$
Copper	1.72
Lead	22.00
Mercury	95.00
Tungsten	5.25
Manganin	44.00
Constantan	49.00

Semi conductors	$\rho\,(\Omega\,\text{m})$
Pure carbon	3.5×10
Pure hermanium	0.60
Pure silicon	2300

Insulators	$\rho\,(\Omega\,m)$
Glass	$10^{10} - 10^{14}$
Mica	$10^{11} - 10^{15}$
Wood	$10^{8} - 10^{11}$

The conductivity is given by the expression

$$\frac{1}{\rho} = \sigma$$

$$= \frac{l}{RA}$$

in Siemens per metre (Sm^{-1}).

The conductivity, σ, of a material of a unit length and a unit cross-sectional area is the reciprocal of the resistance of the material. Semiconductors (e.g. silicon, germanium) have resistivities intermediate between those of metals and those of insulators.

The resistivity of a metallic conductor increases with increase in temperature. As temperature increases, the free electrons gain more kinetic energy and move with higher velocity within the volume of the material. Further the ions of the conductor vibrate with greater amplitude giving rise to more collisions within the atoms and at temperature, t,

$$\rho_t = \rho_o [1 + \alpha(t - t_o)]$$

ρ_o is the resistivity at temperature, t_o and α is the coefficient of resistivity.

The resistivity of an alloy such as manganin is practically independent of temperature.

The resistivity of graphite (a non-metal) decreases with increase in temperature. Thus, it has a negative coefficient of resistivity. However, metals have positive coefficient of resistivity.

31.3 Ohm's law

This has been discussed in chapter 7 but is restated here for emphasis.

The electric current flowing through a metallic conductor (wire) at constant temperature is directly proportional to the potential difference between its ends.

If V represents the p.d. between the ends of a wire in volts and I represents the current flowing through the wire in amperes, ohm's law can be expressed by the equation as:

$$V = kI$$

The constant of proportionality, k is the resistance, R of the wire such that

$$V = IR \qquad 31.1$$

This relationship is ohm's law provided R is a constant.

Internal resistance

The p.d. across a real source in a circuit is not equal to the e.m.f. The reason is that the quantity of charge moving through the material of the source encounters some opposition. This is called internal resistance of the source, denoted by r.

From ohms Law,
The e.m.f. $E = V + Ir$
$\qquad = IR + Ir$

We see that the terminal voltage, V (the p.d. across external circuit) is less than the e.m.f., E because of the term Ir representing the potential drop across the internal resistance, r, it is sometimes called 'lost volts'

The current, I, through the external circuit and connected to the source is

$$I = \frac{E}{R + r} \qquad 31.2$$

Example 31.2

A voltmeter of 800ohm resistance reads 180V when connected across a battery of 30Ω internal resistance. calculate the e.m.f. of the battery.

Solution

From equation 31.1,
$$V = IR$$

$$I = \frac{180}{800} = \frac{9}{40}\ A$$

and from equation 31.2,
$$E = I(R + r)$$

$$= \frac{9}{40}\ (830) = 186.75V$$

Resistors

These are components in the form of lengths of wire or pieces of carbon of which the resistance is accurately known. Standard resistors of various known resistances can be constructed by cutting measured lengths of wire such as manganin or constantan and winding them non-inductively round a wooden block or cardboard rolled in cylindrical form and providing terminals for connection. The values of these resistors can be measured and labelled using established methods. This is shown in fig. 7.7(a) of Chapter 7, Book I.

Carbon resistors with resistance marked with a standard code using three or four colour bands near one end according to the scheme is shown in table 31.2. The first two bands (starting with the band nearest to an end) are digits, the third is a power of ten (multiplier). The fourth band indicates precision or tolerance as shown in Fig. 31.3.

Fig. 31.3(a) Carbon resistor with bands.

Fig. 31.3(b) Symbolic representation of a resistor

Table 31.2 Table of codes

Colour	Value of digit	Multiplier value
Black	0	1
Brown	1	10
Red	2	10^2
Orange	3	10^3
Yellow	4	10^4
Green	5	10^5
Blue	6	10^6
Violet	7	10^7
Grey	8	10^8
White	9	10^9
Silver	± 10%	
Gold	± 5%	
No band	±20%	

For a material that obeys ohm's law (ohmic conductors) a graph of current as a function of potential difference (voltage) is a straight line Fig. 31.4(a), the slope of the line is $1/R$.

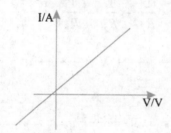

Fig. 31.4(a) Current-voltage characteristics for metal.

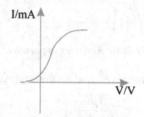

Fig. 31.4(b) Current-voltage characteristics for vacuum tube.

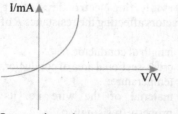

Fig. 31.4(c) Current-voltage characteristics for silicon diode.

Typical examples are metals, mercury, and hydrous copper sulphate.

In devices that do not obey ohm's law (non-ohmic conductors) the relation of voltage to current is not in direct proportion.

Fig. 31.4(b) shows the behavior of a vacuum diode. Here, I is approximately proportional to $V^{3/2}$.

Other substances that do not obey ohm's law are neon gas, tetraoxosulphate (VI) acid (H_2SO_4).

Verification of Ohm's law

In order to verify ohm's law, the apparatus in fig. 31.5(a) is set to complete a circuit.

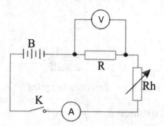

Fig. 31.5(a) Verification of Ohm's law.

The circuit consists of a battery, B, a key, K, a resistor R, a rheostat, Rh, an ammeter, A, and a voltmeter, V, the circuit is connected as shown.

Starting with the setting of Rh to a large value, the key K is closed and the readings of V and A are recorded. The setting of Rh is then gradually reduced to obtain a series of readings of the p.d. V and current I which are also read and recorded. The procedure is repeated four more times. The readings are then tabulated as V(volts) and I(amperes). The graph of V against I is plotted and a straight line passing through the origin is obtained Fig. 31.5(b). The slope of the graph $\frac{\Delta V}{\Delta I}$ gives the value of the resistance of R in ohms.

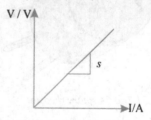

Fig. 31.5(b) Graph to verify Ohm's law.

In the set up, the following precautions should be taken:
(i)   Tight connections ensured.
(ii)   Zero error on meters noted and corrected.
(iii)   Parallax error on meters avoided.
(iv)   Key open when reading is not being taken.
(v)   Readings repeated.

31.4   Resistors in series

In electrical circuits, more than one resistor may be connected end to end in a way that the same current passes through each resistor when connected to a source of e.m.f, such connection is said to be in "series".

Consider the circuit of Fig 31.6 where three resistors R_1, R_2 and R_3 are connected in series. The combined or equivalent resistance, R of R_1, R_2 and R_3 can be measured by connecting a voltmeter, V, across the three of them as shown and noting the reading on V and ammeter, A.

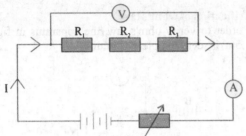

Fig. 31.6   Resistors in series.

Combined resistance $R = \dfrac{V}{I}$

Where $\quad R = R_1 + R_2 + R_3 \qquad\qquad$ 31.3

Rheostats
These are variable resistors used to adjust current flowing in the circuit. A diagram of a rheostat is shown in Fig. 31.7(b). It consists of a long resistance wire coiled round on insulator. The resistance introduced in the circuit depends on the length of the coil as determined by the slide position.

A rotary rheostat or potentiometer (pot) with a high value of total resistance is shown in fig. 31.7(a).

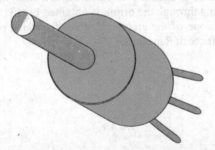

Fig. 31.7(a)   A rotary rheostat

Resistance boxes
Standard resistors also appear in the form of resistance boxes. A simple plug type is shown in Fig 31.7(b) when the box is connected in the circuit, the removal of any plug introduces the resistance marked. When the plug is in, current passes across the top but when pulled out the current has to pass through the coil of resistance of which the value is marked by the plug as shown in fig. 31.7(b).

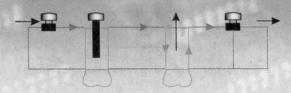

Fig. 31.7(b)   Resistance box

Resistors in parallel
In household wiring, lamps are connected as in fig. 31.8(a). This is done such that turning off or on of one lamp L does not affect the others. The lamps are said to be connected in parallel with each other.

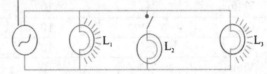

Fig. 31.8a   Lamps connected in parallel.

Here, L_1, L_3 are ON, L_2 is OFF.

The resistors R_1, R_2, R_3, of Fig 31.8(b) are connected in parallel. Here, their ends are joined together between the same points such that the p.d, V across each resistor is the same. The current in each resistor will not be the same but will depend on the resistance of the resistor. A larger current will pass through the resistor with small resistance. If R is the equivalent resistance,

$$\frac{1}{R} = \frac{1}{R_1} + \frac{1}{R_2} + \frac{1}{R_3} \qquad\qquad 32.4$$

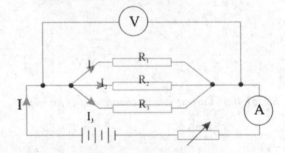

Fig. 31.8(b)   Resistors in parallel.

For two resistances R_1, and R_2, the equivalent

resistance $R_{12} = \dfrac{R_1 R_2}{R_1 + R_2} \qquad\qquad$ 31.5

Factors affecting electrical resistance
The factors affecting the resistance R of a conductor are the:
(i)   length of conductor, l;
(ii)   cross-sectional area of conductor, A;
(iii) temperature;
(iv)   material of the wire i.e. its conducting property (resistivity ρ).

$$R = \frac{\rho l}{A}$$

31.5 Measurement of resistance by the ammeter voltmeter method

Applying ohm's law, the resistance of a circuit component can be determined. A non-inductive coil is connected in series with a cell, E, a rheostat, Rh, an ammeter, A, and a key, K. A voltmeter is connected in parallel across the component as shown in Fig 31.9.

A potential difference, V, is recorded by the voltmeter that is set up across the coil, C. If I is the ammeter reading, then by ohm's law, $R = \frac{V}{I}$ and R which is the resistance of the coil can be calculated. The process is repeated four more times and the average found.

A resistor of known resistance, R, can be constructed from a length, l, of manganin wire of known resistivity, ρ.

$$l = \frac{R\pi d^2}{4\rho}$$

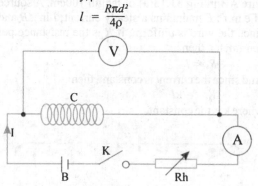

Fig. 31.9 Determination of resistance of a resistor.

where d is the diameter in metres and can be measured accurately using a micrometer screw guage. The value of resistivity, ρ, can be obtained from the book of constants or table 31.1.

Arrangement of cells and resistors in circuits

We have studied in chapter 7 that cells and resistors in circuits can be connected in circuits either in parallel or in series. Many electrical networks may require a combination of such arrangements. This is illustrated in fig. 31.10.

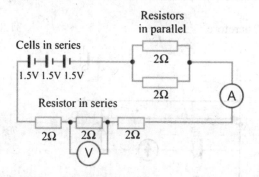

Fig. 31.10(a) Cells connected in series with a series and parallel combination of resistance.

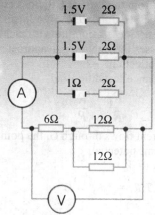

Fig. 31.10(b) Cells joined in parallel with a series and parallel combination of resistance.

Example 31.3

Calculate the current flowing in the ammeter, A, and determine the voltage reading in the voltmeter, V, in (i) fig. 31.10(a) and (ii) fig. 31.10(b).

Solution

(i) From equation 31.1, the effective resistance in fig. 31.10(a) is:

$$R_s = 2 + 2 + 2 + \frac{2 \times 2}{2 + 2} = 7\Omega$$

Total e.m.f. $= E_s = 1.5 + 1.5 + 1.5 = 4.5$V.

Current flowing in ammeter A from ohm's law,

$$I = \frac{4.5}{7} \text{ A} = 0.643\text{A}$$

and the p.d. across 2Ω,

$$V = \frac{2 \times 4.5}{7} = \frac{9}{7} \text{ V.} = 1.29\text{V}$$

(ii) In fig. 31.10(b),

Total e.m.f. $E_p = 1.5$V

Effective resistance $= \frac{2}{3} + 6 + 6 = \frac{38}{3}$ Ω.

Current $I = \frac{1.5 \times 3}{38} = 0.12\text{A}$

p.d. across $6\Omega + (12//12)$,

$$V = 12 \times 0.12 = 1.44$$

The Wheatstone bridge

About 1843, Wheatstone designed a bridge circuit which gave an accurate method for measuring resistances. It consists of four resistors of resistances R_1, R_2, R_3 and R_4 connected as shown in Fig. 31.11.

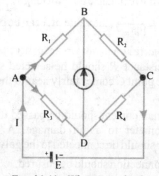

Fig. 31.11 Wheatstone bridge

The current I from the battery E divides at A along the two branches ABC and ADC. By adjusting one or more of the resistances, a condition is reached when no current passes through the galvanometer, G and indicates no deflection.

This is "balance" condition and

$$\frac{R_1}{R_2} = \frac{R_3}{R_4} \qquad 31.7$$

When no current flows through G, the points B and D are at the same potential.

Therefore, $V_{AB} = V_{AD}$

i.e. $I_1 R_1 = I_2 R_3$

Also $V_{BC} = V_{DC}$

$I_1 R_2 = I_2 R_4$

So

If R_1, R_2 and R_3 are known, R_4 can be determined

The metre bridge method

Fig 31.12 shows a practical and simple arrangement of the Wheatstone bridge. It is also called a slide-wire bridge, since the wire AB is arranged such that a slide S (jockey) can be made to slide along the wire.

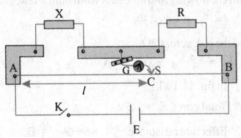

Fig. 31.12 Metre bridge

The unknown resistance, X and a known resistance R are connected as shown in the set up above. ASB is a wire of uniform cross sectional area and of length 100cm stretched along a meter rule. With key K closed, with the jockey S, connected to a galvanometer G, a balance point C is found where there is no deflection of G. This occurs when :

$$\frac{X}{R} = \frac{l\,\sigma}{(100-l)\sigma}$$

Where σ is the resistance per unit length.

Hence, $\frac{X}{R} = \frac{l}{100-l}$, the value of X can be calculated.

1. The resistance R should be selected so that the balance point C comes fairly near to the center of the wire.

2. Very small current should be passed through the galvanometer to avoid damage. A protective resistor should be connected to the galvanometer.

3. Tight connection should be ensured.

4. The jockey should not be dragged along the wire.

Example 31.4

In a metre bridge circuit, a balance (zero deflection in the galvanometer) is obtained at 60.0cm mark when a 2 ohm resistor is connected in the left gap (as in fig. 31.12), calculate the value of the resistance in the right gap of the circuit.

Solution

Using the equation:

$$\frac{X}{R} = \frac{l}{100-l}$$

$$\frac{2}{R} = \frac{60}{40}$$

$$R = \frac{80}{60} = \frac{4}{3}\ \Omega.$$

The potentiometer

A potentiometer consists of a uniform resistance wire AB in Fig 31.13(a) of length 100cm. A source of e.m.f., E maintains a steady current, I in AB and since the wire is uniform, if R is the resistance per centimeter, then :

$$R \propto l$$

And since the current is constant, then

$$V_{AC} = kl$$

where k is the constant.

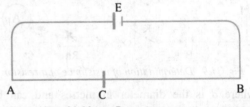

Fig. 31.13(a) Potentiometer

Comparison of e.m.fs. of two cells

In the circuit shown in fig 31.13(a), the battery E provides a steady current through the wire. A cell C_1 of e.m.f. E_1 is connected as shown in fig 31.13(b) through a galvanometer and a balance point is obtained at D_1. This means that the e.m.f. $E_1 = kl_1$ for C_1. With a second cell C_2 in place of C_1, a new balance, l_2 is obtained i.e. the e.m.f. $E_2 = kl_2$ for C_2

Therefore, $\dfrac{E_1}{E_2} = \dfrac{l_1}{l_2}$ $\qquad 31.8$

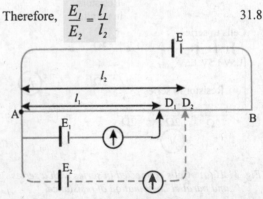

Fig. 31.13(b) Comparison of e.m.f. of cells.

Hence, the e.m.fs. of the two cells can be compared. If one of them is a standard cell of known e.m.f., the e.m.f. of the other can be calculated.

Accuracy

1. When the potentiometer is used to compare the e.m.fs. of cells, no errors are introduced by internal resistances since no current flows at balance.

2. It is more accurate than the moving coil voltmeter for measuring e.m.f.

3. For very sensitive galvanometer, a high precision of the balance point of the potentiometer is possible.

Example 31.5

A potentiometer wire carrying a steady current is 100cm long. When a standard cell of e.m.f. 1.5V is connected to a balance length of 60.0cm was obtained. Calculate the e.m.f. of a cell that gives a balance length of 80.0cm.

Solution

Using equation 31.8,

$$\frac{E_1}{E_2} = \frac{l_1}{l_2}$$

$$\frac{1.5}{E_2} = \frac{60}{80}$$

$$E_2 = \frac{4 \times 1.5}{3} = 2.0V$$

31.6 Kirchhoff's law

Many practical resistor network (Fig. 31.14) cannot be reduced to simple series-parallel combinations. Techniques to handle such problems and compute currents in such networks were developed by a German physicist, Gustav Robert Kirchhoff.

Definitions of terms

(i) A junction (node) in a circuit or electrical network is a point where three or more connecting wires meet.

(ii) A loop is any closed conducting path: The circuit in fig 31.14(a) has two junctions a and b. Also in the Fig 31.14(b) points a, b, c and d are junctions

(iii) Possible loops are closed paths $acdba$, $acdefa$.

(a)

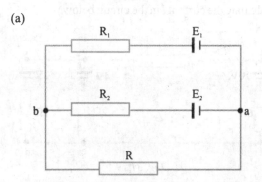

(b)

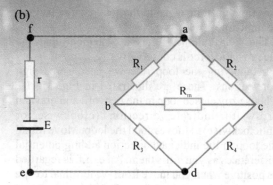

Fig. 31.14 Networks that cannot be reduced to simple series-parallel combinations.

Kirchhoff's laws consist of the following two statements:

1. Kirchhoff's current law (KIL)

The algebraic sum of the currents flowing into any junction N is zero. The sum of the currents flowing towards a junction, N is equal to the sum of the currents flowing away from the junction (see Fig 31.15)

$$\Sigma I = 0$$

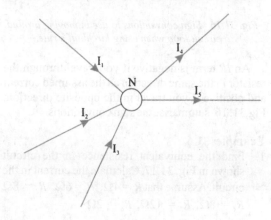

Fig. 31.15 Currents into and away from a node, N.

$$I_1 + I_2 + I_3 = I_4 + I_5$$
$$\text{i.e. } I_1 + I_2 + I_3 - I_4 - I_5 = 0$$
$$\Sigma I = 0$$

2. Kirchhoff's voltage law (KVL)

The algebraic sum of the potential difference in any closed loop (including those associated with e.m.f's and those of resistive elements) must equal to zero. The algebraic sum of the e.m.fs. in any closed loop of an electrical network is equal to the algebraic sum of the voltage (IR) drops in that loop.

$$\Sigma E - \Sigma IR = 0$$

The junction rule above is based on conservation of electric charge. No charge can accumulate at a junction, so the total charge entering the junction per unit time must be equal to the total charge leaving per unit time.

The loop rule (*KVL*) is a statement that the electrostatic force is conservative.

In applying the loop rule we need some sign conventions. These are illustrated in Fig. 31. 16. Choose any closed loop in the network and draw an arrow to indicate direction (clockwise or anticlockwise) to move round the loop. Move round the loop in the indicated direction adding potential differences as you cross them. An e.m.f. is regarded as positive when you move from -ve terminal to +ve terminal of the source of e.m.f. and it is negative otherwise.

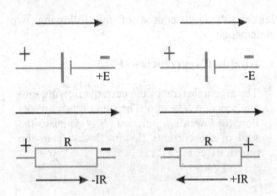

Fig. 31.16 Sign conventions to use in moving around a circuit loop when using kirchhoff's rule.

An *IR* term is negative if you travel through the resistor in the same direction as the assumed current and positive if you travel in the opposite direction. Fig.31. 16 summarise the sign conventions.

Examples 31.6

1. Find the equivalent resistance in the circuit shown in Fig. 31.17. Calculate the current in the circuit. Assume that $R_1 = 4\Omega$, $R_2 = 6\Omega$, $R_3 = 8\Omega$ $R_4 = 8\Omega$, $R_5 = 12\Omega$, $R_6 = 2\Omega$

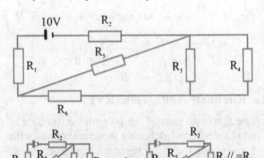

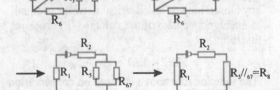

Fig. 31.17

Solution

The circuit can be reduced stage by stage using series –parallel equivalent method.

$$R_7 = R_3//_4 = \frac{R_3 R_4}{R_3 + R_4} = \frac{8 \times 8}{8 + 8} = 4\Omega$$

$$R_{67} = R_6 + R_7 = 4 + 2 = 6\Omega$$

$$R_8 = R_5//_{67} = \frac{R_5 R_{67}}{R_5 + R_{67}} = \frac{12 \times 6}{12 + 6} = 4\Omega$$

$$R_{eq} = R_1 + R_2 + R_8 = 4 + 6 + 4 = 14\Omega$$

Using Ohm's law,

$$V = IR$$

$$\therefore I = \frac{10}{14} \text{ A}$$

Example 31.7

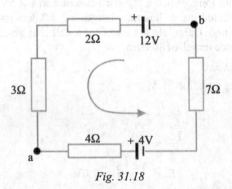

Fig. 31.18

The circuit shown in Fig 31.18 contains two batteries each with an e.m.f. and an internal resistance and two resistors in series.

Calculate: (a) the current in the circuit

(b) the potential difference, V_{ab}

Solution

(a) We assume a direction for the current (anticlockwise)

$$\Sigma E = \Sigma IR$$

$$12 - 4 = 3I + 2I + 4I + 7I$$

$$8 = 16I, \text{ hence, } I = 0.5A$$

(b) $V_{ab} = (11 \times I + 4)$

$$= 9.5V$$

Example 31.8

Calculate the current I in the circuit below.

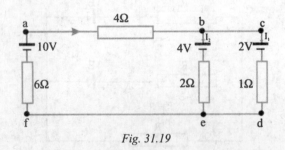

Fig. 31.19

Using junction rule at b,
$$I = I_1 + I_2 \qquad (1)$$
For loop bafeb,
$$6I + 4I + 2I_2 = 10 - 6$$
$$10I + 2I_2 = 4 \qquad (2)$$

For loop bcdeb
$$-2I_2 + I_1 = 4 - 2$$
$$I_1 - 2I_2 = 2 \qquad (3)$$
$$10I_1 + 12I_2 = 4 \qquad \text{(substitute } I = I_1 + I_2)$$
$$6I_1 - 12I_2 = 12 \qquad \text{(multiplying (3) by 6)}$$

$$16I_1 = 16$$
$$I_1 = 1A$$
From equation (3), $I_2 = -0.5A$
Similarly, from equation (1), $I = 0.5A$

31.7 Instrument used for commercial purposes

Instrument used for commercial purposes called multimeters provide different ranges of current and potential difference by turning a knob (switch). Such switches connect appropriate resistors in parallel for current ranges or in series for p.d. ranges.

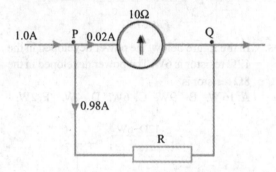

Fig. 31.20 Converting a milliammeter to an ammeter.

Conversion of a galvanometer to an ammeter

Fig. 31.20 shows the method of changing from a small current range 0-20 mA to a large current 0-1A. A suitable resistor R is connected in parallel with the galvanometer between the terminals P and Q. Suppose a current of $1A$ is required to flow through the galvanometer to give it full scale deflection (*fsd*) but the galvanometer can only allow 20mA (0.02A) through the coil of the galvanometer.

We therefore require a resistance R to divert the excess current i.e. $(1 - 0.02)A$ or 0.98A. If the coil resistance is 10Ω, and the p.d. across the coil and the "shunt" resistance R is the same, the resistance can be calculated.
$$0.02 \times 10 = 0.98 \times R$$
$$R = \frac{0.2}{0.98}\Omega \text{ or } 0.2\Omega$$
On switching to the $0.1A$ range, a resistance of this value is connected in parallel.

Conversion of a galvanometer to a voltmeter

Fig. 31.21 illustrates the principle of converting a galvanometer to a voltmeter to measure 0-5V. In this situation a suitable resistor S is connected in series with the coil of the galvanometer.

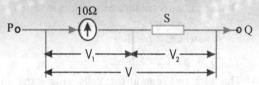

Fig. 31.21 Converting a milliammeter to a voltmeter.

If a maximum p.d. of 5V is between the terminals P and Q as shown. A current of 20mA (0.02A) flowing in the coil of the galvanometer also flows through the series resistance S since they are joined in series. The p.d. $V = V_1 + V_2$ where V_1 is the p.d. across the coil and V_2 is the p.d. across the resistance S. Therefore,
$$V = 0.02(10 + S)$$
$$5 = 0.2 + 0.02S$$
$$S = \frac{4.8}{0.02}$$
$$= 240\Omega$$

On switching to 0-5V range, then a resistance of 240Ω is connected in series.

Summary

1. Continuous d.c. current is produced by batteries (a group of cells). These sources of electromotive force (e.m.f.) drive current through electric circuits.

2. Electromotive force e.m.f., E is the work done when one coulomb of electric charge is moved through both the external circuit (resistor) and the inside of the cell.
$$E = IR + Ir$$
$$= \text{p.d. across external circuit + p.d. across internal resistance.}$$

3. The resistivity, ρ, is the ability of a material to oppose the flow of current through it. It is defined as the ratio of electric field ($E = V/l$) to the current density J (current per unit area)
$$\rho = \frac{E}{J}.$$

It is also defined as the resistance R of a wire of a unit length l and a unit cross sectional area A.
$$\text{i.e. } \rho = \frac{RA}{l} \text{ in } \Omega\text{m}.$$

Conductivity is the reciprocal of resistivity.
$$\sigma = \frac{1}{\rho}$$
$$= \frac{l}{RA}$$

4. For ohmic conductors, i.e. materials that obey ohm's law, a graph of current against voltage is

a straight line through the origin for both positive and negative values.

For non-ohmic conductors, the relation of current to voltage is not in direct proportion.

5. The combined resistance of resistors in series,
$$R = R_1 + R_2 + R_3 + \ldots\ldots\ldots + R_n$$
For resistances in parallel,
$$\frac{1}{R} = \frac{1}{R_1} + \frac{1}{R_2} + \frac{1}{R_3} + \ldots\ldots\ldots + \frac{1}{R_n}$$
The effective e.m.f. for cells connected in series.
$$E = E_1 + E_2 + E_3 + \ldots\ldots\ldots + En$$
The total internal resistance is the sum of the internal resistances. For identical cells connected in parallel total e.m.f. equals e.m.f. of one cell, but total internal resistance, r, is
$$\frac{1}{r} = \frac{1}{r_1} + \frac{1}{r_2} + \frac{1}{r_3} + \ldots\ldots\ldots + \frac{1}{r_n}$$

6. The Wheatstone bridge method is an accurate method to measure resistance. At balance, when no current flows through the detector
$$\frac{R_1}{R_2} = \frac{R_x}{R_4}, R_x \text{ is to be determined, } R_1, R_2, R_3, \text{ have known values.}$$

The practical bridge is the metre bridge. A resistance wire with uniform cross section area of 1m long replaces two of the known resistances. Since $R \propto l$, at balance $R_1 = kl$, and $R_2 = k(100-l)$
$$\frac{R_1}{R_2} = \frac{l}{100-l}$$

7. The potentiometer is used to compare and measure e.m.fs. of cells. It is very accurate since at balance no current flows.
$$\frac{E_1}{E_x} = \frac{l_1}{l_x}$$

E_1 is the known e.m.f. of a cell.
E_x is the unknown e.m.f.

Resistances can be measured by either the ammeter – voltmeter method or by the metre bridge (null method).

8. Kirchhoff's laws are employed to solve circuit problems which cannot be reduced to simple series parallel networks.
The current law (KIL): States that the algebraic sum of all currents flowing into a junction is zero.
    i.e $\Sigma I_n = 0$
The voltage law (KVL): The algebraic sum of the potential differences (IR drops), in any closed loop is equal to the algebraic sum of the e.m.fs in that loop.

$$\Sigma I_n R_n = \Sigma E_n \Rightarrow \Sigma E_n - \Sigma I_n R_n = 0$$

In applying the loop rule (KVL), some sign conventions are required.

Exercise 31

1. A battery consists of 6 accumulators in series each having an e.m.f. of 2V. The e.m.f. of the battery is
   A. 12 V. B. 8V.   C. 6V.   D. 4V.

2. The current, I, flowing through the circuit below is

   A. $\frac{3E}{2R}$. B. $\frac{2E}{R}$. C. $\frac{3E}{R}$. D. $\frac{6E}{R}$.

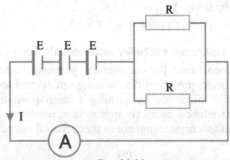

Fig. 31.22

3. In the figure below, the power developed in the 12Ω resistor is 6W. The power developed in the 8Ω resistor is
   A. 16 W. B. 9W. C. 6W. D. 4W. E. 2W.

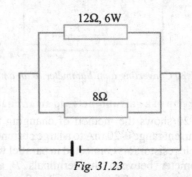

Fig. 31.23

4. In the figure below, a current of 2.8A flows towards the bridge circuit and no current flows in the galvanometer, G. Calculate the current flowing in the 4Ω resistor.
   A. 2.8A B. 2.4A C. 2.0A D 1.2A

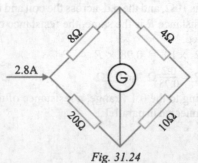

Fig. 31.24

5. The diagram below illustrates the conversion of a milliammeter of resistance 2Ω to an ammeter to read 10A. The milliammeter gives a full scale deflection (fsd) for a current of 10mA. Calculate the value of R.
   A. $2.0 \times 10^{-3} \Omega$ B. $2.0 \times 10^{-2} \Omega$
   C. $2.0 \times 10^{-1} \Omega$ D. $2.0 \times 10^{2} \Omega$

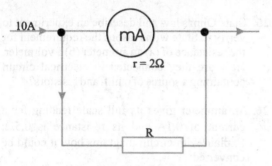

Fig. 31.25

6. A wire of length 100cm and cross sectional area of 2×10^{-3} cm² with electrical conductivity $5.0 \times 10^{5} (\Omega m)^{-1}$. Calculate the resistance of the wire.
   A. 100Ω   B. 5.0Ω   C. 10Ω   D. 0.10Ω

7. A cell of e.m.f. 1.5V is connected in series with a resistor of resistance 3Ω. A high resistance voltmeter connected across the cell registers only 0.9V. Calculate the internal resistance of the cell.
   A. 5.0Ω   B. 4.5Ω   C. 2.4Ω   D. 2.0Ω

8.

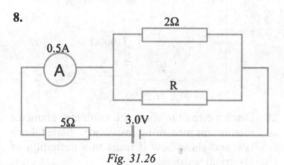

Fig. 31.26

Calculate the value of R in the circuit diagram above.
A. 6.0Ω   B. 4.0Ω   C. 3.0Ω   D. 2.0Ω

9.

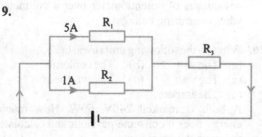

Fig. 31.27

Which of the following is/are correct of the arrangement of resistors in the circuit above?
I.   The current in R_3 is 6A.
II. The resistance R_1 is greater than that of R_2.
III. A voltmeter connected across R_1 will give the same reading as one connected across R_2.
A. I only   B. II only
C. III only   D. I and III only

10. A battery of e.m.f. of 10V and internal resistance of 2Ω is connected to an external resistance of 6Ω, calculate the p.d. across the terminals.
    A. 1.25V   B. 2.5N
    C. 5.00V   D. 7.50V

11. A cell of e.m.f. 1.5V and internal resistance 2Ω is connected in series with an ammeter of resistance, 1Ω and a resistor of resistance, 7Ω. Calculate the current in the circuit.

    A. 6.60A   B. 3.00A
    C. 2.10   D. 0.15 A

12. Calculate the terminal potential difference across a 20Ω resistor connected to a battery of e.m.f. 15V and internal resistance 5Ω.
    A. 0.5V   B. 6.3 V
    C. 12.0V   D. 15.0V

13. The balance length of a potentiometer wire for a cell of e.m.f. 1.50V is 90.00cm. If the cell is replaced by a Daniell cell of e.m.f. 1.08V. Calculate its new balance length.
    A. 84.32cm   B. 73.24cm
    C. 64.80cm   D. 56.54cm

14. A potentiometer wire carrying a steady current is 100cm long when a standard cell of e.m.f. 1.IV is connected to a balance length of 44.0cm was obtained. Calculate the e.m.f. of a cell that gives a balance length of 68.0cm.
    A. 2.2V   B. 1.7V   C. 1.5V   D. 0.7V

15. Which of the following instruments is most accurate for comparing the e.m.f. of two cells?
    A. Voltmeter   B. Ammeter
    C. Metre bridge   D. Metre rule

16. Which of the following is/are ohmic conductors?
    I CuSO₄ II Constantan III Thermistor
    IV Silicon
    A. I only   B. II only
    C. III only   D. I and II only

17. To convert a galvanometer to a voltmeter
    A. a high resistance is connected in series.

B. a low resistance is connected in parallel.
C. a low resistance is connected in series.
D. a high resistance is connected in parallel .

18. Which of the following instruments is **not** suitable for measuring current?
    A. Ammeter   B. Voltameter
    C. Milliammeter   D. Microammeter

19. In a metre bridge circuit, it is found that zero deflection is obtained in the galvanometer when the sliding contact is at 50.0cm mark. When a 6Ω resistor is connected in series with the resistor in the left gap, the balance point moves to 75.0 cm mark. Calculate the value of the resistance originally in the bridge circuit.
    A. 1.5Ω   B. 3.0Ω
    C. 4.5Ω   D. 6.0Ω

20. What length of resistance wire of diameter 0.6mm and resistivity $1.1 \times 10^{-6} \Omega$ m would be cut in order to make a 44Ω resistor?
    A. 11.3m   B.   8.1m
    C. 7.5m   D.   6.4m

21. What is meant by the internal resistance of a cell? A cell of e.m.f. 1.5V is connected in series with a resistance R and an ammeter of resistance 0.2Ω. The potential difference between the terminals of the cell is 1.35V and the ammeter reading is 0.3A. Calculate the value of R and the internal resistance of the cell.

22. Two resistors of 20ohm and 30 ohm are connected in parallel across the terminals of a torchlight battery of e.m.f. 1.5V and internal resistance 3.0 ohm, calculate the potential difference across the terminals of the cell.

23. Four identical cells each of e.m.f. 1.5 volts with internal resistance are connected to form a battery of 6.0V. The battery is then joined in series with an ammeter of negligible resistance and fixed external resistance of 12 ohms. The ammeter then reads 0.3A.
    (a) Draw diagram of the circuit.
    (b) Calculate:
        (i) the internal resistance of the battery; and
        (ii) the value of the resistor which must be joined in parallel with the 12-ohm resistor to increase the ammeter reading to 0.5A.

24. State Kirchhoff's laws of electrical network. Determine the currents, I_1, I_2 and I_3 in the circuit in fig 31.28.

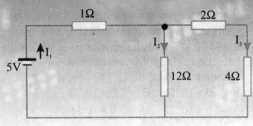

Fig. 31.28

25. State Ohm's law and describe an experiment to verify it. State with reasons the requirement for the resistance of (a) an ammeter (b) a voltmeter. How are they connected in electrical circuit containing a source of e.m.f. and resistors?

26. An ammeter gives its full scale reading for a current of 0.1A and its resistance is 0.5Ω. Explain with circuit diagrams how it could be converted:
    (i) to give a full scale reading of 2A;
    (ii) for use as a voltmeter to read up 10V.

27. Calculate the potential difference between A and B in the circuit of fig. 31.29:
    (i) as shown   (ii) if an additional 500□ were connected from A to B.

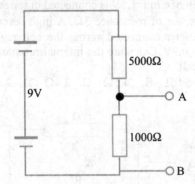

Fig. 31.29

28. Draw a circuit to show the voltmeter-ammeter method for measuring resistance. State Ohm's law and show how it leads to a definition of electrical resistance.

29. Describe how you would compare the electromotive force of two cells using a potentiometer. Illustrate with a labelled diagram the circuit you would use. List the advantages of potentiometer over a voltmeter when measuring voltages.

30. What do the following units measure?
    (a) The volt   (b) The coulomb
    (c) The watt   (d) Kilowatt hour
    (e) The ampere
    A bulb is marked 240V, 60W. How much energy does it consume per hour and calculate the current it passes.

31. A battery of four cells each of e.m.f. of 2.5V and internal resistance 0.5Ω are connected in series with a 4Ω resistor with a parallel combination of two 4Ω resistors.

Draw a diagram of the circuit and calculate :
(i) the effective external resistance
(ii) the current in the circuit
(iii) the lost volts in the battery
(iv) the current in one of the 4Ω parallel resistors

32. (a) List four factors which can determine the resistance of a coil of wire.
(b) Deduce an expression for the equivalent resistance R_q of three resistors R_1, R_2, and R_3 when connected (i) in series (ii) in parallel and deduce an expression for the series and parallel combination if the values of the resistance of the resistors are the same.

33. Two heating coils P and Q connected in parallel in a circuit, produce powers of 5W and 10W respectively. Calculate the ratio of their resistances R_P/R_Q when used.

34. A boiling ring of power 100W is required when the p.d. across it is 200V. Calculate the length of nichrome wire required to make the ring if the cross-sectional area of the wire used is $1\times10^{-7}m^2$ and resistivity of nichrome is $1\times10^{-6}\Omega\,m$.

35. Illustrate, by means of graphs, the relation between the current and voltage:
(a) for uniform manganin wire,
(b) for a diode valve.
How do you account for the differences between the two sources?

MAGNETIC FIELD

32.1 Concept of magnetic field

Everybody uses magnetic forces, without them, there would be no electric motors, TV tubes, loudspeakers and computer printers. The most familiar aspects are those associated with permanent magnets which attract unmagnetised ferromagnetic materials and can attract or repel other magnets. Magnetic forces unlike electric forces act only on moving charges. We shall describe these magnetic forces using the concept of a field. A magnetic field is established by a permanent magnet, by electric current in a conductor or by moving charges. The Magnetic field, in turn, exerts forces on other moving charges and current carrying conductors.

The concept of magnetic field was introduced in Chapter 6.

The magnetic field is a region around a magnet in which the influence of the magnet can be felt.

1. Magnetic interactions can be represented by a moving charge or current that creates a **magnetic field** in the surrounding space (in addition to the electric field).

2. The magnetic field which exerts a force $\vec{F}$ on any other moving charge or current that is present in that field.

Magnetic field is a vector field and we use the symbol B for the magnitude of the field. At any position, the direction of $\vec{B}$ is defined as that in which the north pole of a compass needle tends to point. The magnetic force $\vec{F}$ is always perpendicular to both $\vec{B}$ and the velocity $\vec{v}$ of the moving charge. The direction of $\vec{F}$ is always perpendicular to the plane containing $\vec{v}$ and $\vec{B}$. Its magnitude is given by:

$$F = |q|\, vB \sin \phi$$

where $|q|$ is the magnitude of the charge, ϕ is the angle measured from the direction of v to the direction of B.

The units of B is the tesla ($T = N\,(Am)^{-1}$). The magnetic force is zero when v is parallel or antiparallel to B. i.e when $\phi = 0$, or $180°$. The largest force is obtained when v is perpendicular to B and $F = qvB$. When a charged particle moves through a region of space where both electric and magnetic fields are present, both fields exert forces on the particle. The total force F_T is the vector sum of the electric and magnetic forces. $F_T = q\,(\vec{E} + \vec{v} \times \vec{B})$.

The magnitude of force:

$$|F| = qE + qvB \sin \phi. \qquad 32.1$$

We can represent any magnetic field by magnetic field lines. These magnetic field lines are sometimes called "*magnetic lines of force*" or *magnetic flux*.

Magnetic lines of force are imaginary lines along which a free-north pole would tend to move if placed in the field. A line of force may also be considered as a line such that the tangent to it at any point gives the direction of the field at that point.

Patterns of magnetic field

Magnetic field lines produced by several common sources of magnetic field are shown in Fig. 32.1.

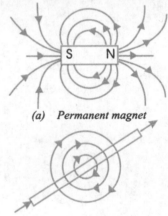

(a) Permanent magnet

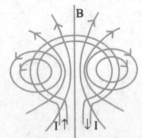

(b) Perpendicular to a straight current carrying wire.

(c) The axis of circular current carrying loop.

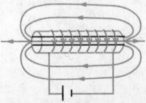

(d) Centre of a cylindrical coil/solenoid.

Fig. 32.1 Magnetic lines of force.

Magnetic flux ϕ_B, is a scalar quantity and is given as
$\phi_B = BA\cos\phi$.

Where A is the cross sectional area where the flux threads.

Angle of dip or the inclination

A uniform copper bar which is non-magnetic will stay horizontal if suspended at its middle Fig. 32.2. However a magnetic needle will produce a different result when suspended at its centre of gravity. It is found that the needle will point downwards at an angle to the horizontal. This angle is called angle of dip.

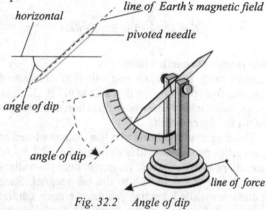

Fig. 32.2   Angle of dip

The angle of dip is the angle between the direction of the earth's resultant magnetic field and the horizontal.

The angle of dip varies all over the earth's surface from 90° near the geographic poles to 0° near the equator. The earth's magnetic field can be resolved into vertical and horizontal components as shown in Fig. 32.3.

The horizontal component (H) of the earth's magnetic field at a point is the magnetic force in a horizontal direction. The vertical component (V) of the earth's magnetic field at a point is the magnetic force in a vertical direction. From Fig. 32.3, the angle of dip ϕ can be calculated in terms of these components, using the expression:

$$\tan\phi = \frac{V}{H}. \qquad\qquad 32.2$$

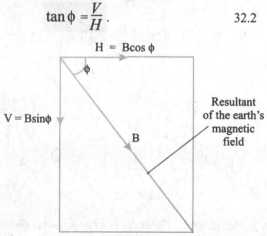

Fig. 32.3   Components of the earth's magnetic field.

Wilhelm Weber, in the middle of the nineteenth century considered that every molecule of a magnetic material is itself a magnet with two poles. If a magnet is broken in half, instead of separating the north and south poles, we obtain two magnets. Additional north and south poles are formed and each of the two small magnets has half the strength of the original magnet. No matter how many times a magnet is broken, each piece was found to be magnets with two poles. This process can be continued, repeatedly dividing a magnet in two and obtaining more smaller magnets until molecules are reached. This clearly demonstrates that the original magnet might have been made of tiny molecular magnets.

It has been established that atoms that make matter contain moving electrons which form tiny current loops that produce magnetic fields of their own. In many materials, their currents are oriented at random and do not cause any net magnetic field. But in some materials, an external magnetic field can cause these loops to align with the field such that their magnetic fields add to the external field and the material is said to be magnetized.

Diamagnetism

In many materials, there are as many electrons spinning or orbiting in one direction as in the opposite direction so that their effects neutralise one another. With an applied magnetic field, the electron orbits are slightly disturbed by induced electromagnetism which reduces the field strength inside the material giving rise to a little magnetic effect called diamagnetism. Diamagnetic substances are oriented perpendicular to strong magnetic fields. Examples, are bismuth, mercury, silver, carbon and lead and such materials are not affected by temperature. The susceptibility of such material is very small and negative.

Paramagnetism

In materials with unbalanced electrons, the individual molecules behave like tiny magnets. In the absence of external magnetic field, these molecular magnets are randomly arranged giving no net magnetic effect to the material; but with the application of external magnetic field, the molecular magnets become partially aligned and the magnetic strength increases. This small effect is called paramagnetism. Examples are platinum, aluminium and sodium. Such materials have very small but positive susceptibility.
Paramagnetic materials are affected by temperature.

Ferromagnetism

In some magnetic materials of which iron, nickel cobalt, gadolinium and certain alloys such as alnico are examples, there are strong interactions between atomic magnetic moments so that their magnetic axes line up with each other in regions called **magnetic domains**. Even in the absence of external field when unmagnetised, the magnetic axes of the domains point in all directions at random and the bar indicates no polarity. If the bar is placed in a gradually increasing magnetic field, e.g. inside a solenoid with d.c. current, in some of the domains, all the atomic magnets align with the direction of the magnetising field. If the magnetising field is strong enough, the axes of all the domains will be said to be saturated. The free atomic poles results in the poles of the magnet.

Ferromagnetic materials can be used in electromagnets, transformer cores, motors and generators. Steel and alnico can be used in the construction of permanent magnets. The susceptibility is very high.

32.3 Earth's magnetic field

A magnetic needle or bar magnet when freely suspended will always point approximately in a north-south direction. This is due to the earth's magnetic field. The earth behaves as though it contained a short bar magnet inclined at a small angle to the axis of rotation of the earth. This imaginary bar magnet has its south pole in the northern hemisphere while its north pole is in the southern hemisphere. Fig 32.4. illustrates the earth's magnetic field.

Magnetic elements of a place

The magnetic elements that determine the earth's magnetic field at a place are:

a) angle of declination or variation;
b) angle of dip/inclination;
c) the horizontal component of the earth's magnetic field.

At a particular place on the earth, the magnetic north is not usually in the same direction as the geographic north at that place. Two planes have to be distinguished:

(i) The magnetic meridian at any place is a vertical plane passing through the magnetic axis of a magnet suspended freely under the influence of the earth's magnetic field.

(ii) The geographic meridian at any place is a vertical plane containing the geographic north and south pole of the earth.

The angle between the geographic north and magnetic north at a place is called the angle of declination at that place.

Mariners called the declination, **the variation of the compass**. The declination is said to be east or west depending upon whether the north pole of the needle is east or west of the geographic north.

The true declination is calculated by adding the reading of compass bearing to the declination at that place.

Fig. 32.4(a) The Earth's field

Bar magnet in earth's field

Earth's field: The earth's magnetic field consists of parallel lines pointing north wards as in Fig. 32.4(a). A uniform field is one whose direction and strength of the field is constant.

The magnetic field due to a bar magnet placed in the earth's magnetic field is shown in fig. 32.4(b). At certain points, the earth's magnetic field neutralizes completely the field due to the bar magnet. Such points are called neutral points. At each neutral point, the direction of the force due to the earth's field on a north pole of a compass needle placed there is exactly equal and opposite to the force due to the magnet. The resultant flux density is zero at neutral points.

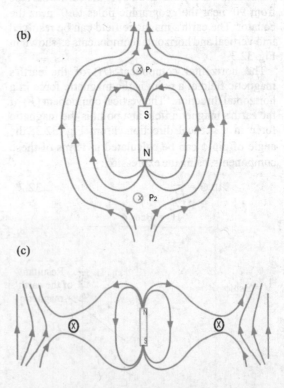

Fig. 32.4(b,c)   Fields due to a bar magnet in the earth's field.

32.4 Electromagnets and the applications of electromagnetic fields

Electromagnetism

An electromagnet is a temporary magnet which is constructed by winding solenoids in opposite directions round soft iron bar bent into a U-shape. The end of the U-shaped iron where the current enters the iron is the south pole and the other end through which the current leaves the iron is the north pole as shown in fig. 32.5.

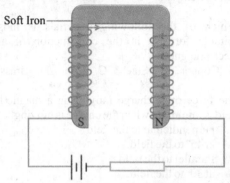

Soft Iron

Fig. 32.5   Electromagnet

Electromagnets find many common applications in industry:

(a) They are used in the construction of devices such as electric bell and telephone receiver.

(b) For lifting and transporting heavy equipment made from pieces of iron and steel.

(c) To separate iron from mixtures containing non-magnetic elements.

(d) To produce strong magnetic fields required in generators and electric motors.

Electric bell

The electric bell consists of two solenoids wound in opposite directions on two of the iron cores connected with a soft iron bar. One end of the windings is connected to a terminal T, and the other to a metal bracket which supports a spring mounted soft iron armature. The armature carries a light spring which is soldered to a disc which acts as a contact taken to second terminal T_2. The circuit is completed through a battery of cells and a push switch connected to terminals, T_1 and T_2. This set up is in Fig. 32.6.

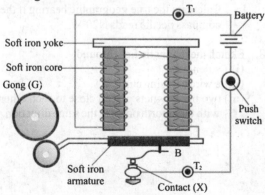

Fig. 32.6 Electric bell

Working principle of electric bell

When the push switch is pressed, current flows and the iron cores become magnetized. The iron bar B is now attracted to the electromagnet. The circuit is then broken and B is released. It falls back again to make contact with X and T_2 once more. Thus, contact is remade and the process is repeated, consequently, the armature vibrates to-and-fro and the hammer attached to the armature strikes the gong repeatedly.

The telephone receiver

A telephone receiver consists of an electromagnet formed by placing a short permanent bar magnet across the ends of two iron bars Fig. 32.7. This is placed so that it exerts a pull on the magnetic diaphragm constructed from a soft alloy. Two solenoids are wound in opposite directions on the soft-iron bars.

When one speaks into the microphone at the other end of the line, a varying electric current is set up having the same frequency as the sound waves. The same current is made to pass through the solenoids of the earpiece. This causes the strength of the magnetic flux to vary in sympathy with the pull of the diaphragm and therefore vibrates as the sound waves which entered the microphone.

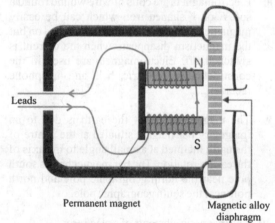

Fig. 32.7 Telephone receiver

Summary

1. Magnetic field is the space around a magnet or a current carrying conductor where a magnetic force can be detected.

2. A magnetic field exerts a force on a moving charge but not on stationary charged particles. The direction of the force is perpendicular to both the magnetic field and the velocity of the particle.

3. Magnetic fields can be represented by field maps using magnetic field lines. Magnetic flux is the product of the surface area and the average component of magnetic field perpendicular to the surface.

4. Magnetic fields exert forces on conductors carrying currents. These forces are essential for the operation of electric motors and many other devices.

5. Magnetic field lines can be visualised by the use of iron filings, which line up tangent to the field lines like little compass needles.

6. A line of force is a line along which a north pole would tend to move if it were free. Magnetic fields would tend to move if it were free. Magnetic fields are vector fields and their directions can be plotted using compass needle. Neutral points are obtained where the earth's magnetic field is exactly equal and opposite to the field due to a bar magnet.

7. The field pattern round a straight current conductor is circular. With a circular coil, the field lines are straight and perpendicular to the coil at the centre but becomes circular as we move away from the centre. The field pattern round a solenoid is of a similar pattern to that round a bar magnet and it is straight at the centre.

8. Electromagnets are coils of wire wound round a soft E or V shaped iron which can be easily magnetized when d.c. current is switched on but the magnetism disappears when the current is switched off. Electromagnets are used in the construction of electric bell and telephone receiver.

9. The magnetic field of the earth is due to an imaginary bar magnet situated at the centre of the earth inclined at a small angle to the axis of the earth's rotation. The bar magnet has its south pole near the north geographic pole and north pole near the south geographic pole.

10. The magnetic elements of a place are:
    (i) angle of dip/inclination;
    (ii) angle of declination; and
    (iii) horizontal component of the earth's field.

11. The magnitude of the magnetic force, F_m, on a charged particle, q, moving in a magnetic field, B with a velocity, v, is given by $F_m = q \, Bv\sin\theta$ and the force is greatest when $\theta = 90°$ i.e. the charged particle moves perpendicular to B.
    When a bar magnet is placed in the earth's field, the points in the field at which the resultant flux density is zero are called neutral points.

1. Which of the following is a vector quantity?
   A. Magnetic field   B. Magnetic flux
   C. Flux density   D. Magnetic element

2. The magnitude of the magnetic force F on a charge q moving in a magnetic field B with a velocity v parallel to the field is given by
   A. $F = qvB$.   B. $F = 0$.
   C. $F = B/qv$.   D. $F = q/Bv$.

3. Which of the following materials is most suitable for use in the construction of an electromagnet?
   A. Copper B. Steel C. Iron D. Brass

4. The force on a charge moving in a magnetic field is minimum when the charge is moving
   A. perpendicular to the field
   B. at 45° to the field.
   C. Parallel to the field.
   D. at 30° to the field.

5. Which of the following is not a magnetic element?
   A. Vertical component of the earth's magnetic field.
   B. Angle of declination.
   C. Horizontal component of the earth's magnetic field.
   D. Angle of dip.

6. The direction of the magnetic force on a charge moving in a magnetic field is
   A. perpendicular to the plane containing v and B.
   B. parallel to the plane containing v and B.
   C. normal to the plane containing q and B.
   D. in the direction of the field, B.
   E. in the direction of the velocity, v.

7. (a) Define the terms declination, inclination and illustrate with a diagram how the earth's magnetic field may be resolved into two components.
   (b) If the angle of declination at a place is 30°. Calculate the true geographic bearing if the compass needle reads N20°W.

8. Sketch the magnetic field around:
   (i) solenoid;
   (ii) a wire carrying current;
   (iii) two bar magnets placed close to each other with their north poles in the same direction.

260

9. (a) Explain what is meant by a neutral point in a pattern of magnetic flux.
    (b) Describe how the magnetic flux pattern may be plotted in a horizontal plane in which a bar magnet is placed in the earth's magnetic field. If the magnet lies with its north pole pointing south, sketch the pattern you would expect to obtain and mark the position of any neutral points.

10. Draw a well labelled diagram showing the essential parts of an electric bell and describe its operation.

11. A proton of charge 1.6×10^{-19}C is projected into a magnetic field of flux density 5.0T with a velocity 2.7×10^{5} ms^{-1}. Calculate the magnitude of the force experienced by the proton in a direction:
    (i) at 45° to the field;
    (ii) parallel to the field; and
    (iii) perpendicular to the field.

12. (a) State with reason the material used to construct the core of the electromagnet in a telephone receiver.
    (b) Describe the operation of a telephone receiver with the aid of a labelled diagram.

ELECTROMAGNETIC FIELDS

Chapter 33

33.1 Concept of electromagnetic field

When a charged particle with charge q moves through a region of space where both electric and magnetic fields with E and B vectors respectively are present, both fields exert forces on the particle. The total force $\vec{F}$ is the vector sum of both the electric and magnetic forces, $\vec{F_e}$ and $\vec{F_m}$ respectively.

Then $F = \vec{F_e} + \vec{F_m}$

$$F = q(\vec{E} + \vec{v} \times \vec{B}) \qquad 33.1$$

where v is the velocity of the particle in the magnetic field.

This is known as Lorentz Force of a current carrying conductor placed in a magnetic field. The strength of a magnetic field is usually measured in terms of a quantity called **magnetic flux density** of the field, B. When a wire carrying a current I is placed in a magnetic field, the wire experiences a force due to the interaction between the field and the moving charges in the wire. The field of the wire is shown in fig. 33.1.

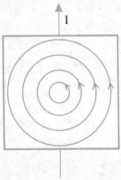

Fig. 33.1 Field around a current carrying conductor.

The force F on the wire can be shown to be proportional to:
(a) current, I, flowing in the conductor,
(b) the length, l, of the conductor in the field,
(c) the sine of the angle that the conductor makes with the field
(d) the strength of the field known as flux density.
The force is given by the equation

$$F = BIl \sin\theta \qquad 33.2$$

Example 33.1

The force experienced by a current carrying conductor of length 100cm is 2.0N. Calculate the

current in the conductor if it is flowing in a direction 45° with the field of 1.0T.

Solution

From equation 33.2,
$$F = BIl \sin\theta$$
$$2 = 1 \times I \times 10^{-2} \times 100 \times \sin 45°$$
$$I = \frac{2}{\sin 45°} = 2.83A$$

The greatest force occurs when $\theta = 90°$ i, i.e. when the conductor is at the right angle to the field. The units of B is tesla or weber per square metre (Wbm^{-2}).

> One tesla is defined as force per unit length on a wire carrying a current of one ampere at right angle to the field.

Fleming's left-hand-rule gives the direction of motion for the case when the field and current are perpendicular, it states that "If the first three fingers of the left hand are held at right angles to each other the First finger represents the Field (N to S), the seCond finger, the Current direction (positive to negative) and the thuMb gives the direction of Motion. The magnetic flux (Φ) passing through a surface is BA, where A is the area of the surface at right angles to the field, $\Phi = BA$,

Magnetic flux (Φ) is measured in webers (Wb).

$$\Phi = BA\cos\theta \qquad 33.3$$

33.2 Force on a moving charge in a magnetic field

Consider a charged particle q moving with a velocity $\vec{v}$ in a magnetic field of flux density B, it is acted upon by the magnetic force $\vec{F_m}$ given by $F_m = q \times \vec{v} \times B$ and the motion is determined by Newton's laws. If $\vec{v}$ and B are perpendicular, the magnitude is given by:

$$F = q v B \sin\theta \text{ and } F = q v B, \text{ if force is}$$
perpendicular to velocity.

Example 33.2

Calculate the force on a charge $+2\mu C$ moving with a velocity $2 \times 10^6 ms^{-1}$ in a field of magnetic flux density 0.5T:
(i) parallel to the field;
(ii) perpendicular to the field.

Solution

Using equation $F = qvB\sin\theta$,

(i) $F = 2 \times 10^{-6} \times 2 \times 10^6 \times 0.5\sin 0$
      $= 0\text{N}$

(ii) $F = 2 \times 10^{-6} \times 10^6 \times 2 \times 0.5 \times 1$
      $= 2\text{N}$

The motion of a charged particle under the action of a magnetic field alone is always a motion with constant speed and the trajectory is circular.

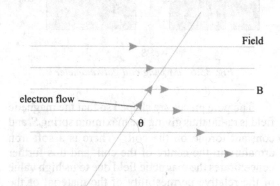

Fig. 33.2 Moving charge in a magnetic field.

33.3 Force and field patterns of two current carrying conductors

As observed, when a current flows in a wire, a magnetic field is produced around the wire; if two conductors are placed close together as in Fig. 33.3, then the field of one wire affects the other and a force exists between the two wires.

The force F per unit length between the conductors is directly proportional to the product of the currents flowing through them and is inversely proportional to their separation.

$$\frac{F}{l} = \frac{\mu_o I_1 I_2}{2\pi r} \qquad 33.4$$

μ_o = permeability of vacuum = $4\pi \times 10^{-7} \text{Am}^{-1}$ and r is the separation.

Fig. 33.3 Current flow in two long parallel wires.

Example 33.3

Two conductors carrying equal currents of 2A in opposite directions are separated by 2.0m. Calculate the repulsive force per unit length between the two conductors. (Take $\mu_o = 4\pi \times 10^{-7}\text{Am}^{-1}$).

Solution

From equation 33.4,

$$\frac{F}{l} = \frac{\mu_o I_1 I_2}{2\pi r} = \frac{4\pi \times 10^{-7} \times 2 \times 2}{2 \times \pi \times 2} = 4 \times 10^{-7}\text{N}$$

When currents flow in the same direction, the force is a force of attraction but if currents flow in opposite directions, the force is that of repulsion.

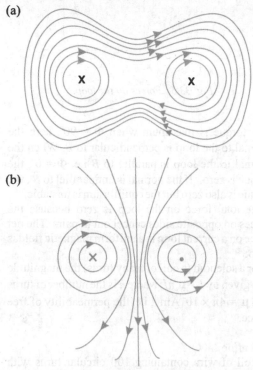

Fig. 33.4 Magnetic field

The magnetic fields for the two wires are shown in: fig 33.4 (a) for currents in the same direction and Fig. 33.4 (b) for currents in opposite directions.

33.4 Current in loops and coils

Coils of wire with a large number of turns and spaced so closely that each turn is very nearly a plane circular loop have been used in the construction of doorbell, transformer or electric motor. A current in such loop is used to establish a magnetic field.

Forces on the sides of a current carrying loop in a uniform magnetic field are as shown in Fig. 33.5. The resultant force is seen to be zero but the magnitude of the net moment of a force (torque), Γ is found to be $\Gamma = IAB\sin\Phi$, where I is the current carried by the loop of area, A, which makes an angle, Φ with the direction of the magnetic field, B.

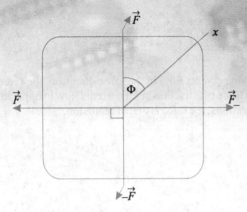

Fig. 33.5 Forces on the loop.

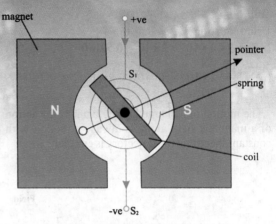

Fig. 33.6 Moving coil galvanometer

The torque is maximum when $\Phi = 90°$, here the normal to the loop is perpendicular to B. When the normal to the loop is parallel to $\vec{B}$ i.e. $\Phi = 0°$, the torque is zero. If the normal is antiparallel to $\vec{B}$, the torque is also zero but the equilibrium is unstable.

The total force on the loop is zero because the forces on opposite sides cancel out in pairs. The net force on a current loop in a uniform magnetic field is zero.

For a solenoid (a coil of many turns) the magnitude B is given by $B = \mu_o nI$, where n is the number of turns and $\mu_o = 4\pi \times 10^{-7} Am^{-1}$, i.e. the permeability of free space.

Example 33.4

A coil of wire containing 100 circular turns with radius 5.0cm is placed between the poles of an electromagnet where the magnetic field is uniform and at an angle of 60° with the plane of the coil. If the field decreases at a rate of 0.30 Ts^{-1}, calculate the magnitude of the induced e.m.f.

Solution

From equation 33.3,

$$\Phi = BA\cos\theta \text{ where } \theta = (90-60)° = 30°$$

$$\frac{dB}{dt} = -0.30 \, Ts^{-1}$$

and $A = \pi \times (5 \times 10^{-2})^2 = 78.6 \times 10^{-4} = 0.00786 m^2$

$$\frac{d\Phi}{dt} = \frac{dB}{dt} A\cos 30° = -0.30 \times 0.00786 \times 0.866$$

$$\frac{d\Phi}{dt} = -2 \times 10^{-3} \, Wbs$$

$$\Sigma = -N\frac{d\Phi}{dt} = -100 \times (-2 \times 10^{-3}) \, V = 0.20V$$

33.5 Applications of electromagnetic field

The moving coil galvanometer

A very common use of the forces on a coil in a magnetic field is that of a moving coil galvanometer shown diagrammatically in Fig. 33.6.

The coil is suspended between the poles of a magnet on jeweled bearings and is held in place by two finely coiled springs (S_1 and S_2) through which the current to be measured passes in and out of coil.

The pole pieces are shaped so that the magnetic field is radial thus giving the maximum spring S_1 and constant torque on the coil. There is a soft iron armature in the centre of the coil, and this further concentrates the magnetic field due to its high value of the relative permeability of the material of the core.

When in equilibrium, with current passing through it, the torque on the coil produced by the magnetic field is balanced by an opposing torque due to the rigidity of the springs. The more delicate the springs, the bigger the deflection for a given current.

The torque Γ due to the field is given by:

$$\Gamma = BANI$$

i.e. torque is directly proportional to current flow.

The electric motor

The electric motor is a device that converts electrical energy into rotational kinetic energy by the action of the force on a coil pivoted in a magnetic field. It differs from the moving coil galvanometer in that in practical motors, there is usually more than one coil and these coils are free to rotate. A cylindrical laminated iron core provides inertia and a radial field.

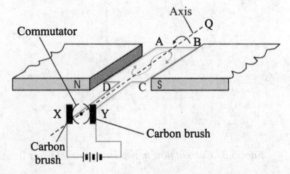

Fig. 33.7 The d.c. motor

Fig. 33.7 shows the essential features of a d.c. motor which consists of:

(a) a number of coils of fine wire wound on a laminated soft iron armature;

(b) a set of brushes *X, Y* to allow current to enter and leave the windings;

(c) a commutator to reverse the current in the coils; and

(d) a set of external field coils.

Advantages of moving coil ammeter

1. The field produced by the horse shoe magnet and the soft iron core is very strong, as such external magnetic fields cannot influence it.

2. The instrument has a uniform space because of the radial field provided by the soft iron core.

3. It can be converted to read different ranges of current, and potential differences by suitably fitting appropriate resistances.

Conversion of galvanometers to ammeters and voltameters

Ammeters are used for measuring currents and are always connected in series into a circuit. A galvanometer is used to indicate the passage of current (small values – on the order of a milliampere (mA) or micro ampere (μA).

To convert a galvanometer to an ammeter a low resistance is connected in parallel with the galvanometer as in Fig. 33.8(a). The low resistance connected in parallel is termed a **shunt**. It will divert a greater part of the current being measured but will allow a certain portion to pass through the coil. Shunt of very low value would take the form of a short piece of fairly thick manganin wire whose resistance does not change with temperature.

$$1.485 \ S \ = \ 0.075$$
$$S \ = \ 0.051\Omega$$

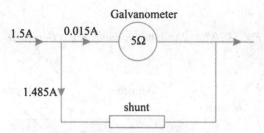

Fig. 33.8(a)   *Conversion of galvanometer to an ammeter.*

Voltmeters

A voltmeter is used to measure the potential difference between the ends of a resistor and is therefore connected across (in parallel with) the resistor. Voltmeters have high resistance and they take negligible current. To convert a galvanometer to a voltmeter, a high resistance or **multiplier** is connected in series, with the galvanometer as shown in the diagram Fig. 33.8(b).

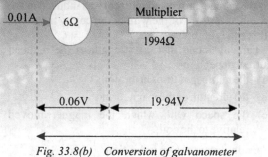

Fig. 33.8(b)   *Conversion of galvanometer to a voltmeter.*

33.6 Electromagnetic flux induction

If the magnetic flux through a coil is altered, then an electromotive force (e.m.f.) will be generated in the coil. Faraday discovered that e.m.f. could be generated by:

(a) either moving the coil or source of flux relative to each other, or

(b) changing the magnitude of the source of flux in some way.

Note: e.m.f. is only produced while the flux is changing, consider two coils as shown in fig. 33.9 when a magnet was plunged into the coil, the galvanometer needle, gave a momentary deflection, showing that a current has been induced in the coil. On withdrawing the magnet from the coil, the galvanometer gave another deflection, this time in the opposite direction. This effect is called **electromagnetic induction**. No current would be induced if the magnet remained stationary inside or outside the coil.

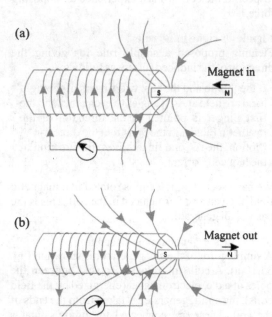

Fig. 33.9   *Electromagnetic induction apparatus*

As the magnet moved, the current was induced in the circuit as a result of the wire being cut by magnetic (flux) lines of force.

Faraday found that the strength of the induced current depends on:

(a) the number of turns in the coil;

(b) the strength of the magnet; and

(c) the speed with which the magnet moved relative to the coil.

Faraday's law of e-m induction

Whenever there is a change in the magnetic flux linked with a circuit, an electromotive force, E is induced, the strength of which is proportional to the rate of change of the flux Φ linked with the circuit.

The magnitude of the induced e.m.f. depends on:

(i) the rate of change of flux;

(ii) the number of turns in the coil; and

(iii) the cross-sectional area of the coil.

The faster the flux is changed the greater is the e.m.f. produced.

$$E = -\frac{d\Phi}{dt} \qquad 33.5$$

Lenz's law of e-m induction

The direction of the induced e.m.f. is such that it tends to oppose the change that produced it.

This law is an application of the law of conservation of energy. Energy is expended when the induced current flows and the source of this energy is the work done when the magnet is moved. Hence, if work is to be done when the magnet moves with respect to the coil, it must experience an opposing force.

Fleming's right-hand rule

Fleming proposed a simple rule for giving the direction of the induced current as follows:

If the thumb and the first two fingers of the right hand are held at right angles to each other and the first Finger is pointed in the direction of the magnetic Field and the thuMb in the direction of Motion, the seCond finger gives the direction of the induced Current.

We have seen that, if a coil is rotated in a magnetic field then an e.m.f. is induced in the coil. This is the basis of all generators.

33.7 The a.c. generator or alternator

A simple form of the a.c. generator is shown in Fig. 33.10(a). A coil (the rotor) is rotated between the poles of a d.c. electromagnet (energized by the field coils), the e.m.f. generated is taken from the ends of the coil. These are connected to sliding contacts known as slip rings on the axle and contact is made with these by two pieces of carbon brushes which press against the slip rings.

As the coil rotates, it cuts through the lines of magnetic flux, thus producing an induced e.m.f., the variation of which is shown in Fig. 33.10. A much smoother output is obtained by having a number of coils wound on an iron core which is laminated to reduce eddy currents, the output of such a generator is shown in fig 33.10(b).

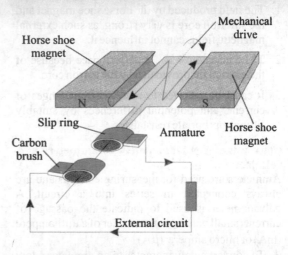

Fig. 33.10(a)   A.C. Generator

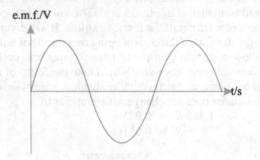

Fig. 33.10(b)   The output variation of a.c. Generator.

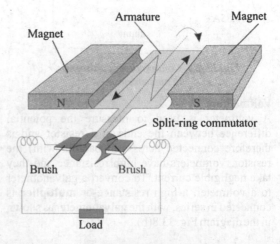

Fig. 33.11(a)   The simple direct current generator.

266

If the slip rings and brushes of the simple a.c. dynamo are replaced by a single split ring with two diametrically opposed brushes called commutator the machine becomes converted into a simple d.c. dynamo (motor), this means that a varying but unidirectional e.m.f. will be produced as a d.c. generator and its output is shown in Fig. 33.11(b).

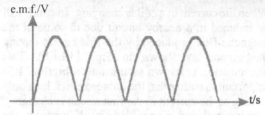

Fig. 33.11(b)   The output variation of d.c. generator

As with a.c. generator, the d.c. machine usually uses rotating field coils, a series of them would be in slots in the core, the rotating coils and the core are known as the armature. The output is then much steadier.

The laws of electromagnetic induction [when the magnetic flux through a coil changes, the e.m.f., E generated in the coil] can be expressed as   33.6 where N is the number of turns in the coil, $N\Phi$ is the flux linkage and $d(N\Phi)/dt$ is the rate of change of flux linkage in webers per second (Wbs^{-1}).

$$E = -\frac{Nd\Phi}{dt} \qquad 33.6$$

E.M.F generated in a rotating coil

Consider a coil of N turns and area A being rotated at a constant angular velocity ω in a magnetic field of flux density B with its axis perpendicular to the field. When the normal to the coil is at an angle θ to the field, the flux through the coil is:

$$BAN\cos\theta = BAN\cos(\omega t)$$

since $\theta = \omega t$. Therefore the e.m.f., E, generated between the ends of the coil is:

$$E = \frac{-d(BAN\cos\omega t)}{dt}$$

$$E = BAN\omega\sin t \qquad 33.7$$

the maximum value of the e.m.f., E_o, is when
$$\theta = \omega t$$
$$= 90°$$
i.e. the coil is in the plane of the field and is given by
$$E_o = BAN\omega.$$

Therefore, $E = E_o \sin\omega t$.

The variation is illustrated in Fig. 33.12

The r.m.s. value of the e.m.f. is $E_{rms} = \dfrac{E_o}{\sqrt{2}}$

(The concept of r.m.s. value will be discussed later).

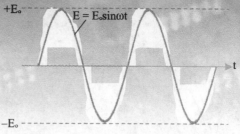

Fig. 33.12   Variation of e.m.f. of a rotating coil

33.8   Inductance
Self inductance
If the current through a coil Fig. 33.13 is altered, then the flux through that coil also changes, and this will induce an e.m.f. in the coil. This is self-induction and the property of the coil is the self-inductance (L) of the coil.

The e.m.f. generated is given by the equation:

$$E = \frac{LdI}{dt} \qquad 33.8$$

Example 33.5
If the current in the solenoid (coil of wire) increases uniformly from zero to 3A in $3\times10^{-3}s^{-1}$. Calculate the:

(i)   magnitude of the self induced e.m.f. (Take the inductance as 25mH).

(ii) energy stored.

Solution
From equation 33.8,
$$E = L\frac{dI}{dt} \; ; \qquad = \frac{dI}{dt} = \frac{3}{3\times10^{-3}} = 10^3 As^{-1}$$
$$E = 25 \times 10^{-3} \times 10^3 V = 25V.$$

From 33.8; $W = \frac{1}{2}LI^2 = 0.5 \times 25 \times 10^{-3} \times 9 J = 0.113J$

> The unit of inductance is the henry (H) and it is defined as the inductance of a coil (or circuit) in which an e.m.f. of one volt is induced when the current changes at the rate of one ampere per second.

The coil and iron rod is termed choke.

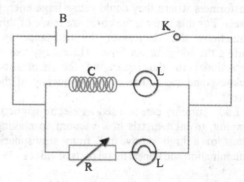

Fig. 33.13(a)

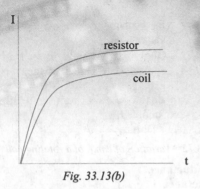

Fig. 33.13(b)

The energy stored in an inductor

Since a changing current in an inductor produces an e.m.f. if the source supplying the current is to maintain a p.d. between its terminals, the inductor must gain energy.

Let the inductor carry an instantaneous current i, which is changing at the rate di/dt. The induced e.m.f. is Ldi/dt and the power, P supplied to the inductor is:

$$P = Ei = \frac{Lidi}{dt}$$

The energy supplied in time, dt, is:
$$dW = Pdt = Lidi$$

Integrating, then
$$W = \frac{1}{2}LI^2$$

The energy, W, stored in an inductor of inductance, L is:

$$W = \frac{1}{2}LI^2 \qquad 33.9$$

This energy is used to produce the magnetic field in and around the coil.

Eddy currents

These are induced currents in metal objects larger than pieces of wire, the induced e.m.f. is not generally great but because the resistance of a lump of metal is very small, the induced currents can be large. Since the induced currents always act to oppose the motion (Lenz's law) eddy currents can be used as a very effective electromagnetic brake. Eddy currents become a problem in the cores of transformers where they could cause large energy losses. For this reason, the cores are made of thin laminations, thus increasing the resistance and limiting the eddy current flow. The energy loss is proportional to the square of the lamination thickness and the square of the frequency of the current.

Eddy currents can be used as electromagnetic damping, to melt metals in a vacuum so making metals of a high purity free from atmospheric contamination and to heat metal parts of valves.

Speedometer

A rotating magnet driven by a flexible cable sets up eddy currents in a pivoted aluminum disc. The magnetic reaction of the eddy currents sets up a couple on the disc which varies with the speed of the car. The disc therefore rotates until the electromagnetic couple is just balanced by an opposing couple set up by a hairspring. A pointer attached to the disc spindle indicates the speed on a suitably calibrated scale.

Mutual inductance

When the current in a coil is changing, an e.m.f. will be induced in a nearby circuit due to some of the magnetic flux produced by the first circuit linking the second as shown in Fig. 33.14(b). This phenomenon is known as **mutual induction**. It is important to realise that the induced e.m.f. lasts only as long as the current in the first circuit is changing. The mutual inductance, M, is defined by the equation

$$E_2 = M\frac{dI_1}{dt}$$

where E_2 is the e.m.f. induced in the secondary coil and $\frac{dI_1}{dt}$, the rate of change of current in primary coil.

Two coils are said to have a mutual inductance of 1 henry if an e.m.f. of 1 volt is induced in the secondary when the current in the primary changes at the rate of $1As^{-1}$.

An expression for mutual inductance, M is given by:

$$M = \mu_o\frac{AN_1N_2}{l}$$

Where N_1 and N_2 are the number of turns for the primary and secondary coils respectively. A is the cross sectional area of the coil with magnetic length, l, μ_o = magnetic permeability of free space = $4\pi \times 10^{-7}Am^{-1}$.

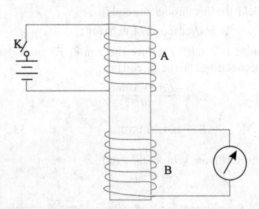

Fig. 33.14(a) e.m.f. induced in B by a changing the current in A.

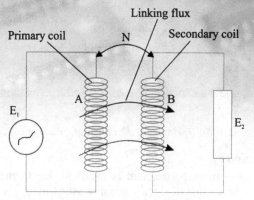

Fig. 33.14(b) Induced e.m.f.

When a current flows through a coil, it sets up a magnetic field and that field threads the coil which produces it. If the current, I, through the coil is changed, the flux linked with the turns of the coil changes and an e.m.f. is induced in the coil.

Self induction opposes the growth of current in the coil. So, current increases gradually to its final value.

$$E_2 = L_2 \frac{dI_1}{dt}$$

$$E_1 = L_1 \frac{dI_2}{dt}$$

$$M = \sqrt{L_1 L_2}$$

33.9 The transformer

The transformer uses the property of mutual inductance to change the voltage of an alternating supply. It may be used in the home to give a low voltage output from the mains for a cassette recorder or in a power station to produce very high voltages from the national grid.

It consists of two coils known as primary and secondary wound on a laminated iron core that links both coils as in Fig. 33.15. The core must be laminated to avoid large eddy currents. The laminations are usually E-shaped, and the primary and secondary coils are wound one on top of the other to improve magnetic linkage.

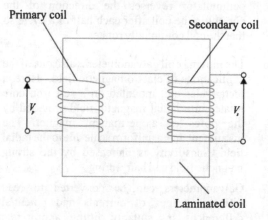

Fig. 33.15   A simple transformer

An a.c. voltage is applied to the primary and this produces a changing magnetic field within it. This changing magnetic field links the secondary coil and therefore induces an e.m.f. in it. The magnitude of this induced e.m.f. (V_s) is related to the e.m.f. applied to the primary (V_p) by the equation:

$$\frac{V_s}{V_p} = -\frac{N_s}{N_p}$$

where N_s and N_p are the number of turns on the secondary and primary coils respectively. The secondary voltage is 180° out of phase with that of the primary. If the output voltage is greater than input voltage, the transformer is known as a **step up transformer** and if the input voltage is greater than the output voltage, the transformer is called a **step down transformer**. For a step-up transformer, $N_s > N_p$, while for a step-down transformer, $N_p > N_s$.

It is assumed here that there is no flux leakage that is, that all flux produced by the primary links with the secondary and that there are no energy losses. This is the ideal transformer and this equation hold

$$\frac{V_s}{V_p} = \frac{N_s}{N_p} = \frac{I_p}{I_s}$$ 33.10

Where I_p and I_s are the currents flowing in the primary and secondary coils respectively.

In practice however, energy is lost from a transformer in the following ways:

(a) Heating in the coils (I^2Rt losses); this can be reduced by keeping their resistance low.

(b) Eddy current losses in the core can be reduced by the laminated core.

(c) Hysteresis loss; every time the direction of the magnetizing field is changed, some energy is lost due to heating as the magnetic domains in the core realign. This is reduced by using a "soft" magnetic material for the core e.g. silicon-iron, permalloy.

(d) Flux leakage is reduced by having efficient core design (soft iron core) to ensure that all the primary flux is linked with the secondary.

Transformer efficiency is the ratio of output power to the input power.

Example 33.6

A transformer which can produce 12V from a 220V$_{r.m.s}$ supply has an efficiency of 80%. If the current in the secondary coil is 10A, calculate the current in the primary coil.

Solution

From equation 33.10,

$$\frac{V_s}{V_p} = \frac{N_s}{N_p} = \frac{I_p}{I_s} \Rightarrow V_s I_s = V_p I_p$$

and efficiency $= \frac{80}{100} = \frac{V_s I_s}{V_p I_p}$

Substituting, $4 \times 220 \times I_p = 5 \times 12 \times 10$

$$I_p = \frac{600}{4 \times 220} = \frac{60}{88} \text{ A}$$
$$= 0.68A$$

33.10 The transmission of electricity

The transformer is an essential component of the national grid which distributes electrical energy around the country. Electrical energy is generated in power stations by generators at a potential of about 25kV. It is first stepped up to 400 kV by a transformer and then transmitted across the country in aluminum cables roughly 2cm in diameter.

High voltages are used because the power loss (I^2R) per kilometer for a given power output will be much less at high voltage, low current than at low voltage and high current.

33.11 The induction coil

The induction coil is the basis of many ignition systems for cars. It uses the mutual induction between two coils to produce a high voltage. A diagram of an induction coil is shown in Fig. 33.16(a).

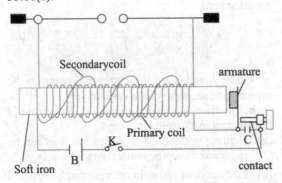

Fig. 33.16(a)   Induction coil

A primary coil consisting of a small number of turns of thick copper is wound round a bundle of iron rods which are insulated from each other. The secondary coil, which consists of many hundreds of fine wire is wound over the primary. On closing the switch, K, a current flows in the primary and magnetises the core which attracts the armature and the circuit is broken. The magnetic field dies away and the armature is pulled back by the spring contact and the circuit is complete again and current flows. The process repeats itself. The rapidly changing magnetic field produces a high voltage in the primary coil, the greater the rate at which the field changes the greater the induced e.m.f. A capacitor C is connected across the make and break contacts to reduce sparking and causes the field to die away much rapidly. This makes the induced e.m.f. in the secondary coil much greater when the circuit is broken than when it is made. The secondary current therefore appear in pulses though in the same direction. Sparks of several centimeters may be obtained through air at atmospheric pressure with small induction coils.

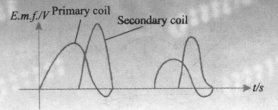

Fig. 33.16(b) Variation of the output of induction coil.

Summary

1. Electromagnetic field is the field due to the interaction of electric and magnetic forces. The magnitude of the force is given by the equation:
$$F = qE + qv\,B\sin\theta,$$ where θ is the angle between field and velocity.

2. A current carrying conductor with a length, l, and carrying current, I, in a field, B, experiences a force, F, given by the equation:
$$F = B\,Il\sin\theta.$$

3. The direction of the force is given by Fleming's left hand rule and the force is always directed perpendicular to the direction of current and magnetic field.

4. The magnitude of the force per unit length between two conductors carrying currents I_1, I_2 flowing in the same direction and separated by a distance, r, in a vacuum is given by: $\frac{F}{l} = \frac{\mu_o I_1 I_2}{2\pi r}$.

   and the force is attractive if the directions of the current are the same, the force per unit length is repulsive if otherwise.
   The resultant force on the sides of a current carrying loop in a uniform magnetic field is zero but the moment of a force, Γ, is found to be $\Gamma = IAB\sin\theta$, where A is the area of the loop.

5. An electric motor is an application of electromagnetic field. It consists of a rectangular coil of insulated wire (armature) that rotates in a magnetic field between two pole pieces of a magnet. A split ring commutator reverses the direction of the current in the coil after each half of a cycle so that the coil continually rotates.

6. The moving coil galvanometer is also one of the applications of electromagnetic field. Here, a rectangular coil mounted on a soft iron core rotates in a radial magnetic field provided by the poles of a permanent magnet. The instrument has a uniform scale due to the radial field. Sensitivity is increased by the strong magnetic field and hair spring.

7. Galvanometers can be converted to read different ranges of currents and potential differences by suitably fitting appropriate resistances.

8. An induced e.m.f. is produced in a circuit whenever there is a change in the magnetic flux linked with the circuit. The induced e.m.f. in a coil rotating in a magnetic field can be increased by increasing: (i) the number of turns in the coil; (ii) the area of the coil; (iii) the speed of rotation of the coil; and (iv) the strength of the magnetic field.

9. Faraday's law of electromagnetic induction states that whenever there is a change in magnetic flux linked with a circuit, an e.m.f. is induced in the circuit. The induced e.m.f. is proportional to the rate of change of flux.

10. Lenz's law gives the direction of the induced e.m.f. The induced current or e.m.f. flows in such a direction as to oppose the motion producing it:

$$\varepsilon = -\frac{Nd\Phi}{dt}.$$

11. An a.c. generator is a device for converting mechanical energy into electrical energy. The current produced by this device is an alternating current. To obtain a d.c. from the generator, the slip-rings are replaced by a split ring cummutator. A d.c. generator works on the same principle as the a.c. generator except that the split ring commulator in a d.c. generator helps to produce a current flowing in one direction.

12. A transformer is a device for changing the voltage of an a.c. supply. A step up transformer converts low voltage to high voltage. A stepdown transformer brings down a high voltage to an appropriate low voltage. The transformer equation is:

$$\frac{V_s}{V_p} = \frac{N_s}{N_p} = \frac{I_p}{I_s}$$

where V_s, N_s and I_s are the e.m.f., number of turns and current in the secondary winding of the transformer, while V_p, I_p and N_p are the corresponding primary e.m.f., current and number of turns. Practical transformers suffer from: (i) Eddy current losses; (ii) Hysterisis losses; (iii) flux linkage losses; and (iv) heat losses. These losses which can be minimized, reduce the efficiency of the transformer.

$$\text{Efficiency} = \frac{\text{Power developed in the secondary coil}}{\text{Power developed in the primary coil}}$$

13. An induction coil is a device which enables us to obtain a high e.m.f. from a low d.c. voltage. An induction coil is frequently used in the manufacture of ignition systems of motor vehicles.

Exercise 33

1. Which of the options A-E is suitable for converting an a.c. generator to a d.c. generator?
   A. By replacing the armature with a commutator or split ring.
   B. By replacing the slip-rings with split-ring commutator.
   C. By replacing the slip rings with brushes.
   D. By replacing the brushes with split ring commutator.

2. Transformers are constructed so that energy losses are reduced to a minimum. This is achieved by
   I. laminating the core.
   II. using soft iron core.
   III. using coils of thin wire.

   A. I only   B. II only   C. I and II only
   D. I, II and III

3. A transformer is connected to a 220 V$_{rms}$ supply. The primary coil has 22 000 turns and the secondary voltage is found to be 20V; calculate the number of turns in the secondary coil.
   A. 44 000   B. 11000   C. 2000   D. 11

4. To convert an alternating current generator into a direct current generator, the
   A. coil is wound on a soft iron core.
   B. slip rings are replaced with split ring commutator.
   C. number is turns in the coil is decreased.
   D. strength of the magnetic field is decreased.

5. Which of the following statements about a generator is **not** correct?
   A. It requires an external supply of current to the coil.
   B. It may require the use of slip rings.
   C. It requires an external supply of energy to rotate the coil.
   D. It can produce alternating current.

6. Induced current depends on the:
   I. Number of turns in the coil.
   II. Strength of the magnet.
   III. Speed with which the magnet is plunged into the coil.
   A. I only   B. II only   C. I and II only
   E. II and III only

7. If a current carrying coil is mounted on a metal frame, the back e.m.f. induced in the coil causes
   A. inductance.   B. eddy currents.
   C. electromagnetism.   D. mangetic moment.

8. The force F experienced by a current carrying conductor parallel to the magnetic field B in Newtons is

   A. 0.   B. BIl.   C. $\frac{BI}{l}$.   D. $\frac{Bl}{I}$.

9. Two conductors carrying equal currents of 1A in the same direction are separated by 1m. The magnitude of the force per unit length between the conductors is (assume that μ_o $4 \times 10^{-7} Am^{-1}$)
   A. $+6.4 \times 10^{-8}N$ and attractive.
   B. -2×10^{-7} and repulsive.
   C. $+2 \times 10^{-7}$ and repulsive.
   D. -2×10^{-7} and attractive.

10. A galvanometer of resistance 5.0Ω has full scale deflection for a current of 100mA. How would its range be extended to 1.0A? by placing a resistance of
    A. $\frac{5}{9}\Omega$ in parallel. B. $\frac{9}{5}\Omega$ in series.
    C. $\frac{4}{5}\Omega$ in series.   E. $\frac{9}{5}\Omega$ in parallel.

11. A dynamo primarily converts
    A. potential energy into kinetic energy.
    B. mechanical energy into electrical energy.
    C. electrical energy into kinetic energy.
    D. kinetic energy into potential energy.

12. The principle of operation of an induction coil is based on
    A. Ohm's law.   B. Ampere's law.
    C. Faraday's law. D. Coulomb's law.

13. Which of the following ammeters may be used to measure alternating currents?
    I. Moving coil ammeter.
    II. Moving iron ammeter.
    III. Hot-wire ammeter.

    A. I and II only   B. II and III only
    C. I and III only   D. III only

14. The core of an efficient transformer should consist of laminated pieces of metal in order to
    A. increase the heat produced by increasing the eddy current.
    B. increase the heat produced by reducing the eddy current.
    C. reduce the heat by increasing the eddy current.
    D. reduce the heat by reducing the eddy current.

15. A galvanometer has a resistance of 5Ω. By using a shunt wire of resistance of 0.05Ω, the galvanometer could be converted to an ammeter capable of reading 2A. What value of current flows through the galvanometer?
    A. 2mA   B. 10mA   C. 20mA
    D. 25mA   E. 30mA

16. The magnetic flux in a coil having 200 turns changes at the time rate of $0.08Wbs^{-1}$, the induced e.m.f. in the coil is

A. 250.0V B. 16.0V C. 2.5V D. 1.6V

17. A transformer which can produce 8V from a $240 V_{rms}$ a.c. supply has an efficiency of 80%. If the current in the secondary coil is 15A. Calculate the current in the primary coil.
    A. 0.500A   B. 0.625A   C. 1.600A
    D. 2.500A

18. If a current carrying coil is mounted on a metal frame, the back e.m.f. induced in the coil causes
    A. inductance.   B. eddy current.
    C. electromagnetism. D. inertia.

19. A current carrying conductor experiences a force when placed in a magnetic field because the
    A. conductor is magnetized.
    B. magnetic field of the current interacts with external field.
    C. force is due to motor principle.
    D. electric field intensity is equal to magnetic field strength.

20. Describe, with the aid of a well labelled diagram, an a.c. generator. Explain why the output is an alternating one.
    State:
    (i) What circumstances determine the instant when the peak value of the voltage occurs.
    (ii) The factors which affect the magnitude of the peak voltage.

21. With the aid of labelled diagrams, explain the action of:
    (a) an induction coil; and
    (b) a simple d.c. generator.

22. Describe a simple a.c. generator and how it is modified by a commutator to provide d.c. What are the advantages to be gained by using a.c. at high voltage when electrical power is to be transmitted over a long distance?

23. State the laws which determine the magnitude and direction of a current produced by electromagnetic induction. What is the effect on the e.m.f. of using a coil of:
    (a) greater number of turns?
    (b) greater area.?

24. A moving coil galvanometer has a resistance of 20Ω and gives a full-scale deflection of 1.5mA.
    (a) Calculate the potential difference across its terminals when this current is flowing.
    (b) How can the galvanometer be converted into a voltmeter?

25. Draw a diagram to show the magnetic field set up by a current flow up a vertical wire. Describe an experiment to show that a straight conductor carrying a current and placed in a magnetic field experiences a mechanical force. Name two practical applications of this principle.

26. Explain what is meant that the efficiency of a transformer is 88% and give two reasons why this can be so. Draw a labelled diagram of a transformer suitable for transforming from $240V_{ac}$ to $20V_{ac}$. Give details of the materials used in its structure.

27. What are eddy currents? Describe one application of their use. The secondary of a transformer supplies 12V when connected to $240V_{rms}$. If this transformer takes 2A from the mains when used to light six 12V 40W lamps in parallel, find its efficiency.

28. Write down an expression for the force on a charge, q, moving with a velocity, v perpendicular to a magnetic field, B. Hence, calculate the magnitude of a force on an electron moving with a speed of $2.5 \times 10^6 ms^{-1}$ perpendicular to the field of 0.5T.
    $[e = 1.602177 \times 10^{-19}C]$.

29. Sketch the form of the magnetic flux pattern due to a current flowing:
    (i) in a long solenoid
    (ii) through two long straight parallel wires when the direction of the current are opposite (Neglect the earth's magnetic field).
    (iii) Draw a labelled diagram of an electric bell and explain how it works.

30. State the Faraday's laws of electromagnetic induction and Lenz law. Describe an experiment to verify the laws of electromagnetic induction.

31. Explain the terms:
    (i) step up transformer; and,
    (ii) step down transformer. Why are the coils of a transformer wound on an iron core? A transformer is required to give 15V from the 220Vrms mains supply. If the primary coil has 20 000 turns, calculate the number of turns in the secondary coil.

32. Sketch the field due to two current-carrying straight wires close to each other:
    (a) when the current in both wires flow in the same direction;
    (b) when the current flow in opposite directions. State whether the acting forces on the pairs of wire are attractice of repulsive.

33. (a) Describe with the aid of a labelled diagram, the mode of operation of a moving coil galvanometer.
    (b) State three methods by which the sensitivity of a galvanometer can be increased.
    (c) State two essential differences between a moving coil galvanometer and a d.c. generator.
    (d) Explain the term eddy current and state two devices in which the currents are applied.

34. (a) Draw a well labelled diagram illustrating the principle of a step-up transformer and explain how it works.
    (b) State three ways by which energy is lost in a transformer and how they can be minimized.
    (c) If a transformer is used to light a lamp rated 40W 240V from a 400V a.c. supply; calculate the:
    (i) ratio of the number of turns of the primary coil to the secondary coil in the transformer;
    (ii) current drawn from the mains circuit if the efficiency of the transformer is 90%.

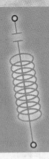

SIMPLE ALTERNATING CURRENT (A.C.) CIRCUITS

Chapter 34

Introduction

We have studied direct currents produced by cells, batteries and other sources in chapter 7. The defects of such sources were also outlined. During the 1880s, George Westinghouse invented the alternating current (a.c.) with sinusoidally (sine wave) varying voltage and current employing the use of transformer which can be used to step up and down *a.c.* which *d.c.* cannot, low voltages are safer for consumer use but high voltages with low currents are best for long distance power transmission to minimise heat losses in cables.

Most present-day household and industrial power distribution systems operate with alternating current. Any appliance plugged into a wall outlet uses *a.c.* and even many battery powered devices such as radio receivers, cordless phones make use of *d.c.* power supplies derived from *a.c.* mains source; circuits in modern communication equipments also make extensive use of *a.c.*

In this chapter, we shall learn how resistors, inductors and capacitors behave in circuits with sinusoidally varying voltages and currents.

34.1 Nature of alternating currents and voltages

We define an alternating current or voltage as one which varies with time about a mean value. It is produced by an *a.c.* source, a coil of wire rotating with angular velocity, as in a magnetic field as described in chapter 33. Such a source develops an alternating e.m.f. The term *a.c.* source is used for any device that supplies a sinusoidally varying voltage (potential difference) or current.

The usual circuit symbol for an *a.c.* source is shown in fig. 34.1.

Fig. 34.1 Symbol for an a.c. source.

A sinusoidal voltage is described by a function such as $V = V_p \sin\omega t$

Where V is the instantaneous potential difference (p.d.) at a time, t. V_p is the maximum or peak p.d. which is called voltage amplitude and ω is the angular frequency equal to $2\pi f$, where f is the frequency of alternation expressed in hertz. In Nigeria and Ghana, the electric power distribution systems use a frequency, $f = 50$ hertz (Hz) and ($\omega = 314$ rad s^{-1}). Similarly a sinusoidal current is described as

$$i = I_p \sin\omega t \qquad 34.1$$

where i is the instantaneous current and I_p is the peak or maximum current termed current amplitude.

34.2 Graphical representation

If an *a.c.* current and voltage are of the same frequency but not in step (phase) in a circuit, there is a phase difference, ϕ between them, then the equations for current and voltage are respectively.

$$i = I_p \sin \omega t \text{ and } V = V_p \sin(\omega t + \phi). \qquad 34.2$$

The graphs of *a.c.* current and voltage are illustrated in Fig. 34.2(a) and fig 34.2(b) respectively.

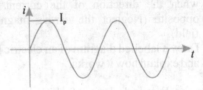

Fig. 34.2 (a) Graph of i against t .

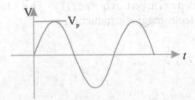

Fig. 34.2(b) Graph of V against t.

Fig. 34.3 below illustrates the graph of *a.c.* current and voltage with a phase difference, ϕ.

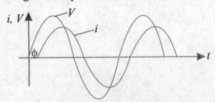

Fig. 34.3 Graph of i, V and ϕ.

34.3 Peak and root mean square value of a.c.

Important definitions in a.c. theory

Consider the sine wave shown in Fig. 34.4. Let it represent the variation of current with time (or voltage with time) alternating between two extremes.

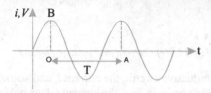

Fig. 34.4 Sine wave representation of a.c. Current/voltage.

The period T of the variation is the time for one complete alternation (oscillation), OA The frequency, f, is the number of alternations (times the current changes direction) per second $f = \frac{1}{T}$ s^{-1} (Hz) or number of complete cycles per second. The peak value OB is the maximum displacement from O (I_p or V_p).

The average value of the current or voltage is zero.

The rectified average value or half average value is
$$\frac{2I_p}{\pi} = 0.637 I_p.$$

The root-mean-square (r.m.s.) value is a most useful way to describe a quantity that varies either positively or negatively. It is also termed the effective value. This is the square root of the mean value of the squares of the current or voltage taken over a whole cycle.

Consider the d.c. power, P_{dc}, developed across a load resistance, R, in a d.c. circuit of Fig. 34.5(a) given as: $P_{dc} = I_{dc}^2 R$.

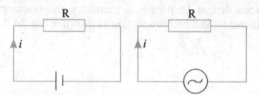

Fig. 34.5(a) A d.c. circuit   fig. 34.5(b) An a.c. circuit

and for the a.c. power P_{ac} across the same value of resistor, R, in an a.c. circuit of Fig. 34.5(b) such that
$$P_{ac} = i^2 R$$
$$= I_p^2 R \sin^2 \omega t.$$
If $P_{ac} = P_{dc}$, the current flowing in the a.c. circuit is the effective (r.m.s.) current.

$$i^2 = I_p^2 \sin^2 \omega t$$
$$= I_p^2 \left[\frac{1}{2} - \frac{1}{2} \cos 2\omega t \right]$$

and since the average value of cos2ωt is zero

$$I_{effective}^2 = I_{r.m.s.}^2 = \frac{I_p^2}{2} \qquad\qquad 34.3$$

$$I_{r.m.s.} = \frac{I_p}{\sqrt{2}} = 0.707 I_p \text{ (root mean square value of a}$$
sinusoidal current)
$$V_{r.m.s.} = \frac{V_p}{\sqrt{2}} = 0.707 V_p \text{ (root mean square value of a}$$
sinusoidal voltage)

In Nigeria, the voltage supply (mains voltage) is $240 V_{r.m.s.}$ and so its peak value is 340V.

The r.m.s value of an alternating current is defined as that value of steady current which would dissipate heat at the same rate in a given resistance.

$$I_{r.m.s.} = \frac{I_p}{\sqrt{2}}$$
$$= 0.707 I_p.$$

The d.c. meters such as the moving coil type are not used to measure a.c. currents/voltages because of their alternating nature. However, hot wire ammeters, moving iron ammeters and rectified meters are included in a.c. circuits to measure their effective values. i.e. the average values of the squares of the currents/voltages.

Example 34.1

The current drawn from a personal computer is 2.0A from a $220V_{rms}$ – 50Hz line. Calculate the:

(a) average current;

(b) r.m.s. current;

(c) amplitude current;

(d) half average value of the current.

Solution

(a) the average of any sinusoidal current alternating over any number of cycles is zero.

(b) 2.0A is the r.m.s. value of the current.

(c) from equation $I_{rms} = \frac{I_p}{\sqrt{2}}$

amplitude current $I_p = \sqrt{2} \times 2 = 2.83 A$

(d) half average value of current
$$I_{av} = 0.637 I_p = 0.637 \times 2.83 = 1.80 A.$$

34.4 Alternating currents in resistors, inductors and capacitors (R.L.C.)

Resistor in an a.c. circuit

Let us consider a resistor with resistance R through which a sinusoidal current, i, flows given by:

$i = I_p \sin \omega t$, where I_p is the peak value. The circuit is shown in Fig. 34.6.

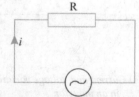

Fig. 34.6 An a.c. circuit with a resistor.

From Ohm's law discussed in 31.3, the instantaneous potential diffence (p.d.) across R is:

$V_R = iR = (I_pR) \sin \omega t$.

The maximum voltage V_R is the voltage amplitude.
Hence, $V_R = I_pR$
and $V_R = V_R \sin \omega t$.

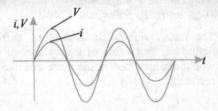

Fig. 34.7(a) Variation of current and voltage in a resistor.

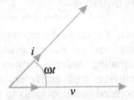

Fig. 34.7(b) Rotating phasors of current and voltage.

Fig. 34.7(a) shows the variation of current and voltage in a resistor. As phasors rotate, shown in Fig. 34.7(b) current and voltage remain in phase i.e. the maximum, zero and minimum values of current and voltage are reached at the same instant of time.

Inductor in an a.c. circuit

A pure inductive circuit as in Fig 34.8(a) behaves quite differently from the one containing resistance alone. The resistor in Fig 34.6 is replaced by a pure inductor (a coil of wire) with self inductance, L and zero resistance.

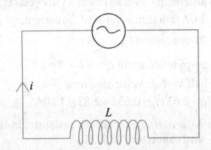

Fig. 34.8(a) Inductive circuit

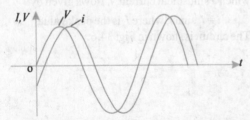

Fig. 34.8(b) Current and voltage variation in an inductor.

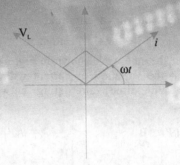

Fig. 34.8(c) Current and voltage phasors

In the inductive circuit, the current i, and voltage V, are not in phase; in fact, the current i, lags behind by $90°$ ($\frac{\pi}{2}$ radians) as in the phase vector diagram in Fig 34.8(c).

If $i = I_p \sin \omega t$

$V_i = L\frac{di}{dt} = \omega L I_p \cos \omega t$

$= \omega L I_p \sin(\omega t + \frac{\pi}{2})$

$\therefore V_i = V_L \sin(\omega t + \phi)$

where $\phi = \frac{\pi}{2}$ is the phase angle for a pure inductor.

The amplitude of the inductor voltage, V_L is given as $V_L = I_p \omega L$.

We define inductive reactance:

$$X_L = \omega L = 2\pi f L \qquad 34.4$$

Hence, $V_L = I_p X_L$ is the amplitude of voltage across a pure inductor in an a.c. circuit.

> Reactance is the opposition to the flow of current in an a.c. circuit containing either a capacitor or an inductor.

From the expression for inductive reactance, X_L, it is seen that as frequency, f, increases, the reactance increases in direct proportion as shown in Fig 34.9.

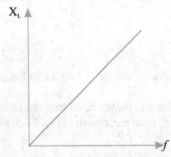

Fig 34.9 Graph of X_L versus f

Example 34.2
If the current amplitude in a pure inductor in a radio receiver is $120\mu A$ when the voltage amplitude is $3.0V$ at a frequency of $1.2MHz$.
Calculate the:(i) inductive reactance (ii) inductance.

Solution

The voltage across the inductor $V_L = IX_L$ where X_L is the inductive reactance:

$$X_L = \frac{3}{120 \times 10^{-6}} = 2.5 \times 10^4 \Omega$$

From equation 34.4,

$$X_L = \omega L = 2\pi f L$$

$$L = \frac{X_L}{2\pi f} = \frac{2.5 \times 10^4}{2 \times \pi \times 1.2 \times 10^6} = 3.3\text{mH}$$

Capacitor in an a.c. circuit

When a capacitor is connected to an a.c. voltage supply as in Fig. 34.10(a), the plates of the capacitor are continually charging and discharging and so a.c. current flows in the circuit.

The current and voltage are not in phase (out of step). Current is 90° ($\frac{\pi}{2}$ radians) ahead of the voltage.

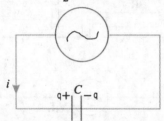

Fig. 34.10(a) A.C. current in a capacitive circuit .

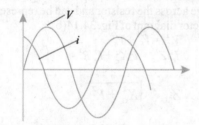

Fig. 34.10(b) Variation of current and voltage in the capacitive circuit.

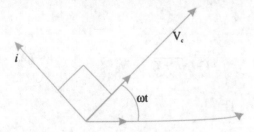

Fig 34.10(c) Current and voltage phasors.

If a.c. supply voltage, V, is given as: $V = V_p \sin\omega t$
The charge, q, on the capacitor plates is:

$q = CV = CV_p \sin\omega t$ (where C is the capacitance of the capacitor)

but current $i = \dfrac{dq}{dt} = \omega CV_p \cos\omega t$

$$i = \omega CV_p \sin\left(\omega t + \frac{\pi}{2}\right)$$

Here, current leads voltage by 90° or $\frac{\pi}{2}$ radians. The capacitive reactance, X_c, is given as:

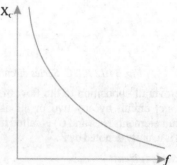

$$X_c = \frac{V_c}{i_c}$$
$$= \frac{V_p \sin\omega t}{\omega CV_p \sin(\omega t + \frac{\pi}{2})}$$
$$= \frac{1}{\omega C} \qquad 34.5$$

Therefore $V_c = I_p X_c$ is the amplitude of voltage across a capacitor in an a.c. circuit and from the graph of reactance X_c versus frequency f in Fig. 34.11. X_c is inversely proportional both to frequency f and capacitance, C. As frequency increases, the capacitive reactance decreases i.e. it blocks low frequency current but allows high frequency current to pass.

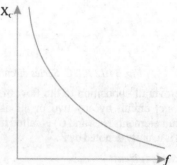

Fig. 34.11 Graph of X_c versus frequency

Table 34.1
Circuit elements with alternating current

Circuit element	Amplitude relation	Circuit quantity	Phase of V
Resistor	$V_R = IR$	R	In phase with i
Inductor	$V_L = IX_L$	$X_L = \omega L$	Leads i by 90°
Capacitor	$V_c = IX_c$	$X_c = 1/\omega C$	Lags i by 90°

Example 34.3

A 400Ω resistor is connected in series with a 5.0μF capacitor. The voltage across the resistor

$$V_R = 2 \sin(100\pi)t.$$ Calculate the:

(a) current in the circuit;

(b) capacitive reactance of the capacitor;

(c) voltage across the capacitor.

Solution

(a) Since it is a series circuit, the same current flows through the circuit elements.

$$i = \frac{V_R}{R} = 5 \times 10^{-3} \sin(100\pi)t \ \text{A}$$

(b) from equation 34.5,

Capacitive reactance $X_c = \dfrac{1}{\omega C}$ where $\omega = 100\pi$

$$= \frac{10^6}{100 \times \frac{22}{7} \times 5} = \frac{100}{15.71} \times 10^2$$

$$= 6.36 \times 10^2 \Omega$$

(c) voltage across a capacitor of capacitance, C

$V_c = I X_c = 3.18 \sin\left(100\pi t - \frac{\pi}{2}\right) V$

Note: Current leads voltage by $\frac{\pi}{2}$ radians in a capacitive circuit.

34.5 The L.R., R.C. and L.R.C. series circuit

Many *a.c.* circuits used in practical electronic systems involve resistance, inductive reactance and capacitive reactance. A simple example is a series circuit containing a resistor R, an inductor L, and a capacitor C and an *a.c.* p.d. as illustrated in Fig. 34.12.

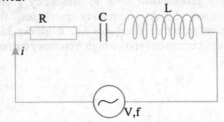

Fig. 34.12 R.L.C. Series circuit

> The overall opposition to the flow of current in the a.c. circuit by any two or all of the three circuit elements (R, L and C) is called **impedance** and is usually denoted by Z.

L.R. series circuit

The *L.R.* circuit is shown in Fig 34.13(a).

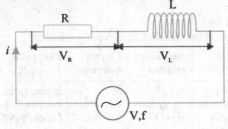

Fig. 34.13(a)

The same current flows through the series circuit and therefore

$V_L = I_p X_L$

$V_R = I_p R$

But since the voltages across the resistor and the inductor are not in phase the composite voltage V_{LR} will be a vector sum of V_L and V_R as in the Fig 34.13(b).

$V_{LR}^2 = V_L^2 + V_R^2$

$I_p^2 Z_{RL}^2 = I_p^2 X_L^2 + I_p^2 R^2$

$$Z_{RL} = \sqrt{X_L^2 + R^2} \qquad 34.6$$

Z_{RL} is the impedance offered by the combination of the inductor and the resistor in an *a.c* circuit.

The phase angle ϕ_{RL} between current and voltage in a *R.L.* series circuit is

$$\phi_{RL} = \tan^{-1}\left(\frac{X_L}{R}\right) \qquad 34.7$$

(i.e. the angle whose tangent is $\frac{X_L}{R}$)

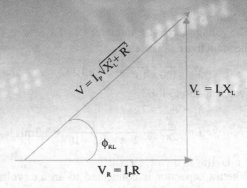

Fig. 34.13(b) Vector representation of the L.R. series circuit

R.C. series circuit

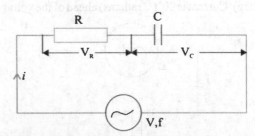

Fig.34.14(a) R.C. series circuit

The voltage across the capacitor lags behind the voltage across the resistor and can be represented by the vector diagram of Fig. 34.14(b).

$V_{RC}^2 = V_C^2 + V_R^2$

$I_p^2 Z_{RC}^2 = I_p^2 X_C^2 + I_p^2 R^2$

$$Z_{RC} = \sqrt{X_C^2 + R^2} \qquad 34.8$$

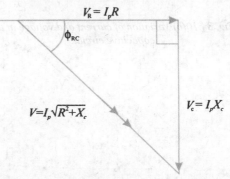

Fig. 34.14(b) Vector sum of V_R and V_c

Z_{RC} is the impedance offered by the combination of a capacitor and a resistor in an *a.c.* circuit. The phase angle ϕ_{RC} between current and voltage in the R–C series circuit is given as

$$\phi_{RC} = \tan^{-1}\left(\frac{X_c}{R}\right) \qquad 34.9$$

L.C. series circuit

See the circuit in Fig 34.15(a).

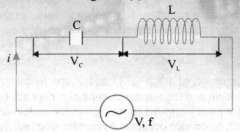

Fig. 34.15(a) L.C series circuit

The voltages across the inductor and the capacitor V_L and V_C as indicated in fig. 34.15(b) are $180°(\pi -$ radians) out of phase and when added vectorially gives

$$V^2 = (V_L - V_C)^2$$
$$V = V_L - V_C$$
and $Z_{LC} = X_L - X_C$

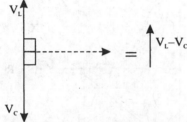

Fig. 34.15(b) Vector representation of V_L and V_C

Example 34.4

In the series circuit of Fig. 34.13(a), $R = 300\Omega$ and $L = 60mH$, $V = 50V$ and $\omega = 100\pi$ rads^{-1}.
Calculate the:

(i)   inductive, X_L;

(ii)   impedance, Z_{LR};

(iii) phase angle between the voltage and current, ϕ.

Solution
From equation 34.4,

(i) $X_L = \omega L = 100\pi \times 60 \times 10^{-3} = 6\pi$ ohms

(ii) $Z_{RL} = \sqrt{X_L^2 + R^2} = \sqrt{(300)^2 + (6\pi)^2}$

        $= 300.59\Omega$

(iii) $\phi = \tan^{-1} \dfrac{6\pi}{300} = 3.6°$.

34.6 Vector diagram of series R.L.C. circuit

The voltages V_R, V_L and V_C across R, L, and C respectively in Fig. 34.16(a) would be summed vectorially to give the resultant voltage given by:

$$V_{RLC}^2 = (V_{L2} - V_C)^2 + V_R^2$$
$$I^P Z^{RLC} = I^P (X_L - X_C)^2 + I^P R^2$$

$$Z_{RLC} = \sqrt{(X_L - X_C)^2 + R^2} \qquad 34.10$$

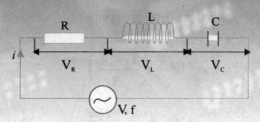

Fig. 34.16(a) R.L.C. circuit

Example 34.5

For the circuit in Fig. 34.14(a), $R = 300\Omega$ and $C = 100\mu F$, $V = 50V$, and $f = 50Hz$. Calculate the:

(i)   capacitive reactance, X_c.

(ii)   impedance Z_{RC}.

(iii) phase angle between the voltage and current in the circuit.

Solution
From equation 34.5,

(i) $X_C = \dfrac{1}{\omega C} = \dfrac{1}{2\pi f C} = \dfrac{1}{100\pi \times 10^{-4}}$

        $= \dfrac{10}{\pi} \times 10\Omega$

        $= 31.83\Omega$

(ii) $Z_{RC} = \sqrt{R^2 + X_C^2}$

        $= 301.68\Omega$

(iii) $\phi = \tan - \dfrac{X_C}{R} = -10.05°$

(i)

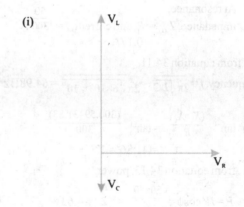

(ii)

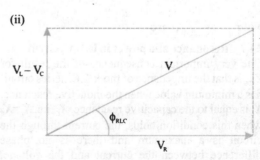

Fig. 34.16 (b) –Vector summation

The phase angle ϕ_{RLC} between current and voltage in a R-L-C series circuit is given as

$$\phi_{RLC} = \tan^{-1}\left(\frac{X_L - X_C}{R}\right)$$

$$= \tan^{-1}\left(\frac{\omega L - 1/\omega C}{R}\right) \qquad 34.11$$

If $X_L > X_C$, ϕ_{RLC} is positive and voltage leads current and the circuit is inductive.

If $X_L < X_C$, ϕ_{RLC} is negative and voltage lags current and the circuit is capacitive.

Example 34.6

In the series circuit of Fig. 34.16(a). Suppose $R = 300\Omega$ $L = 60$mH and $C = 100\mu$F, $V = 50$V and $\omega = 100\pi$ rads^{-1}. Calculate the:

(i)   impedance, Z, of the circuit;

(ii) current and frequency at resonance;

(iii) phase angle between voltage and current;

(iv) power absorbed in the circuit.

Solution

(i) From equation 34.10,

$$Z_{RLC} = \sqrt{(X_L - X_C)^2 + R^2}$$

$$= \sqrt{(300.59 - 31.83)^2 + (300)^2}$$

$$= 402.78\Omega$$

(ii) At resonance,

impedance, $Z_{RLC} = R$, and current, $I = \dfrac{50}{300}$ A

$$= 0.17\text{A}$$

and from equation 34.11,

Frequency, $f = \dfrac{1}{2\pi\sqrt{LC}} = \dfrac{1}{2\pi\sqrt{6\times10^{-2}\times10^{-4}}} = 64.98$Hz

(iii) $\tan^{-1}\dfrac{(X_L - X_C)}{R} = \tan^{-1}\dfrac{(300.59-31.83)}{300}$

$$= 41.86° = 42°$$

(iv) from equation 34.13, power

$$P = IV\cos\phi = \frac{50\times50}{Z} \times \frac{R}{Z} = 4.63\text{W}$$

Note: $I = \dfrac{V}{Z}$, $\cos\phi = \dfrac{R}{Z}$

34.7   Resonance and power in R.L.C. circuit

One very important consequence of the result for Z_{RLC} is that the impedance of the $R.L.C.$ series circuit has a minimum value when the inductive reactance, X_L is equal to the capacitive reactance, X_C, i.e. $X_L = X_C$ when this condition holds, the current through the circuit is a maximum and there is no phase difference between the current and the voltage, further the voltage of the circuit is the same as the source voltage.

This is known as the resonant condition for the

$L.C.R.$ series circuit.

Resonance occurs in an $L.C.R.$ series circuit when the inductive reactance has the same value as the capacitive reactance. The resonant frequency, f, is:

$$f_r = \frac{1}{2\pi\sqrt{LC}}$$

It is observed that X_L, X_c and Z are frequency dependent and the resonance condition depends on the frequency applied to a.c. for every series a.c. circuit, resonance occurs at a resonant frequency, f, when $X_L = X_C$.

That is, $2\pi f_r L = \dfrac{1}{2\pi f_r C}$

and is given by $f_r = \dfrac{1}{2\pi\sqrt{LC}}$ 34.12

Fig 34.17(a) shows how X_L, X_C, R, and Z vary with frequency, f and Fig. 34.17(b) shows the variation of current I_a versus frequency, f.

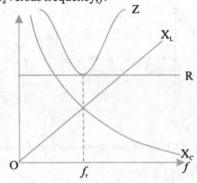

Fig. 34.17(a) Graph of variation of Z,X,R versus f

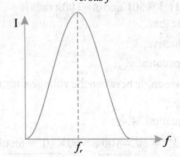

Fig. 34.17(b) Current versus frequency

Since at f_r, impedance, Z is minimum, current I is maximum but note that R does not change with frequency.

Effects of resonance

The resonance effects in an $L.C.$ circuit may be used to filter out selected regions of the frequency spectrum. Fig 34.18(a) shows an acceptor filter whose frequencies of $\dfrac{1}{2\pi\sqrt{LC}}$ will be passed by the filter. Fig. 34.18(b) shows a rejector filter where all frequencies except those of frequency $\dfrac{1}{2\pi\sqrt{LC}}$ will be passed by the filter.

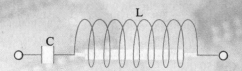

Fig. 34.18(a) Acceptor filter

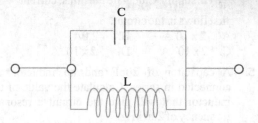

Fig. 34.18(b) Rejector filter

If the capacitor (or inductor) is variable, the circuit may be tuned to resonate at a particular frequency. This is used in tuning of amplifiers (selectivity) in radio receivers and television. The L.C. (tank) circuit is tuned to the incoming signal.

The aerial receives a broad band of frequencies and the capacitor is varied such that the circuit resonates at the frequency of the required station. A simple circuit for the tuner section of the radio receiver is shown in Fig. 34.19(a). The frequency response of a tuned circuit is shown in Fig. 34.19(b)

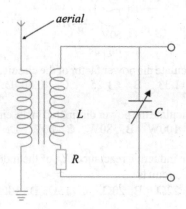

Fig. 34.19(a) Tuner circuit

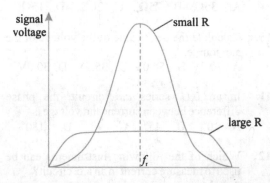

Fig. 34.19(b) Frequency response of a tuned circuit.

34.8 Power in a.c. circuits

Power absorbed in any a.c. circuit is given by the equation $P = iV$

$$P = I_p \sin(\omega t + \phi) . V_p \sin \omega t$$

It can be shown that the average power

$$P_{av} = V_p I_p \cos \phi \qquad 34.13$$

Where ϕ is the phase angle between the voltage and current in the circuit. If i and V are in phase, ϕ is zero as in a resistor and the average power P_{av} is equal to $P_{av} = V_{rms} I_{rms}$ and when i and V are out of phase as in inductive or capacitive circuit, $\phi = 90°$ and the average power $P_{av} = 0$.

The factor $\cos\phi$ is termed power factor and is given by $\cos\phi = R/Z$.

In general, capacitor and inductor absorb no power since $\cos\phi = 0$, but store electric energy, $\frac{1}{2}Cv^2$ and magnetic energy, $\frac{1}{2}LI^2$ respectively.

Summary

1. In an alternating current (*a.c.*) circuit, voltages and currents vary sinusoidally (like a sine wave) with time at a given angular frequency $\omega = 2\pi f$. The voltage and current amplitudes for individual circuit elements (resistor with resistance R inductor with inductance, L, and capacitor with capacitance, C) may be proportional but in general, there is a phase difference ϕ between voltage V and the current, i.
   $$V = V_p \sin \omega t \text{ and } i = I_p \sin(\omega t + \phi).$$
   where V_p is the peak/maximum voltage or voltage amplitude and I_p is the peak/maximum current or current amplitude.

2. The ratio of the voltage and current amplitudes is called the resistance, R, reactance, X or the Impedance Z in the resistive, capacitive/inductive and a series *L.R.C.* circuit respectively.
   $$R = \frac{V_R}{I},$$
   $$X_L = \frac{V_L}{I} = \omega L,$$
   $$X_c = \frac{V_c}{I} = \frac{1}{\omega C}$$
   $$Z_{RLC} = \frac{V_{RLC}}{I} = \sqrt{(X_L - X_C)^2 + R^2}$$

3. Sinusoidally, varying voltages and currents can be represented by rotating vectors called *phasors*.

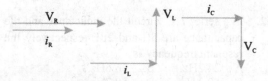

Fig. 34.20

The amplitudes of sinusoidally varying voltages and currents can be described in terms of root-mean-square (effective) values.

$$I_{rms} = \frac{I_p}{\sqrt{2}}$$
$$= 0.707 I_p$$

$$V_{rms} = \frac{V_p}{\sqrt{2}}$$
$$= 0.707 V_p$$

4. Hot wire ammeter and moving iron ammeter are used to measure values of *a.c.* currents. Opposition to flow of current in *a.c.* circuit by an inductor or capacitor is termed reactance, X. Inductive reactance, $X_L = \omega L = 2\pi f L$

capacitive reactance, $X_C = \frac{1}{\omega C} = \frac{1}{2\pi f C}$.

5. Capacitive and inductive circuits are termed reactive because they depend on frequency. If any two or all of the three elements R, L, and C offer opposition to the flow of current in an a.c. circuit, such opposition is termed impedance, Z

$$Z_{RL} = \sqrt{X_L^2 + R^2},$$
$$Z_{RC} = \sqrt{X_C^2 + R^2},$$
$$Z_{RLC} = \sqrt{(X_L - X_C)^2 + R^2}$$

6. When inductors and capacitors are combined in a series circuit, the effects of their reactances may cancel out i.e. $(X_L - X_C = 0)$ at particular frequencies leading to a minimum impedance in an *L.C.R.* series circuit equal to the value of resistance R and consequently maximum current. This effect is called resonance and can be used in tuned amplifiers of radio receivers and *TV*.

The resonant frequency, $f_r = \frac{1}{2\pi\sqrt{LC}}$

7. Power absorbed in an a.c. circuit is given by the expression $P_{ac} = I_{rms} V_{rms} \cos \phi = \frac{I_p V_p}{2} \cos \phi$,

where $\cos \phi = \frac{R}{Z}$ is the power factor.

In an inductive or a capacitive circuit, power absorbed is zero since $\cos \phi$ is zero because $\phi = \pm 90°$.

Exercise 34
1. Calculate the peak voltage of a mains supply of $240 V_{rms}$.
   A. 121V   B. 156V   C. 340V   D. 311V

2. In a series *L.C.* circuit the inductance and the capacitance are 5H and 2μF respectively the resonant frequency is
   A. 24.2Hz.   B. 36.6Hz.
   C. 50.3 Hz.   D. 58.7Hz.

3. An alternating current with a peak value of 5A passes through a resistor of 10.Ω. Calculate the rate at which energy is dissipated in the resistor.
   A. 250.0W   B. 125.0W
   C. 50.0W   D. 12.5W

4. A 5μF capacitor is placed across a $200 V_{rms}$, $\frac{100}{\pi}$ Hz supply. Calculate the r.m.s. current that flows in the circuit.
   A 2×10^5 A   B.   2.0A
   C. 2×10^{-1} A   D. 2×10^{-2} A

5. A capacitor of 20pF and an inductor are connected in series. Calculate the value of the inductor that will give the circuit a resonant frequency of 200 kHz.
   A. 0.03 mH   B.   0.3mH
   C. 3.0mH   D.   30.0mH

The diagram below illustrates an *a.c.* source of $50 V_{rms}$, $\frac{100}{\pi}$ Hz connected in series with an inductor of inductance L and a resistor of resistance R the effective current in the circuit is 2A and the p.d. across L and R are 30V and 40V respectively. Use this information to answer questions 6–10.

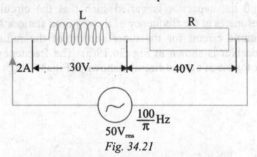

Fig. 34.21

6. Calculate the power factor of the circuit.
   A.   1.33   B.   1.25   C.   0.80   D.   0.60

7. Calculate the power dissipated in the circuit.
   A.   100W   B.   80W   C.   60W   D.   20W

8. The inductive reactance, X_L, of the inductor in the circuit is
   A.   22Ω.   B.   20Ω.   C.   15Ω.   D.   10Ω.

9. The impedance of the circuit is
   A.   35Ω.   B.   25Ω.   C.   20Ω.   D.   15Ω.

10. Calculate the peak value of the voltage of the a.c. source.
    A.   70.7V   B.   50.0V   C.   35.4V   D.   30.0V

11. In an *L.C.* series *a.c.* circuit, the phase difference between current and voltage is
    A.   0°.   B.   45°.   C.   90.   D.   180°.

12. Which of the following instruments can be used to measure current in an a.c. circuit?
    A.   Moving coil ammeter.

B. Tangent galvanometer.
C. Hot wire ammeter.
D. Moving coil galvanometer.

13. In a capacitive circuit with an a.c. source of variable frequency, which of the graphs respresents the variation of capacitive reactance, X_c, and frequency, f_o?

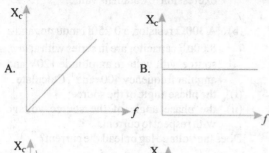
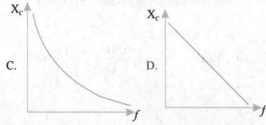

A.

B.

C.

D.

Fig. 34.22

14. The vector diagram of the relationship of I_L and V_L for an a.c. circuit containing a pure inductor is

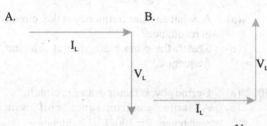
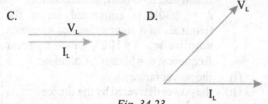

A.

B.

C.

D.

Fig. 34.23

15. In an $L.C.R.$ series circuit with an a.c. source and variable frequency, which of the following statements is **not** correct at resonance?
A. Impedance is R.
B. Voltage across R is the source voltage.
C. Impedance is maximum.
D. The phase difference is zero.

16. Average power dissipated in $L.C.R.$ series circuit is given by the expression

A. $I^2 X_c$. B. $I^2 X_L$. C. IV. D. $I^2 R$.

17.

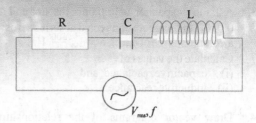

Fig. 34.24

The diagram above is a series $R.L.C.$ circuit, the current in the circuit at resonance is

A. $\dfrac{V}{R}$. B. $\dfrac{V}{\omega L}$. C. $\dfrac{V}{\omega^2 LC}$. D. $\dfrac{V}{RLC}$.

18. At what frequency will an inductor with inductance of 10.0mH have a resistance of 800 ohm?

A. $\dfrac{4}{\pi} \times 10^4$Hz   B. $\dfrac{4}{\pi} \times 10^3$Hz

C. $\dfrac{40}{\pi}$ Hz   D. 1.6π Hz

19. What is the peak value of current whose r.m.s. value is 10A?
A. 7.1A B. 10.0A C. 14.1A D. 20.0A

20. At what frequency is the reactance of a capacitor with $C = 100\mu F$ be equal to the reactance of an inductor with $L = 10$mH?

A. $\dfrac{100}{\pi}$ Hz   B. $\dfrac{250}{\pi}$Hz

C. $\dfrac{370}{\pi}$ Hz   D. $\dfrac{500}{\pi}$Hz

21. (a) Explain "electrical resonance" in an $L.C.R.$ series circuit.
    (b) In an $L.R.C.$ series circuit, $R = 250\Omega$
        $L = 0.40$H and $C = 0.02\mu F$.
    Calculate:
    (i) The resonant angular frequency of the circuit.
    (ii) The value of the current if the source voltage is $30.0V_{rms}$ at resonance.
    (iii) tThe phase difference between current and voltage at resonance.

22. An instantaneous alternating voltage is expressed by the equation
$V = 7.1 \sin(1000t - \dfrac{\pi}{6})$
and the instantaneous alternating current is
$i = 3.5 \sin 1000t$
Sketch the variational graph of the voltage and the current and determine:
(i) The effective value of the current.

283

(ii) The impedance of the circuit.
(iii) The phase difference between the current and the source voltage.

23. A 0.50μF capacitor, a 30.0 ohm resistor and a 0.050H inductor are connected in series across a voltage source of e.m.f. 50V$_{rms}$, $\frac{100}{\pi}$ Hz. Calculate the values of:
(i) capacitive reactance; and
(ii) inductive reactance.

24. Draw vector diagrams of the relationship between I and V for an a.c. circuit containing:
(a) a **pure** inductor
(b) a capacitor
(c) a resistor
Explain the need for qualifying (a) as pure.

25. A circuit consists of an inductor, a capacitor and a lamp connected in series across an a.c. source of variable frequency.
(i) Draw the circuit.
(ii) Discuss the variation in the brightness of the lamp as the frequency is increased from zero. Explain the phenomenon.
(iii) How can the circuit be modified, such that the lamp does not go dim?

26. (a) Draw circuits with:
(i) a resistor with a resistance, R;
(ii) a capacitor with a capacitance, C; and
(iii) an inductor with an inductance, L, connected across an a.c. source in turn.
(b) Sketch the graphs of instantaneous voltage and current for (a) (ii) and (a) (iii).
(c) The voltage and current in the circuit of a (iii) is given respectively as:
$V = 7\sin(100\pi t)$
$i = 3.5\sin(100\pi t + \frac{\pi}{2})$
Determine the:
(i) frequency of the alternating voltage;
(ii) effective value of the current;
(iii) phase difference between current and voltage;
(iv) reactance of the circuit.

27. (a) Explain the following in relation to alternating current circuits:
(i) impedance;
(ii) reactance; and
(iii) power factor.
(b) for an $L.C.R.$ series circuit, $R = 300\Omega$, $L = 60$mH and $C = 0.5\mu$F, source e.m.f $= 50$V$_{rms}$ and $\omega = 5000$ rads^{-1}.
(i) Draw the circuit containing the circuit elements. Hence, find:
(ii) the impedance Z of the circuit;
(iii) the phase angle between the current and

voltage in the circuit;
(iv) the voltage across each element in the circuit.

28. (a) Draw and discuss the variational graphs of Z, X_L, X_C and R versus frequency. Locate on the graphs the reasonable frequency, f_r and write down the expression to obtain its value.

(b) A 300Ω resistor, a 0.250H inductor and a 8.00μF capacitor are in series with an $a.c.$ source with voltage amplitude 120V and angular frequency 400 rads^{-1}. Calculate :
(i) the phase angle of the source;
(ii) the phase angle of the source voltage with respect to current.
Does the voltage lag or lead the current?

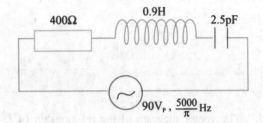

29. Consider the $L.C.R.$ series circuit below.
Fig. 34.25
(a) At what angular frequency is the circuit in resonance?
(b) Sketch the phasor diagram at resonant frequency.

30. (a) Define power factor in an a.c. circuit.
(b) A large electromagnet coil with resistance, $R = 300\Omega$, an inductance, $L = 4.30$H is connected across the terminals of a source that has a voltage amplitude, $V = 180$V and angular frequency, $\omega = 50$ rads^{-1}. Calculate:
(i) the power factor;
(Ii) the power delivered by the source.

31. In an $L.C.R.$ series circuit, $R = 300\Omega$, $L = 0.9$H and $C = 2.0\mu$F and the supply has an r.m.s. voltage of 240V at a frequency of 50Hz.

Calculate the:
(i) inductive reactance;
(ii) capacitive reactance;
(iii) combined reactance of both the capacitor and inductor;
(iv) impedance of the circuit; and
(v) phase angle between the current and the source voltage.

32. A 150mH inductor is connected in series with a variable capacitor which can be varied between 500pF and 20pF. Calculate the maximum and minimum frequencies to which the circuit can be tuned.

33. Calculate the magnitude and determine the phase of the current when the following are connected to a $200V_{rms}$, 50Hz supply, a:
  (a) coil of inductance 0.2H and negligible resistance;
  (b) capacitor of 60μf;
  (c) coil of inductance 0.2H and a resistance of 20Ω.

34. What is meant by r.m.s. value of alternating current? A capacitor with capacitance $C = 20\mu F$ is connected to a source of alternating e.m.f. of r.m.s. value 240V and frequency 50Hz.
  (a) Calculate the r.m.s. value of the current.
  (b) If this capacitor is replaced by an inductor of inductance, $L,$ of 60mH, calculate the r.m.s. value of the resulting current.

35.

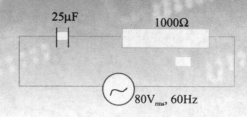

Fig. 34.26

Calculate the following in the series circuit shown above:
  (i) reactance of the capacitor;
  (ii) impedance of the circuit;
  (iii) current through the circuit;
  (iv) voltage across the capacitor; and
  (v) average power absorbed in the circuit.

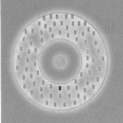

MODELS OF ATOM AND NUCLEAR PHYSICS

Chapter 35

35.1 Models of atom

J.J. Thomson discovered the electron and measured its specific charge, $\frac{e}{m}$ (ratio of electron charge, e to electron mass, m)in 1897. The experiments performed showed that almost all of the mass of the atom was associated with the positive charge, not the electrons. With atomic size of diameter $10^{-10}\,m$, only hydrogen contains one electron. Then Thomson proposed that the atom consisted of a sphere of positive charge of $10^{-10}\,m$ diameter with electrons embedded in it. In his model, the positive charge and the negative electrons are distributed throughout the whole of the atom as shown in fig. 35.1. In his own experiment, alpha particle is scattered only through a small angle.

From the Rutherford scattering experiments, it was established that the atom has a nucleus, a very small but very dense structure with diameter $10^{-14}\,m$ and which occupies $10^{-12}\,m$ of the total volume of the atom but that it contains all the positive charge, at least 99.5% of total mass of the atom. An alpha particle can be scattered through a large angle by dense positively charged nucleus. He also suggested that the electrons revolve in orbits about the nucleus.

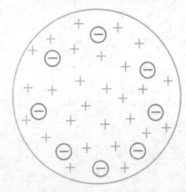

Fig. 35.1 Thomson's model of the atom.

Limitation

According to classical electromagnetic (*e-m*) theory, any accelerating electric charge radiates *e-m* radiation, and the energy of the orbiting electron should therefore decrease continuously, and its orbit should decrease in size until the electron collapses into the nucleus and the frequency of the *e-m* waves should be equal to the frequency of revolution of the particle emitting continuous spectrum, and not the

line spectrum observed. Furthermore, the prediction that atoms were unstable could not be justified experimentally.

In Niels Bohr's proposal, he postulated that the electron moves round the nucleus in certain stable orbits without emitting radiation and a definite amount of energy is attributed to each stable orbit. He also postulated that electron cannot lose energy in continuous fashion but in discrete jumps.

Energy is only radiated when the electron jumps from one orbit to another. The energy is radiated in the form of a photon of light with energy, E, and frequency, f, given by:

$$E_2-E_1 = \Delta E = hf \qquad 35.1$$

where h is the planck's constant ($h = 6.6\,26 \times 10^{-34}$ Js). This model accounts for the line spectrum. He also found that the angular momentum of electrons was in discrete values (quantized) and the magnitude for the electron is:

$$m_e v_n r_n = \frac{nh}{2\pi} \qquad 35.2$$

Where m_e is the mass of the electron,
$\quad v$ is the velocity,
$\quad r$ is the radius of the orbit,
and $n = 1,2,3\ldots$ corresponding to the value of the permitted orbit.

For the Bohr's model of the hydrogen atom, the proton is assumed to be at rest, the electron revolves in a circular orbit of radius r_n with speed v^n. This model gave the atomic diameter as $10^{-10}\,m$ which is consistent with other models.

In summary, the Bohr's model:
(i) explains the existence of line spectra and predicts accurately the frequencies of lines in the hydrogen spectrum,
(ii) offers an explanation for absorption spectra,
(iii) ensures the stability of atoms by proposing that the ground state is the lowest energy state,
(iv) predicts accurately the ionization energy for hydrogen as -13.6eV.

Ionization energy is the energy required to remove the electron completely from the atom. This ionization process corresponds to a transition from the ground state (n=1) to infinitely large orbit radius with $n = \infty$.

Limitations:
Bohr's model predicted the energy levels of hydrogen completely but:
(i) provides no insight into what happens during transition from one orbit to another;
(ii) cannot be extended to multi-electron atoms i.e. atoms with two or more electrons;
(iii) an electron moving in one of Bohr's circular orbits form a current loop and should produce a magnetic moment-but a hydrogen atom in the ground state has no magnetic moment due to orbital motion.

Electron cloud model: This model considers the atom as consisting of the nucleus with the electron moving rapidly around the nucleus and spending most of its time in high probability regions. Hence, the electron is not considered as a particle orbiting round the nucleus but as a wave with a specified energy having only a certain probability of being in a region in the space outside the nucleus. As such, the electron is visualised to spread out around the nucleus like a cloud. This is the electron-cloud model. Fig. 35.2 illustrates the density distribution of the electrons. The spherical boundary indicates where the electron is located and hence the probability of finding the electron within the boundary is high.

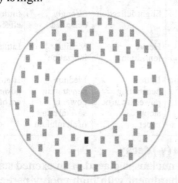

Fig. 35.2 Electron-cloud model

35.2   Atomic structure and properties

The basic building blocks of the nucleus are the proton and the neutron. In a neutral atom, the dense positively charged nucleus is surrounded by one electron for every proton in the nucleus. The proton and the neutron together make up what is called **nucleon**. The radii of most nuclei are represented by $r = r_o A$, where $r_o = 1.2 \times 10^{-15}$m. The proton which carries positive charge has a mass, m_p of 1.673×10^{-27}kg and a positive charge of $e^+ = 1.62 \times 10^{-19}C$. The electron which carries a negative charge has a mass, m_e, of 9.11×10^{-31}kg and an electronic charge $e^- = 1.62 \times 10^{-19}C$.

In a neutron atom of sodium, there are 11 protons and 11 electrons (i.e number of electrons equal number of protons).

The neutron carries no charge but its mass, m_n, is about the same as a proton $m_n = 1.675 \times 10^{-27}$ kg.

The number of protons in a nucleus is the proton (atomic) number and is designated by Z. The number of neutrons is called **neutron number,** N. The **nucleon number** (mass number), A is the sum of the number of proton, Z and the number of neutrons, N that is, $A = Z + N$.

A single nuclear species having specific values of both Z and A is called a nuclide. We denote the nuclide of X by ${}_Z^A X$ (when A = nucleon number, Z = proton number).

Table 35.1 illustrates a list of values of A, Z and N for a few nuclides.

Table 35.1 Values of A, Z and N for a few nuclides

Nuclide	Nucleon number A	Proton number Z	Neutron number $N=A-Z$
Hydrogen ${}_1^1 H$	1	1	0
Carbon ${}_6^{12} C$	12	6	6
Sodium ${}_{11}^{23} Na$	23	11	12
Copper ${}_{29}^{65} Cu$	65	29	36
Uranium ${}_{92}^{238} U$	238	92	146

The electron structure of an atom responsible for the chemical properties is determined by the charge, Z_e, of the nucleus.

35.3   Nuclides and isotopes

Nuclide of an element with the same proton number, Z, but different nucleon number, A, or neutron number, N, are called isotopes of that element.

The chemical properties of isotopes are the same but they have slightly different physical properties such as melting and boiling points, and diffusion rates.

In general, isotopes have the same position on the periodic table having the same chemical properties but different nuclear properties.

Uses of radioactive isotopes
These materials have a variety of uses, these include:
A.   Technological uses
  (i) dating of geological specimens using uranium,
  (ii) treatment of tumours,
  (iii) dating archaeological specimens using carbon-14,
  (iv) sterilization of foodstuffs,
  (v) liquid flow measurement,
  (vi) checking blood circulation and blood volume,
  (vii) checking silver contents in coins,
  (viii) testing for leaks in pipes.

B. Medical uses

(i) iodine – 131 with half-life of 8 days and activity of 8μ-curie taken as liquid or capsule;

(ii) technetium – 99 with half-life of 6 hours yield gamma-rays of 140eV energy;

(iii) cobalt – 60 sources of up to 10^4C;

(iv) iodine – 123 is suitable for medical studies.

Isotopes can be produced artificially by bombarding elements with neutrons, e.g.

$$^{34}_{16}S + ^{1}_{0}n \longrightarrow ^{35}_{16}S + \text{Energy}$$

Isotopes thus produced are unstable and decay with the emission of α-particles, β-particles and even γ-rays. They are called **radioisotopes**.

Radioisotopes or radioactive isotopes are produced artificially by bombarding elements with neutrons.

Table 35.2 List of some isotopes

$^{12}_{6}C$	$^{14}_{6}C$
$^{35}_{17}Cl$	$^{37}_{17}Cl$
$^{238}_{92}U$	$^{235}_{92}U$

35.4 Radioactivity

For over 2500 nuclides, only fewer than 300 are stable. The others are unstable structures that decay to form other nuclides by emitting particles and electromagnetic radiation through a process called *radioactivity*. The radioactive elements are those elements that spontaneously emit particles and radiation from their nucleus e.g. radium, radon, polonium, and uranium.

In this process, nothing is done to initiate it and nothing can be used to control it.

> Radioactivity is the spontaneous decay or disintegration of unstable nuclei of the atom of an element by the emission of alpha (α-) particles, beta (β–) particles and gamma (γ-) radiation with the production of energy.

Alpha (α-) decay

An alpha particle is a helium ($^{4}_{2}He$) nucleus with two protons and two neutrons bound together with a total spin of zero. When a nucleus emits an alpha particle, its neutron number, N, and proton number, Z, values each decrease by two and the nucleon number, A, decreases by four, moving it closer to a stable state.

For a nuclide

$$^{A}_{Z}X \longrightarrow ^{A-4}_{Z-2}Y + \alpha \text{- particle} (^{4}_{2}He)$$

$$^{226}_{88}Ra \longrightarrow ^{222}_{86}Rn + ^{4}_{2}He + Q$$

$$\text{Radium} \quad \text{Radon} \quad \text{Helium} \quad \text{Energy}$$

The mass of α - particle $m_\alpha = 6.65 \times 10^{-27}$ kg

The energy Q produced in this decay is $Q = 9.0 \times 10^{-13}$ J Alpha particles can travel only a few *cm* in air or 10^{-3} cm through solid before being brought to rest by collisions.

Beta (β-) decay

In β- decay, N decreases by one and Z increases by one; A does not change. The β-particle is an electron with a speed of 99.5% the speed of light $(2.99 \times 10^8 ms^{-1})$ and they are emitted with continuous spectrum of energies: for β- emission:

$$^{11}_{4}Be \longrightarrow ^{0}_{-1}e + ^{11}_{5}Be$$

Table 35.3 The properties of the emitted particles (α-,β-) and γ-radiation.

Radiation	Alpha (α-) particles	Beta (β-) particles	Gamma (γ) rays
Nature	Helium nuclei $^{4}_{2}He$	High speed electrons	Electromagnetic waves of very short wavelength
Velocity	(0.15–0.21) $\times 10^8 ms^{-1}$	$2.9 \times 10^8 ms^{-1}$	Speed of light $3.0 \times 10^8 ms^{-1}$
Charge	$+Ze(3.2 \times 10^{-19}C)$	$-e(-1.6 \times 10^{-19}C)$	No charge
Mass	6.65×10^{-27} kg	9.1×10^{-31} kg	Negligible
Effect of magnetic field	Slight deflection	Strongly deflected	Little or no effect
Ionizing power	Heavy ionization	Medium ionization	Little ionization
Penetrating power	Little penetrating power, it can be stopped by paper	Medium penetrating power in several mm of aluminium	High penetrating power in several cm of lead.

Gamma (γ-) decay

When a nucleus is placed in an excited state, either by bombardment with high energy particles or by radioactive transformation, it can decay to the ground state by emission of one or more photons called gamma (γ-) rays, with typical energy range of 10keV–5MeV

In γ-decay, the element does not change in nucleus, it only goes from an excited state to a lower state. Gamma emission takes place from an excited nucleus with no change in nucleon or proton number.

$$^{60}_{27}C_o \longrightarrow ^{0}_{0}\gamma + ^{60}_{27}C_o$$

In γ-radiation, A and Z do not change. Such radiations travel in straight lines and has negligible mass with little ionizing power but high penetrating power.

The radioactive decay law

For a radioactive decay, it is found that the number of radioactive nuclei (dN) decaying in a unit time at dt is directly proportional to the number N present at the instant of time, that is

$$\frac{dN}{dt} \propto N \Rightarrow \frac{dN}{dt} = -\lambda N$$

Where λ is the constant of proportionality known as the *radioactive decay constant*. The unit is per second (s^{-1}). The negative sign indicates that the number of radioactive nuclei decreases with time.

The quantity $\frac{dN}{dt}$ is called the *activity* of the sample.

If at time, t_o, the undecayed nuclei is N_o, then

$$\frac{dN}{N_o} = \lambda dt,\ \text{when integrated gives}$$

$$N = N_o e^{-\lambda t}$$

From the above equation, the radioactive decay is seen to be a random process following exponential decay. The decay constant, λ is the fractional number of nuclei present in the material that decays in a unit time if interval is small. i.e.

$$\lambda = \frac{dN}{N_o t} \qquad \text{35.3}$$

The half life of a radioactive source

The half-life is defined as the time it takes for the activity of the sample to reduce to half of its original value or the time it takes for the number of radio active nuclei in the sample to reduce to half.

$$T_{\frac{1}{2}} = \frac{0.693}{\lambda}$$

For half life,

$$N = \frac{N_o}{2} \text{ at } t = T_{\frac{1}{2}}$$

i.e. $\frac{N}{N_o} = \frac{1}{2}$, we can write from:

$$\frac{N}{N_o} = e^{-\lambda T_{\frac{1}{2}}}$$

and taking log of both sides,

$$ln\left(\frac{N}{N_o}\right) = -\lambda T_{\frac{1}{2}}$$

$$ln\,2 = \lambda T_{\frac{1}{2}}$$

$$T_{\frac{1}{2}} = \frac{0.693}{\lambda} \qquad \text{35.4}$$

Fig. 35.3 shows a typical decay curve

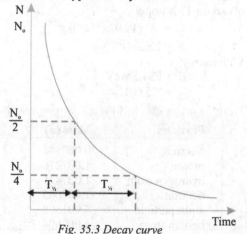

Fig. 35.3 Decay curve

Isotope	Half-life $(T_{\frac{1}{2}})$	Decay Constant (λ)
Uranium −238	4.5×10^9 years	5.10×10^{-18}
Carbon −14	5.57×10^3 years	3.90×10^{-12}
Radium −226	1.62×10^3 years	1.35×10^{-4}
Helium −5	6×10^{-20}s	1.20×10^{19}

Radioactive transmutations

There are two types of radioactivity:
(a) natural, and (b) artificial.

Natural radioactivity

Natural radioactivity is the spontaneous disintegration of an unstable nuclide by the emission of α-particle or β-particle or γ-radiation or a combination of any two or all the three with energy released.

For natural radioactivity to occur, the proton number $Z \geq 82$ e.g. Radon -222 decays to Radium-222 by emitting two β-particles:

$$\underset{86}{^{222}}\text{Rn} \longrightarrow 2\,\underset{-1}{^{0}}\text{e} + \underset{88}{^{222}}\text{Ra} + Q\,\text{(energy)}$$
$$\text{(Radon)} \qquad \beta\text{-particle} \qquad \text{Radium}$$

Thorium-234 decays by emitting a β-particle to Protactinium-234.

$$\underset{90}{^{234}}\text{Tn} \longrightarrow \underset{91}{^{234}}\text{Pa} + \underset{-1}{^{0}}\text{e} + Q$$

In general, for an α-decay,

$$\underset{Z}{^{A}}\text{X} \longrightarrow \underset{2}{^{4}}\text{He} + \underset{z-2}{^{A-4}}\text{Y}$$

Parent nuclide, $\longrightarrow$ α-particle + daughter nuclide

For β-decay,

$$\underset{Z}{^{A}}\text{X} \longrightarrow \underset{-1}{^{0}}\text{e} + \underset{z+1}{^{A}}\text{Y}$$
$$\beta\text{-particle}$$

and for γ-radiation

$$\underset{Z}{^{A}}\text{X} \longrightarrow \gamma + \underset{Z}{^{A}}\text{Y}$$
$$e\text{-}m\text{ radiation}$$

Artificial transformations

Artificial radionuclides can be produced by bombarding stable nuclides $(Z<<82)$ with small nuclear particles such as γ- radiation, β-particles, α-particles or even neutrons and protons.

$$\underset{7}{^{14}}\text{N} + \underset{2}{^{4}}\text{He} \longrightarrow \underset{8}{^{17}}\text{O} + \underset{1}{^{1}}\text{H}$$

Here, the alpha particle had been absorbed by the nucleus and the reaction has changed nitrogen into oxygen.

$$\underset{12}{^{24}}\text{Mg} + \underset{0}{^{1}}\text{n} \longrightarrow \underset{11}{^{24}}\text{Na} + \underset{1}{^{1}}\text{P} + \text{energy}$$

$$\underset{3}{^{7}}\text{Li} + \underset{1}{^{1}}\text{H} \longrightarrow \underset{2}{^{4}}\text{He} + \underset{2}{^{4}}\text{He}$$

In artificial radioactivity, a non-radioactive material, when bombarded with small nuclear particles (α-, β-particles) is made radioactive.

35.5 Nuclear reactions

In the preceding section we studied the decay of unstable nuclei, especially spontaneous emission of an α-or β-particle atimes followed by γ-emission. In this decay, nothing was done to initiate this decay and nothing could be done to control it. This section examines some nuclear reactions that result from the bombardment by a particle rather than a spontaneous natural process.

Nuclear fission

When a radionuclide (with $Z > 80$) is bombarded with neutrons, two roughly equal parts are produced with the release of a huge amount of energy.

> Nuclear fission is a decay process in which an unstable nucleus splits into two parts of comparable mass.

Fission was discovered by Hann and Strassman in 1938 when they bombarded uranium ($Z=92$) with neutrons. They found the resulting radiation to be a radioactive isotope of barium ($Z=56$)) and krypton ($Z=36$). These results were interpreted as showing that uranium nuclei were splitting into two parts (fragments) called fission fragments. Two or three free neutrons also appear along with the fission fragments.

^{238}U and ^{235}U can easily be split by neutron bombardment. The latter by slow neutrons but the former by neutrons of energy greater than 1MeV.

Two typical fission reactions are:

(a) $^{235}_{92}U + ^{1}_{0}n \rightarrow ^{236}_{92}U \rightarrow ^{144}_{56}Ba + ^{89}_{36}Kr + 3^{1}_{0}n + Q$

(b) $^{235}_{92}U + ^{1}_{0}n \rightarrow ^{236}_{92}U \rightarrow ^{148}_{57}La + ^{85}_{35}Br + 3^{1}_{0}n + Q$

Where Q is the nuclear energy produced

The total energy of the fission fragments is quite high about 200 MeV. (compared to α-, β-energies of a few MeV). This is because nuclides with nucleon number $A \geq 240$ are less tightly bound than those at $90 \leq A \leq 145$.

Nuclear fusion

> Nuclear fusion is the joining of two or more light nuclei to form a heavy nucleus with the release of enormous energy.

Fusion reactions release energy in the same way as the fission reactions i.e. the binding energy (to be discussed in the next section) per nucleon after reaction is greater than before reaction.
Here are some examples of fusion reactions.

$^{1}H + ^{1}H \longrightarrow ^{2}H + \beta^{+} + \nu + Q$

$^{2}H + ^{1}H \longrightarrow ^{3}He + \gamma + Q$

$^{2}H + ^{2}H \longrightarrow ^{3}He + ^{0}n + Q$

In the first reaction, two protons combine to form a deuteron (^{2}H) with the emission of positron (β^{+}) and an electron neutrino. In the second, a proton and a deuteron combine to form the nucleus of isotope of helium (^{3}He) with the emission of gamma ray. The third is a reaction in which two deuterons (heavy hydrogen) are fused to produce Helium-3 and a neutron.

In all the three reactions, energy, Q, is released. The biggest problem with the fusion reaction is making the nuclei to fuse, because the electrostatic repulsion between them at very small distances become extremely large. For this reason, the hydrogen gas has to be raised to a very high temperatures of 10^{6} °C even under very high pressure, thus giving the nuclei sufficient thermal kinetic energy to overcome the electrostatic repulsion.

35.6 Nuclear energy

Binding energy

The neutrons and protons in a stable nucleus are held together by nuclear forces and energy is needed to pull them apart. This energy is called the binding energy of the nucleus; the greater the binding energy, the more stable is the nucleus. This energy shows itself as a difference between the mass of the nucleus and the sum of the masses of the nucleons within it.

The Einstein mass-energy relation

In 1905, Albert Einstein published his special theory of relativity, one of the conclusions from this is that mass and energy are equivalent and are related by the equation

$$E = \Delta mc^{2} \qquad 35.5$$

The difference between the masses before and after the reaction Δm, corresponds to the reaction energy, E, where c is the speed of electromagnetic radiation. For Δm to equal 1kg, the amount of energy, E, produced is 9×10^{16} J.

If we estimate the amount of electrical energy used in the home as 2.5×10^{10} kWh; this would supply 10 000 houses in a town with a 1 kWh of heat for nearly 300 years.

Conversely, a 1 MeV gamma-ray can be converted into a mass giving 1.78×10^{-30} kg. Because the masses of atomic particles are so small, the atomic mass unit ($a.m.u.$) is adopted.

1 $a.m.u.$ (u) is defined as $\frac{1}{12}$ of the mass of one atom of carbon-12 isotope.

$$1u = \frac{1}{12} (19.92 \times 10^{-27}) kg$$
$$= 1.66 \times 10^{-27} kg$$

With energy
$$E = 931.5 MeV$$
$$= 1.5 \times 10^{-10} J$$

Table 35.4 The masses of some common particles

Particles	Mass (u)
electron	0.000548
proton	1.007276
hydrogen atom	1.007825
neutron	1.008665
alpha particle	4.001508
helium atom	4.002604

Binding energy calculation

Consider the alpha particle, ($^4_2$He) containing two protons and two neutrons. The mass of the nucleons is 4.031882u, but mass of helium nucleus is 4.002604 u.

The binding energy (the difference between the mass of the nucleons and the nucleus) is the mass defect.

i.e. $\Delta m = (4.031882 - 4.002604)$ u
$= 0.029278$ u
$= 27.27$ MeV.

If the binding energy is positive, like in the example above, the nucleus is stable, but if it is negative, the nucleus would decay simultaneously.

Energy from fission reaction

The fission of ^{235}U produces two radioactive nuclei, some neutrons, and release of nuclear energy as shown by the equation:

$$^{235}_{92}U + \, ^1_0n \longrightarrow \, ^{236}_{92}U \Rightarrow \, ^{148}_{57}La + \, ^{85}_{35}Br + 3^1_0n + Q$$

The mass equation for this reaction is
$235.124u + 1.009u \longrightarrow 147.961u + 84.938u + 3.027u$

$\Delta m = 0.207u$
$= 193MeV$ and for 1kg of U-235

the fission energy is 8.19×10^{13}J

Energy from fusion reaction

From the fusion reaction in which two deuterons are fused to produce Helium -3 nucleus and a neutron.

$$^2_1H + \, ^2_1H \longrightarrow \, ^3_2He + \, ^1_0n + Energy$$

From the mass equation, the mass defect

$\Delta m = 0.004u$ or 3.27 MeV.

i.e. the energy released per deuterons is 3.04×10^{-13} J. But since there are 3×10^{26} deuterons in 1 kg of deuteron, energy released per kg is 9.12×10^{13} J which is greater than the fission energy produced by uranium.

Atomic explosions

If one of the neutrons produced by the first fission hits a second uranium nucleus, the latter will also split, the process will continue, causing a very large number of fission reactions. This is called *chain reaction*.

Chain reaction occurs on the fission of uranium $^{235}_{92}$U only when the quantity of uranium is large. If the uranium is small, and undergoes fission reaction, the secondary neutrons escape from the sides before they cause fission. So, to sustain chain reaction, there must be sufficient pure uranium – 235 known as the **critical mass** to avoid many neutrons from being lost from the sides before they can cause further fission.

These thermal neutrons are slowed down by a moderator usually carbon (graphite blocks) or heavy water (H_2O_2).

In atomic bomb, there is explosion because two pieces of uranium with both masses below the critical mass but whose sum is greater than the critical mass are brought together at the right time. There is then an increasing, uncontrolled chain reaction, and massive explosion with extensive destructive effects.

Nuclear reactors

A nuclear reactor is a system in which a controlled nuclear chain reaction is used to produce energy. In a nuclear power plant, the energy is used to generate steam, which operates a turbine and rotates the electrical generator (dynamo). The most familiar application of nuclear reactors is for the generation of electric power. Others include the production of:

(a) artificial radioactive isotopes for medical research, e.g. ^{131}I, ^{60}Co have application in radiotherapy; and

(b) high intensity neutron beams and fissionable nuclides.

Peaceful uses of nuclear energy

From previous sections, we know that nuclear energy is the energy released when nuclear reaction or radioactive decay occurs. Presently, nuclear energy is an important source of energy and many nuclear power stations have been built for generating electricity. Some spacecrafts are even powered by small nuclear plants.

Relative advantages of fusion over fission

1. Fusion is easily achieved with hydrogen; nuclear repulsion is overcome as nuclei approach each other at very high temperature. (The required high temperature can be obtained by passing a very large current through the plasma).

2. The raw materials required for fusion are more readily available. Hydrogen can be produced from sea water quite cheaply; one major difficulty is the control of impurities due to plasma interaction with vessel walls.

3. Fusion process produces less dangerous by-products.

4. Fusion reaction produces much larger release of nuclear energy.

Summary

1. The models of atom include Thomson, Rutherford, Bohr and electron-cloud models. The accepted model of the atom is that the atom consists of a small nucleus with radius 1.2×10^{-15}m and composed of protons and neutrons with a number of electrons located in orbits some distance away.

2. The mass of the nucleus is slightly less than the total mass of its constituents. All nuclei have about the same density.

3. Nuclear stability is determined by the interaction between the attractive nuclear force and the electric repulsion of the protons. Hence the atom is held together by nuclear and electric forces.

4. The proton carries a positive charge, the electron carries a negative charge and the neutron carries no charge. The mass of the electron is 1/1860 that of the proton or the neutron.

5. Electrons occupy certain fixed orbits around the nucleus of an atom. When electron is in one of these circular orbits, it does not radiate any energy but retains a fixed energy level. An electron absorbs radiation when it moves from a lower energy level to a higher energy level and it gives off radiation when it moves from a higher to a lower energy level.

6. Nucleon is the name for both protons and neutrons. The proton (atomic) number, Z, is the number of protons in the nucleus which is also equal to the number of electrons. The nucleon (mass) number, A, is the total number of nucleons in the nucleus.
$A = Z + N$, where N is the number of neutrons.

7. A nuclide is a given nucleus with a specified number of neutrons and protons. Isotopes are two or more nuclides of the same element having the same number of protons but different number of neutrons. Unstable nuclei usually decay into different nuclei by emitting alpha ($\alpha-$), beta (β-) particles sometimes followed by gamma (γ) ray photon.

8. The rate of decay is described in terms of the half-life and decay constant.
The process of the decay is radioactivity i.e. the spontaneous decay of the nucleus with the emission of α-particles, β-particles and γ-ray in addition to release of energy.

9. α-particles are positively charged helium nuclei ^{4}He with a low penetrating power. They are quite massive and they ionize air, but are only slightly deflected by electric and magnetic fields.

10. β-particles are fast moving electrons ($^0_1$e) which are strongly deflected by electric and magnetic fields.
β-particles have very small masses and can be stopped by a thin sheet of lead. Their speed is 99.5% speed of light.

11. γ-rays are electromagnetic waves. They have very high penetrating power but are electrically neutral. γ-rays are not affected by electric and magnetic fields and they move with the speed of light.

12. Half life ($T_{\frac{1}{2}}$) is the time required for one-half of the atoms in an element present to decay.
Decay constant (λ) is the rate of decay per unit atom of a substance. It is related to the half-life by the equation $T_{\frac{1}{2}} = \frac{0.692}{\lambda}$.

13. Artificial radionuclides may be manufactured by bombarding stable nuclides with small nuclear particles such as α-, β-particles or neutrons.

14. Nuclear fission is the splitting of a heavier nucleus into two smaller nuclei of comparable masses with the release of energy and neutrons.

15. Nuclear fusion is the joining of two light nuclei into a large nucleus with the release of a large amount of energy.

16. Nuclear energy is used in the production of hydrogen bomb but its peaceful uses include generation of electric power for domestic and industrial use; even spacecrafts are powered by small nuclear plants.

17. $1 eV = 1.6 \times 10^{-19}$J, 931.5 MeV $= 1$u

Exercise 35

1. The binding energy of the nickel nuclide $^{62}_{28}$Ni is 545.3 MeV. Calculate the binding energy per nucleon in eV.

   A. 3.38×10^{10} B. 1.53×10^{10}
   C. 1.95×10^{7} D. 8.80×10^{6}

2. The particles found in the nucleus of an atom are I–protons, II–electrons III–neutrons.
   A. I- only   B. II- only
   C. I and II only   D. I and III.

3. 8 α-decays and 6β-decays are necessary before an atom of $^{238}_{92}$U achieves stability, the final product has the proton number
   A. 70.   B. 78.   C. 82.   D. 90.

4. Nuclear fusion is a nuclear reaction in which

   I   the total mass of the products is less than that of the reactants.

   II two light nuclei are joined together to form a heavy nucleus.

   III energy is released.

   IV a heavy nucleus is split into two parts of about the same mass.

   A. I and II only   B. II and III only
   C. III and IV only   D. I, II, and III only

5. The effect on the nucleon number of a radio nuclide when it emits an alpha-particle is that it
   A. decreases by 4.   B. decreases by 2.
   C. decreases by 3.   D. remains the same.

6. $^{27}_{13}$Al + $^{1}_{0}$n $\longrightarrow$ $^{24}_{11}$Na + γ

   In the nuclear reaction above, the product denoted by γ is
   A. a proton.   B. a β-particle.
   C. an α-particle.   D. a neutron.

7. How many particles and protons are emitted in the radioactive decay of $^{224}_{88}$Ra to $^{214}_{92}$Pb?

   A. 10,6   B. 4,2   C. 2,2   D. 2,1

8. A radioactive substance has a half life of 3s. After 6s, the count rate was found to be 500. What is the initial count rate?

   A. 150   B. 1500   C. 2000   D. 2500

9. Which of the following rays originates from the nucleus of an atom?

   A. *IR*- rays   B. *UV*- rays

   C. *X*-rays   D. γ-rays

10. Which of the following symbolic representations is correct for an atom *A* with two electrons and 32 neutrons?

    A. $^{32}_{20}$A   B. $^{34}_{2}$A   C. $^{30}_{12}$A   D. $^{20}_{12}$A

11. The number of electrons contained in the nucleus of $^{235}_{92}$U is

    A. 30.   B. 92.   C. 143.   D. 235.

12. If a nuclide $^{4}_{2}$He decays, a nucleus is formed accompanied with the emission of a

    A. γ-ray.   B. α-particles
    C. neutron.   D. proton.

13. Beta-particles are

    A. protons.   B. neutrons.
    C. He-nuclei. D. electrons.

14. Which of the following is different from the others?

    A. *X*-rays   B. γ-rays

    C. Cathode rays   D. *UV* rays

15. A neutron exists in the atomic nucleus. Which of the following also exists in the nucleus?

    A. an electron.   B. a β-particle.
    C. an α-particle. D. a proton.

16. Natural radioactivity consists of the emission of: I- α-particles; II - β-particles; III - γ-rays; IV-*X*-rays.

    A. I- only   B. II only
    C. I and II only   D. I, II and III only

17. The activity of a radionuclide depends on
    A. age and temperature.
    B. age, purity and temperature.
    C. purity and temperature.
    D. age and purity.

18. Which of the following is most strongly affected by a magnetic field?

    A. γ-rays   B. *X*–rays
    C. β- particles D. α - particles

19. What type of reaction is represented by the following scheme?

    $^{1}X + ^{2}Y \longrightarrow ^{3}Z + ^{0}n + \text{energy}$

    A. Fusion reaction   B. Fission reaction

C. Chain reaction   D. Radioactive decay

20. A radioactive sample initially contains 64 atoms, after three half-lives, the number of atoms that have disintegrated is

    A. 8.   B. 24.   C. 32.   D. 56.

21. Explain: (i) fusion (ii) fission. List three advantages of fusion over fission in the generation of power. Calculate in joules the binding energy for $^{60}_{28}$Co.

22. State briefly what would happen to a stable element if is bombarded by alpha-particles, explain how the bombardment of uranium ($^{235}_{92}$U) with neutrons could lead to nuclear fission reaction and hence nuclear explosion.

23. State (a) three characteristics of nuclear activity.
    (b) three applications of nuclear energy.
    (c) two postulates of Bohr's atomic model and two limitations of such a model.

24. Explain the following:

    (i) nucleon number; (ii) proton number; and

    (iii) a half life of a radioisotope. A sample of a radio active element with half life of 10mins has an initial mass of 4000g. Sketch the decay curve and use the graph to determine the time at which the mass is 125g.

25.
    $^{238}_{92}$U $\xrightarrow{\alpha}$ $^{a}_{b}$Th

    $^{a}_{b}$Th $\xrightarrow{\beta}$ $^{c}_{d}$Pa

    $^{c}_{d}$Pa $\xrightarrow{\beta}$ $^{e}_{f}$Y

    The reactions illustrate a decay scheme. Determine the values *a, b, c, d, e, f*. What radioisotope is *Y*?

26. Distinguish between natural and artificial radioactivity. Mention two ways in which artificial radioactivity can be induced in a nucleus.

27. Explain (i) half-life (ii) decay constant and (iii) activity. In 360mins, the activity of a certain radioactive substance decays to 1/8 of its original value calculate (i) half-life (ii) decay constant (iii) activity of the substance.

28. Explain the terms atomic mass unit (*a.m.u.*) and electron volt (eV). Find the energy equivalents of the masses of proton and neutron in eV. (Assume that $m_p = 1.0078$u, $m_n = 1.0089$u). The deuteron may be split into a proton and a neutron by bombarding it with a photon according to the equation

    $\gamma + ^{2}H \longrightarrow ^{1}n + ^{1}P$

Explain the meaning of the symbols used in this equation and determine the energy of the photon to cause the splitting. (Mass of deuteron is 2.0140u). Take 1u = 931MeV

29. Briefly discuss the atomic models as outlined by (a) Rutherford (b) Niels Bohr. State the limitations of each type of model described.

30. What is radioactivity?

    Distinguish between natural and artificial radioactivity. Give two applications of radioactivity and discuss the hazards of exposure to nuclear radiations.

31. (a) The isotope $^{238}_{92}U$ emits an α-particle and $^{214}_{92}Pb$ emits a β-particle and an X-ray. Comment on and explain the values of the proton and nucleon numbers of the new isotopes formed.

    (b) The sodium nuclide $^{23}_{11}Na$ absorbs a deuterium (^2_1H) nucleus and ejects a proton (^1_1H). Write out the reaction and identify the new nuclide.

    Define: (i) radioactivity and (ii) isotope.

32. Part of a uranium decay series can be represented as follows:

    $$^{238}_{92}U \xrightarrow{\alpha} A. \xrightarrow{\beta} B. \xrightarrow{\beta} C. \xrightarrow{\alpha} D.$$

    Where α, β represent the α-particle and β-particle emission respectively, where for example uranium produces a daughter nucleus A by emitting an α-particle and so on.

    (a) Explain the numbers 238 and 92 for element U.

    (b) Calculate the corresponding numbers for the elements A,B,C,D, stating briefly the method.

    (c) What do the α-and β-emissions represent?

    (d) Which of the species in the series above are isotopes?

33. Discuss α-particles, β-particles and γ-rays under the following headings: identity, mass, charge and velocity. Show what part these qualities play in making α-particles cause the greatest ionization and γ-rays have the greatest penetration.

34. Nuclear reactions are symbolically expressed as follows $Q(P,R)S$.

    Where Q is the initial radionuclide,
    P is the incoming particle
    R is the outgoing particle
    and S is the final nuclide
    Complete the following reaction by calculating the proton and nucleon numbers of the missing terms.

    (i) $^{238}_{92}U$ (n, β)..?.

    (ii) ^7_3Li (...,α) ^4He

    (iii) $^{14}_7N$ (n, p) .....

35. The following are nuclear reactions:

    (a) $^{118}_{50}Sn + ^1_1P \rightarrow ^{66}_{31}Ga + ^{49}_{20}Ca + 4^1_0n$

    (b) $^7_3Li + ^1_1P \rightarrow ^4_2He + ^4_2He$

    (i) Name and explain briefly the type of nuclear reactions. What hazards does the type (a) reaction present?

    (ii) If the proton is accelerated through a p.d. of 0.37 MeV, calculate the ratio of the neutron to that of the proton in (a).

    The atomic masses are $^{118}Sn = 117.940u$, $^{66}Ga = 65.947u$, $^{49}Ca = 48.963u$, $p = 1.008u$, $^1n = 1.009u$).

36. State Bohr's postulates concerning the motion of an electron round the nucleus of an atom and explain the problem in Rutherford's model of the atom which these postulates solve.

37. The following are recorded about the two processes by which energy may be obtained from the nucleus when:

    (i) a heavy nucleus is required;

    (ii) very high temperatures are necessary.

    Name the two processes involved and relate the facts above to their respective processes.

38. (a) $^{234}_{90}Th$ is a radioactive isotope of thorium which has a half-life of 24 days and disintegrates with the emission of beta particles and gamma rays. Explain the underlined terms.

    (b) It is given that the following reaction takes place $^{238}_{92}U \longrightarrow ^{234}_{90}Th + ^4_2He$

    Calculate the total energy in joules released per atom in the disintegration.

    [The atomic masses are: ^{238}U, 238.0508u; ^{234}Th, 234.0436u. ^4He, 4.0026u]

39. The following equations represent two nuclear reactions;

    (i) $^{235}_{92}U + ^1_0n \rightarrow ^{236}_{92}U \rightarrow ^{141}_{56}Ba + ^{92}_{36}Kr + 3^1_0n$

    (ii) $^2_1H + ^2_1H \longrightarrow ^4_2He$

    State the two kinds of reaction and distinguish between them. How is each reaction used as a source of energy?

40. (a) The neutron (^1_0n) required in the fusion reaction can be obtained from the reaction $^9_4Be + ^4_2\alpha \Rightarrow A + ^1_0n$. Identify the element A.

    (b) Define the terms nucleus, nuclides, isotopes: The following are examples of neutron bombardment reactions.

    $^{59}_{27}Co + neutron \longrightarrow Y + \gamma ray$

    $^{14}_7N + neutron \longrightarrow Z + proton$

    Determine the proton and nucleon numbers of Y and Z and explain how each number is obtained.

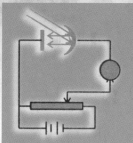

ENERGY QUANTIZATION

Chapter 36

Introduction

In 1910, Rutherford showed that the atom was composed of a heavy central nucleus, positively charged with a large number of negatively charged electrons circling or orbiting round it and that such a system would be unstable and would decay in about 10^{-10}s as the attractive force between the nucleus and the electrons caused the electrons to spiral into the nucleus. However, in 1913, Niels Bohr overcame this difficulty by applying the quantum theory to the problem and suggested that electrons in the atom exist in discrete (or quantized) energy states. He also stated that the allowed values of the angular momentum would be integral multiples of $h/2\pi$.

This theory was developed in 1900 by Max Planck to explain the radiation curves from a black body and he stated that the energy of the electrons was distinct values of energy, (energy quanta) and could be represented as allowed orbits around the nucleus spiraling is not allowed; electron could only lose its energy in well defined steps.

Thus, the energy, E_n, of radiation can be:

$$E_n = n\,hf \qquad 36.1$$

where $n = 1,2,3$ where h is the Planck's constant and there cannot be radiations whose energy lies between these values. This implies that energy radiated is not continuous but exists in discrete amounts (i.e. Quantized).

36.1 Energy levels in atoms

From Bohr's theory of the hydrogen atom, the energy levels in multielectron atoms could not be predicted. However, the fundamental ideas of Bohr's theory that the angular momentum of the electron has quantum (discrete) values and that energy levels of the atom have only allowed separated values which characterize the atom were valid. So, it is supposed that a given atom has a series of discrete energy levels E_o, E_1, E_2 and that no intermediate energy level is possible. The lowest energy level systems in this state are in stable equilibrium.

If the atom absorbs energy, and the energy of the atom reaches one of its allowed values, E_1, the atom is said to be in an **excited state**. Once an atom has been excited to a higher energy level, E_n, it will try to

reduce its energy. The energy lost if the atom reverses to the ground state is $(E_n - E_o)$. This energy is radiated in the form of electromagnetic radiation. The energy, ΔE, of the photon emitted is expressed as

$$\Delta E = E_n - E_o = hf_n = \frac{hc}{\lambda_n} \qquad 36.2$$

where f is the frequency and λ is the wavelength.

In some cases, the atom may change back to the ground state through an intermediate allowed energy level, E_m. In this case two different frequencies f_1, f_2 are radiated and are given respectively by the equations

$$hf_1 = E_n - E_m, \qquad hf_2 = E_m - E_o.$$

Energy levels are usually drawn on a vertical scale and transitions from one energy level to another energy level with an arrow. Fig. 36.1 shows roughly the energy levels of an atom. Its ground state E_o and excited states $E_1, E_2 \ldots E_\infty$

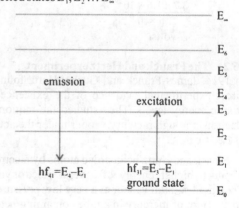

Fig. 36.1 Energy levels in an atom.

The energy E_x required to raise an atom from its ground state to an excited state is called excitation energy given by: $\quad E_x = eV_x \qquad 36.3$

where V_x is the excitation potential of the atom.

If the atom is in its most stable state (ground) E_o, and absorbs an amount of energy, eV which just removes an electron completely from the atom, V is known as *ionization potential* of the atom.

E_∞ is taken as zero energy of the atom.

The ionization energy, E_i is the energy required to remove an electron completely from an atom in its most stable state.

$$E_i = E_\infty - E_o = eV_i \qquad 36.4$$

Where V_i is known as ionization potential.

Example 36.1

An electron has energy 6.7eV, to what level will the mercury atom be excited? Assuming that the ionization energy is 10.4eV. Calculate the (i) wavelength of the light emitted if the atom drops from excited state to the second level, (ii) excitation potential (assume $h = 6.626 \times 10^{-34}$Js).

Solution

The energy received from the bombarding electron,

$E_n - E_o = 6.7$eV.

$E_n - (-10.4) = 6.7$eV.

Therefore, $E_n = -3.7$eV

But this is the energy of the third level:

$E_2 - E_1 = -3.7 - (-5.5) = 1.8$eV

(i) The energy lost by the atom is equal to the energy of the emitted photon:

i.e. $1.8\text{eV} = \dfrac{hc}{\lambda}$

$\lambda = \dfrac{6.6 \times 10^{-34} \times 3 \times 10^8}{1.8 \times 1.6 \times 10^{-19}} = 6.9 \times 10^{-7}$m

since $1\text{eV} = 1.6 \times 10^{-19}$J

$\lambda = 6.9 \times 10^{-7}$m.

(ii) From the equation:

$E = eV$

$V = \dfrac{3.7 \times 1.6 \times 10^{-19}}{1.6 \times 10^{-19}}$

$\quad = 3.7$ volts

36.2 The Franck and Hertz experiment

In 1914, James Franck and Guslav Hertz found a direct experimental evidence of the existence of atomic energy levels. They studied the motion of electrons through mercury vapour under the action of electric field.

Franck and Hertz bombarded atoms by electrons of much higher energy of several electronvolts. They used sodium vapour at a very low pressure of about 1mm of mercury in a tube containing heated tungsten filament F, a grid plate G and an anode plate A as shown in Fig. 36.2. Electrons were emitted from F and the distance FG was arranged to be much greater than the mean free path of the electrons in the gas. Before reaching G, electrons would make collisions with the atoms. The potentiometer, S, is used to vary the p.d. between F and G.

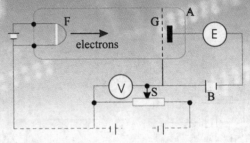

Fig. 36.2(a) Franck and Hertz experiment set up

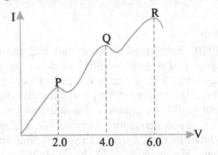

Fig. 36.2(b) I–V characteristic for Franck and Hertz experiment

The emitted electrons from F were accelerated to kinetic energies depending on the magnitude of V as measured by a voltmeter. A p.d. less than 1 volt was applied between A and G so that A was negative with respect to G, electrons reaching G and passing through A were subjected to a retarding potential. The electro-meter E measured the number of electrons reaching A per second.

As the p.d. V_{FG} was increased from zero, the current recorded by E increased and rose to a value P as shown in fig 36.2(b). As V was increased the current diminished to a minimum and rose again to a new higher p.d. peak at Q, diminished and rose again to a higher peak at R. The p.d. V_c termed critical potential between successive peaks was found to be constant and equal to 2.10V for sodium vapour from the graph. It is seen that the current begins to drop at the critical potential, V_c. Here the electrons have an energy of eV_c joule, that is sufficient to raise the internal energy of the sodium atom by collision.

As the voltage across the tube is increased, the current increases as the electrons collide elastically with the atoms of the gas. The field in most of the tube is small since most of the p.d. occurs near the wire of the filament. Therefore when the electrons reach the grid, they have insufficient kinetic energy to overcome the retarding field between the grid, G, and the anode plate, A, and the anode current falls. This shows that no increase in the energy of the atom can occur if the energy of the electrons is less than eV_c. The existence of definite series of energies with no intermediate values suggests that the atom has a set of well defined energy levels.

The transition of electrons from one energy level to another gives the characteristics and unique spectrum of the material.

36.3 Types of spectra

There are two main types of spectra:

(a) *emission spectra* – where light is given out by a source; and

(b) *absorption spectra* – where light from a source is absorbed when it passes through another material, usually a gas or a liquid.

(a) Emission spectra

These show different characteristics that depend on the nature of the source:

(i) A continuous spectrum contains all the wavelengths in a certain region of the spectrum. A continuous spectrum in the visible region may be emitted by a hot solid at a temperature above some 800K. The sun emits a continuous spectrum as does a piece of iron heated in a flame and other incandescent solids and liquids. Here, all wavelengths are found over a wide range.

(ii) A line spectrum: here, only certain lines are visible and is emitted by a monatomic gas (Fig 36.3(a)) such as hydrogen in a discharge tube. Another example is the visible spectrum of a sodium salt vaporized in a bunsen flame and consists of two lines close together.

(iii) A band spectrum: consists of a series of bands and is emitted by gases or liquids such as oxygen, carbonmonoxide, carbondioxide, blood or potassium permanganate.

(iv) Solution, consisting of molecules. Here the linkages between two or more atoms give groups of lines as in Fig. 36.3(b).

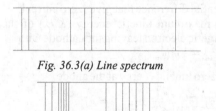

Fig. 36.3(a) Line spectrum

Fig. 36.3(b) Band sepctrum

If a gas is excited by a high voltage to produce a discharge and the light is examined in a spectrometer, an emission spectrum is seen. As they move through the discharge in the gas, some electrons have sufficient energy to excite atoms to a higher energy level. Neon gas for example produces *a line spectrum* which consist of a number of well defined lines having a particular frequency or wavelength. These separated lines are experimental evidence of separate (quantized) energy levels in the atom.

(b) Absorption spectra

If light from a white light source is passed through a gas, then the continuous spectrum is crossed by a series of dark lines that correspond exactly to the lines observed in the emission spectrum which involve transitions to the ground state. This is because in a gas, almost all the atoms are in their ground state.

Absorption occurs by the electrons in the atom absorbing the energy from the incoming radiation and then re-radiating it in all directions. Thus, the energy that was originally travelling in one direction is spread out and when compared with the rest of the spectrum, the wave lengths appear dark.

Atoms can absorb energy in a number of ways.

(i) In a flame, inelastic collisions with energetic molecules can raise atoms to higher energy levels.

(ii) In a discharge tube, inelastic collisions with bombarding electrons can raise atoms to higher energy levels.

(iii) From a photon.

If the photon energy $E = hf$ is just sufficient to excite an atom to one of its higher energy levels, the photon will be absorbed with it returns to the ground states; the excited atom emits when the same wavelength as the photon but equally in all directions. So, the intensity of the radiation in the direction of the incident photon is reduced. A dark line is thus seen whose wavelength is that of the absorbed photon.

Absorption of photons explains the dark lines in the sun's visible spectrum. The sun emitting continuous spectrum is crossed by many dark absorption lines sometimes called fraunhofer lines. These are due to absorption by the outer gaseous layers of the sun and a study of such lines gives the astronomer a method for determining the composition of the sun.

36.4 Colour and light frequency

In electric discharge tubes, atoms are raised or excited to higher energy levels mainly through inelastic collision with electrons. Emitted or absorbed photons give rise to characteristic colour of light and wavelength/frequency.

According to Bohr, an atom can make a transition from one energy level to a lower energy level by emitting a photon with energy equal to the energy difference between the initial and final levels (Fig. 36.4).

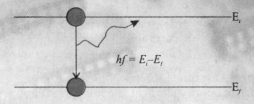

$$hf = E_i - E_f$$

Fig. 36.4 Transition between energy levels.

If E_i is the initial energy before transition and E_f is the final energy after transition and the photon's energy is $hf = \frac{hc}{\lambda}$ the conservation of energy gives (energy of emitted photon)

$$hf = \frac{hc}{\lambda} = E_i - E_f \qquad 36.5$$

For example, when a krypton atom emits a photon of orange light with wavelength:

$\lambda = 606 \times 10^{-9}$ m, the photon energy is 2.05eV.

For sodium energy levels, yellow-orange light is emitted by sodium vapour. Sodium atoms emit this characteristic yellow-orange light with wavelengths (589.0 and 589.6) x 10^{-9}m when they make transitions from two closely spaced excited levels.

If an atom absorbs a photon in the ultra-violet region to reach an excited level and then drops back to the ground level in steps emitting two or more photons with smaller energy and longer wavelength. This phenomenon is termed **fluorescence**. For example, the electric discharge in a fluorescent tube causes the mercury vapour in the tube to emit ultra violet radiation.

In electric discharge tube, atomic hydrogen emits a series of lines of different wavelength. The visible line, H_α is in the red with wave length, 656.3nm. The next line in the blue-green, H_β has a wavelength 486.1nm and a formula gives the wavelengths of these lines called the **Balmer series:**

$$\frac{1}{\lambda} = R\left(\frac{1}{2^2} - \frac{1}{n^2}\right) \qquad 36.5$$

for the visible region where λ is the wavelength and R is the Rydberg's constant and $R = 1.097 \times 10^7 \text{m}^{-1}$ and $n = 3, 4, 5$. Other series proposed by Lyman and Paschen are in the ultraviolet and infrared regions. The energy levels E_n of the hydrogen atom are given by:

$$E_n = -\frac{13.6eV}{n^2}, \quad n = 1, 2, 3, \ldots \qquad 36.6$$

36.5 Photoelectric effect

It was discovered that electrons could be emitted from a metal surface when electromagnetic radiation falls on the surface. For some surfaces such as sodium, this radiation had to have short wavelength (X-rays or ultraviolet) to cause emission while for others such as caesium, electrons were emitted when irradiated by infra-red radiation which is of much longer wavelength. This phenomenon, first observed in 1887 by Hertz is known as **photoelectric effect.** This is the emission of

electrons when radiation of appropriate frequency strikes a metal surface. The liberated electrons absorb energy from the incident radiation and are thus able to overcome the attraction of positive charges.

These effects can be summarised as follows:

(a) No electrons are emitted from the positive plate due to the mutual attractive force between the electrons and the plate.

(b) The number of photoelectrons emitted per second is directly proportional to the intensity of radiation.

(c) The energy of the emitted electrons depends on the frequency of the incident radiation.

(d) There exists a *threshold frequency* (f_o) for all surfaces, and below this frequency, no electrons are emitted no matter the intensity of radiation. As long as the radiation with a frequency above the threshold value is used, the emission of electrons is instantaneous. This minimum frequency depends on the material of the cathode. The set up in Fig 36.5 demonstrates the photoelectric effect.

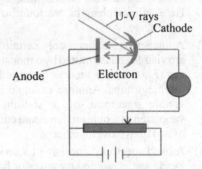

Fig. 36.5 Experimental set up for photoelectric effect.

Electrons emitted from the cathode are pushed toward the anode by the electric field force. Even when the direction of the electric field is reversed, some electrons still reach the anode. The stopping potential, V_o is the minimum value of the reverse potential difference that gives zero current.

The maximum kinetic energy ($K.E.$) of the most energetic electron leaving the cathode with $K.E._{max} = \frac{1}{2}mv_{max}^2$

has zero kinetic energy at the anode.

$$K.E_{max} = \frac{1}{2}mv_{max}^2 = eV_o \qquad 36.7$$

i.e. maximum kinetic energy of photoelectrons.

By measuring the stopping potential, V_o, the maximum kinetic energy with which the electrons leave the cathode can be determined.

Photoelectric effect and the quantum theory

To explain photoelectric effect, we have to resort to the quantum theory proposed by Max Planck in 1900. This states that *radiation is emitted in quanta or packets of energy.* The energy, E, of a quantum of radiation is given by:

$$E = hf$$

where h is the planck's constant and f is the frequency of radiation, $h = 6.62 \times 10^{-34}$ Js. From experiments, it has been found that only quanta of sufficient energy and hence of sufficiently high frequency would produce photoelectric emission from a metal surface. The minimum energy, E_o, required to remove an electron from the metal surface can be written as:

$$E_o = hf_o$$

and this is known as *work function* (ϕ) of the metal. Therefore, $K.E._{max} = \frac{1}{2} mv^2_{max} = hf - \phi$ and from equation 36.7,

$$eV_o = hf - \phi \qquad 36.8$$

Table 36.1 Work functions of some elements

Element	Work Function (ϕ) (eV)	Element	Work function (ϕ)
Sodium	2.40	Nickel	5.10
Caesium	1.88	Silicon	4.80
Copper	4.70	Platinum	6.75
Gold	5.10	Carbon	5.00

Einsten's photoelectric equation

An equation proposed by Einstein in 1905, relates the energy E, of the incident quantum to the work function and the kinetic energy of the emitted electron. If the work function of the metal is ϕ and the incident frequency is f, Einsteins photoelectric equation is expressed as $E = hf = \phi + \frac{1}{2} mv^2$

If $\phi = hf_o$, where f_o is the threshold frequency, then

$$\frac{1}{2} Mv^2 = h(f - f_o) \text{ and } eV_o = h(f - f_o). \qquad 36.9$$

Example 36.2

The threshold frequency for lithium is 5.5×10^{14} Hz. Calculate the work function for lithium. If lithium surface is illuminated by light of wavelength 450nm. Calculate the maximum velocity of the most energetic photo electrons.

Solution

For the equations 36.8 and 36.9,

Work function $\phi = hf_o$

$$= 6.63 \times 10^{-34} \times 5.5 \times 10^{14}$$

$$= 3.64 \times 10^{-19} J = 2.27 eV$$

Maximum $K.E., E_{max} = hf_o - \phi = \frac{hc}{\lambda} - \phi = \frac{1}{2} mv^2$

$$\frac{hc}{\lambda} = \frac{6.63 \times 10^{-34} \times 3.0 \times 10^8}{450 \times 10^{-9} \times 1.6 \times 10^{-19}} = 2.76 eV$$

$$E_{max} = 2.76 - 2.27$$

$$= 0.49 eV.$$

$$\frac{1}{2} mv^2 = 0.49 eV$$

$$v^2 = \frac{0.98 \times 1.6 \times 10^{-19}}{9.1 \times 10^{-31}}$$

$$v = \sqrt{0.172 \times 10^{12}} = 4.15 \times 10^5 \text{ ms}^{-1}$$

36.6 Thermionic emission

Edison in 1880 noticed that current could flow in an evacuated (without air) bulb from one glowing filament to another filament if the hot filament was negatively charged. This emission of electrons was called **thermionic emission**.

> Thermionic emission is the emission of free electrons from a hot metal surface. The energy required to cause this emission varies from metal to metal.

The emitting surface is usually a metal plate in a vacuum tube. The plate is indirectly heated with a hot wire. The cloud of electrons produced near the plate could be accelerated away by placing a second plate in the valve and maintained at a much more positive potential forming a thermionic diode as in Fig 36.6(a).

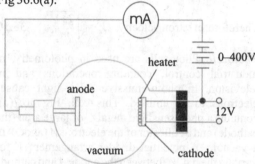

Fig 36.6(a) Experimental set-up for thermionic emission .

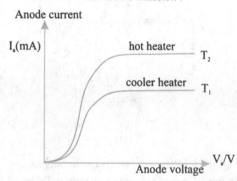

Fig. 36.6(b) Anode current I_a vs Anode voltage (V_a)

There was a flow of current which was indicated by the milliameter. The hotter the cathode, the greater the current since more electrons are emitted per second; this is shown in Fig 36.6(b), the lower curve represents a lower temperature, T_1. The greater the anode potential, the greater the electron velocity. Thermionic emission occurs because the free electrons within the metal are given sufficient energy to escape from the surface. The energy is provided by the heater of the filament.

The streams of electrons emitted from the cathode are called **cathode rays.**

The cathode rays have the following properties; they:

(a) Move in straight lines.

(b) Cause fluorescence.

(c) Possess kinetic energy which is changed to heat when brought to rest.

(d) Are deflected by electric and magnetic fields – traveling in circles in magnetic fields and in parabolas in electric fields at right angles to their motion.

(e) Possess a negative charge.

(f) Can produce X-rays if they are of very high energy.

The gain in kinetic energy of the electrons comes from their loss in electrical energy.

Gain in kinetic energy = $\frac{1}{2} m_e v_e^2$

Loss in electric energy = eV

Where V is the p.d. applied to the anode and e, the electron charge and m_e is the mass of electron.

Therefore, electron velocity, $V_e = \sqrt{\dfrac{2eV}{m_e}}$ 36.10

Photocell: Photocells are used in photometry, in industrial control, counting operations and in television. In photo-emissive cells, light causes electrons to be emitted. This cell, Fig 36.7(a), contains a photosensitive metal C of large area (the cathode) and a collector of the electrons A (anode) in a vacuum. A potential divider arrangement V for varying the p.d. V_{ac} between the anode A and cathode C and E, an electrometer is used to measure small current.

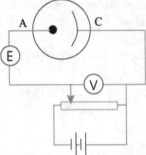

Fig. 36.7(a) Photoelectricity experimental set-up.

As shown, A is made negative in potential relative to C. The photo-electrons emitted from C then experience a retarding potential. The p.d., V is increased until the current becomes zero and the stopping potential, V_o is read from the voltmeter V. This is repeated for different wavelengths λ_1, λ_2 and λ_3.

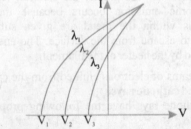

Fig 36.7(b) I-V characteristic of a photocell.

Fig 36.7(c) V_o versus f

36.7   X-ray production

The production and scattering of X-rays provide examples of the quantum nature of e-m radiation. X-rays are produced when rapidly moving electrons that have been accelerated through a potential difference of the order of 10^3 to 10^6V strike a metal target. Using an apparatus as illustrated in Fig. 36.8, electrons are emitted (boiled off) by thermionic emission from the heated cathode and accelerated towards the anode (the target) by a large potential difference, V_{AC}. The bulb is an evacuated glass globe (with a residual pressure of 10^{-7} atmosphere or less) so that the electrons can travel from the cathode to the anode without colliding with air molecules. When V_{AC} is of the order of 10^3 volts or more, the electrons strike the target (Tungsten anode) and X-rays are produced. With a cold cathode however, the voltages required are 10^5V and these tubes produce hard X-rays with wavelength $10^{-9} - 10^{-13}$m. Since X-rays are emitted by accelerated charges, it is clear that they are e-m waves, energy of an X-ray is related to its frequency and wavelength.

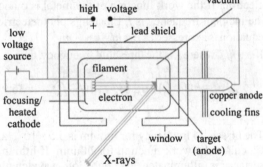

Fig 36.8 Apparatus for the production of X-rays.

Typical X-ray wavelengths range from 10^{-12} to 10^{-9}m.

$$E_{x-ray} = hf = \frac{hc}{\lambda} = eV \qquad 36.11$$

Example 36.3

Calculate the minimum wavelength of X-rays when a voltage of 45kV is applied to an X-ray tube.

Solution

From equation 36.7,

$$E = hf = \frac{hc}{\lambda} = eV$$

$$\frac{6.63 \times 3 \times 10^8 \times 10^{-34}}{1.6 \times 10^{-19} \times 45 \times 10^3} = \lambda = 2.8 \times 10^{-11} \text{m}$$

X-ray emission is the inverse of the photoelectric effect. In photoelectric emission, there is transformation of the energy of a photon into the kinetic energy of the electron; in X-ray production, there is a transformation of the kinetic energy of an electron into the energy of a photon. The intensity of X-rays depends on the number of electrons striking the target per second controlled by the heater current in hot cathodes. The wavelength depends on the voltage across the tube. The penetrating power depends on the accelerating voltage and the intensity of the beam. When X-rays collide with target, they lose their kinetic energy producing 99.5% heat and only 0.05% X-rays. Anode has to be cooled.

Compton scattering: A phenomenon called Compton scattering provides a direct confirmation of the quantum (particle) nature of X-rays. When X-rays strike matter, some of the radiation is scattered. Compton discovered that some of the scattered radiation has longer wavelength than the incident radiation and that the change in wavelength depends on the angle through which the radiation is scattered as shown in Fig. 36.8. If the scattered radiation energy is at an angle ϕ with respect to the incident direction and if λ and λ' are the wavelengths of the incident and scattered radiation, respectively, then

$$\lambda' - \lambda = \frac{h}{mc}(1 - \cos \phi) \text{ (Compton scattering)}$$

where m is the electron rest mass 9.11×10^{-31} kg

h = Planck's constant = 6.63×10^{-34} Js, and

c is the speed of e-m wave = 3×10^8 ms^{-1},

$$\frac{h}{mc} = 2.43 \times 10^{-12} \text{m.}$$

$$\lambda' - \lambda = \frac{h}{mc}(1 - \cos \phi) \qquad 36.12$$

Compton scattering cannot be explained using classical e-m theory which predicts that the scattered wave has the same wave length as the incident wave.

$\overrightarrow{P'}$	=	$\overrightarrow{p_i}$	−	$\overrightarrow{p_s}$
momentum of recoiling electron		*momentum of incident photon*		*momentum of scattered photon*

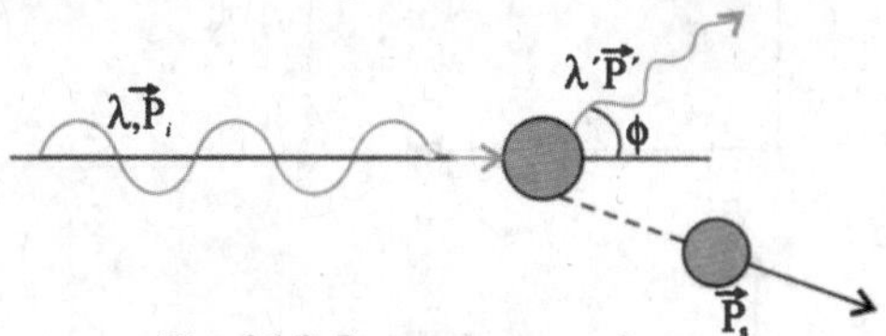

Fig. 36.9 Compton scattering

Properties of X-rays
X-rays were shown to have the following properties; they:
(a) Pass through many materials more or less unchanged;
(b) Cause fluorescence in materials such as rock salt, calcium compounds or uranium glass;
(c) Affect photographic plates;
(d) Cannot be refracted;
(e) Are not affected by magnetic and electric fields;
(f) Discharge electrified bodies by ionizing the surrounding air;
(g) Can cause photoelectric emission;
(h) Are produced when a beam of high energy electrons strike a metal target. (The higher the nucleon number of the target, the greater the intensity of the X-rays produced).

Uses of X-rays
(a) Diagnostic: X-rays are used in the detection of a broken bone or a tooth cavity. With the addition of an absorber such as iodine, X-rays are used to check respiratory or digestive disorder.
(b) Therapeutic: Used for the treatment of malignant cancers and tumors.
(c) Doses of X-rays for medical purposes to patients should be controlled as they can damage living tissues.
(d) X-ray diffraction can be used in determining atomic spacing in crystals.

Calculation of X-ray wavelengths
If electrons are accelerated to a velocity, v, by a potential difference, V, and then allowed to collide with a metal target, the maximum frequency, f, of the X-rays emitted is given by the equation:

$$\frac{1}{2}mv^2 = eV = hf$$
$$f = \frac{eV}{h}$$

This shows that the maximum frequency is directly proportional to the accelerating voltage.

Summary
1. The energy in electromagnetic waves is carried in packets (packages) called photons or quanta. The energy, E, of one photon for a wave with frequency, f, and wavelength, λ, is:

$$E = hf = \frac{hc}{\lambda}$$

2. In the photoelectric effect, a surface can absorb a photon and eject an electron if the photon energy hf is greater than the work function ϕ. The stopping potential, V_o for the electrons emitted can be deducted from $eV_o = hf - \phi$ and $\phi = hf_o$ where f_o is the threshold frequency. Hence, $eV_o = h(f - f_o)$, frequency f_o is, the minimum frequency below which, no electron can be emitted for a given surface. The kinetic energy (K.E.$_{max}$) of the most energetic electron leaving the cathode is given as:

$$K.E_{max} = \frac{1}{2}mv^2_{max} = eV_o$$

When an atom makes a transition from an initial energy level E_i to a final level E_f by emitting a photon, the frequency, f, and the wavelength, λ, of the photon are given by:

$$hf = \frac{hc}{\lambda} = E_i - E_f$$

3. The energy, E_x required to raise an atom from its ground state to an excited state is called excitation energy given by:
$$E_x = eV_x$$
where V_x is the excitation potential of the atom.

4. The energy required to remove an electron completely from the atom is termed ionization energy, E_i given by $E_i = E_\infty - E_o = eV_i$ (E_∞ is zero energy, $E_o =$ ground state and V_i is the ionization potential).

5. The Franck and Hertz experiment gives direct evidence that energy levels exist in atoms. The values of the energy are discrete multiples of eV_c where V_c is the critical potential of the atom.

6. There are two main types of spectra:
   (a) Emission spectra where light is given out by a source. Emitted or absorbed photons give rise to characteristic colour of light and wavelength/frequency ($c = f\lambda$), krypton atom emits a photon of orange light with a wavelength of 6.06×10^{-7}m. Sodium vapour emits photon of yellow-orange light with wavelengths $(5.890$ and $5.896) \times 10^{-7}$m. The hydrogen (H_α) series emits photon in the red colour with wavelength 6.563×10^{-7}m.
   Emission spectra include (i) continuous spectrum e.g. sun, here all wavelengths are found (ii) the line spectrum e.g. monatomic gases, neon gas produce line spectrum which consists of well defined lines of a particular wavelength.
   (b) Absorption spectra result when light from a source is absorbed as it passes through a gas or liquid.

7. For the hydrogen series,
$$\frac{1}{\lambda} = R\left[\frac{1}{2^2} - \frac{1}{n^2}\right]$$
where $R = 1.097 \times 10^7$m^{-1} and $n = 3,4,5\ldots$
The energy levels of the hydrogen atom are given by:
$$E_n = -\frac{13.60}{n^2} eV \quad \text{for } n = 1,2,3,4\ldots n$$

8. The Compton scattering provides a strong evidence of the quantum (particle) nature of X-rays.

Exercise 36
Useful constants:
$h = 6.63 \times 10^{-34}$Js $\quad c = 3 \times 10^8$ms^{-1}
$e = -1.6 \times 10^{-19}$C $\quad m_e = 9.1 \times 10^{-31}$kg
$eV = 1.6 \times 10^{-19}$J

1. A photon of orange light has a wave length of 600nm. The photon frequency is
   A. 5.0×10^{12} Hz. B. 5.0×10^{13}Hz.
   C. 5.0×10^{14}Hz. D. 5.0×10^{15}Hz.

2. Calculate the photon energy of light having a wavelength of 600nm.
   A. 0.021eV B. 0.21eV
   C. 2.1eV E. 21eV

3. A nucleus in a transition from an excited state emits a gamma ray photon with an energy of 3.2 MeV. Calculate the photon frequency.
   A. 7.72×10^{14}Hz. B. 7.0×10^{14}Hz.
   C. 8.5×10^{20}Hz. D. 7.72×10^{20}Hz.

4. A continuous spectrum may be emitted by
   A. Neon gas. B. Sodium vapour.
   C. Carbon dioxide. D. Sun.

5. The number of electrons emitted per second when a metal is irradiated with appropriate frequency depends on
   A. intensity of radiation.
   B. frequency of radiation.
   C. energy of a radiation.
   D. momentum of the radiation.

6. The energy of the emitted electrons from the metal surface depends on
   A. frequency. B. Wavelengths.
   C. intensity. D. momentum of the radiation.

7. The work function of a metal is expressed as
   A. hc. B. $h\lambda_o$. C. $\frac{hc}{\lambda_o}$. D. $\frac{hc^2}{\lambda_o}$. E. $\frac{h^2c}{\lambda_o}$.

8. Which of the following depicts the curve of current against voltage in the process of thermionic emission?

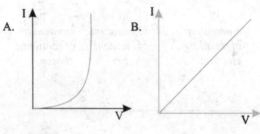

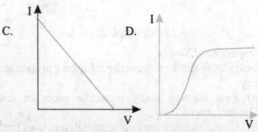

Fig. 36.10

9. Cathode rays are
   A. photons. B. electrons.
   C. neutrons. D. γ-rays.

10. Which of the following is **not** a property of X-rays? They
    A. are *e-m* waves.
    B. are deflected by electric field.
    C. can cause photoemission.
    D. can cause fluorescence.

11. An X-ray tube is operated at 40kV, the shortest wavelength of the X-rays produced is
    A. 3.11×10^{-11}m. B. 3.01×10^{-10}m.
    C. 3.01×10^{-9}m. D. 3.01×10^{-8}m.

12. The process by which a metal, heated to a high temperature, boils off electrons from its surface is known as
    A. photoelectric emission.
    B. thermionic emission.
    D. field emission.
    E. radio active emission.

13. Which of the following gives rise to line spectra obtained from atoms?
    A. Ionization of an electron from the atom.
    B. Excitation of an electron in the atom.
    C. Kinetic energy of a moving atom.
    D. Change of an electron from a higher to a lower energy level in the atom.

14. The minimum energy required to remove an electron completely from a given atom is known as
    A. potential energy.
    B. binding energy.
    C. excitation energy.
    D. ionization energy.

15. The work function of a metal is 8.6×10^{-19}J. Calculate the wave length of its threshold frequency.
    A. 80.0nm   B. 100.0nm
    C. 124.0nm   D. 231.0nm

16. (a) Define "work function" of a metal.
    (b) Sodium has a work function of 2.1 eV and it is illuminated by radiation whose wavelength is 150nm.
    Calculate:
    (i) the maximum energy;
    (ii) the speed of the emitted electrons;
    (iii) the least frequency of radiation for which electrons are emitted.

17. (a) When light is incident on a metal plate electrons are emitted only when the frequency of the light exceeds a certain value. Explain this phenomenon.

(b) The maximum kinetic energy of the electrons emitted from a metallic surface is 1.6×10^{-19}J when the frequency of the incident radiation is 7.5×10^{14}Hz. Calculate the minimum frequency of radiation for which the electrons are emitted.

18. (a) Explain what is meant by (i) ionization potential and (ii) excitation potential.
    (b) The ground state of the electron in the hydrogen atom is represented by the energy -13.6eV and the first excited state by -3.4 eV on a scale in which the electron is completely free is at zero energy. Calculate:
    (i) The ionization potential of the hydrogen atom.
    (ii) The wavelengths of two lines in the emission spectrum of hydrogen.

19. (a) What are X-rays? List two properties of X-rays.
    (b) Protons are accelerated by a potential difference of 5.0×10^3V and strike a target calculate the minimum wavelength of the resulting X-rays.

20. (a) Briefly describe, using a modern X-ray tube how X-rays are produced.
    (b) List four properties of X-rays and two applications.

21. (a) Distinguish between *hard* and *soft* X-rays.
    (b) A certain source generated X-ays with an acceleration voltage of 17.0 kV in a tube. Calculate the shortest wavelength of X-rays produced in the tube.

22. An atom that is initially in an energy level with $E = -8.92$eV absorbs a photon that has a wavelength 735nm. Calculate the internal energy of the atom after it absorbs the photon.

23. Explain what is meant by:
    (i) photoelectric effect; and
    (ii) work function.

24. (a) Distinguish between photoelectric emission and thermionic emission.
    (b) List four properties of electrons.
    (c) Compare the velocity of electrons produced in a thermionic emission process and a photo-emission process using the following data.

Thermionic		Photoelectric
Voltage	2000V	200V
Work function	4eV	2eV

25. Determine the minimum potential difference between the filament and the target of an *X*-ray tube if the tube is to produce *X*-rays with a wavelength of 0.120nm.

26. (a) Explain the term "photoelectric effect".

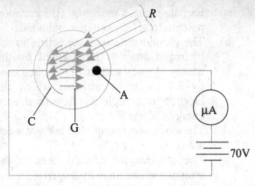

Fig. 36.11

The diagram above represents a photocell with its associated circuit.

(a) Identify the physical quantities represented by letters *A*, *C*, *G* and *R*.

(b) State two applications of photoelectric effect.

(c) A light of wavelength 510nm is incident on a metal resulting in the emission of photoelectrons. If the work function of the metal is 2.20 eV, calculate the:

(i) maximum kinetic energy of the photoelectrons.

(ii) energy of the incident photon.

27. (a) What are photoelectrons?

(b) State two features of photoelectric emission.

(c) An incident radiation of energy, *E*, falls on a photoemissive surface with a *work function*, φ and a *threshold frequency*, f_o resulting in the photoemission of electrons with *maximum kinetic energy, K.E.$_{max}$*. Explain the italised words.

28. (a) Briefly explain the following terms:

(i) ground state energy;

(ii) excitation energy;

(iii) ionization energy;

(iv) emission line spectra;

(v) line-absorption spectra.

(b) An electron jumps from an energy level of –3.2eV to one of –10.6 eV in an atom, calculate the energy and wavelength of the radiation emitted.

29. (a) Explain what is meant by photoelectric emission.

(b) Draw a labelled diagram to illustrate the structure of a photocell and explain its operation.

(c) In a photoemissive cell, no electrons leave the surface until the threshold of the incident radiation is reached. Explain what happens to the energy of the light before the emission of electrons starts.

State one factor that determines the number of electrons emitted.

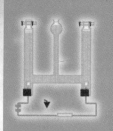

ELECTRICAL CONDUCTION THROUGH LIQUIDS AND GASES

We shall study the effect of passing an electric current through certain classes of liquids. Not all liquids will conduct electricity, only those that contain ions. Some molten compounds, and solutions such as inorganic acids, bases and salts dissolved in water, and fused inorganic solids allow electricity to pass through them. In the process, the substances break up into their component parts. This process is termed **electrolysis** and the liquid in which this takes place is known as **electrolyte**. At the negative electrode (*cathode*) the product liberated is always either a metal or hydrogen while at the positive electrode (*anode*), it is oxygen or non-metal or the anode may dissolve in solution.

Some of these terms need to be defined

Electrolysis is the process of decomposing certain liquids and solutions into their component parts by the passage of electricity through them.

An electrolyte is a liquid which will conduct electricity and which can be decomposed into its component parts in the process.

Ions are charged particles which exist in electrolytes and take part in electrolysis. The ions which move to the anode are called anions; those that move to the cathode are called cations.

A voltameter is the vessel containing the electrolyte and the electrode.

Electrolysis takes place in the voltameter as in figure 37.1.

Electrodes are materials in the form of rods or plates through which current enters or leaves the electrolyte.

37.1 Conduction through liquid: ionic theory

The ionic theory was developed by a Swedish scientist, Arrhenius. He considers an electrolyte as dissociating into charged particles called **ions**. This dissociation occurs irrespective of whether or not an electric field is applied to the electrolyte. For example, copper tetraoxosulphate (VI), ($CuSO_4$) in

solution dissociates into a copper ion and a tetraoxosulphate (VI) ion. Using chemical symbols.

$$CuSO_4 \rightarrow Cu^{2+} + SO_4^{2-}$$

The copper ion is a copper atom that has lost two electrons and is therefore positively charged while a tetraoxosulphate (VI) ion is a group of atoms that has gained two electrons and therefore is negatively charged. In an electrolyte, the negative (–ve) and positive (+ve) ions move randomly in solution until positive and negative electrodes are placed in the electrolyte and a battery connected to the electrodes. The +ve ions drift towards the cathode (–ve plate) and the -ve ions move towards the anode (+ve plate). The rate of movement of charge is the current flowing in the electrolyte. This is illustrated in Fig. 37.1. Such movement ceases as soon as the battery is disconnected. Electrolytic solutions are able to conduct electricity because the electrolytes in solution can dissociate into ions.

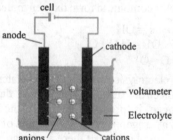

Fig. 37.1 The voltameter

Examples of electrolysis

Electrolysis of acidulated water

The Hoffmann voltameter is used in the electrolysis of acidulated water. It consists of two graduated tubes connected to another tube which has a reservoir through which the electrolyte is introduced. The electrodes are made of platinum. The electrolyte is water to which a few drops of tetraoxosulphate (VI) acid have been added to increase its conductivity. With the taps closed, a steady current is passed into the electrolyte through the platinum electrodes. It is observed that bubbles of gases form at the upper end of the graduated tubes as the levels of the electrolyte fall. The volume of the hydrogen gas collected at the cathode is twice that of the oxygen gas collected at the anode. This set up is illustrated in figure 37.2.

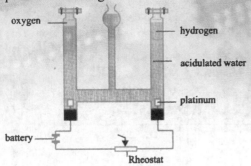

oxygen — hydrogen — acidulated water — platinum — battery — Rheostat

Fig. 37.2 Hoffmann voltameter

According to ionic theory, water (H_2O) dissociates into hydrogen (H^+) ions and hydroxyl ions (OH^-), that is;

$$H_2O \longrightarrow H^+ + OH^-$$

The tetraoxosulphate (VI) acid, (H_2SO_4) dissociates into hydrogen ions and tetraoxosulphate (VI) ions.

$$H_2SO_4 \longrightarrow 2H^+ + SO_4^{2-}$$

When current is passed through the platinum electrodes in acidutated water, the H^+ ions drift towards the cathode where they receive electrons and form neutral hydrogen atoms which combine in pairs to form hydrogen molecules, H_2

$$H^+ + e^- = H, \quad H + H = H_2$$

At the same time, the hydroxyl and the tetraoxosulphate (VI) ions move towards the anode where the tetraoxosulphate (VI) ions remain in solution while the hydroxyl ions lose electrons to the anode and form water and oxygen atoms. The oxygen atoms combine to form oxygen molecules.

$$OH^- + e^- = OH$$
$$OH + OH = H_2O + O$$
$$O + O = O_2$$

Thus, in electolysis of acidulated water using platinum electron, oxygen is formed at the anode and hydrogen is produced at the cathode. The volume of hydrogen is twice the volume of oxygen collected. This shows that, there are twice as many hydrogen atoms as oxygen atoms in water and confirms that the chemical formula for water is H_2O.

Electrolysis of copper tetraoxosulphate (VI) solution using copper electrodes

Using the set up of apparatus in fig. 37. 3 and as described previously, the copper tetraoxosulphate (VI) in solution dissociates into copper ions and tetraoxosulphate (VI) ions and water dissociates into hydrogen ions and hydroxyl ions.

$$CuSO_4 \longrightarrow Cu^{2+} + SO_4^{2-}$$
$$H_2O \longrightarrow H^+ + OH^-$$

When electricity is passed, the copper and hydrogen ions drift to the cathode where copper is discharged in preference to the hydrogen (H^+) ions from water. So, copper is deposited at the cathode

$$Cu^{2+} + 2e^- \longrightarrow Cu$$

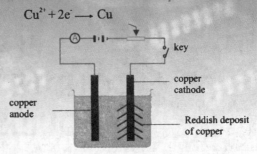

key — copper cathode — copper anode — Reddish deposit of copper

Fig. 37.3 Electrolysis of copper tetraoxosulphate (VI) using copper electrodes.

The SO_4^{2-} and OH^- ions drift to the anode. The SO_4^{2-} combine with the copper of the anode to form more copper tetraoxosulphate (VI). The concentration of copper tetraoxosulphate (VI) remains the same because the copper goes into solution from the copper anode at the same rate as copper is being discharged on the cathode from the solution. The anode therefore dissolves and is deposited in the cathode.

$$Cu^{2+} - 2e^- = Cu^{2+}$$
$$Cu^{2+} + SO_4^{2-} = CuSO_4 \text{ (at the anode)}$$

From experiments, it can be shown that the amount of substance liberated at either electrode depends on the:

(a) mass of substance liberated;
(b) current passed through the electrolyte; and
(c) time for which the current is passed.

37.2 Electrolysis and Faraday's laws

Based on these experiments, Faraday formulated two laws:

1. The mass, m, of a given element liberated during the process of electrolysis is directly proportional to the quantity of electricity, Q, that has passed during the electrolysis,

i.e. $$m \propto Q \Rightarrow m = zIt \qquad 37.1$$

where z is a constant of proportionality for each element and is known as its electrochemical equivalent, (i.e. mass of the element liberated by the passage of one coulomb of electricity) its units are $kg\,C^{-1}$.

2. The relative masses of substances liberated by the same quantity of electricity are proportional to their chemical equivalents C,

i.e. $$\frac{m_1}{m_2} = \frac{c_1}{c_2} \qquad 37.2$$

or the number of moles of different elements liberated in electrolysis by the passage of the same quantity of charge are simply related to each other.

The quantity of charge required to liberate or dissolve one mole of any singly charged ion in electrolysis is termed Faraday constant (F), it's value is $9.65 \times 10^4\,C\,mol^{-1}$.

Example 37.1

The electrochemical equivalent of a metal is $0.12 \times 10^{-6} kgC^{-1}$. Calculate the mass of the metal deposited in 2 hours after a current of 2.0A flows through the electrolyte.

Solution

From the equation 37.1,

$$m = zIt$$
$$= 0.12 \times 10^{-6} \times 2 \times 2 \times 60 \times 60 \, kg$$
$$= 1.728 \times 10^{-3} kg.$$

Example 37.2

The masses of copper and silver deposited are 10.00g and 34.28g respectively when the same current flows through copper and silver voltameters for 30 minutes. If the chemical equivalent of silver is 108, calculate the chemical equivalent of copper.

Solution

From equation 37.2,

$$\frac{m_1}{m_2} = \frac{c_1}{c_2}$$
$$\frac{10}{34.28} = \frac{c}{108}$$

Chemical equivalent for copper

$$c = \frac{10 \times 108}{34.28} = 31.5$$

Electrolysis of copper sulphate solution using platinum electrodes.

It is observed in this process that the platinum cathode is covered with a bright red layer of pure copper. The copper sulphate solution loses its blue colour. During electrolysis, Cu^{2+} and H^+ ions drift to the cathode where copper is discharged in preference to hydrogen. At the anode, the OH^- ions are discharged and combine to form water and oxygen.

$$4OH^- \longrightarrow 2H_2O + O_2 + 4e^-$$

The net result is the deposit of copper on the cathode, the production of oxygen around the anode and the reduction in the concentration of the copper tetraoxosulphate (VI) solution.

Verification of Faraday's Laws of electrolysis.

The required apparatus which consists of a copper voltameter with copper electrodes, a rheostat, ammeter, a battery of cells is connected as shown in Fig 37.4. A stop clock is also provided to record the time.

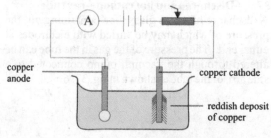

Fig. 37.4(a) Set up to verify Faraday's first law

The surface of the cathode is cleaned with emery cloth and washed in distilled water. It is weighed on a beam balance and then dipped into the copper tetraoxosulphate (VI) solution and connected to the -ve terminal of the battery. The current is switched on and adjusted to a value of 1.0A and made to flow for about 20 minutes using the rheostat. The cathode is removed, rinsed with distilled water and dried. It is weighed again to find the mass of copper deposited. The cathode is placed back into the voltameter and the process is repeated for four more times. If the mass of copper deposited is plotted against the total time for which current flowed in each case, a straight line graph passing through the origin will be obtained. This shows that the mass of copper deposited is directly proportional to the time for which 1A current flowed.

The electrochemical equivalent, z, of copper can be found from the gradient of the graph.

Hence, $z = \frac{m}{It} = \frac{Gradient}{I}$

where current $I = 1A$

(b) Using the same apparatus, the voltameter is run four times for about 20 minutes for different values of current (e.g. 0.5, 1.0, 1.5, 2.0, 2.5A) each time. If the mass of copper deposited by each flow of current is plotted against the current, a straight line graph is again obtained showing that the mass of copper deposited is directly proportional to current. From the gradient of the graph, $\frac{m}{I}$,

$$z = \frac{gradient}{20 \times 60}$$

The two sets of experiments demonstrate that the mass of substances deposited in electrolysis is directly proportional to the current and to the time for which current flowed.

Experiment to calibrate an ammeter

A copper voltameter with copper electrodes, a key, a battery, a rheostat and the ammeter to be caliberated are connected in series as set up as in Fig. 37.4(a). The cathode plate is first cleaned, washed in distilled water and dried in a current of warm air. The plate is weighed and placed in the voltameter with copper tetroxosulphate (VI) solution as the electrolyte with the key closed and by adjusting the rheostat, the ammeter gives the full scale reading to within a few amperes. The stop clock is started at the same time the key is closed. After the current has passed for some time as recorded by the stop clock, the current is switched off. The cathode is washed and reweighed. The difference in the mass gives the mass of copper deposited.

Let the initial mass of cathode be $m_i \, g$

Let the final mass of cathode be $m_f \, g$

Let time for which current is passed be t

If the electrochemical equivalent of copper, $z = 0000339C^{-1}$

Mass of copper deposited is $(m_f - m_i)$g

$$\therefore \text{current} = \frac{m_f - m_i}{zt}$$

This current can be marked on the scale of the ammeter and the scale between this value and zero can be graduated.

Experimental verification of Faraday's second law

A copper voltameter and a silver voltameter are connected in series as shown in fig. 37.4(b) The copper and silver cathodes are weighed and then rinsed in distilled water, dried and re-weighed to determine the masses of copper and silver deposited. If the masses are compared, they will be found to be in the following ratio.
Copper: silver as 32: 108 which is their respective chemical equivalent.

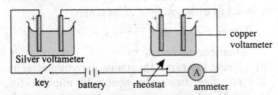

Fig. 37.4(b) Set up for Faraday's second law

37.3 Applications of electrolysis

In industry, electrolysis is used in electroplating of metals, purification of metals and electrolytic production of metals from compounds.

Electroplating

This process is used in coating cutlery (spoons, forks) and other articles with copper, silver, chromium or gold. The material to be plated is placed as the cathode and the coating material is made the anode of a voltameter. The solution of a salt of the plating material is made the electrolyte. When a spoon is to be silver plated, it is made the cathode, pure silver is made the anode and silvertrioxonitrate (V) ($AgNO_3$) solution is the electrolyte (Fig. 37.5).

Two anodes are placed one on each side of the spoon such that the front and back of the spoon is plated at the same time.
The silver trioxonitrate (V) ($AgNO_3$) in solution dissociates into silver ions (Ag^+) and trioxonitrate (V) ion(NO_3^-).

$$AgNO_3 \longrightarrow Ag^+ + NO_3^-$$

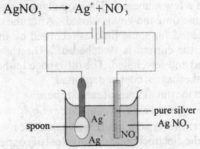

Fig. 37.5 Electroplating

When electricity is passed through the solution, Ag^+ ions drift to the cathode where they are discharged and the spoon is coated with silver. The NO_3 ions remain in solution, combining with silver from the anode to form more silver trioxonitrate(V), thus maintaining its original concentration.

The need for electroplating of a metal is to improve its appearance and prevent it from being corroded. Bumpers of cars and handlebars of bicycles are chromium plated to give them bright appearance and protect them from rusting.

The purification of metals

In the electrolysis of copper tetraoxosulphate (VI) using copper electrodes, copper is deposited at the cathode while at the same time the copper from the anode got into solution.

In order to purify a copper metal, the impure copper is made the anode while pure copper is made the cathode. With the passage of electricity, copper ions are dissolved from the anode and deposited at the cathode, leaving the impurities in solution. The pure copper is used in the manufacture of connecting wires and electric cables because of its low resistance.

Preparation of metals from their compounds

Electrolytic processes can be used to prepare metals such as aluminum, sodium and potassium from their molten chloride or hydroxide solutions.

37.4 Conduction of electricity through gases

We are all familiar with the electric spark formed when a *high-voltage* discharge occurs across a region of air, and also with the bright yellow light emitted by a sodium vapour lamp. These are examples of the conduction of electricity through gases. The different results are due not only to the different gases but also the different pressures under which conduction takes place. The pressure in neon lamp is about 10mm of mercury.

In dry air at atmospheric pressure 760mm Hg, a voltage of about 30kV is required to produce a spark between two electrodes, 1cm apart. For pointed electrodes the p.d. is reduced to 12kV due to the higher field at a point. For small potential differences, a gas is almost a perfect insulator. At lower pressures the p.d. to give sparking is reduced.

37.5 Discharge and hot cathode-ray tube

A discharge tube is a glass tube containing air, the pressure of which may be varied with electrodes at either end. The pressure of the gas in the tube can be altered through the vacuum pump connected to a side arm of the tube as shown in fig. 37. 6.

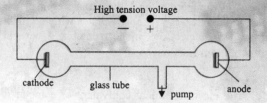

Fig. 37.6 Discharge tube

Experiments with discharge tube show that gases conduct electricity under *low pressure* and *high potential difference* (greater than 100V). Under these conditions, a gas in discharge tube will glow because its atoms are given energy by the flow of electricity through the tube.

At very low pressure (*0.01mm Hg*) and high voltage (*> 1 kV*) the gas in the tube breaks into ions. The positive ions move towards the cathode and the negative ions and free electrons move towards the anode. The positive ions knock off electrons from the metal plate of the cathode. These electrons produced at the cathode are called cathode rays.

As the pressure is reduced still further, the p.d. needed to maintain the discharge rises again, and at pressures less than 0.001mmHg the tube becomes a good insulator again.

Goldstein, in 1896 observed that when a discharge occurred in a tube of low pressure, gas rays appeared to be produced from the anode which are called positive rays and originated within the gas itself. These positive rays were composed of particles which were positive ions of the gas in the tube.

The positive rays showed the following properties, they;
(a) could be deflected by electric and magnetic fields.
(b) showed a spectrum of velocities.
(c) were dependent of the gas in the tube.
(d) could cause ionization.
(e) cause fluorescence and affected photographic plates.

Nature and properties of cathode rays: They
(a) consist of streams of fast moving particles of negative electricity called electrons;
(b) cause materials (glass or zinc) to fluoresce;
(c) travel in straight lines;
(d) are deflected by electric and magnetic fields;
(e) can ionize gas;
(f) can affect photographic plates;
(g) can produce X-rays from high density metals when they are suddenly stopped by such metals;
(h) are highly penetrating (can penetrate aluminum plate, and even steel plate).

From the stated properties, it is concluded that cathode rays are highly energetic electrons used for lighting and display of signs. For example, the tube contains mercury vapour or sodium vapour which at low pressure fluoresce or glow at the passage of cathode rays. The cathode rays (or electrons) produced in the tube cause the emission of ultra-violet rays when they bombard the vapourised atoms of mercury. The interior of the fluorescent lamps are coated with phosphorus which gives off visible light when the ultra-violet rays strike it. Fluorescent tubes are also used as display signs. The most widely used gas is the neon gas which gives bright orange-red colour while fluorescent lamps are more efficient than filament lamps.

Cathode ray tube

Cathode ray tubes are found in oscilloscopes and similar devices and are used in *TV* picture tubes and computer displays. Cathode ray tubes use an electron beam which was called cathode ray since it emanated from the cathode (-ve electrode) of a vacuum tube.

The cathode ray oscilloscope was developed in 1897 by Brown from the cathode tube. It has many applications, including voltage measurement (a.c. and d.c.), observation of wave forms, frequency and phase comparison and time measurement. Fig 37.7 is a simplified diagram of a cathode ray oscilloscope *(CRO)*.

At the centre of the *CRO* is a highly evacuated cathode ray tube with the following features:
(a) a heated cathode *C* to produce a beam of electrons (a typical beam current is of the order of 0.1mA);
(b) a grid *G* to control the brightness of the beam;
(c) an accelerating anode A_2 at a potential of about 1kV;
(d) a pair of plates Y_1 and Y_2 to deflect the beam in the vertical direction;
(e) a pair of plates X_1 and X_2 to deflect the beam in the horizontal direction;
(f) fluorescent screen *F* on which the beam of electron falls. Such screens are coated with zinc sulphide, which emits a blue glow when electrons collide with it;
(g) a graphite coating to shield the beam from external electric fields and to provide a return path for the electrons;
(h) a metal screen which surrounds the tube and shields it from stray magnetic fields.

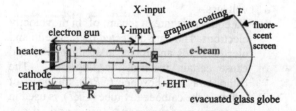

Fig. 37.7 Cathode ray oscilloscope

The focusing and accelerating systems are connected at different points along a resistor chain. Focusing is achieved by varying the voltage applied between the two anodes A_1 and A_2.

The *CRT* has a hot cathode, brightness control and electron lens. It has *X*- and *Y*-plates which deflect the beam of electrons in horizontal a d vertical directions respectively.

Summary

1. Liquids containing +ve ions and –ve ions conduct electric current and are known as electrolytes.

2. Electrolysis is the process of decomposing certain liquids and solutions into their component parts by the passage of electricity through them.

3. A voltameter is the vessel containing the electrodes and the electrolyte and is a device used to study the process of electrolysis.
   In the electrolysis of copper tetraoxosulphate (VI) solution, with copper electrodes, copper is transferred from anode to cathode. With platinum electrodes, copper is deposited at the cathode and oxygen is formed at the anode leaving the solution less dense.

4. Faraday's laws of electrolysis:
   (a) The mass, m, of an element deposited or liberated during electrolysis is directly proportional to the quantity of electricity, Q (current and time) which is passed through the electrolyte.
   $m = zQ = zIt$
   The constant of proportionality, z is the electro chemical equivalent (mass deposited per coulomb).
   (b) When the same current passes through different electrolytes for the same time, the mass of any element deposited is proportional to its chemical equivalent (atomic mass/valency).

5. In electroplating, the material to be electroplated is made the cathode in a voltameter containing an electrolyte which is the solution of the metal to be deposited while the anode is the electroplating material.

6. Electrolysis can also be applied to purify some metals and certain metals may be prepared from their compound using electrolytic process.

7. Cathode rays are produced in gas discharge tubes under very low pressure and high voltages.

8. Cathode rays are a beam of high velocity electrons. They are deflected by magnetic and electric fields and travel in straight lines and cause certain materials to fluoresce. The cathode ray oscilloscope (*CRO*), the heart of which is the cathode ray tube (*CRT*), is used in voltage measurement (a.c. and d.c.), observation of waveforms, frequency and phase comparison and time measurement.

Exercise 37

1. The electrochemical equivalent of a metal is 0.126×10^{-6} kg C^{-1}, the mass of the metal that a current of 2.5 A will deposit in 2 hours is
   A. 0.595×10^{-3} kg.   B. 2.268×10^{-3} kg.
   C. 0.227×10^{-3} kg.   D. 0.378×10^{-3} kg.

2. A charge of one coulomb liberates 0.0033g of copper in an electrolytic process. How long will it take a current of 1A to liberate 0.99 g of copper in such a process?
   A. 60 minutes   B. 50 minutes
   C. 30 minutes   D. 5 minutes

3. The electrochemical equivalent of silver is $0.0012gC^{-1}$, if 18.0g of silver is to be deposited by electrolytic process on a surface by passing a steady current for 500 minutes, the current should be
   A. 400mA.   B. 450mA.
   C. 500 mA.   D. 550mA.

4. The electrochemical equivalent of a metal is 1.3×10^{-7} kgC^{-1}. The mass of the metal X which 2.0×10^4 C of electricity will deposit from a suitable electrolyte is
   A. 6.5×10^{-2} kg.   B. 2.6×10^{-2} kg.
   C. 6.5×10^{-3} kg.   D. 2.6×10^{-3} kg.

5. To electroplate with 1.0kg of platinum, a current of 100A was passed through an appropriate vessel containing a platinum electrolyte for 2.0×10^4 hours, the electrochemical equivalent for platinum is
   A. 5.0×10^{-7} kgC^{-1}.   B. 2.5×10^{-7} kgC^{-1}.
   C. 1.38×10^{-10} kgC^{-1}.   D. 1.38×10^{-8} kgC^{-1}.

6. In a *CRO*, the grid controls the
   A. voltage.   B. current.
   C. frequency.   D. brightness.

7. Which of the following instruments is not required in the set up of experiment on electrolysis?
   A. Voltameter   B. voltmeter
   C. ammeter   D. Electrodes

8. Which of the following graphs correctly illustrates the variation of mass with quantity of electricity in electrolysis?

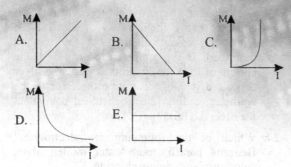

Fig. 37.8

9. Which of the following statement(s) correctly describe(s) cathode rays?
   I   They consist of particles carrying negative electric charges.
   II They are deflected in a magnetic but not in an electric field.
   III They consist of fast moving neutrons and are deflected in an electric field.
   A. I only   B. II only
   C. III only   D. I and II only

10. Which of the following is not true of a discharge tube?
   A. The gas in the tube must be carbon dioxide.
   B. The glass tube must have two electrodes.
   C. The pressure of the gas must be very low.
   D. Air is gradually pumped out of the tube.

11. The mass of an element liberated by one coulomb of electricity during electrolysis is
   A. atomic mass.
   B. molecular mass.
   C. chemical equivalent.
   D. electrochemical equivalent.

12. In the cathode ray oscilloscope, the anodes are
   A. at higher positive potential than the cathode.
   B. at the same potential as the cathode.
   C. at lower positive potential than the cathode.
   D. at a more negative potential than the cathode.

13. Which of the following is **not** a component of the electron gun in *CRT*?
   A. Heated filament   B. Grid
   C. Y-Y plate   E. Electron lens

14. The masses of copper and silver deposited are 5.00g and 17.14g respectively when the same current flows through copper and silver voltameters for 15 minutes. If the chemical equivalent of silver is 108, calculate the chemical equivalent of copper.
   A. 30.5   B. 31.5
   C. 32.0   D. 32.5

15. The process by which cathode-rays are emitted in the cathode ray tube is
   A. photoelectric emission.
   B. thermionic emission.
   C. field emission.
   D. cathode emission.

16. (a) Explain the following terms:
      (i)   electrolysis;
      (ii) electrodes;
      (iii) electrolyte; and
      (iv) voltameter.
   (b) State Faraday's laws and briefly describes an experiment to illustrate the first law.
   (c) Calculate the time it will take to coat evenly a copper plate in a copper voltameter if the mass of copper deposited on the cathode is 1.3g when a current of 1.5A is passed through the voltameter. (z of copper $= 0.000339 gC^{-1}$).

17. Present an account of the processes occurring when dilute tetraoxosulphate (VI) acid is electrolysed between platinum electrodes.
   An ammeter and a copper voltameter are placed in series in a circuit. After 10 minutes the mass of copper deposited is 0.18g. The ammeter reading is 0.8A. If the e.c.e of copper is 0.0003 gC^{-1}, what can you deduce from the ammeter reading?

18. Explain the terms anode and cathode in relation to an electrolytic process. Calculate the cost of depositing a layer of silver 0.2mm thick on an iron spoon of surface area 100cm^2 if a current of 1.5A for an hour cost ₦20. (Density of silver is 10.5gcm^3, z of silver is $1.12 g C^{-1}$).

19. List two industrial applications of electrolysis. Describe an experiment to illustrate Faraday's second law of electrolysis.
   A copper and a silver voltameter are connected in series and for a given period; 5.0g of copper was deposited, calculate the mass of silver deposited within the same period of time. Assume the chemical equivalent of copper to be 31.5, chemical equivalent of silver to be 108.

20. (a) What are charge carriers of electric current in: (i) metals? (ii) electrolytes? (iii) semiconductors?
   (b) Explain the origin and nature of cathode rays. List four of their properties. State two ways in which they are produced.
   (c) Sketch and label the diagram of a cathode ray oscilloscope. State the function of each component part.

21. (a) List four properties and the nature of positive rays.
    (b) Briefly discuss the conduction of electricity through gas.

22. Distinguish between chemical equivalent and electrochemical equivalent of metal electrodes. An electric current of 2A is required to electroplate a metal block of total area 500cm² with a layer of silver 0.02mm thick. Calculate the length of time required for this process (Assume density of silver to be 10.5gcm⁻³ and electrochemical equivalent of silver is 0.001118gC⁻¹).

23. Describe an experiment to calibrate an ammeter using the process of electrolysis. Draw the circuit diagram of the method described. If the ammeter records a steady current of 1.0A for 20 minutes while the silver deposited is 0.8g, determine the error in the ammeter reading [electrochemical equivalent for silver is 0.001118gC⁻¹].

24. Which of the following are electrolytes? Benzene, paraffin, pure water, molten silver, solution of ammonium chloride.

25. Draw a labelled diagram to show the structure of a hot-cathode tube designed for sending a narrow beam of electrons onto a fluorescent screen. Indicate and explain the need for inserting deflection plates.

312

WAVE-PARTICLE PARADOX

Chapter 38

Light and other electromagnetic radiation sometimes act like waves and sometimes like particles. Interference and diffraction show wave behaviour while emission and absorption of photons demonstrate particle behaviour.

Electrons are not the only set of particles which behave as waves. These effects are less noticeable with more massive particles because their momenta are much higher and so the wavelengths are correspondingly shorter. Appreciable diffraction is observed only when the wavelength is of the same order as the grating spacing, though protons are diffracted much less (its mass, m_p is 2000 x m_e). It is clear that particles can exhibit wave properties and that waves can behave as particles. As seen in photoelectric effect, electromagnetic waves appear to have a particle nature. Furthermore, gamma rays which behave like e-m waves of short wavelength but detection by Geiger Muller tubes which count pulses, show that they behave as particles. A paradox therefore exists since wave and particle structure appear to be mutually exclusive.

The two aspects, wave and particle are linked through the two relations.

$$E = hf \quad \text{and} \quad p = \frac{h}{\lambda} \qquad 38.1$$

Where E is the energy of the particle and p is the momentum of the particle.

E and p refer to particle description while f and λ refer to a wave description: with h, the planck's constant being the constant of proportionality in both equations.

In addition, frequency, f, of the wave is proportional to the energy, E, and the wavelength, λ, is inversely proportional to the momentum, p.

In the case of a photon of frequency f, $\lambda = \frac{c}{f}$

Thus, $E = hf$

$$p = \frac{h}{\lambda}$$

$$= \frac{hf}{c}$$

$$= \frac{E}{c}$$

Hence, $\quad E = pc = mc^2 \qquad 38.2$

So, as a particle, the mass of a photon is:

$$m = \frac{E}{c^2} = \frac{hf}{c^2}.$$

This is what Compton showed when he assumed that a particle of mass $\frac{hf}{c^2}$ collided elastically with an electron in the atom.

38.1 Wave nature of matter

After the discovery of photoelectric effect, it was realized that matter can possess particle-like properties and wave-like properties. In 1923, Louis de Broglie proposed that a particle of mass, m traveling with a velocity, v, would have a wavelength, λ given by the equation:

$$\lambda = \frac{h}{mv} \qquad 38.3$$

Where h is the planck constant.

This expression is valid also for electrons, protons and neutrons.

Example 38.1

Calculate the wavelength of (i) an electron moving with a velocity of $2.3 \times 10^6 \text{ms}^{-1}$ (ii) a ball of mass 0.2kg moving with a speed of 20ms^{-1}. Comment on your results.

Solution

From equation 38.3,

$$\lambda = \frac{h}{mv}$$

(i) $\quad \lambda_e = \dfrac{6.63 \times 10^{-34}}{9.1 \times 10^{-31} \times 2.3 \times 10^6} = 3.2 \times 10^{-10} \text{m}$

$$= 3.2 \overset{\circ}{A} (1 \overset{\circ}{A} = \text{Amstrong unit} = 10^{-10}\text{m})$$

(ii) $\quad \lambda_b = \dfrac{6.63 \times 10^{-34}}{0.2 \times 20} = 1.66 \times 10^{-34} \text{m}.$

The wavelength of the electron is so small and thus an electron can be diffracted using a slit as small as 1A, whereas for the ball, the wavelength is so small that it will be impossible to observe diffraction or interference which are wave properties.

Example 38.2

(a) Calculate the speed of an electron having a wavelength of 2×10^{-10}m.

(b) Through what potential difference must the electron be accelerated to attain this speed?

Solution

(a) From equation 38.3,

$$v = \frac{h}{m\lambda} = \frac{6.63 \times 10^{-34}}{9.1 \times 10^{-31} \times 2 \times 10^{-10}} = 3.64 \times 10^{6}\, ms^{-1}$$

(b) Loss in potential energy = gain in kinetic energy

$$eV = \frac{1}{2}mv^2$$

$$V = \frac{9.1 \times 10^{-31} \times (3.64 \times 10^6)^2}{2 \times 1.6 \times 10^{-19}}$$

$$= 37.7V$$

Experimental verification of wave-nature of matter- de Broglie's hypothesis

If the electron has wave properties, then it ought to be possible to observe these: electrons show the characteristics of waves such as interference and diffraction. The very small wavelength means that the obstacles used to diffract them must be very small and as with X-rays, it was the atomic lattice that was found suitable (i.e. of the order of $\overset{\circ}{A} = 10^{-10}\, m$).

The diffraction of electrons was first shown by Davisson and Germer in 1927. While studying the nature of crystal surfaces, they directed a beam of electrons at the surface of the crystal and observed the possibility of electrons being reflected at various angles. They found that the electrons were reflected in almost that same way that X-rays would be reflected from the same crystal. Using de Broglie's equation: $\lambda = \frac{h}{mv}$, the computed wavelengths were comparable to those obtained using X-rays which lend a strong support to the hypothesis of de Broglie.

Apart from the reflection experiment, the wave nature of matter was confirmed by the electron-diffraction experiment. In this experiment, a beam of electrons was passed through a crystalline solid (a very thin sheet of graphite) the electrons diffract from the carbon atoms and the resulting circular pattern obtained on the screen is a series of concentric rings. This is due to the regular spacing of the carbon atoms in different layers in the graphite.

Davisson and Germer found that electrons and molecules exhibit wave properties of diffraction and interference. Broglie's equation is thus of universal validity and must express something very fundamental.

For an electron, $\lambda_e = \frac{h}{m_e v}$

$$\therefore \lambda_e = 1.2\overset{\circ}{A}$$

$$= 1.2 \times 10^{-10}m, \text{ where } v = 6 \times 10^6 ms^{-1}.$$

The slit required in the diffraction of an electron is as small as 10^{-10}m.

For a classical particle such as a ball of 0.15kg moving with a velocity of 30ms^{-1}.

$\lambda = 1.49 \times 10^{-34}$m. The wavelength is so small that neither interference nor diffraction can be observed.

Such a classical particle cannot exhibit wave properties.

38.2 Particle nature of matter

(a) Photoelectric effect

We now consider another way in which electrons can be emitted. If light is shone on a suitable material, electrons may be emitted from the material. This process of release of electrons is called *photoelectricity*.

For example, if ultraviolet radiation falls on zinc, electrons are emitted from the zinc atoms. It should be noted that electrons are emitted from the metal provided that the wavelength of the radiation is less than a certain value, depending on the kind of metal. Using radiation of wavelength that is too long, the intensity of radiation may be as strong as we can make it and we may run the experiment for as long as we like, but no electrons will be emitted. Weak radiation of a short wavelength causes electron emission immediately.

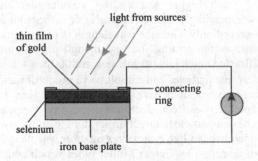

Fig. 38.1 The photoelectric effect

If we direct a low intensity beam of radiation at the material, relatively few electrons are emitted. If the intensity of the directed beam is high the number of electrons emitted per second increases.

A photoelectric cell has a glass bulb containing a large metal plate as the cathode and a small metal plate or rod as the anode. A p.d. of about 100V is required between the cathode and the anode. When light falls on the cathode, electrons are emitted, and are attracted towards the anode. The current through the cell increases. In this way, variations in the amount of light falling on the cathode control the amount of current through the cell. The current is small but it can be amplified to operate burglar alarms and many other applications.

The fact that the strength of the current is proportional to the intensity of incoming light, makes it possible to use photocells as instruments for measuring the illumination of a surface.

The kind of cell used in most photographic lightmeters produces its own voltage and needs no battery or power supply. Such cells are known as **photovoltaic cells**.

(b) Compton effect

The confirmation of the concept of the photon as a concentrated bundle or packet of energy was provided by the compton effect. It was noticed that there is a change in the frequency of X-rays when they lose energy in collision with electrons, which they knock off from a metal surface.

In the photoelectric effect, all the energy of the photon goes into the energy necessary to remove the electron from the surface and the kinetic energy of the electron and the photon continue to exist, but does lose energy as shown by the change in the wavelength or frequency of the incident X-rays.

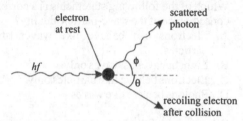

Fig. 38.2 Compton effect

The phonemena of interference and diffraction can be explained only by treating light as a wave. Yet in order to explain the results of the photoelectric and Compton effects, we must consider light as consisting of packets of energy or photons.

Thus, light appears to have a wave-particle duality. Light has the properties both of waves and of particles: a dual nature.

38.3 Wave particle duality

The study of the behaviour of light and other electromagnetic radiation including interference and diffraction demonstrate the wave nature of light. Others, such as photo electric effect, Compton scattering phenomenon point to the particle nature of light.

These two theories seem to be incompatible but both have been shown to be valid. This is the wave-particle duality.

38.4 The Heisenberg's uncertainty principle

If it were possible to measure the exact position and velocity of every particle in the universe at a certain time, then by applying the basic laws of physics, we should be able to predict their state at any future time e.g. we should be able to predict how much rain would fall in Abuja on the second of June in the year 2009! The uncertainty principle of Heisenberg states that it is actually impossible to make such a measurement.

If the measurement of a co-ordinate x has an uncertainty Δx and the corresponding momentum component, p has an uncertainty Δp, then the uncertainties are found to be related by the inequality:

$$\Delta x \Delta p \geq \frac{h}{2\pi} \qquad 38.4$$

This is the Heisenberg's uncertainty principle for position and momentum.

The uncertainly principle states that neither the position nor the momentum of a particle can be determined with great precision simultaneously .

Using more sophisticated instruments and detectors would not yield to greater accuracy (precision).

To measure (detect) a particle, the instrument (detector) has to interact with it which unavoidably changes the state of motion of the particle thus introducing an uncertainty about its original state. There is also an uncertainty principle for energy. The energy, E, of a system has an in-built uncertainty, ΔE. The uncertainty, ΔE depends on the time interval Δt during which the system remains in the given state. The relation is:

$$\Delta E \Delta t \geq \frac{h}{2\pi} \qquad 38.5$$

This is **Heisenberg's uncertainty principle** for energy and time interval.

A system that remains in a state for a very long time (large Δt) can have a very well defined energy (small ΔE) but if it remains in that state for a short time Δt, the uncertainty in energy must be correspondingly greater. (large ΔE).

It is impossible to make exact determination of a co-ordinate of a particle and of the corresponding component at the same time. The precision of such measurements is limited by the Heisenberg's uncertainty principle and for the x-component is given by: $\Delta x . \Delta p_x > \frac{h}{2\pi}$.

The uncertainty, ΔE, is energy of a state that is occupied for a time, Δt, is given by:

$$\Delta E = \frac{h}{2\pi \Delta t} .$$

The modern view of a particle is that it has both wave and particle properties described by the wave mechanical model. This model states that we cannot fix the position of a particle but can only predict the probability of its being at a given point at a certain time.

Example 38.3

Determine the uncertainty in the:
(i) energy of a photon which is radiated in a time interval 10^{-5}s;
(ii) momentum of a 0.2kg football moving with a speed of 20ms^{-1} and restricted to a region of 25cm. Determine the fractional uncertainty in momentum.

Solution

Using equations 38.4 and 38.5,

(i) $\Delta E . \Delta t \geq \frac{h}{2\pi}$

$$\Delta E \geq \frac{6.63 \times 10^{-34}}{2 \times \pi \times 10^{-5}}$$

$$\geq 1.06 \times 10^{-29} \text{J}$$

(ii) $\Delta p . \Delta x \geq \dfrac{h}{2\pi} = \dfrac{6.63 \times 10^{-34}}{2\pi}$

$\Delta p_x = \dfrac{6.63 \times 10^{-34}}{2\pi . \Delta x} = \dfrac{6.63 \times 10^{-34}}{2 \times \pi \times 25 \times 10^{-2}}$

$= 4.2 \times 10^{-34}$

Fractional uncertainty,

$\dfrac{\Delta p_x}{P_x} = \dfrac{4.2 \times 10^{-34}}{4} = 1.05 \times 10^{-34}$

Summary

1. Electromagnetic radiation behaves as both waves and particles.

2. The phenomena that can be fully explained by assuming that matter behaves like a wave are: diffraction (electron, light) and interference. On the other hand a number of phenomena that can be explained by assuming that matter behaves like a particle are: emission and absorption of light, photoelectric effect, thermionic emission and compton effect.

3. The wave-particle duality implies that light has both the properties of a wave as well as the properties of a particle. The de Broglie hypothesis $\lambda = \dfrac{h}{mv}$ is valid for electrons and other elementary particles e.g. Protons and neutrons.

4. According to the uncertainty principle

$\Delta p . \Delta x \geq \dfrac{h}{2\pi}$ i.e. the uncertainty in the measurement of position (Δx) and the uncertainty in the measurement of momentum (Δp) is equal to $\dfrac{h}{2\pi}$, h is planck's constant.

5. Momentum and position, energy and time, velocity and position are known as complementary variables. The two variables cannot be measured to desired accuracy simultaneously. The higher the accuracy in measuring one variable (e.g. energy) the lower the accuracy in measuring the complementary variable (time).

Exercise 38

1. The uncertainty principle can be written as

   I. $\Delta p \, \Delta x > \dfrac{h}{2\pi}$.

   II. $\Delta x \, h \geq \dfrac{\Delta p}{2\pi}$.

   III. $\Delta E \, \Delta t \geq \dfrac{h}{2\pi}$.

   IV. $\Delta t \, h \geq \dfrac{\Delta h}{\Delta \pi}$.

   A. I only.   B. III only.
   C. I and III only.   D. II and IV only.

2. De Broglie's relation may be stated as
   A. $E = hf$.   B. $\lambda = \dfrac{h}{p}$.
   C. $E = eV$.   D. $\lambda < \dfrac{h}{p}$.

3. Which of the following statements is **not** correct?
   A. Neutrons can be diffracted.
   B. Both neutrons and electrons are matter waves.
   C. Protons are waves and not particles.
   D. Electron beam can be diffracted.

4. Which of the following statements is a correct consequence of the wave-particle duality?
   A. Electrons can behave like waves and particles.
   B. Light behaves as waves only.
   C. Electrons behave like particles only.
   D. Photons behave like waves.

5. Which of the following is **not** endowed with wave-particle duality?
   A. Electrons.   B. Protons.
   C. Light.   D. Sound.

6. Which of the following statements is a correct consequence of the uncertainty principle?
   A. The uncertainty in our knowledge of energy and the duration taken to measure it are each less than the planck's constant.
   B. The complete knowledge of the position of a particle implies the complete ignorance of its energy.
   C. A particle's kinetic energy cannot be measured accurately at any time.
   D. Both momentum and energy of a particle can be known with absolute certainty.

7. (a) Briefly explain what is meant by:
       (i) the uncertainty principle;
       (ii) wave particle duality.

   (b) Determine the uncertainty in the energy of a photon which is radiated in a time interval 10^{-36}s?
   (Assume $h = 6.63 \times 10^{-34}$ Js).

8. State the de-Broglie hypothesis. Calculate:
   (i) The wavelength of an electron whose mass is 9×10^{31}kg and moving with a velocity 5.7×10^{7}ms^{-1}.
   (ii) The wavelength of a ball of mass 0.15kg moving with a speed of 30ms^{-1}. Comment on your results and discuss why the ball cannot be regarded as a matter wave.

9. A 0.10kg football moving with a speed of $25\,ms^{-1}$ is restricted to a region of 20cm. Calculate the:
    (i)   tuncertainty in the momentum;
    (ii) fractional uncertainty in momentum. Discuss the result (ii).

10. From de Broglie's relation, deduce an expression for the wavelength of an electron beam if the accelerating voltage is V. Estimate the wavelength of an electron beam with $V = 3.6\,kV$ and for an electron beam $m_e = 9.1 \times 10^{-31}\,kg$, $e = 1.6 \times 10^{-19}\,C$ and $h = 6.63 \times 10^{-34}\,Js$.

11. List and describe three observable phenomena in which matter behaves like a wave and three other phenomena in which matter behaves like a particle.

FUNDAMENTALS OF ELECTRONICS

Chapter **39**

39.1 Conduction in solids

Every solid conductor of electricity can be classified as either a metal, a semiconductor, or a non-conductor termed insulator.

Metals

Metals are characterised by low values of electrical resistivity of about 10^{-8} to 10^{-6} ohm meter, e.g. silver, gold, copper and aluminum. Such conductors contain free electrons in large concentration, which are not bound to the metal atoms but are free to move throughout the volume of the metal and for most purposes can be regarded as "free electron sea". The free electrons have a volume concentration of the order of $10^{29} m^{-3}$. A metal exhibits charge neutrality because the negative charges on the free electrons are balanced by the positive charges associated with the nuclei. Conduction in metals is a single carrier process in which the mobile charge is negative, and the equation $E = \rho J$ which is a form of Ohm's law holds at constant temperature. Here, J is the current per unit area, E is the electric field, and ρ is the resistivity. As temperature increases the resistance of metallic conductors increases due to higher collision between atoms.

39.2 Semiconductors

These are materials with resistivities intermediate between conductors and insulators. Germanium has resistivity of 0.6×10^3 Ω-m and silicon has resistivity of 1.5×10^3 Ω-m. Semiconductors belong to group IV in the periodic table with four electrons in their outermost shells. The valence electrons of the atoms of semiconductors are not wholly free to move throughout the volume of the semiconductor, instead, they participate in *covalent bonds* that hold the assembly of the semiconductor atoms together and consequently, they cannot move about freely.

When all the valence electrons are constrained in covalent bonds, no charge carriers are free to move and hence there is no conduction. Most covalent bonds are like this except diamond with conductivity of 10^{-18} $(\Omega\text{-m})^{-1}$. At 290K, the conductivity of pure silicon is 0.3×10^{-7} $(\Omega\text{-m})^{-1}$ and germanium is about 0.2×10^{-3} $(\Omega\text{-m})^{-1}$. Since none of these values is zero, there must therefore be a few electrons that can participate in conduction. This means that the covalent bonds are incomplete and some electrons are free to move at normal temperatures due to the thermal vibration of the valence electrons. The fraction of the valence electrons that are disengaged from covalent bonds is small.

At 300K, for Ge, there are 10^{19} broken bonds per m^3. As a consequence of these broken covalent bonds, there exists two distinct and independent groups of charge carriers, the "free electrons" produced when bonds are shaken loose and they carry negative charge and the other set of charge carriers associated with the valence electrons, which remain, bound in covalent bonds. This gives rise to a localized positive charge called **hole** since it results from a vacancy in the bond structure. Since valence electrons near a broken bond can fill the vacancy, this causes the hole to move in the opposite direction. Hence, the hole can move throughout the material without involving the conduction electrons. The model assumes that holes and conduction electrons are present exactly in equal numbers. Holes and conduction electrons are produced in pairs when bonds are broken and disappear in pairs when recombination occurs i.e. when the electrons revert back to holes or vacancies. As temperature increases, conductivity increases due to hole-electron pair generation.

Insulators have very high resistivities of between 10^7 to 10^{18} Ω-m. Examples are quartz, polyethylene and diamond. Here, all electrons are bound to the crystal and none is free to participate in conduction.

Energy band model

In the band model, every solid material has three bands; filled valence bands and empty conduction bands separated by an energy gap. Energy level diagrams for a conductor, insulator and semiconductor are depicted in Fig. 39.1. A metal always contains overlapping valence and conduction bands i.e. the conduction band remains partly filled and occupation of states is easily altered to produce a current by the application of an electric field. There is no separation and hence no energy gap. This overlap gives rise to many conduction

(a)

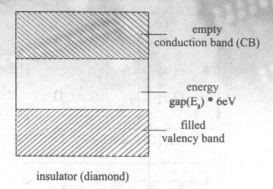

insulator (diamond)

(b)

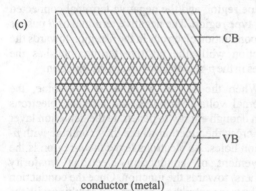

semi conductor (silicon)

(c)

CB

VB

conductor (metal)

Fig. 39.1 Energy band model

electrons even without the application of external energy.

In insulators, at temperatures up to several hundred Kelvin and in semiconductors at temperatures near 0K, all bands are either practically filled completely or practically completely empty. In these circumstances, there is no conductivity. However, electrons may be excited into the conduction band at room temperature if the energy gap, E_g, is between 0.2eV and 1.5eV as in semiconductors. Silicon has E_g = 1.15eV, and germanium has E_g = 0.75eV. The energy gap, E_g, between the valence band and conduction band for insulators may be as much as 6eV; for diamond, E_g is 7eV. This makes it very difficult for the electrons to acquire sufficient energy to cross to conduction band. Conduction electrons increase in number, as

temperature increases since lattice vibration energy increases with temperature and the energy required to break bond decreases. Semiconductors such as silicon and germanium are characterized by negative temperature coefficient of resistance i.e. as temperature increases, resistivity decreases.

39.3 Types of semiconductors

Impurities in semiconductors

Pure semiconductor materials do not conduct current very well because of the limited number of free electrons in the conduction band. In addition they require that the holes and electrons be present in exactly equal numbers; holes and electrons are produced in pairs and disappear (recombine) in pairs. The resistivities of silicon or germanium can be drastically reduced and controlled by the addition of impurities, which strongly influence the relative concentrations of the charge carriers. These impurities called *dopants* (about one atom per million) are added to semi-conductors during fabrication. This process is called *doping*.

Donor impurities: are atoms with five valence electrons such as arsenic, antimony and phosphorus. Atoms of these dopants fit readily into the regular crystalline structure of the host Group IV semiconductor. Such pentavalent impurity atoms have five valence electrons; one electron is "leftover" after the covalent bonds are completed. The extra electron, which is losely bound becomes dissociated from the impurity atom and moves about through the semi conductor as a conduction electron. Consequently, donor impurities contribute conduction electrons to the semiconductor without contributing holes. Since most of the charge carriers are electrons, semiconductor materials doped in this way are termed *n*-type (negative type). The electrons are called the majority carriers while the holes are the minority carriers.

Acceptor impurities: are elements that have three valence electrons rather than four. Examples are aluminum, gallium, indium and boron. These also fit into the periodic crystalline structure of tetravalent semiconductor but they have one few valence electrons to complete the valence bonds. Thus, there is a vacancy with each acceptor atom. They augment the population of holes without contributing electrons. Since most of the current carriers are holes, holes are the majority carriers in a *p*-type semi-conductor material while electrons are called minority carriers. If a semiconductor contains negligible quantities of donor or acceptor impurities, the hole and electron concentrations are equal.

The semiconductor is said to be *intrinsic* since its electrical properties are intrinsic to the semiconductor material and are not as a result of impurities. If on the other hand, a semiconductor contains a significant quantity of donor atoms, it will have more electrons than holes (*n*-type) and if the dominant impurity atoms are acceptor type in the semiconductor, it will have a majority of holes over the electrons (*p*-type). Both *n*-type and *p*-type semiconductor materials are termed *extrinsic* because their electrical properties are governed more by the impurities than by the semiconductor itself.

39.4   P–N junction diode

A *p-n* junction is made by growing in a single semiconductor crystal, part of which is *n*-type and the other *p*-type. The boundary inside the crystal between *p*-and *n*-regions is termed *p-n* junction; *p-n* junction occurs whenever the impurity concentration changes from a predominance of donors to a predominance of acceptors over a sufficiently small distance. In silicon or germanium, this distance is about 10^{-7}m.

At the junction plane, holes tend to diffuse from the *p*-type region to the *n*-type region leaving the *p*-region slightly negative. Similarly, electrons from the *n*-region will diffuse into the *p*-region leaving the *n*-region slightly positive.

In a layer between *n* and *p* regions, holes and electrons recombine and since this layer is now depleted of free charge carriers, it is called the **depletion layer**. This layer acts as a potential barrier, which opposes any further diffusion of charge. This condition is illustrated in fig. 39.2. In equilibrium, the net (drift and diffusion) holes and electrons vanish, the diffusive flows are balanced by the drift flows associated with the potential barrier that exists near the junction plane.

At 25°C, the barrier potential is approximately 0.7V for silicon and 0.3V for germanium. As the junction temperature increases, the barrier potential decreases and vice versa.

Biasing the p-n junction

At equilibrium, there is no current across a *p-n* junction. The primary usefulness of the *p-n* junction is its ability to allow current to flow in only one direction and to inhibit the flow in the other direction as determined by the bias. *Bias* is a fixed d.c.voltage that sets operating conditions for a semiconductor device. There are two bias conditions for a p-n junction-forward and reverse; either of these conditions is created by application of an external voltage of appropriate polarity.

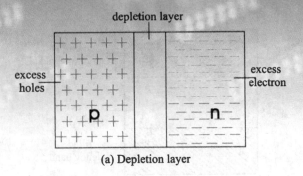

(a) Depletion layer

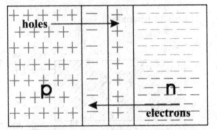

(b) Diffusion of electrons/holes across the junction.

Fig. 39.2 p–n. junction

Forward bias in fig 39.3(a) shows a d.c. voltage connected in a direction to forward bias the *p-n* junction such that *A* is positive with respect to *C*, i.e. the positive terminal of the battery *B* is connected to *p*-type region and the negative terminal connected to *n*-type region. The negative terminal of *B* pushes the conduction electrons in the *n*-region towards the junction while the positive terminal pushes the holes in the *p*-region also toward the junction.

When the barrier potential is overcome, the external voltage provides the *n*-region electrons with enough energy to penetrate the depletion layer and cross the junction where they combine with *p*-region holes. As electrons leave the *n*-region is the movement of conduction electrons (majority carriers) towards the junction. Once the conduction of electrons enter the *p*-region and combine with the holes, they become valence electrons and then move from hole to hole toward the positive terminal of *B*. Conduction occurs at approximately 0.7V for silicon and 0.3V for germanium. The effect of forward bias is to reduce the potential barrier and current will flow. This current increases exponentially with increasing voltage until the potential barrier is zero when it is limited by the bulk resistance of the semiconductor material which gives rise to a negligible drop limits it.

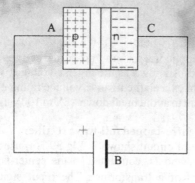

Fig. 39.3 (a) Forward bias p–n junction

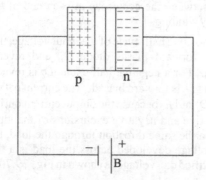

Fig. 39.3(b) Reverse bias p–n junction

Reverse bias is the condition that prevents current across the *p-n* junction. Fig. 39.3(b) shows a d.c. voltage source connected to reverse bias the *p–n* junction; with negative terminal of *B* connected to the *p*-region and the positive terminal to the *n*-region. Here, the negative terminal of *B* attracts holes away from the *p*-region of the junction while the positive terminal also attracts electrons away from the junction. This makes the depletion layer widen until the potential difference across it is equal the external bias voltage. At this point, the holes and electrons stop moving away from the junction and majority carriers between layers of oppositely charged ions–form an effective capacitance (1-20pF). Since majority current quickly becomes zero there is however a very small leakage current produced by minority carriers that is thermally generated; germanium has a greater leakage current than silicon. This current (*nA*) is thermally produced by electron-hole pairs in the depletion layer and some diffusive current due to external voltage, the reverse biased voltage.

Thus, if a junction is biased in the forward direction, a fairly large current will flow; but under reverse bias conditions, provided the turnover voltage is not reached, the current is extremely small. In other words the device acts as a rectifier. However, due to leakage current, the use of germanium devices is restricted to temperature below 70°C, whereas silicon is usable up to 150°C.

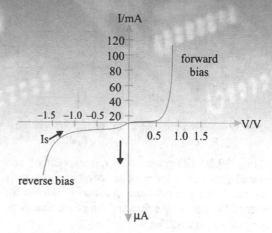

Fig. 39.4 Current-voltage (I-V) characteristics of a p-n junction diode .

39.5   Diode characteristic curve

Fig.39.4 depicts the current-voltage characteristics for the forward and reversed biased situations of a silicon *p-n* junction

A *p-n* junction diode conducts current when it is forward biased, i.e. the bias voltage exceeds the barrier potential, V_B and the diode prevents current when it is reverse biased at less than the breakdown voltage.

From fig. 39.4, the upper right quadrant of the graph represents the forward biased condition. As the forward voltage approaches the value of the barrier potential, 0.7V for silicon and 0.3V for germanium, the current begins to increase. Once the forward voltage reaches the barrier potential, the current increases drastically and must be limited by a series resistor. The voltage across the forward biased diode remains approximately equal to the barrier potential.

The lower left quadrant of the graph represents the reverse biased condition. As the reverse voltage increases to the left, the current remains near zero until the breakdown voltage V_{BR}, is reached. When breakdown occurs, there is a large reverse current which if not limited can destroy the diode. Typically, the breakdown voltage is greater than 50V for most rectifier diodes.

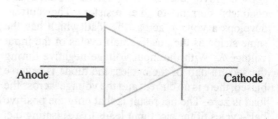

Fig. 39.5(a) Diode circuit symbol

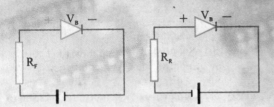

Fig. 39.5(b) Forward bias   *Fig. 39.5(c) Reverse bias*
   (R_F 10Ω)   *(R_R 10^6Ω)*

Fig. 39.5 Illustrates the circuit symbol and biased junction diodes. The reverse current is temperature dependent and is found to double for every 10°C rise. In the forward direction, change in forward voltage is 2.5m V°C⁻¹.

Half-wave rectifiers

Because of their unique ability to conduct current in one direction, diodes are used in rectifier circuits. Rectification is the process of converting a.c. to pulsating d.c.

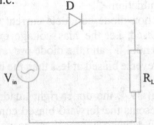

Fig. 39.6(a) Half-wave rectifier

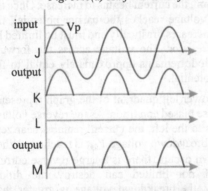

Fig. 39.6(b) Output variations

In fig. 39.6 an a.c. source is connected to a load resistor R_L through a diode D. When the sine wave goes positive, the diode is forward biased and conducts current to the resistor. The current develops a voltage across the load which has the same shape as the positive half cycles of the input voltage K. With the input voltage negative during the second half of the cycles, the diode is reverse biased, there is no current and the voltage across the load is zero. The net result is that only the positive half-cycles of the a.c. Input leads to a pulsating d.c. voltage output as shown in M. The variation is in fig. 39.6(b). This is half-wave rectification. Time

average (d.c.) value of the half-wave rectified output is $V_{av} = \frac{V_p}{\pi}$,

i.e. $0.318 V_p$, where V_p is the peak voltage. The voltage applied across the diode during negative half-cycles is known as the inverse voltage, which should not exceed the inverse voltage rating of the component to avoid breakdown. (2V to 100V).

39.6   Centre-tapped full-wave rectifier

This type of circuit shown in Fig 39.7(a) uses two diodes D_1 and D_2 connected to the center-tapped secondary of a transformer. The input signal is coupled through the transformer to the center-tapped secondary. Half of the secondary voltage appears between the center-tap at each end of the secondary winding.

For a positive half-cycle of the input voltage, this condition forward biases diode D_1, and reverse biases D_2. For a negative half cycle, D_1 is reverse biased and D_2 is forward biased. The current path is through D_2 and R_L because the output current during both positive and negative excursions of the input cycle is in the same direction through the load, the output voltage developed across the load is a full wave rectified d.c. voltage as shown in Fig. 39.7(b).

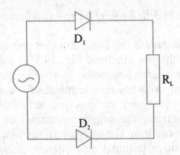

Fig. 39.7(a) Centre-tapped full wave rectifier.

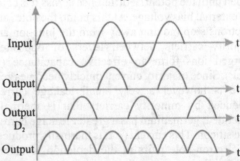

Fig. 39.7(b) output waveforms from a full wave rectifier.

The output voltage of a center-tapped full wave rectifier is always one half of total secondary voltage.

$V_{out} = \frac{V_2}{2} V_B$,if diode drop V_B is included.

The peak inverse voltage (PIV) for a full wave rectifier (center-tapped) is $2V_p$ (out).

Filter circuits

The lowest frequency-alternating component present in the full wave rectifier circuit is twice the supply frequency, f which makes the removal of the harmonics easy with filter circuits. Filters make the d.c. output current sufficiently smooth for most uses, by preventing the a.c. components from passing through the load resistance. Filter circuits are employed to reduce rectifier output ripple either by passing the alternating output components around the load by a shunt capacitor, or limiting their magnitude to a low level in the load by a series inductor. Combinations of capacitors and inductors are found to be more efficient.

Capacitor input filter

A half wave rectifier with a capacitor input filter is shown in Fig 39.8 and R_L represents the load resistance.

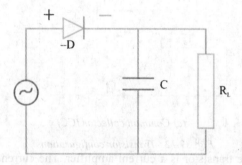

Fig. 39.8(a) Half wave rectifier with capacitor filter.

During the positive first quarter of the cycle of the input, the diode D, is forward biased, allowing the capacitor to charge within a diode drop of the input peak as in Fig. 39.8(b). When the input begins to decrease below its peak, the capacitor retains its charge and the diode becomes reverse biased. During the remaining part of the cycle the capacitor can discharge only through the load resistance at a rate determined by the time constant, $R_L C$, and period of the input voltage. It is desirable to have a large time constant by making X_c much less than R_L. During the first quarter of the next cycle, the diode will again become forward biased and the input voltage exceeds the capacitor voltage by approximately a diode drop.

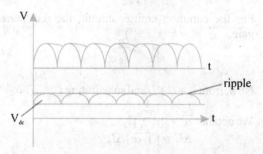

Fig. 39.8(b) Output from capacitor filter.

Junction transistors belong to a group of two families of transistor types, one is the bipolar junction transistor (*BJT*), the second being the field effect transistor (*FET*). Amplifiers designed using BJTs are current controlled while those designed using *FET*s are voltage controlled. The *BJT* is however, more widely used than the *FET*.

Construction of BJT

A bipolar junction transistor is a three-terminal device with two *p-n* junctions formed back-to-back. There are two types of *BJT*- the *n-p-n* and the *p-n-p*. In the *n-p-n* type, a *p*-type region is sandwiched between two *n*-type regions. On the other hand, the *n*-type region is sandwiched between two *p*-type regions. The schematic diagrams of the two types of *BJT* are illustrated in Fig. 39.9.

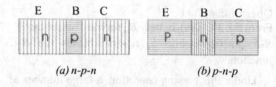

(a) n-p-n   *(b) p-n-p*

Fig. 39.9 Schematic diagram of BJT

The three terminals of the *BJT* are emitter (*E*), base (*B*) and collector (*C*). The base region is thin and very lightly doped while the emitter and collector regions are more heavily doped. The two *p-n* junctions are emitter-base junction (*E-B*) and base-collector junction (*B-C*). For normal amplifier operation, the *E-B* junction is forward biased while the *B-C* junction is reverse biased as in fig 39.10. The circuit symbols of the n-p-n and p-n-p

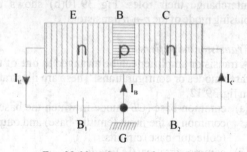

Fig. 39.10(a) Biasing of n-p-n BJT

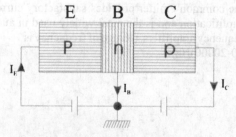

Fig. 39.10(b) Biasing of p-n-p BJT

transistors are shown in Fig. 39.11.

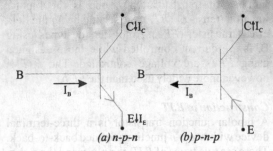

Fig. 39.11 circuit symbol of BJT

The currents flowing in the terminals are also indicated in Fig. 39.10. I_E represents the emitter current, I_C is the collector current and I_B is the base current.

Operation of BJT
From fig. 39.10(a), battery B_1, forward biases the B-E junction while B_2 reverse biases the B-C junction.

Under this biasing condition, a large number of electrons in the emitter region are pushed into the lightly doped and thin base region. Some of these electrons recombine with the holes in the base region. These holes constitute the base current, I_B in the external circuit. Almost all the injected electrons (95%) are drifted to the collector region by the positive potential of battery B_2 to form the collector current, I_C; electrons ejected from the emitter form the emitter current, I_E.

The operation of the *p-n-p* type of *BJT* is similar to that of the *n-p-n* except that holes and electrons interchange their roles. Fig 39.10(b) shows the biasing mode of the *p-n-p* transistor.

Transistor amplifiers
A transistor amplifier can be arranged in one of the three modes or configurations. These are illustrated in fig. 39.12.
(a) common-base (*CB*) mode in which the base is common to the input (emitter-base) and output (collector base) circuits.
(b) common emitter (*CE*) mode.
(c) common collector (*CC*) mode.

The common emitter provides satisfactory current amplification and is the most widely used in audio frequency amplifiers. (Range of frequency is (20-20000)Hz).

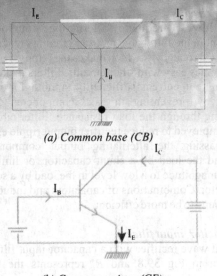

(a) Common base (CB)

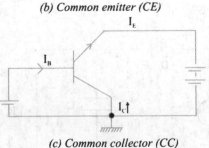

(b) Common emitter (CE)

(c) Common collector (CC)

Fig. 39.12 Transistor configurations

The transistor is a current amplifier. The currents flowing in the transistor are the emitter current, I_E, the collector current, I_C and the base current, I_B. From Kirchoff's current law,
$$I_E = I_B + I_C.$$
In the n-p-n transistors, the carriers of the current are mainly electrons while the carriers of the current in the *p-n-p* are mainly holes.

Electrons have greater mobilities than holes, as such, *n-p-n* transistors are used in high frequency and computer circuits where the carriers are required to respond very quickly to signals. Current amplification (gain) is the ratio of output current to input current.

For the common base mode, the d.c. current gain α

is given as $\qquad \alpha = \dfrac{I_C}{I_E}$.   39.1

For the common emitter circuit, the d.c. current gain,
$$\beta = \frac{I_C}{I_B} .$$ 39.2

Now, from $I_E = I_C + I_B$ and substituting $I_E = \dfrac{I_C}{\alpha}$

We obtain $\dfrac{I_C}{\alpha} = [\dfrac{1}{\dfrac{1-\alpha}{\alpha}}] I_B$

$$\Delta I_C = [\frac{1}{1-\alpha}] \Delta I_B$$

$$\frac{\Delta I_c}{\Delta I_B} = \beta$$

Hence, $\beta = \dfrac{\alpha}{1-\alpha}$

So, for $\alpha = 0.95$

$$\beta = \frac{0.95}{0.05}$$

$$= 19$$

Voltage amplification, $A_V = \dfrac{V_o}{V_i}$

and power gain = current gain x voltage gain.

CE circuit is very sensitive to temperature variation and must be stabilized for excessive rise in temperature. Silicon transistors are less sensitive to temperature change than germanium transistors.

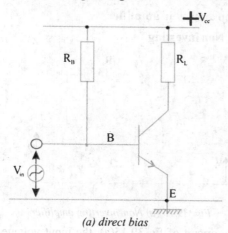

(a) direct bias

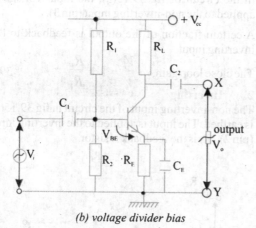

(b) voltage divider bias

Fig. 39.13 A single stage common emitter amplifier circuit.

(i) R_1, R_2 provides the necessary bias.

(ii) a load R_L produces output across XY, Y is grounded, OV.

(iii) C_1, C_2 are blocking capacitors, they stop noise and d.c. at the input and output of the amplifier. They are used to couple signals in and out of amplifier.

(iv) C_E across R_E prevent undesirable feedback of the amplified signal to the base emitter circuit.

(v) R_E stabilizes the circuit against excessive temperature rise and thermal runaway.

For silicon transistor, $V_{BE} = 0.7V$

Note: $R_B = \dfrac{R_1 R_2}{R_1 + R_2}$, $V_{CC} = V_{CE} + I_C R_L$

$$I_B = \frac{V_\alpha - V_{BE}}{R_B} \qquad R_L = \frac{V_\alpha - V_{CE}}{I_C}$$

$$I_C = \beta I_B \qquad V_{BB} = I_B R_B + V_{BE}$$

39.8 Integrated circuits

In the early days of solid state electronics, computing and electronic circuits were constructed from discrete and individual components such as diodes, transistors, resistors and capacitors. In the 1950s, it was realized that it would be possible to form all the components for such circuits in a single chip (wafer) of semiconductor material and this became known as integrated circuit (*IC*).

There are two major types of *IC*:

(a) Linear or analogue, containing amplifying and oscillating circuits.

(b) Digital, involving switch circuits.

The digital integrated circuits are of two types:

(i) *TTL* (transistor-transistor logic) which produces faster switching but require a stable power supply and larger operating (quiescent) currents.

(ii) *CMOS* (complementary metal-oxide semiconductor logic) which gives slower switching but can work from low power supply. A larger density of components may be achieved with *CMOS* circuits and this makes large scale integration (*LSI*) easier having 100-1000 components per chip.

Four basic steps are required to create small regions that form *MOS* transistors on the silicon slice:

(a) *oxidation* – a layer of silicon dioxide is grown on top of the substrate, silicon.

(b) *photomasking* – parts of the oxide layer are selectively removed by chemical etching.

(c) *diffusion* – unprotected regions of silicon are changed to *p* – or *n* – type by diffusion of impurity materials.

(d) *metallization* – a thin metal layer is grown over the slice to interconnect the transistors and diodes electrically.

Most digital systems use *IC* (intergrated circuit) for the following reasons:

(i) *IC* pack a lot more circuitry in a small package such that the overall size is reduced (miniaturization).

(ii) Cost is drastically reduced due to mass production.

(iii) Systems are more reliable since the number of interconnections from one device to another has been reduced.

(iv) There is improved performance.

(v) *ICs* have drastically reduced the amount of

power needed to perform a given function and do not require cooling.

However, *ICs* have the following disadvantages:

(i) *ICs* cannot handle very large currents and voltages due to heat generated and excessive temperature rise.

(ii) *ICs* cannot implement devices such as inductors, transformers and large capacitors.

(iii) Repairs become difficult if not impossible.

(iv) *ICs* can only perform low power circuit operations.

Operational amplifier

The operational amplifier (*op amp*) is one of the most versatile *IC*. It has wide applications because of its ability to carry out simple mathematical operations such as addition, subtraction, multiplication, differentiation and integration, it is used as inverting and non inverting amplifiers, voltage comparator or oscillator. It is a differential input d.c. amplifier with the following properties:

(a) a very high open loop gain (*AOL*).

(b) a very high input impedance such that it draws no current.

(c) a very low output impedance such that it does not load circuits connected to it.

(d) gives an amplified output signal proportional to the difference between the input signals.

A common form of operational amplifier is the μ 741. It is fabricated in an eight pin dual, in-line (*DIL*) form.

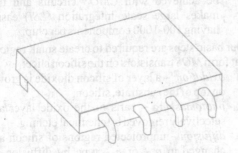

(a) Schematic amplifier

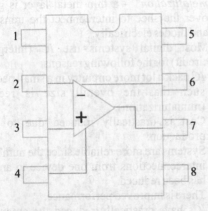

(b) pin configuration

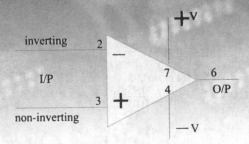

(c) Circuit symbol

Fig. 39.14 Operational amplifier

The internal circuitry is quite complex containing about twenty transistors, eleven resistors and one capacitor.

The op amp as an amplifier

1. **Non inverting**

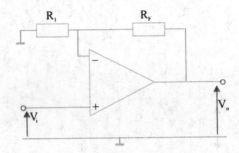

Fig. 39.15 (a) Non-inverting amplifier

In the circuit of fig 39.15(a), the input voltage is applied to the non-inverting input (pin 3).

A certain fraction of the output is feedback to the inverting input.

The close loop gain, $\dfrac{V_o}{V_i} = 1 + \dfrac{R_F}{R_I}$　　39.3

2. **Inverting**

The non-inverting input of the circuit in fig 39.15(b) is earthed. The input is applied to the inverting input (pin 2). R_F is the feedback resistor.

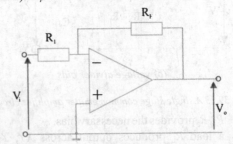

Fig. 39.15(b) Inverting amplifier

Close loop gain, $\dfrac{-R_F}{R_I} = \dfrac{V_o}{V_i}$　　39.4

The output is 180° out of phase while the input and the gain depend only on external resistors.

Example 39.1

(a) Calculate the gain of a µ741 *IC* amplifier connected in a non-inverting mode if the feedback resistor, R_F is 20kΩ and R is 2kΩ in Fig. 39.15(a).

Solution

From equation 39.3,

$$\text{Gain} = 1 + \frac{R_F}{R_1}$$

$$= 1 + \frac{20}{2} = 11$$

(b) For the inverting amplifier in Fig. 39.15(b), Calculate the gain if $R_F = 20$kΩ and R, is 2kΩ.

Solution

From equation 39.4,

$$\text{Gain} = -\frac{R_F}{R_1} = -\frac{20}{2} = -10$$

Summary

1. Semi conductors have resistivity (conductivity) values between insulators and good conductors. Pure (intrinsic) semi conductors have two sets of charge carriers **electrons** and **holes** in the same proportion. (i.e. number of electrons is equal to number of holes) however, conductivity increases as temperature increases, (resistivity decreases).

   Silicon and germanium are the two best known semiconductor materials and they both belong to group IV on the periodic table, i.e. they have four electrons on their outermost shell. In their energy profile, they have forbidden gaps. Silicon has energy gap, E_g (forbidden gap) of about 1.1eV, while germanium has, E_g • 0.7eV.

2. At low temperatures, semiconductors behave like insulators with the valence band filled and the conduction band empty. In insulators, e.g. diamond, E_g • 7 eV and all the charge carriers are bound. Conductors have overlapping valence and conduction bands with free electrons moving through the wire at all temperatures. However as temperature increases, resistivity increases.

3. In order to improve the conductivity in semiconductors, impurities are added chemically, a process called doping. Doping with a pentavalent (Phosporus, Arsenic) or trivalent (Gallium or Indium) impurity results in an *n*-type or *p*-type semiconductor which is highly temperature dependent. These semiconductors are said to be extrinsic.

4. A *p-n* junction diode is made from a single crystal in which a section is doped with *p*-impurity (acceptor atom) and the other section with an *n*-impurity (donor atom) when the junction is formed, diffusion of majority carriers across the junction gives rise to a potential barrier which results in a junction free of carriers. The region within the junction is called a depletion layer. With *p-n* junction forward biased, current flows as the barrier potential is reduced. On the other hand, reverse biasing increases the barrier potential and no current flows. The junction diode then operates as a rectifier. The rectifier output may be half wave or full wave. The pulsating output consists of gaps for the half wave circuit whereas there are no gaps in the output of the full wave circuit (with two or four diodes).

5. When capacitors operating (low pass filters) are applied across the output of a rectifier circuit, the pulsating d.c. output is smoothened. i.e. the ripple and a.c. variations on the output are greatly reduced.

6. A bipolar junction transistor (*BJT*) is a three terminal device (Emitter, Base and Collector) and is made of two *p-n* junctions connected back to back. When appropriately biased, emitter-base junction is forward biased and base-collector junction is reverse biased. *BJT* can operate as an amplifier in three modes i.e. (i) common base where the base is grounded and output from the collector (ii) common emitter with emitter grounded and output from the collector (iii) common collector (emitter follower) with collector grounded but output from emitter. The current gain of each configuration can be computed (output current/input current).

7. In the BJT the two sets of currents (electron and hole) participate in amplification and such amplifiers are said to be current controlled. Employing a voltage divider bias and emitter resistor applied to prevent thermal runaway, a common emitter amplifier can be designed with a high current gain.

8. When discrete components (resistors, capacitors, diodes and transistors) are formed on a single chip of a semiconductor material (silicon) circuits thus formed are called integrated circuits (*IC*). Such circuits may be analogue (producing continuously varying signals) or digital (discrete signals). A most useful *IC* is the operational amplifier which can be used to design amplifier and oscillator circuits and circuits to perform mathematical operations.

1. A solid material with an energy gap of 1.2eV is
   A. a metal.   B. a semi conductor.
   C. an insulator.   D. a crystal.

2. On the periodic table, semi conductors belong to group
   A. I.   B. II.   C. III.   D. IV.

3. A semiconductor material doped with arsenic will become
   A. *p*-type.   B. *n*-types.
   C. intrinsic.   D. pure.

4. Which of the following is an acceptor impurity?
   A. Phosphorus   B. Gallium
   C. Arsenic   D. Antimony

5. The majority carriers in a *p*-type semiconductor material are
   A. positive ions.   B. holes.
   C. electrons.   D. negative ions.

6. Which of the following is an extrinsic semiconductor material?
   A. *n*-type   B. Silicon
   C. Germanium   D. Tin

7. Which of the following graphs represent the current-voltage of a *p-n* junction biased in the forward mode?

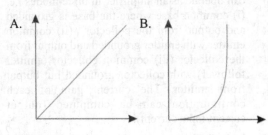
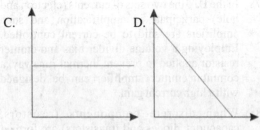

Fig. 39.16

8. The current flow in a reverse-biased *p-n* junction is on the order of μA. This is due to
   A. thermally generated minority carriers.
   B. thermally generated majority carriers.
   C. negative voltage applied.
   D. positive voltage applied in reverse direction.

9. In an energy band diagram of a solid material,

the energy band gap is 6eV. The solid material is a
   A. a semi conductor.   B. an insulator.
   C. an intrinsic solid. E. an extrinsic solid.

10. Which of the following is **not** a trivalent impurity atom?
    A. Arsenic   B. Boron
    C. Aluminium   D. Gallium

11. Which of the following is an extrinsic semi conductor?
    I.   *n*-type
    II. *P*-type
    III. Silicon
    IV. Germanium
    A. IV only   B. III only
    C. I & II only D. I,II & III only

12. Which of the following *p-n* junction is forward biased?

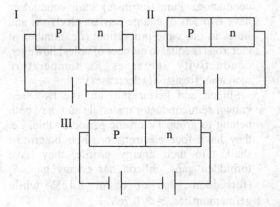

Fig. 39.17
    A. I only   B. II only
    C. III only   D. I and II only

13. Which of the following is the circuit symbol for a *p-n* junction diode?

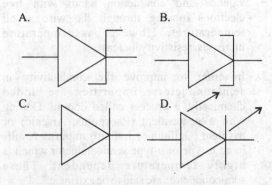

Fig. 39.18

14. The variational output waveform of a full wave rectifier to a sinusoidal input is

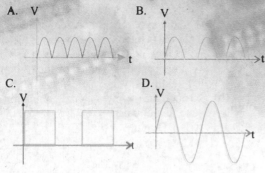

Fig. 39.19

15. Which of the following is the circuit symbol for *n-p-n* transistor?

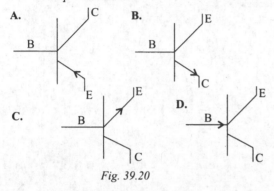

Fig. 39.20

16. The d.c. forward current gain in a common base amplifier circuit is

A. $\frac{I_E}{I_C}$.   B. $\frac{I_E}{I_B}$.   C. $\frac{I_C}{I_E}$.   D. $\frac{I_E}{I_B}$.

17. The forward current gain for a common emitter amplifiers, β can be expressed in terms of the common base current gain, α, as

A. $\frac{\alpha}{1+\alpha}$.   B. $\frac{\alpha}{1-\alpha}$.   C. $\frac{1+\alpha}{\alpha}$.   D. $\frac{1-\alpha}{\alpha}$.

18. In the design of a high gain power amplifier, the preferred configuration is

A. Common Base.   B. Common Emitter.
C. Common Collector.   D. Emitter Follower.

19. In an eight pin-dual-in line μ 741 integrated operational amplifier, the output is taken out of pin is

A. 2.   B. 3.   C. 4.   D. 6.

20. In an inverting μ741 amplifier, with feed back resistor $R_F = 22k\Omega$ and input resistor $R_1 = 10 \, k\Omega$ the amplifier gain is

A. –3.2.   B. –2.2.   C. +2.2.   D. +3.2.

21. (a) (i) Use charge carrier model to distinguish between metals, semiconductors and insulators.

     (ii) Give two examples each.

   (b) Show that $\vec{E} = \rho \vec{J}$ is a form of ohms law, where $\vec{E}$ is the electric field, $\vec{J}$ is current per unit area and ρ the resitivity.

22. (a) (i) Describe the energy band model of matter and use it to characterize metal conductors, semiconductors and insulators.

     (ii) Give one example each with the approximate values of their energy gap.

   (b) Explain the following terms in relation to **seminconductors:**

     (i) Doping

     (Ii) Acceptors

     (iii) Donors

23. (a) Describe the formation of *n*-type, and *p*-type semiconductors.

   (b) Sketch and discuss the origin of the I-V characteristic of a:

     (i) forward bias *p-n* junction

     (ii) reverse bias *p-n* junction

24. (a) Explain what is meant by rectification.

   (b) Describe with necessary diagrams the operation of a: (i) half-wave rectifier (ii) full wave rectifier using two diodes.

   (c) Draw and explain the input and output variation.

25. (a) The input waveform to the circuit shown below is $e = 5\sin 100\pi t$.

   (b) Sketch three cycles of its output and briefly discuss the variations.

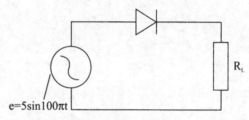

$e = 5\sin 100\pi t$

Fig. 39.21

   (c) (i) What is the frequency of the signal voltage?

     (ii) Estimate the peak value of the output voltage across R_L if the diode is of silicon type.

26. (a) List four advantages and two disadvantages of integrated circuits (*IC*).

   (b) Sketch the pin configuration of *IC* μ741 operational amplifier.

27. (a) Draw and label a single stage common emitter amplifier biased against thermal runaway.

   (b) State the use of the components.

28. If $\alpha = \frac{I_C}{I_E}$ is the common base amplifier d.c. current gain and $\beta = \frac{I_C}{I_C}$ is the forward current gain for common emitter amplifier, deduce that $\beta = \frac{\alpha}{1-\alpha}$.

ANSWERS

Exercise 1
1. D
2. D
3. A
4. D
5. B
6b 1sec, 0.1cm, 1°, 0.01cm, 1°
7. 0.001cm
8. $L^3T^{-2}M^{-1}$
9. $ML^{-1}T^{-2}$
10. x=1, y=1, z=0
11. (i) $ML^{-1}T^{-2}$ (ii) s^{-1}
12. $M^4kg^{-1}s^{-1}$

Exercise2
1. B
2. C
3. A
4. B
10. 3m
11. (i) $4ms^{-2}$ (ii) 0 (iii) 20m
12. 450m
13. 20m
14. 4sec
15. $2ms^{-2}$, 25m
16. $40ms^{-1}$
17. $20ms^{-1}$

Exercise 3
1. A
2. C
3. C
4. A
7. 40J
8. 4000J, 0.4m
9. 2400J
10. 300 watts
11. 10J
12. 3000 watts
13. 200J
14. 0.25J
15. (a) 39.3kW (b) 27.5kW

Exercise 4
1. B
2. A
3. A
4. A
5. B
6. D
7. A
8. B
9. C
10. (b) 5:1
11. (b) $400.15cm^3$
12. (b) 455g
16. (c) $5.1 \times 10^{-7}K^{-1}$

Exercise 5
1. B
2. B
3. D
4. B
5. B

Exercise 6
1. A
2. B
3. D
4. A
5. A
11. True

Exercise 7
1. A
2. D
3. D
4. D
5. A
6. A
7. B
8. D
9. A
10. A
11. A
12. A
13. B
14. B
15. B
16. D
17. D
18. C
19. A
20. B
23. 1A
26. 2Ω, 2A, 2V, 1A
27. $4.0 \times 10^2 Ω^{-1} m^{-1}$
28. 1.62kJ, 324J
29. 4.16A
30. 62.5Ω, ₦30
32. 0.5Ω
34. 0.6V, 1.0A, 2.5A
35. 0.21Ω

Exercise 8
1. D
2. D
3. A

Exercise 9
1. A
2. B
3. B
4. A
5. C
6. 30 cm
7. 1.52cm

11. (a) 1000Ncm^{-1}
    (b) 0.15J

Exercise 10
1. D
2. D

Exercise 11
1. C
2. D
3. D
4. A
5. A
6. C
7. B

BOOK 2
Exercise 12
1. A
2. B
3. A
4. $\sqrt{2}$ km
5. $2^{\frac{1}{2}}$F or $\sqrt{2}$ F
6. 1000N
8. (a) 25N
   (b) 32.4N
9. 85.4kmh^{-1}, N75°W
10. 63.4° to the direction of the current
11. 5km
12. 26.5N, 17.32N
13. D
14. C
15. (3units) in south direction
16. 16N

Exercise 13
1. D
2. D
3. C
4. B
5. (a)17.32s
   (b) 375m
   (c) 866m
6. (a) 11.07s
   (b) 32.84°
   (c) 930m
7. 511.2ms^{-1}
8. (a) 2.02s
   (b) 16.2m
   (c) 19.8ms^{-1}
9. 34.6sec, 3464m

Exercise 14
1. B
2. A
3. C
4. B
5. A
6. B
7. B

8. C
9. C
10. 2N
11. 33.3g
12. 173.2N, 86.6N
13. 240N
14. 125N, 95N
15. 0.68m
16. 6N
17. 0N, 0.5Nm
19. b(i) 80g   (ii) 33cm
20. (C) 160N
23. 41200N
24. 0.9
25. 6096kgm^{-3}
26. 3.46cm^3
27. 300g
28. 89g
29. (a) 12.5gm^{-3} (b) 1.13gcm^{-3}
30. (a) 25.5cm, (b) 20.4cm
31. 20N, 15N, 16N
32. 0.08m^3, 0.056m^3,0.108kg
33. (a) 36N (b) 32N (c) 31.2N
    (B) 7500kgm^{-3}

Exercise 15
1. B
2. B
3. D
4. C
5. C
7. 196Nm^{-2}
8. 1960Nm^{-2}
9. 2000Nm^{-2}
10. 0.5m
11. 2.97 × 10^{5}Pa
12. 1.02 bar
13. (a) 500Nm^{-2}
    (b) 2500N

Exercise 16
1. B
2. A
3. A
4. A
5. B
10. 1.2s
13. (a) 0.02s
    (b) 0ms^{-1}, 4936ms$^-$
    (c) 15.7ms^{-1}, 0ms^{-1}
16. (a) 4.47m
    (b) 9.99ms^{-2}

Exercise 17
1. B
2. D
3. D
4. A
5. A
6. B
7. D

8.   1600N
11. 30Ns
13. $1ms^{-1}$
14. $4.8ms^{-1}$
15. 50N
16. $9.0 \times 10^{-28}N$
18. $2.3ms^{-1}$
19. 150N
20. 18N
21. $60ms^{-1}$
22   1N
23   $300ms^{-1}$
24. 48N
25   10,000N
28. $1.82ms^{-1}$ in the direct of the first ball

Exercise 18
1.   D
2.   D
3.   D
4.   D
5.   C
7.   156.25N
8. $\dfrac{125\%}{\pi}$
9.   101.8
10. 2
11. 150, 150

Exercise 19
1.   D
2.   D
3.   C
4.   C
5.   A
6.   108°C
7.   50°C
9.   (a) 176°F (353K)
     – 22°F (243K)
     (b) –40°C (233K)
     21.1°C (294.11K)

Exercise 20
1.   C
2.   D
3.   D
4.   C
5.   D
6.   C
7.   D
8.   C
9.   (b) 1118.72J
10. (c) $6.6 \times 10^{-3}kg$

Exercise 21
1.   A
2.   B
3.   D
4.   A
5.   C
6.   D

7.   D
8.   D
9.   D
10. (c) $34.62cm^3$
11. (c) $719.8cm^3$
12. 546.0K
13. (a) 59.6cmHg
     (b) $373.4cm^3$

Exercise 22
1.   C
2.   B
3.   C
6. $2 \times10^{-3}m$
7.   (a) 0.06m
     (b) $0.6ms^{-1}$
     (c) 0.1s
8.   0.083s
9.   0.8m, 4m
14. $3ms^{-1}$, 7.5Hz
15. $3ms^{-1}$, 1.2m
16. (i) 1.57m
     (ii) $30ms^{-1}$
     (iii) 0.052s, 19.1Hz
     (iv) 25m

Exercise 23
1.   A
2.   C
3.   B
4.   A
5.   C
6.   B
7.   C
8.   D
9.   C
10. A
11. (c) 375cm
12. (c) The object is 30cm from the mirror and
          the image is 15cm from the mirror.
14. (c) The image is 12cm high and formed
          30cm from the mirror.

Exercise 24
1.   A
2.   C
3.   B
4.   C
5.   A
6.   C
7.   D
8.   D
9.   C
10. B
11. B
12. (b) 19.5°
     (c) 0.67
13. (a) 1.5
     (c) 1.49
14. (a) 6cm
     (b) 5.3cm

C (i) It is between F & 2F on the other side of the lens.
   (ii) It is formed at 2F on the other side of the lens.

15. (c) The image is virtual erect and of height 2/3 that of the object.

Exercise 25
1. D
2. B
3. C
4. C
5. D
6. D
8. (b) 60cm
   (c) 66.7cm
9. 10.17cm
12. 22.7cm

Exercise 26
1. C
2. B
3. C
4. D
5. B
6. D
7. D
8. C
9. C
10. C
11. A
17. 0.26m
19. $338.8ms^{-1}$
20. 15 hoots
22. (a) 2s
   (b) 1.0s
24. 85m
25. 0.005s

BOOK 3

Exercise 27
1. B
2. D
3. B
4. D
5. B
6. D
11. 150m

Exercise 28
1. B
2. C
3. D
4. B

Exercise 29
1. D
2. B
3. C

4. C
5. 5.34×10^{-6}N
7. $1.12 \times 10^{4}ms^{-1}$
9. See text book worked example
12. 0.8W, $8ms^{-2}$

Exercise 30
1. B
2. D
3. B
4. A
5. C
6. C
7. B
8. D
9. C
10. D
11. C
12. D
13. B
14. C
15. A
16. A
17. D
18. C
19. A
20. (c) 2.7×10^{6}
21. (i) 4.43×10^{-10}F
   (ii) 88.6×10^{-9}C
   (iii) $10^{5}NC^{-1}$
   (iv) 8.86×10^{-6}J
22. 1.8μF
23. 0.016J
24. (a) 8.85×10^{-12}F
   (b) 8.85×10^{-12}C
   (c) $10^{4}NC^{-1}$
25. 29J
26. 23.04×10^{9}N
27. $1.88 \times 10^{13}NC^{-1}$
28. 2.36×10^{-7}C
29. (c) 1.92×10^{-17}N
30. 7.2 J
32. 5.6×10^{6}N
33. (c) (i) 5×10^{-3}C, 2×10^{-2}C
   (ii) 7.5J

Exercise 31
1. A
2. D
3. B
4. C
5. A
6. C
7. D
8. D
9. D
10. D
11. D
12. C
13. C

14. B
15. C
16. B
17. A
18. B
19. D
20. A
21. $R = 4.5\Omega, r = 0.5\Omega$
22. 1.2V
23. b(i) 6Ω
    (ii) 18Ω
24. $I_1 = 1A, I_2 = \frac{1}{2}A, I_3 = \frac{2}{3}A$
27. (i) 1.5V (ii) 1.29V
30. (i) 216000J, 0.25A
33. 2:1
34. 40m

Exercise 32

1. A
2. B
3. C
4. C
5. A
6. A
7. (b) N50°W
11. (i) 1.53×10^{-13}N (ii) 0
    (iii) 21.6×10^{-14}N

Exercise 33

1. B
2. C
3. C
4. B
5. A
6. C
7. B
8. A
9. A
10. A
11. B
12. C
13. B
14. D
15. C
16. B
17. B
18. B
19. B
24. (a) 0.03V
27. 50%
28. 2.00×10^{-13}N
31. (ii) 1364 turns
34. c (i) 5:3 (ii) 0.111A

Exercise 34

1. C
2. C
3. B
4. C
5. D

6. C
7. B
8. C
9. B
10. A
11. C
12. C
13. C
14. B
15. C
16. C
17. A
18. A
19. C
20. D
21. b(i) 7.7×10^4Hz
    (ii) 0.17A
    (iii) 0
22. (i) 2.47A
    (ii) 2.03Ω
    (iii) 30°
23. (i) $10^4\Omega$
    (ii) 10Ω
26. (i) 50Hz
    (ii) 2.47A
    (iii) $\pi/2$
    (iv) 2Ω
27. (ii) 316.23Ω
    (iii) 18.43°
    (iv) $V_L = 47.4V, V_c = 63.2V, V_R = 47.4V$
28. b(i) $\theta = 35.3°$
29. (a) 1.1×10^5Hz
30. (b) (i) 0.81
    (ii) 34.68W
31. (i) 282.6Ω
    (ii) $1.6 \times 10^3\Omega$
    (iii) 1882.6Ω
    (iv) 1351.13Ω
    (v) $\phi = 77.2°$
32. 9.2×10^4Hz, 1.8×10^4Hz
33. (a) 3.18A, +90°
    (b) 3.77A, −90°
    (c) 3.03A, 72.35°
34. (a) 1.51A
    (b) 12.74A
35. (i) 106.09Ω
    (ii) 1005.6Ω
    (iii) 7.95×10^{-2}A
    (iv) 8.43V
    (v) 6.32W

Exercise 35

1. D
2. D
3. C
4. D
5. A
6. C

7. C
8. C
9. D
10. B
11. B
12. C
13. D
14. C
15. D
16. D
17. D
18. C
19. A
20. D
28. 2.5MeV
35. (ii) 4:1
38. (b) 6.87×10^{-13} J
40. (a) $^{10}_{6}$A $\rightarrow$ carbon
    (b) Y $\rightarrow$ 60 nucleons and 27 protons
        Z $\rightarrow$ 14 nucleons and 6 protons

Exercise 36
1. C
2. C
3. D
4. D
5. A
6. A
7. C
8. D
9. B
10. B
11. A
12. B
13. B
14. D
15. D
16. (b)(i) 6.2eV
    (ii) 1.47×10^{6}ms^{-1}
    (iii) 5.1×10^{14}Hz
17. (b) 5.1×10^{14}Hz
18. (b) (i) 10.2V
    (ii) 1.2×10^{-7}m
19. (b) 2.5×10^{-10}m
21. (b) 7.3×10^{-11}m
22. 7.2 eV
25. 10.36kV
26. (c) (i) 0.38×10^{-19}J
    (ii) 3.9×10^{-19}J
28. (b) 11.84×10^{-19}J, 168nm

Exercise 37
1. B

2. D
3. C
4. D
5. C
6. D
7. B
8. A
9. A
10. A
11. D
12. A
13. C
14. B
15. B
16. (c) 2556.5s
18. 7k
19. 17.14g
22. 78.3 mins
28. 0.4A

Exercise 38
1. C
2. B
3. C
4. A
5. D
6. B
7. (b) 1.06×10^{2}J
8. (i) 1.3×10^{-11}m, (ii) 1.47×10^{-34}m
9. (i) 5.3×10^{-34} kgms^{-1} (ii) 2.1×10^{-34}
10. 2.05×10^{-11}m

Exercise 39
1. B
2. D
3. B
4. B
5. B
6. A
7. B
8. A
9. B
10. A
11. C
12. A
13. C
14. A
15. C
16. C
17. B
18. B
19. D
20. B
25. c (i) 50Hz

INDEX

341